GROUND WATER

Fig. 1.—View of the group of great piedmont alluvial cones at the foot of the Sierra Nevada, in the vicinity of Independence, Owens Valley, California. Maximum difference in elevation from apex to toe of the piedmont slope is 3,000 ft. The City of Los Angeles obtains most of its water supply from Owens Valley. It utilizes water from Owens River and tributary mountain streams and ground water pumped from the alluvial cones. This region is notorious for the contentions over water rights between land owners and the City of Los Angeles. (*Frontispiece.*)

GROUND WATER

BY

C. F. TOLMAN

Late Professor of Economic Geology,
Leland Stanford Junior University

FIRST EDITION
SEVENTH IMPRESSION

McGRAW-HILL BOOK COMPANY, INC.

NEW YORK AND LONDON

1937

THE MAPLE PRESS COMPANY, YORK, PA.

DEDICATION

To my son and colleague, John van Steen Tolman, who, true to the highest traditions of his profession, gave his life in order to carry out faithfully the obligations imposed upon him as mine superintendent.

PREFACE

This book records the birth and describes the development of a new science—coordinated scientific data regarding the occurrence, motions, and activities of subsurface water, and the hydrologic properties of water-bearing materials—christened by O. E. Meinzer "Ground-water Hydrology."

Ground water is hidden in subsurface interstices and escaped the serious attention of the father of all sciences, scientific curiosity, until intensive investigations beginning about forty years ago revealed the importance of ground water and many of the interesting phenomena accompanying its occurrence.

The critical data regarding ground water are chiefly geologic and engineering, although all the natural sciences have contributed. The ground-water hydrologist has adopted all applicable methods of scientific research and has also developed his own methods for evaluating the hydrologic properties of rocks and for estimating capacities of underground reservoirs and rates of movement in underground conduits.

This book is the first general treatise of the science published in English, and the only one to attempt a summary of the results of the intensive study of subsurface water in western United States, where existence depends upon the exploration and development of ground water. Drought has struck four times in the last six years in regions of the United States where water supply was supposed to be plentiful, and in current literature appears the dawning of the idea that development and utilization of ground water may help to meet not only the periodic deficiency in water supply in semiarid regions, but also the occasional severe deficit caused by drought where normally rainfall and surface water are adequate.

The author feels the responsibility of presenting the pioneer textbook dealing with ground water and trusts that errors, omissions, and criticisms will be called to his attention in order that later editions may be improved. The personal viewpoint from which the subject is reviewed has to some extent apportioned emphasis according to the interest aroused in professional investigations, rather than according to importance. It is hoped that this viewpoint will not defeat the principal object of the book, that is, to present the data, with appropriate references to the literature, required by advanced geological and engineering students and by practicing engineers and geologists.

It is hoped that this book, especially the general review of principles, may assist the attorney in preparing for litigation involving subsurface water, and may possibly assist in the development of sound ground-water law founded on present-day scientific knowledge.

This is the day of development of our natural resources. Ground-water developments vary from the dug well of the homeowner, involving an expenditure of a few hundred dollars, to water conservation and development projects of municipalities, of states, and of the national government. May those responsible for these developments take time to become familiar with the occurrence of underground water before proceeding with the expenditure of millions of dollars!

The author takes pleasure in incorporating the following contributions prepared for this book: "Prospecting for Water by Geophysical Methods," by C. A. Heiland; "Electrical Methods," by J. J. Jakosky; and "The Hawaiian Ground-water Province," by R. G. Sohlberg. Important contributions by O. E. Meinzer on various phases of the science have been extensively quoted. It is with regret that owing to space limitations it has been necessary to omit equally authoritative contributions by N. E. Bradbury, "Air-mass Analysis"; E. W. Galliher, "Mechanical Analysis of Granular Materials"; and R. E. Wright, "Chemical Quality of Natural Waters"; all of which appeared in mimeographed editions of the syllabus on "Ground Water."

The author gratefully acknowledges the assistance of J. F. Poland in preparation of Chap. VIII, Percolation, Ground-water Turbulent Flow, and Permeability; and Chapter XIII, Wells. He expresses his obligation to the late D. W. Murphy and to C. H. Lee, A. E. Sedgwick, and L. C. Hill who were associated with him in detailed ground-water investigations; and to O. E. Meinzer, R. D. Reed, Rollin Eckis, W. A. Packard, F. G. Clapp, D. A. Lane, Irving Crosby, and H. F. Lynn, who furnished original data. He acknowledges with pleasure the assistance of many others who have reviewed and criticized this book, and of Amy C. Stipp who compiled index and tables and made editorial revisions.

C. F. Tolman.

Stanford University, Calif.,
August, 1937.

CONTENTS

xi

alluvial cone—Displacement of contours by irrigation and pumping
—Fluctuations of ground water—Geophysical methods of locating
water table and bedrock—Electrical methods—APPENDIX: Prospecting for water by geophysical methods. Introduction—Definition of problem—Geophysical classification of underground water
—Methods of location—Methods applicable to structural interpretation—Methods applicable to stratigraphic interpretation—
Instruments of water location—Discussion of results—Economic
aspects of geophysical water location—References.

CHAPTER X

Ground water in fractures—Classification of fractures—Deep-
seated fractures—Superficial fractures—Structure and hydrologic
properties of fractured zone—Size of water body—Effect of erosion
and earth movements on water table—Fluctuation of water table
during cycle of erosion—Water table and movements in fractured
zone—Water movements above the water table—Movements of
water at and below the water table—Comparison of water table in
fractured rock with that in pervious granular material—Source of
information regarding ground water in fractured rock—Ground
water in solution openings—Ground water in impervious, flat-lying
limestone—Structural attitude—Development of openings—The
process of solution—Filling of cavities by precipitation—Subsurface
perched streams—Water-table streams—Topographic control of
water table—Solution conduits formed below the water table—
Ground water in impervious, inclined limestone beds—Ground
water in porous limestone—Original openings in porous limestone
—Ground water in lava—Ground water in fractures in limestone—
References.

CHAPTER XI

History of development of artesian wells—Origin of artesian pressure—Hydraulic principles of confined percolation—Comparison of
flow in pipes with percolation in confined aquifers—Effect of change
in cross-sectional area of conduit—Some hydraulic phenomena due
to pumping—Pressure changes due to well flow—Cone of pressure
relief—Depleted pressure surface—Effect of pressure relief on
aquifer and confining formations—Literature on effect of pressure
relief—Phenomena indicating compressibility and elasticity of artesian aquifers and aquicludes—Minor fluctuations of wells due to
barometric and tidal effects—Water-table wells—Wells tapping
confined water—Effects of atmospheric pressure on rigid and elastic
conduits—Pressure effects on intake and well—Characteristics of
aquiclude and overlying strata—Effect of earthquakes on water
levels in wells—Other evidence indicating compressibility of aquifers—Evidence from water production in excess of replenishment

without drawdown at intake—Evidence from continued change in
pressure gradient extending over a limited area—Evidence from
phenomena of recovery—Evidence from laboratory tests—Evidence from surface subsidence around wells—Possible causes of
subsidence—Quantitative estimate of yield due to depletion of pressure—Comparison of pumping confined and free water—Change
from confined to water-table conditions due to overpumping—
Comparison of water-level fluctuations—Effect of pumping from
confined system on water-table wells and streams—References.

CHAPTER XII

Important types of artesian systems—Stratiform aquifers—High-pressure systems, or: water furnished in part by compression of
aquifer—Fractures and joints in crystalline rocks—Solution cavities and lava tunnels—Pressure water in alluvial cones and fans—
Geologic structure of alluvial cone—Effect of slope—Effect of
source rock—Processes of weathering—Rainfall and runoff—
Depositional agencies that build up the alluvial cone—Stream flow
within banks—Flood action—Combined stream and flood action—
Hydrologic structure and ground-water movement in alluvial cone
—Depletion in the average alluvial cone—Isolated sand lens surrounded by incoherent silt and clay—References.

CHAPTER XIII

Hydraulics of wells—Water-table wells—Cone of water-table
depression and area of influence—Derivation of formulas—Confined-water wells—Cone of pressure relief—Factors affecting
quantity of flow—Size of well—Effect of diameter on velocity of
flow into well—Types of wells—Dug wells—Bored wells—Drilled
wells—Percussion-drilled wells—Driven wells—Cable-tool wells—
Casing—California stovepipe method—Hydraulic rotary wells—
Gravel-envelope well—Comparison of cable-tool and hydraulic
rotary wells—Advantages of cable-tool method—Advantages of
hydraulic rotary method—Well perforations—Importance of perforations—Types of perforations—Machine-perforated casing—
Casing perforated in the ground—Well screens—Well development
—Useful formulas—References.

CHAPTER XIV

Occurrence—Organic shales the probable source rocks—Movement
of oil-field fluids—Hydraulic conditions during accumulation of
oil pool—Objections to original hydraulic theory—Role of compaction and buoyancy—Conditions after accumulation and before

drift—Great sheet of Tertiary alluvium—Alluvial deposits of the semiarid Southwest—Superficial lava formations—Soil, weathered rock—Bedrock formations delimiting ground-water provinces— Large bodies of intrusive igneous rocks—The Paleozoic sedimentary formations—Cretaceous formations of northwest Great Plains region, the Rocky Mountains, and Colorado plateau—The Cretaceous and Tertiary formations of the Atlantic coastal plain and the embayment of the Gulf of Mexico—Eocene and later Tertiary deposits of Great Plains, Rocky Mountains, and Colorado plateau region—Classification of ground-water provinces—Western ground-water provinces—Ground-water provinces described by Meinzer —Ground-water provinces of western United States—Great Basin ground-water province—Extent and general structure—Topography—The valley fill—Lake beds and axial stream gravels—The Columbia Plateau ground-water province—The Great Valley of California ground-water province—Location and topography— Structure and ground-water supply—Irrigation and ground water —Water conservation and flood control—Valley fill of Willamette Valley and Puget Sound trough—Ground-water province of Coast ranges of central and southern California—Structure and ground-water supply—San Diego County—The Los Angeles basin—Other important deposits of valley fill—The Northern Coast range ground-water province—The Hawaiian ground-water province— Location and general geology—Water resources—Temperature and rainfall—Occurrence of ground water—Unconfined basal ground water—Confined basal ground water—Ground water confined between dikes—Ground water perched on old alluvial deposits— Ground water perched on ash or tuff—Development of ground water—Island of Maui—Island of Oahu—Island of Kauai—Island of Hawaii—Island of Molokai—Lanai, Niihau, and Kahoolawe— References.

GROUND WATER

CHAPTER I

INTRODUCTION

The principal subject treated in this text is ground water which fills all openings within the saturated zone. The water table is the upper surface of the ground-water body and of the saturated zone and above it is the zone of aeration or zone of suspended water which extends to the ground surface. The water table is a delicate indicator of hydraulic conditions in the upper portion of the saturated zone. It registers fluctuations due to variations in water supply and withdrawals, and its slope gives the hydraulic gradient of free ground water. The water table is discussed in detail in this book because of its importance in the study of ground-water problems.

Ground water properly designates all interstitial water below the water table, but only the superficial portion of ground water, principally within 1000 ft. of the ground surface, has been studied and exploited by those interested in water supply. This extractable body of ground water occurs in openings between grains in alluvial and sedimentary rocks (pore water[1]), in fractures usually abundant only near the ground surface (fissure water[1]), and in tubular openings in soluble rocks, and openings in lava formed by flow and gas expansion during solidification (cavern water[1]).

Types of water bodies to which little attention has been paid by ground-water hydrologists are ground water of oil fields and thermal waters, including ore-forming solutions. Water bodies underlying oil deposits are often stagnant and under high hydraulic pressure (Chap. XIV). The chemical composition and hydraulic head of oil-field waters vary markedly in the successive water-bearing sands, which indicates a marked separation of the water bodies in each aquifer. Thermal water is of com-

[1] Nomenclature of Höfer-Heimhalt, "Grundwasser und Quellen," pp. 115–121, Friedr. Vieweg & Sohn, Braunschweig, Germany, 1920.

1

plex origin and composition and may be meteoric water heated at depth or water of volcanic and magmatic origin.[1] Ore solutions are the best known type of thermal waters and their occurrence and peculiar characteristics are registered in the ore deposits they have formed. Ore solutions are strongly energized, high-temperature water bodies of complex chemical composition and under great telluric pressure, often developed above intrusive igneous masses. Their penetrating power due to pressure, heat, and corrosive chemical composition is enormously greater than that of ordinary types of ground water. They are capable not only of penetrating tight fractures, but also of opening them up by hydraulic pressure. In some cases[2] they break the rock penetrated and act in many respects like intrusive bodies of magma. Ore solutions not only precipitate minerals in cavities held open by hydraulic pressure, but also penetrate apparently solid rock and the chemically active constituents of the solution may react on the rock, profoundly altering it.

Water in superficial fractures and in the large openings in lavas and in soluble rocks is important locally and is discussed (Chap. X), but most of the text deals with ground water in granular formations (alluvial and sedimentary deposits), the tributary water in the atmosphere and on the ground surface, and water in the undersaturated zone above the water table. The interconnected pore spaces in sedimentary and alluvial materials are chiefly of capillary or subcapillary size. In capillary openings ground water moves under the ordinary hydraulic gradients existing underground or produced by a pumping well. Subcapillary openings are dominant in formations such as clay, silt, and shale and ordinary subsurface hydraulic gradients cannot force water through or out of them. Such water is herein called "fixed ground water." Although generally of little importance as a source of water, fixed ground water may be moved into more pervious formations, and thus be made available, by pressure gradients produced by extreme overpumping and by processes of compaction of fine-grained sedimentary rocks, a phenomenon

[1] LINDGREN, W., "Mineral Deposits," 3d ed., pp. 91–101, McGraw-Hill Book Company, Inc., 1928.

[2] Breccia rings at Cananea: V. D. Perry, Copper Deposits of the Cananea District, Sonora, Mexico, "Copper Resources of the World," vol. 1, XVI, pp. 416–418, Inter. Geol. Cong., 1935.

which only recently has attracted scientific investigation and discussion (pages 470–472, 495–498).

Ground water in openings of capillary or supercapillary size may be classified as free and confined water. Free ground water occurs from the water table down to the first confining formation and moves as a single water body, the hydraulic features of which are registered by the water-table slopes. Confined ground water is movable ground water which is separated from overlying bodies of confined or free ground water and, of course, from the overlying water table by less permeable material, with the result that the water table does not control the movements of the underlying confined water and is no indicator of the hydraulic conditions of that water body. Confined water moves usually in a conduit under a pressure head originating at the upper end of the conduit. The movement of confined water and many of the accompanying hydraulic phenomena are quite different from the movement of free water under the control of the water table. Confined water and interpretation of the accompanying pressure phenomena are discussed in detail (Chaps. XI and XII).

All occurrences of water other than ground water are discussed only insofar as they affect the occurrence, movements, and supply of ground water. Influent seepage feeding ground water must first penetrate the soil horizons and the remainder of the zone of aeration before reaching the water table. Therefore the soil and the zone of aeration receive appropriate treatment (Chaps. V to VII).

The investigation of ground water, its replenishment by and losses to overlying water bodies, calls for an understanding of the sciences of meteorology, the science of the air; climatology, the study of present and past climates of the world; and hydrology which deals chiefly with surface water. Detailed study of the supply and losses of ground water involves a critical analysis of evaporation and transpiration and an understanding of the movements of water through the superficial materials above the water table (Chaps. VI and VII). The study of artificial draft due to pumping is based on an understanding of the hydraulics of wells (Chap. XIII). In these studies the investigator must of necessity trespass in the fields of pure and applied science. The study of the mineralization of ground water is a phase of applied chemistry and its pollution, of bacteriology. The motions of ground water in the saturated zone and the movements of water above the water table, where film forces and capillary attraction interfere with the action of gravity, are subject to the laws of physics.

Of all the sciences geology is of greatest importance in the study of subsurface water.[1]   Ground water fills interstices of granular pervious rocks and fractures and solution openings in impervious rocks.   The water-holding capacity of a rock is controlled by its porosity, and the freedom of movement of water in any formation depends upon the size and interconnection of the openings.   The porosity and pattern of the openings are as much the result of geological processes of rock formation and alteration as the solid portion of the rock, and the shape and extent of pervious water-bearing formations and their relation to the impervious formational members are determined by geologic structural studies and pictured in geologic cross sections.

The search for water in the semiarid regions, the intensive exploitation of ground water by wells, and litigation in regard to ownership of ground water have brought to light many peculiarities and idiosyncrasies in the occurrence and movements of subsurface water.   These peculiarities are due chiefly to the structure and hydrologic properties of the water-bearing materials and have stimulated detailed geological investigation of the superficial formations, especially soils, to which little attention has been paid by geologists in the past.

The comprehensive, scientific study of ground water is a relatively recent development.   Most of the detailed methods of ground-water investigation have been developed within the present century.[2]   Until recently the geologist investigating ground-water supplies has confined his studies to the physical characteristics of the water-bearing materials and the engineer has specialized in measuring or estimating ground-water movements and supply.   However, the engineer's estimates are often erroneous if made without an understanding of the size and characteristics of the water-bearing conduits and subsurface

---

[1] All water below the ground surface, including ground water and all types of suspended water, is called subsurface or underground water (see Fig. 4, page 39).

[2] MEINZER, O. E., Outline of Methods for Estimating Ground-water Supplies, *U.S. Geol. Surv. Water-Supply Paper*, 638-C, 1932.

reservoirs. Also the geologist overlooks the best possible check on the accuracy of his conclusions regarding the physical characteristics of the formations and structures controlling ground-water movements if he does not test them by an analysis of engineering measurements.

The importance of combined geological and engineering work in the study of ground water has been emphasized by O. E. Meinzer, Geologist in Charge of the Division of Ground Water of the United States Geological Survey. This emphasis has been justified by the results achieved by combined geological field study, laboratory investigation of hydrologic characteristics of water-bearing materials, and engineering field studies carried out under his direction. He has adopted for this broad field of scientific investigation the designation "ground-water hydrology" and has insisted that the investigator must have a broad foundation in physics, chemistry, engineering, and geology. The Division of Ground Water of the Geological Survey has furnished advanced training for a number of brilliant young investigators in ground-water hydrology.

The entire field of ground-water hydrology as defined by Meinzer cannot be covered in a single textbook, and limitations in size prevent discussion in this text of results of many branches of the scientific investigation of ground water, such as chemical quality, bacteriology and pollution, and many others. Therefore the writer hesitates to assume the responsibility of designating the book a "Textbook of Ground-water Hydrology" and has selected the simple title "Ground Water."

The main portion of this book is a revision of a stenographic record of the lecture course on ground-water geology which has been given at Stanford University since 1927, and prior to that in the courses in economic geology since 1905, first at the University of Arizona and then at Stanford University. The material for these courses and this text has been gathered from the literature and from the author's practice as consulting geologist in the Southwest during the past thirty-five years. Much of this work has been directed to the study of ground water. The examples are taken largely from California, where the greater part of his investigations has been carried on, and where the geologic and engineering aspects of the subject have received more detailed scrutiny than elsewhere.

The author presupposes that the reader is versed at least in the elementary principles of geology and of hydraulic engineering. He is supposed to understand the engineering methods of assembling and analyzing field data, especially hydraulic data; hence description of the details of engineering procedure is generally omitted. The field and laboratory methods developed by the ground-water geologist and engineer are discussed in detail. Sequence and structure of water-bearing materials are determined by geological field studies. Hydrologic properties are determined by laboratory tests on water-bearing materials and interpreted from field measurements of influent seepage, water-table and pressure-surface gradients, and pumping records. From these data the quantity of water in storage or moving toward a well can be estimated. The attempt is made to discuss the principles of occurrence of ground water in sufficient detail so that the engineer with some knowledge of geology and the geologist with an understanding of engineering principles and methods can work out the problems in ground-water hydrology that may be presented to them.

GROUND-WATER DEVELOPMENT BY THE ANCIENTS

In humid regions primitive man paid little attention to water. It was always present and, like air, was taken as a matter of course. However, in semiarid and arid regions the occurrence of water controlled the activities of man. Villages were built on living streams or around water holes, and man's early movements consisted chiefly of migrations to perennial water in the dry season and ventures into new pastures or hunting grounds in the wet season.

Today moderns of the humid regions have no concept of the absorbing interest we within the confines of aridity take in the weather and the water supply. We pass a running stream and stop to guess at its flow in inches or second-feet. We see an alfalfa field and automatically make mental calculations as to the quantity of water transpiring. A swamp land in the center of a desert basin is immediately scrutinized with care, for it may indicate the quantity of water being wasted and available for pumping farther up the slope. The natural vegetation is observed because it may indicate the depth to subsurface water.

Primitive man was taught to dig for water, possibly by observing the actions of wild horses and wolves in search of water. As soon as he learned to domesticate and rear cattle and sheep the well became his most important possession.

In the Bible are recounted many incidents illustrating the importance of ground-water supplies to the tribes of Israel. Abraham and Isaac were renowned for their success as well diggers. As Meinzer[1] states, "the twenty-sixth chapter of Genesis . . . reads like a water-supply paper."[2] The earliest romances recorded in the Bible, those of Rebekah[3] and Rachel[4]

---

[1] MEINZER, O. E., The History and Development of Ground-water Hydrology, *Jour. Wash. Acad. Sci.*, vol. 24, no. 1, p. 6, January, 1934.

[2] Gen. 26: 17–23:

And Isaac departed thence, and pitched his tent in the valley of Gerar, and dwelt there.

And Isaac digged again the wells of water which they had digged in the days of Abraham his father; for the Philistines had stopped them after the death of Abraham: and he called their names after the names by which his father had called them.

And Isaac's servants digged in the valley, and found there a well of springing water.

And the herdmen of Gerar did strive with Isaac's herdmen, saying, The water is ours: and he called the name of the well Esek; because they strove with him.

And they digged another well, and strove for that also: and he called the name of it Sitnah.

And he removed from thence, and digged another well; and for that they strove not: and he called the name of it Rehoboth; and he said, For now the Lord hath made room for us, and we shall be fruitful in the land.

And he went up from thence to Beer-sheba. . . .

And he builded an altar there, and called upon the name of the Lord, and pitched his tent there: and there Isaac's servants digged a well. . . .

And it came to pass the same day, that Isaac's servants came, and told him concerning the well which they had digged, and said unto him, We have found water.

And he called it Shebah: therefore the name of the city is Beer-sheba unto this day.

[3] Gen. 24: 11–19, 50–51:

And he made his camels to kneel down without the city, by a well of water, at the time of the evening, even the time that women go out to draw water.

And he said, O Lord . . .

. . . let it come to pass, that the damsel to whom I shall say, Let down thy pitcher, I pray thee, that I may drink; and she shall say, Drink; and I will give thy camels drink also; let the same be she that thou hast appointed

were enacted at wells.   The Jews suffered for want of water in their forty years of wandering in the deserts of Egypt and Arabia and complained bitterly to Moses and Aaron.   To quell one of these revolts Moses smote the rock with his rod and a fountain of water burst forth.[1]   During their wanderings the Israelites

---

for thy servant, Isaac; . . .

And it came to pass, before he had done speaking, that behold, Rebekah came out . . .

And the damsel was very fair to look upon, a virgin, neither had any man known her; and she went down to the well, and filled her pitcher, and came up.

And the servant ran to meet her, and said, Let me, I pray thee, drink a little water of thy pitcher.

And she said, Drink, my lord: and she hasted, and let down her pitcher upon her hand, and gave him drink.

And when she had done giving him drink, she said, I will draw water for thy camels also, until they have done drinking. . . .

Then Laban and Bethuel answered and said, The thing proceedeth from the Lord . . .

Behold Rebekah is before thee; take her, and go, and let her be thy master's son's wife, as the Lord hath spoken.

[4] Gen. 29: 2–3, 9–11:

And he looked, and behold, a well in the field, and, lo, there were three flocks of sheep lying by it; for out of that well they watered the flocks: and a great stone was upon the well's mouth.

And thither were all the flocks gathered: and they rolled the stone from the well's mouth, and watered the sheep, and put the stone again upon the well's mouth in his place.

And while he yet spake with them, Rachel came with her father's sheep: for she kept them.

And it came to pass, when Jacob saw Rachel the daughter of Laban his mother's brother, and the sheep of Laban his mother's brother, that Jacob went near, and rolled the stone from the well's mouth, and watered the flock of Laban his mother's brother.

And Jacob kissed Rachel, and lifted up his voice, and wept.

[1] Num. 20: 5–11:

And wherefore have ye made us to come up out of Egypt, to bring us in unto this evil place? it is no place of seed, or of figs, or of vines, or of pomegranates; neither is there any water to drink.

And Moses and Aaron went from the presence of the assembly unto the door of the tabernacle of the congregation, and they fell upon their faces; and the glory of the Lord appeared unto them.

And the Lord spake unto Moses, saying,

Take the rod, and gather thou the assembly together, thou and Aaron thy brother, and speak ye unto the rock before their eyes; and it shall give forth his water, and thou shalt bring forth to them water out of the rock;

dug wells under the direction of the Lord who promised them "houses full of all good things, which thou filledst not, and wells digged, which thou diggedst not."[1]

Miracle-working waters are described in John 5: 2–9:

Now there is at Jerusalem by the sheep market, a pool, which is called in the Hebrew tongue Bethesda, having five porches.

In these lay a great multitude of impotent folk of blind, halt, withered, waiting for the moving of the water;

For an angel went down at a certain season into the pool, and troubled the water: whosoever then first after the troubling of the water stepped in, was made whole of whatsoever disease he had.

It has been suggested that this miracle-working spring was an ebbing and flowing spring (pages 438–440).

The pools of Solomon which still supply Jerusalem with water through an aqueduct "are partly hewn in the rock and partly built with masonry, . . . lined with cement, and are formed on successive levels, one slightly above the other, with conduits leading from the upper to the lower, and with flights of steps from the bottom to the top of each pool . . . The main supply of water comes from the spring, or fountain."[2] The lower pool is the larger. It is 582 ft. long, 207 ft. broad at the east end, 148 ft. at the west, and 50 ft. deep.

The pool of Shiloah where Christ healed a blind man is still in use and has a "good supply of water, generally somewhat salty to the taste, perhaps from the soil through which it percolates, and it is, moreover, polluted by the washerwomen and tanners by whom it is constantly used . . . " The water is supplied from the Fountain of the Virgin, by a tunnel 1708 ft. long cut in the solid rock.[3]

---

so thou shalt give the congregation and their beasts drink.

And Moses and Aaron gathered the congregation together before the rock; and he said unto them, Hear now, ye rebels; must we fetch you water out of this rock?

And Moses lifted up his hand, and with his rod he smote the rock twice: and the water came out abundantly: and the congregation drank and their beasts also.

[1] Deut. 6: 11.

[2] SCHAFF, P., "A Dictionary of the Bible," p. 818, New York, 1885.

[3] *Ibid.*, pp. 801–802.

Jacob's well is one of the few localities mentioned in the Bible identified by all authorities. It is in a rectangular enclosure, 151 by 192 ft. surrounded by walls long since crumbled to ruins. The well is now 75 ft. deep and 7½ ft. in diameter. The upper portion is lined with rough masonry. It has been filled up to probably more than half its depth by falling debris.[1]

Regarding Roman ground-water development the archeologist[2] tells us that "before the building of the first aqueduct in 312 B.C., the Romans depended for their water supply upon the Tiber and upon wells, springs, and rain water caught and stored in cisterns. The soil was so rich in springs and underground streams that wells could be sunk successfully at any point and the average depth necessary was only about 5 meters. Such wells were common from the earliest period, and the recent excavations in the Forum have brought to light upward of 30, some of which date from the republic."[3] However, the near-surface ground water of the Pontine marshes was so polluted that the Romans abandoned their wells and imported water by means of remarkable aqueducts, and apparently never utilized the ground-water supplies of their far-flung empire as they might have done if not prejudiced against the use of ground water.

Speaking of the Athens of Pisistratus (middle sixth century B.C.), Butler says, "Many of the houses are provided with deep wells stoned up with polygonal masonry and nearly all have convenient cisterns and granaries. . . . In the wider streets are public wells of great depth, covered by stone slabs, with small apertures, the necks of which are well furrowed by the ropes which for centuries have drawn the dripping buckets from their cool depths. Some of them are again in use."[4]

It is a matter of common knowledge that in semiarid Southern Europe and later in Latin America the well was the center of rural and urban life and of feminine activity and gossip. In some parts of Mexico today water is raised in a hide by men on

[1] SCHAFF, *op. cit.*, p. 414.

[2] The following references on Greek and Roman water development were kindly furnished by H. R. Fairclough, Professor Emeritus of Classical Literature at Stanford University.

[3] PLATNER, "Topography and Monuments of Ancient Rome," 2d ed., p. 90, 1911.

[4] BUTLER, H. C., "The Story of Athens," pp. 74–75, Century Company, 1902.

horseback, just as it was by the ancient Arab cattlemen. Most
of these early wells were small dug wells, but some in Southern
Europe were large and ingeniously constructed. Such a well

Fig. 2.—Famous well at Orvieto, Italy, Pozzo di S. Patrizio.

was built in the City of Orvieto, Italy, and known as *Pozzo di S.
Patrizio* (St. Patrick's well). It was started in 1527 and completed in 1540. The well is located on a bluff overlooking the

valley and penetrates "tufa rock" to an impervious layer of marl
which lies below the level of the adjacent valley. A plentiful
supply of ground water collects in the pervious deposit above the
marl.   Two separate staircases, one above the other, wind around
the shaft and water-carrying asses descend by one staircase and
ascend by the other.   The well is 200 ft. deep and 42 ft. in diameter including the staircases, each of which contains 248 steps.
The photographs (Fig. 2) are reproduced from postal cards collected by a visitor at this famous well.[1]

The drilling of artesian wells in France (in Artois beginning
1126 and in Modena, northern Italy) centered both popular and
scientific interest on the occurrence of spouting water, and here
was developed the art of drilling wells in place of digging them.
The development of the art of well drilling from then on is
described by Norton and by Bowman.[2]   Although it has been
generally recognized that the art of drilling and casing wells
was invented, perfected, and extensively practiced by the
ancient Chinese, it has not been appreciated that by using bamboo
and patience they penetrated to depths rivaling those reached
in modern times with steel and steam.   G. D. Louderback,
Professor of Geology at the University of California, described
to the writer wells sunk 5000 ft. by the method of manual churn
drilling and the use of bamboo casing.   They were started by the
grandfather and completed by the grandson.

Kanats,[3] the Greatest Waterworks of the Ancients

Undoubtedly the most extraordinary works of ancient man for
collecting ground water are the kanats of the Persians.   The
kanats connect the bottoms of shafts, conspicuous over all the
high central valleys of Persia, and are dug by human moles
working over long periods of time.

Thirty-six of these tunnels supply Teheran (population 275,-
000) and the highly cultivated tributary agricultural area.   The
kanats of this system are 8 to 16 miles long and reach a maximum

[1] Information and pictures contributed by Charles Gilman Hyde, Professor
of Civil Engineering, University of California.

[2] NORTON, W. H., Artesian Wells of Iowa, *Iowa Geol. Surv.*, vol. 6, pp. 122–
124; Isaiah Bowman, Well-drilling Methods, *U.S. Geol. Surv. Water-Supply
Paper* 257, 1911.

[3] Also called kariz, kahriz, canaut, ghanat, quanat, kanaut, karazes, and
khanate, as various writers euphoniously translate the Arabic.

of 500 ft. below the ground surface.   One tunnel supplying a
suburb of Teheran passes 200 ft. below the city.[1]

One of the most interesting systems of kanats supplies the city
of Dizful.   Most of the tunnels of this system extend under
gravel bars of the river Ab-i-diz, but a branch kanat penetrates
alluvial outwash gravels, as do most of the kanats of Persia.
The kanats of Dizful are unusually productive, each carrying
about 7.5 sec.-ft. flow.   They pass under the city to irrigate
adjacent fertile land.   The dwellings extend two to six stories
underground and are connected by subterranean passages; hence
it is called the City of Rats.   The lowest story of the houses
usually reaches a kanat, making a cool summer room, delightful
to the natives.   However, to westerners the attractiveness is
reduced because the kanats act both as water supply and sewer
for the dwellings.

History of Kanat Building.—The origin of kanat building is
lost in antiquity.   According to Butler the tunnel of Negoub
was built in 800 B.C. to supply the city of Nineveh.   In 626 B.C.
the Medes captured the city of Hamadan by destroying the kanats
that supplied water to the city.

Water development by building kanats was introduced in
Egypt about 500 B.C. by Admiral Scylox, whom Butler designates
as the father of engineers.   He built an extensive kanat system
irrigating 1800 square miles of fertile land.   These kanats are
said to penetrate sandstone strata, the water of which is concentrated in faults.   In celebration of the completion of this great
project the Egyptians built the temple of Ammon at Thebes and
for the first time officially recognized their conqueror Darius I as
Pharaoh of Egypt.   The outlets of this great Egyptian system
became clogged and covered during the passage of time and until
recently those still flowing were supposed to be springs.   Translation of old inscriptions and subsequent exploration revealed their
true nature.   Their length has not as yet been determined, but
they are believed to extend far to the east under a hundred miles
of rolling desert to intercept seepage from the Nile.

Construction.—The art of kanat building is practiced by a
guild whose members are known as *mukanni*, under whose direction the coolies perform the manual labor.   The chief (the

[1] BUTLER, M. A., Irrigation in Persia by Kanats, *Civil Eng.*, vol. 3, no. 2,
pp. 69–73, February, 1933.

mukanni bashi) locates the exploratory shaft or shafts upslope from the desired portal of the proposed kanat with appropriate mysterious ceremonies to impress his clients, usually a company of land owners. After the exploratory shafts have located a satisfactory bed of water-bearing material, a series of construction shafts are sunk, taking advantage of the terrain. Work begins at the portal and construction shafts are sunk at varying distances; according to Fraser at maximum intervals of 100 yd., where the kanat is deep, and averaging 60 to the mile.[1] The grade and direction of the kanat from shaft to shaft are determined by a crude surveying instrument, consisting of a plumb line with a heavy weight hung from a tripod or crossbar placed over the shaft. The plumb line is tied into a loop above the mouth of the shaft and a notched stick is inserted, spreading the looped portion apart. The sighting stick is adjusted to the desired grade and differences in elevation are recorded by knots in the line. The muck is carried by hand from the working face of the tunnel in a fold of burlap or goatskin and hoisted to the surface by windlass. There is no ventilation in the tunnels. Reflected sunlight has been used since ancient times. Accidents are frequent and the loss of life is great, but there are always others to carry on.

The kanats of Teheran, over 200 years old, are reported to have cost more than the equivalent of $100,000. A kanat constructed at Mazandaran 10,500 ft. long and 42 ft. below the surface,[2] with presumably about 60 shafts to the mile, or approximately 15,000 ft. of sinking and tunneling, cost $9,100, or about 60 cents per foot, a cost which has not been approached by modern occidental miners.

Geology and Ground-water Hydrology.—Most of the Persian kanats are driven into the great alluvial cones that fill all the valleys of the high plateaus in the desert highland. They exceed in size the alluvial cones of western America, even the piedmont cones of the eastern slope of the Sierra Nevada. Clapp[3] describes them as hundreds of miles in breadth and several scores of miles

---

[1] FRASER, DAVID, "The Marches of Hindustan," Blackwood and Sons, London, 1907.

[2] BUTLER, Irrigation in Persia by Kanats, *op. cit.*

[3] CLAPP, F. G., Tehran and the Elburz, *Geog. Rev.*, vol. 20, no. 1, pp. 69–85, 1930.

from mountain slope to the center of the valley, where the gravelly alluvial material grades into silt which supports some crops where not too dry or saline and is highly productive where watered by kanats. The bedrock of the mountains which supply the material for the alluvial cones is predominantly limestone and volcanic tuff. The conglomerates, therefore, are cemented by silt and calcareous material and apparently stand well, but, of course, there is constant caving in the softer formations and this calls for constant cleaning and repair.

The ground-water hydrology of the alluvial cones is interesting. Apparently exploratory shafts are necessary to locate water-bearing sands; the cemented formations carry little water. The productive water-bearing formations are encountered at considerable distance up the slope of the alluvial cones. Long experience handed down from the distant past enables the *bashi* to select a favorable locality for the exploratory shaft. After the water-bearing sand is encountered in the shaft, apparently there is little difficulty in handling the water in the tunnel driven to tap the shaft. A western miner viewing these remarkable constructions would consider them the wonder of ancient civilization.

THE DEVELOPMENT OF GROUND-WATER THEORY[1]

In ancient times springs were considered as miraculous gifts of the gods; they wrought miracles and consequently were places where temples were built. These superstitions continue today, perhaps somewhat modified by time, in the optimistic overestimation of the therapeutic value of "medicinal" springs.

The Greek philosophers were familiar with cavernous limestone terranes and, reasoning by analogy, conceived that great open spaces existed in the depths of the earth and that the natural processes at depth were similar to those observed at the surface. Homer, Thales, and Plato correctly concluded that spring water is derived from the ocean but erroneously supposed that a direct

---

[1] History and Development of Ground-Water Hydrology, by O. E. Meinzer, furnished much of the information outlined in the following discussion and his article is quoted extensively. The reader is referred to the comprehensive references given in his paper. A recent paper entitled, "Historical Development of Ideas regarding the Origin of Springs and Ground Water," by M. N. Baker and R. E. Horton (*Trans. Amer. Geophys. Union*, pp. 395–400, 1936) is an interesting summary from original sources.

return flow takes place through subterranean channels.   Aristotle thought that as "the air surrounding the earth is turned into water by the cold of the heavens and falls as rain," so "the air which penetrates and passes into the crust of the earth also becomes transformed into water owing to the cold which it encounters there.   The water coming out of the earth unites with the rain water to produce rivers.   The rainfall alone is quite insufficient to supply the rivers of the world with water. The ocean into which the rivers run does not overflow because, while some of the water is evaporated, the rest of it changes back into air or into one of the other elements."[1]

Quoting from Meinzer's historical review of the development of ground-water hydrology:

Prior to the latter part of the 17th century it was generally assumed that the water discharged by the springs could not be derived from the rain, first because the rainfall was believed to be inadequate in quantity, and secondly, because the earth was believed to be too impervious to permit penetration of the rain water far below the surface.   With these two erroneous postulates lightly assumed, the philosophers devoted their thought to devising ingenuous hypotheses to account in some other way for the spring and stream water.   Two main hypotheses were developed: one to the effect that sea water is conducted through subterranean channels below the mountains and is then purified and raised to the springs; the other to the effect that in the cold dark caverns under the mountains the subterranean atmosphere and perhaps the earth itself are condensed into the moisture which feeds the springs.

The sea-water hypothesis gave rise to subsidiary hypotheses to explain how the sea water is freed from its salt and how it is elevated to the altitude of the springs.   The removal of the salt was ascribed to processes of either distillation or filtration.   The elevation of the water was by different writers ascribed to processes of vaporization and subsequent condensation, to rock pressure, to suction of the wind, to pressure exerted on the sea by the wind and waves, or later to capillary action. One curious explanation was that, owing to the curvature of the earth, the water in the middle of the ocean is actually at a much higher altitude than the springs and hence furnishes the necessary head.[2]

[1] ADAMS, F. D., Origin of Springs and Rivers, An Historical Review, *Fennia*, vol. 50, no. 1, Finland, 1928; Abst. *Geol. Soc. Amer. Bull.*, vol. 39, pp. 149–150, 1928.

[2] MEINZER, O. E., History and Development of Ground-water Hydrology, *Wash. Acad. Sci. Jour.*, vol. 25, no. 1, pp. 6–32, January, 1934.

The failure of the ancient philosophers to recognize influent seepage from rainfall as the source of springs and rivers was due to the belief that rain water penetrates only a few feet below ground surface. "Rainfall," declared Seneca, "cannot possibly be the source of springs because it penetrates only a few feet into the Earth whereas springs are fed from deep down. . . . As a diligent digger among my vines I can affirm my observation that no rain is ever so heavy as to wet the ground to a depth of more than ten feet."[1] This belief seems to have been undisputed for centuries.

Beginning with the middle of the sixteenth century numerous publications appeared which contained discussions of ground water, but until the close of the seventeenth century the two old Greek hypotheses chiefly occupied the field, although the infiltration theory was explained by a few writers, especially in 1850 by Bernard Palissy.[2] Palissy was reared in poverty and was not educated in Greek and Latin, but at an early age he began to observe nature and based his theories on his observations. He wrote a fascinating dialogue between "Theory" and "Practice."

"When for a long time," says Practice, "I had closely considered the cause of the sources of natural fountains and the place whence they might proceed, at length I became plainly assured that they could proceed from or be engendered by nothing but the rains." Theory replies: "After having heard your opinion I am compelled to say that you are a great fool. Do you think me so ignorant that I should put more faith in what you say, than in so large a number of philosophers who tell us that all waters come from the sea and return thither? . . . "[3]

Two great men of the 17th century who rejected or ignored the teachings of Palissy were the German astronomer Johann Kepler (1571–1630) and the French philosopher René Descartes (1596–1650). The hypothesis that the earth functions somewhat like an animal, or indeed that it is a living being, became current early in the 17th century and had adherents as late as the 19th century. Kepler adopted this hypothesis and expressed the opinion that the earth, like a huge animal, takes in the water of the ocean, digests and assimilates it, and discharges the products of these physiological processes through springs. Descartes taught that the sea water finds its way into the depths of the earth through

[1] BAKER and HORTON, *op. cit.*, p. 399.
[2] PALISSY, B., Discours admirable de la nature des eaux et fontaines tant naturelles qu'artificielles, 1580.
[3] MEINZER, *op. cit.*, p. 1.

underground channels and is there vaporized by the heat of the earth's interior; furthermore that the vapor rises through caverns, is condensed at higher levels, and thus supplies the springs.[1]

In the latter part of the seventeenth century Perrault, Mariotté, and Halley abandoned the theories of the past and actively undertook experimental work to determine the source and movements of ground water. Thus the science of ground-water hydrology was born.

Perrault made measurements of the rainfall during three years; and he roughly estimated the area of the drainage basin of the Seine River above a point in Burgundy and of the runoff from this same basin. Thus he computed that the quantity of water that fell on the basin as rain or snow was about six times the quantity discharged by the river. Crude as was his work, he nevertheless demonstrated the fallacy of the age-old assumption of the inadequacy of the rainfall to account for the discharge of springs and streams. Mariotté computed the discharge of the Seine at Paris by measuring its width, depth, and velocity at approximately its mean stage, making the velocity measurements by the float method. He essentially verified Perrault's results. About the same time Halley made crude tests of evaporation, and demonstrated that the evaporation from the sea is sufficient to account for all the water supplied to the springs and streams, thus removing the need for Plato's Tartaros or any other mysterious subterranean channel to conduct the water from the ocean to the springs.[2]

Mariotté, who discovered Mariotté's law of gases, also known as Boyle's law, probably deserves more than any other man the distinction of being regarded as the founder of ground-water hydrology, perhaps I should say of the entire science of hydrology. In his publications, which appeared after his death in 1684, he defended vigorously the infiltration theory and created much of the modern thought on the subject. According to the brief digest of his works by Keilhack (Lehrbuch der Grundwasser und Quellenkunde, 1912 ed., pp. 80, 81) he maintained that the water derived from rain and snow penetrates into the pores of the earth and accumulates in wells; that this water percolates downward till it reaches impermeable rock and thence percolates laterally; and that it is sufficient in quantity to supply the springs. He demonstrated that the rain water penetrates into the earth, and used for this purpose the cellar of the Paris Observatory, the percolation through the cover of which compared with the amount of rainfall. He also showed that the flow of springs increases in rainy weather and diminishes in times of

[1] Meinzer, *op. cit*, pp. 10–11.
[2] *Ibid.*, p. 11.

drought, and explained that the more constant springs are supplied from larger underground reservoirs.[1]

In 1660 John Ray delivered two series of sermons . . . (in which) he described a brook flowing close by his dwelling. This he had ascended to its source, noting that it was fed by numerous rivulets along the way and by a spring at the top which in turn must be supplied with water from adjacent ground. All this water evidently came from rain. Applying these observations to several large European rivers whose courses he had inspected, he wrote that they did not seem to him "to bear any greater proportion to the rivers and rivulets they receive and the immense tracts of land that fed them than my small brook doth to its small rills and compass of ground."[2]

Erasmus Darwin, grandfather of Charles, made practical use of geology to improve the water of a contaminated well by sinking one within it to tap a deeper inclined stratum which he observed at the outcrop.

In the first half of the nineteenth century French engineers, geologists, and drillers made many contributions to the study of ground water, largely because this was the period of great activity in drilling artesian wells in France. In the last half of the nineteenth century French and German scientists and those of other nations began to record conclusions founded on observational data, thus furnishing the foundation upon which the science of ground-water hydrology has been built.

In America the writings of famous engineers, such as Hazen[3] and King,[4] mathematicians such as Slichter,[5] and the classic contributions of geologists such as Chamberlin[6] and Darton,[7] and many others initiated the scientific study of ground water.

[1] MEINZER, *op. cit.*, p. 12.

[2] BAKER and HORTON, *op. cit.*, p. 399.

[3] HAZEN, A., Some Physical Properties of Sands and Gravels, *Mass. State Board of Health, 24th Ann. Rept.* for 1892 (1893).

[4] KING, F. H., Principles and Conditions of Movement of Ground Water, *U.S. Geol. Surv. 19th Ann. Rept.*, pt. II, 1899.

[5] SLICHTER, C. S., Theoretical Investigation of the Motion of Ground Water, *U.S. Geol. Surv. 19th Ann. Rept.*, pt. II, 1899.

[6] CHAMBERLIN, T. C., Requisite and Qualifying Conditions of Artesian Wells, *U.S. Geol. Surv. 5th Ann. Rept.*, 1885.

[7] DARTON, N. H., Artesian Well Prospects on the Atlantic Coastal Plain Region, *U.S. Geol. Surv. Bull.* 138, 1896; Geology and Underground Water Resources of the Central Great Plains, *U.S. Geol. Surv. Prof. Paper* 32, 1905; The Geology and Underground Waters of South Dakota, *U.S. Geol. Surv. Water-Supply Paper* 227, 1909.

Geological concepts of the nature and movements of underground water were strongly influenced by Van Hise's[1] classic discussion of ground water, which he pictured as a great "sea of underground water" permeating the outer shell of the earth to the limits of the "zone of fracture" which he thought extended to a depth of 5 to 6 miles below the earth's surface.

Slichter's theoretical and mathematical studies and field measurements of the motions of ground water,[2] although limited to movements of water in assorted sands, emphasized the slow general motions of ground water throughout the entire mass of pervious material in the general direction of the slope of the water table.

From these sources chiefly was derived the notion generally accepted until recently of an interconnected ground-water body of great extent with a general slow movement distributed throughout the entire body of water. Confined or artesian water in the great sandstone formations where structural conditions were favorable was, of course, recognized and described,[3] but until recently no concept was expressed in the literature of the complexity of the motions of the innumerable disconnected bodies of free-moving water interstratified with bodies of stagnant (fixed) water in fine-grained porous but impervious material.

The laws governing water movement in capillary openings, which predominate in alluvial and sedimentary formations, were deduced experimentally by Hagen (1839), Poiseuille (1840–1842), Darcy (1856), Hazen (1892), and Slichter (1899) (pages 200–207). If these laws had been considered in the light of the character of sedimentary and alluvial materials, ground water would not have been pictured as "a sea" affected throughout by slow general motions.

One of the facts brought out by these experimental studies is that under a given hydraulic gradient the velocity of ground-water percolation varies directly as the square of the size of the capillary openings through which the water moves, or approxi-

[1] VAN HISE, C. R., Treatise on Metamorphism, *U.S. Geol. Surv. Mon.* 47, pp. 123–158.

[2] SLICHTER, *op. cit.*, Chap. I; Motions of Underground Water, *U.S. Geol. Surv. Water-Supply Paper* 67, 1902; Field Measurements of Rate of Movement of Underground Waters, *U.S. Geol. Surv. Water-Supply Paper* 140, 1905.

[3] CHAMBERLIN, *op. cit.*, pp. 131–173.

mately as the square of the average diameter of the constituent grains of water-bearing material. To explain the bearing of this on the motions of ground water, it may be recalled that coarse, sorted sand of average grain size of 1 mm. diameter is very pervious and is a good aquifer; while fine silt, of average particle diameter of 0.01 mm., represents probably about the finest material through which water can be forced by gravity. Now assume, as may easily be the case, a water-table slope or a pressure gradient sufficient to force water through the coarse sand at the rate of $8\frac{1}{3}$ ft. or 100 in. a day, about 3000 ft. a year. Under the same slope or gradient water will move through the silt $\frac{1}{100}$ in. a day or 3.65 in. a year. This example emphasizes the fact that in sorted, pervious materials the grain size is of utmost importance in controlling the movement of ground water. Ready movement takes place only in coarse, sorted material such as sand, gravel, and uncemented sandstone, and in open fractures and solution channels. Fine silt and clay and most unsorted materials and, of course, unfractured crystalline rocks act as barriers to ground-water motions.

The twentieth century has seen painstaking refinements in the methods of field investigation and interpretation of data collected, laboratory methods of investigation of hydrologic characteristics of water-bearing materials, and the development of methods of making a ground-water inventory. Chemistry, physics, and bacteriology of ground water have been closely studied.

The important literature easily available to the American student occurs chiefly in the following publications:

The *United States Geological Survey Water-Supply Papers* which since 1900 include more than 200 papers relating primarily to ground water. Meinzer's writings appear chiefly in these publications and constitute the most comprehensive and most valuable treatment of ground water. His writings have been quoted extensively in this text, especially in the chapters on Springs (Chap. XV), The Ground-water Inventory (Chap. XVI), and Ground-water Provinces (Chap. XVII).

The *Bulletins of the American Society of Civil Engineers* contain many contributions dealing with the engineering phases of ground-water investigations. The *Geological Survey Bulletins* of the various states and *State Engineers' Reports* contain important data on ground water. The *Transactions of the American Geophysical Union* published by the National Research Council of the National Academy of Sciences furnish the best summaries of recent advances in our knowledge of ground-water hydrology and hydrology in general, and also the closely related science of meteorology.

The extensive botanical literature and literature of the agricultural scientist contain important data on the hydrologic properties of soil, as well as detailed discussions of the forces acting on water occurring above the water table. Important contributions appear in the publications of the Carnegie Botanical Laboratory, the *Bulletins of the United States Department of Agriculture*, the *Proceedings* and *Papers of the International Congress of Soil Science*, publications of the various agricultural colleges and experimental stations connected with universities, and in scientific periodicals dealing with soils.

POPULAR SUPERSTITION AND MISINFORMATION REGARDING GROUND WATER

Centuries have been required to free scientists from superstition and wild theories handed down from the dawn of history regarding the unseen subsurface water, and one should learn to control his impatience at the constant reminders that this is still an age of popular superstition with respect to the occurrence of ground water. The elementary principle that gravity controls motions of water underground as well as at the surface is not appreciated by all engaged in the development of ground-water supplies.

The popular belief exists that "rivers of underground water" pass through solid rock devoid of interconnected interstices and flow under intervening mountain ranges. For example, it has been stated that the ground water of the coastal valleys of California originates in the Sierra Nevada, passes under the Great Valley of California and the intervening mountains of the Coast Range, regardless, of course, of geologic structure. It has been repeatedly stated that large springs flow from fissures at the top of the highest peaks of a mountain range. Many people still believe that the magical forked witch stick is able to point to underground water streams and will actually twist in the hands of the operator in its endeavor to do so.

These popular superstitions are examples of the ability to believe without the foundation of facts, and this peculiar ability exists in the minds of both "educated" and "uneducated" men. Inasmuch as the movements of underground water cannot be observed at the surface, they have been subject to wild speculation. Even a judge in our courts has ruled that "percolating water moves in a mysterious manner, in courses unknown and unknowable."

Present-day knowledge in regard to the occurrence of ground water and especially the control of geologic structure over its motions should be of wide interest. People should be freed from superstitions regarding the mysterious and "unlawful" wandering of water underground. Every user of well water should know something about the source and underground motions of his water supply. In this way he may guard against contamination and be able to decide whether or not advice is sound, which is usually given by well drillers, as to the advisability of deepening a well or sinking others. Owners of estates in the rolling foothills or in the pleasant valleys of the Coast Range in the vicinity of San Francisco have put down deep wells to encounter the currents of water that, according to popular belief, must exist at depth. Yet in much of this area ground water occurs in fractures in impervious rocks, and most of these fractures die out with depth.

ECONOMIC IMPORTANCE OF GROUND WATER

The importance of ground water in the semiarid West; the quantity of ground water now pumped; the importance of the industry of manufacturing pumping machinery, water-well-drilling equipment and supplies; and the number of men engaged in well drilling certainly justify the attention now being devoted to ground water. Not only in the United States, but also in arid regions the world over, pumping ground water is one of the major industries.

It has been estimated by Cox[1] that in India alone not less than 20,000,000 acres are under irrigation using pumped well water—an acreage comparable with the total irrigated area of the United States.

A brief summary of information published in the Fourteenth and Fifteenth Federal Census reports of 1920 and 1930, respectively, gives an indication of the importance of water development in California, and also shows the rapid increase in the use of ground water as compared to surface water between the years 1920 and 1930.

The acres irrigated from pumped wells in California increased 76 per cent in these ten years, to 1,453,000; while the acres irrigated by gravity supply from streams decreased 34 per cent

---

[1] Cox, W. G., "Artesian Wells as a Means of Water Supply," Brisbane, South Australia, pp. 3–7, 1895.

(approximately 900,000 acres). The estimated investment to supply irrigation water in California was $450,000,000 up to 1930, of which $240,000,000, or 53 per cent, was invested in pumping wells.

The only figures available at present on the number of irrigation wells in the United States are those given in the 1930 census. These are reproduced below with those for California. Apparently only the large irrigation wells are listed, as the number of wells in the United States is known to be far greater than the census figures.[1]

1930	Flowing wells		Pumping wells	
	Number	Capacity, g.p.m.	Number	Capacity, g.p.m.
Total for California..........	449	65,768	46,737	24,266,167
Total for United States.......	4,811	609,367	56,729	32,467,120

The present development is but a start toward the full utilization of our ground-water resources. In the regions where ground water has been overpumped and the water level lowered unduly, methods of artificial recharge may be used to refill the underground reservoirs and also conserve flood waters (pages 173–187). In the more humid regions crops may be saved in the occasional dry years by recourse to pumping.

The following statement by Henry Morgenthau Jr., Governor, U.S. Farm Credit Administration, was chiefly responsible for the final success in starting the extensive project in the Santa Clara Valley, Santa Clara County, California, to conserve flood water in surface reservoirs and feed it underground to replenish the depleted ground-water reservoir.

Many California complaints came from Santa Clara Valley. There the water table has fallen 90 ft. in fifteen years. Would you put your money there with no assurance that during the next fifteen years the water table would not continue to fall, and pumping costs rise? We are not going to make that kind of a loan. But if a Santa Clara Valley farm is close to water, if the pumping costs are low, we will lend the money.[2]

[1] Fifteenth Census of the United States, 1930, Irrigation of Agricultural Lands (Summary for the United States), 1929 and 1930.

[2] *The Commonwealth*, vol. 9, no. 36, p. 160, Sept. 5, 1933.

The four great droughts that have afflicted central and midwestern United States in the last six years seriously affected ground-water supplies, soil moisture, and locally influent seepage by which ground water is supplied. The conservation of soil and soil moisture is now promised as a national undertaking. It is to be hoped that the conservation and storage of ground water for auxiliary supply in times of deficient rainfall will be undertaken under the direction of those who have scientific knowledge of the occurrence of ground water and practical understanding of the methods of its extraction and conservation.

CHAPTER II

RÉSUMÉ OF ELEMENTS OF GROUND-WATER HYDROLOGY AND APPLICATION TO GROUND-WATER LITIGATION

Before presenting in detail the data gathered by investigators in many lines of scientific research on many different subjects, but all bearing on some phase of the study of ground water, it seems advisable to present in this preliminary chapter the general scheme of the occurrence and motions of ground water with discussion of methods of investigation. The purpose of the chapter is to give a clear picture of the origin, occurrence, and behavior of the unseen subsurface water bodies, with brief reference to the practical application of the principles involved, in order that the more detailed technical discussions in the following chapters may be appreciated. In preparing this chapter the writer has borne in mind the statement of several attorneys that a summary of this type would be of assistance in the lawyer's preparation for ground-water litigation.

Throughout the chapter the writer has embraced the opportunity to mention, and where necessary to define, the technical terms used by ground-water investigators. The important terms are in italics where first mentioned. In order to read or discuss understandingly any scientific subject, the terminology of the particular science involved must be understood. Inasmuch as investigators of ground water have borrowed terms from many different sciences, a glossary of the terms used in this text has been compiled and appears as an appendix. Comprehensive references to the literature are appended to subsequent chapters containing the detailed discussions.

States of Water

Gas.—Water as a gas is known as water vapor. It is the third most abundant gas in nature; nitrogen being first, oxygen second, and carbon dioxide fourth. In order of importance with respect to life and geologic processes they are: oxygen, water vapor, and carbon dioxide. Important

26

subsurface gases are ground air and water vapor which occur above the water table; and hydrocarbon gases, hydrogen sulphide, and carbon dioxide which occur below the water table.

Liquid.—Water as a liquid occurs as running water, standing water, as drops of fog and dew, and as drops of rain. The only other important liquids in nature are the hydrocarbons, found locally where the geologic structure favors accumulation of oil, and lava (molten rock) which is a temporary liquid.

Solid.—Forms of solid water are ice (glacial ice is important as a water reserve); snow, also important where large accumulations occur during the winter; hail; and hoar frost (frozen vapor condensed on solids).

Water Classified According to Origin

Water may be classified as to source under the headings *meteoric water, juvenile water, rejuvenated* or *metamorphic water*, and *connate water*.

Meteoric water is derived from the atmosphere. It is precipitated on the surface of the globe and may enter the subsurface reservoirs, sooner or later to return again to the atmosphere. It constitutes the great body of atmospheric, surface, and subsurface water which has accumulated during geologic time.

Juvenile water is new water. It constitutes an addition to the water supply of the globe, and is further classified according to origin as *magmatic, volcanic*, and *cosmic* water.

Magmatic Water.—Magma is molten rock occurring *at depth* and consists of a mutual solution of melted rock-forming minerals and of gases, the most important of which is water vapor. That magmatic water is given up upon crystallization of magma is shown by the minerals formed at and near the contact of igneous rocks with intruded rocks, and especially by those that replace the intruded rock and penetrate it in veins. Some of these minerals could have been transported only in solution in water vapor and in liquid water. Water driven out of magma during its crystallization is called *magmatic water*.

Volcanic water is a second type of juvenile water, often included with magmatic water. It is furnished by surface lava flows. In the Hawaiian Islands volcanic water has been collected, by means of tubes put down into the molten lava, and analyzed. It contains no argon, which occurs in all atmospheric water, hence it is concluded that it is new water, not derived from atmospheric or ground water. It has further been shown that throughout molten lava oxygen and hydrogen are uniting to form water, and that this action is an important source of volcanic heat.[1]

Cosmic water, or water that comes in from space with meteorites, is a third type of juvenile water. No quantitative estimate has been made of the amount of cosmic water added annually to the water supply of the globe.

Rejuvenated water is water returned to the terrestrial water supply by geologic processes of compaction and metamorphism. Compaction reduces

---

[1] DAY, A. L., and E. S. SHEPHERD, Water and Volcanic Activity, *Bull. Geol. Soc. Amer.*, vol. 24, pp. 573–606, 1913.

the porosity of clayey sediments from as high as 50 per cent in freshly deposited material to 3 to 4 per cent in shales. As compaction takes place, the water filling the pore space thus destroyed is forced into the available aquifers. This type of rejuvenated water may be denominated *water of compaction* (p. 142).

Weathering causes water to combine with the minerals of rocks to form new minerals and thus be abstracted from the water supply of the globe. This water is returned only in part by the reversal of the process due to metamorphism, which involves dehydration and driving out of water fixed in the minerals by weathering. This type of rejuvenated water may be called *metamorphic water.* If there were no additions to the atmospheric and to the terrestrial water supply, fixation of water by weathering would ultimately exhaust the earth's water supply. Fortunately water is constantly being added, as previously stated, and probably makes up in part for the water permanently removed by weathering.

Connate Water.—The openings and interstices of all sedimentary rocks deposited beneath the ocean were originally filled with salt water. After the rocks have been lifted above the sea, fresh water slowly drives out and replaces the salt water. Exploration of oil fields has shown that bodies of sea water are preserved in anticlines and under barriers which prevent access of sweet water descending from the ground surface. Connate water, therefore, exists as pockets of stagnant water, especially in structures which hold oil and gas and which have not been flushed out with fresh water. These occurrences indicate that under unfavorable structural conditions ground-water movement may be restricted even in pervious beds. The occurrence of stagnant bodies of oil-field water is discussed in Chap. XIV.

COMPOSITION OF GROUND WATER

Ground water is never chemically pure. Even rain water contains materials dissolved from the air as well as suspended dust. "Red snow" or "blood rain" is colored by intermixed organisms of microscopic size.[1] The composition of ground water limits its suitability for agricultural and industrial purposes and for drinking water.

The most common substances dissolved in ground water are the salts of the common basic radicals derived from rock disintegration, and acids derived from the disintegration of rocks, from the gases of the air, volcanic gases, and from organic sources. The common bases are sodium, potassium, calcium, magnesium, iron, and aluminum; and the common acid radicals are Cl, SO_4, and CO_3. The rarer bases such as lithium, barium, copper, zinc, and the acids of arsenic and boron may give the water unusual or

---

[1] Geikie, Sir A., "Textbook of Geology," vol. 1, p. 444, 1903, The Macmillan Company, New York.

even toxic properties. Ground water may be classified as mineral and nonmineral. The former includes water that contains unusual amounts of dissolved salts, especially of uncommon composition. The term is usually limited to spring water and is not applied to the general body of ground water. Spring waters are also classified as *thermal* and *nonthermal.* The latter have approximately the average temperature of the rocks at or near the surface. The temperature of ground water may vary from freezing (in caves and ground water derived from snow fields and glaciers) to superheated water above the boiling point at the surface (geysers).

Ground water may suffer *contamination* from natural sources and *pollution* by man and animals. In pervious water-bearing deposits situated at the seashore sweet ground water may float on salt ground water (pages 245–248). Where pervious water-bearing material alternates with impervious material, contamination may be caused by movement of salt water down wells after the static level of the wells has been reduced below sea level by pumping. Certain formations may contain sufficient salts to contaminate water enclosed therein. This type of contamination may be designated *formational contamination.* Pollution is commonly bacterial but may be caused by mixing with industrial wastes and with mine waters. Bacterial pollution is studied in specially equipped bacteriological laboratories.

TYPES AND CAPACITY OF NATURAL RESERVOIRS

The openings in soils, alluvial materials, nonindurated sedimentary formations, and to a less extent fractures and solution openings in crystalline rocks, constitute a great ground-water reservoir, and the level to which the reservoir is filled is recorded by the water table.

Water is stored in other natural reservoirs overlying the ground-water reservoir and is moved from one reservoir to another by the force of gravity, unbalanced film forces, and the molecular forces generated by solar energy, chiefly transpiration, evaporation, and condensation. Ground water is replenished by water from the overlying reservoirs and is depleted by the return of water to them.

The principal reservoirs are (1) the atmosphere, a reservoir of atmospheric moisture which replenishes all the other reservoirs;

(2) the ground surface which supports surface water in streams, lakes, ponds, the ocean, and solid water as snow and ice; (3) the soil zone, acting as a reservoir of soil moisture which is held against the pull of gravity and is thus made available for plant consumption; and (4) the ground-water reservoir.

Water Vapor Stored in the Atmosphere.—Water is a variable constituent of the atmosphere, the quantity varying with the temperature of the air. Large quantities of water vapor are present in warm saturated air of the tropics. Water is largely limited to the atmospheric "zone of convection" which constitutes the basal stratum of the atmosphere about 7 miles thick.[1] The average water vapor content of the atmosphere, if precipitated, is equivalent to a layer about 1 in. thick over the globe or 4 in. thick over the continents.[2] It is the smallest but most active of the terrestrial water bodies. Moisture evaporated from large areas is precipitated in the vicinity of barometric lows by the winds blowing toward them, and rainfall of a single storm (measured in inches) often far exceeds the average moisture content of the atmosphere. Rainfall is the source of all surface and underground water, and therefore rainfall is measured and all available rainfall data are analyzed by the ground-water investigator.

Surface Water.—Surface water consists of two distinct water bodies: (1) the oceanic water body which is highly mineralized by salts, and (2) the surface fresh-water body which covers small portions of the land surface.

The oceanic water body contains sufficient water to cover the entire globe to a depth of a little less than 2 miles, and if spread evenly over the continents, would average about 8 miles in depth.[3] It is by far the largest of the earth's water bodies. It is the chief source of atmospheric moisture and therefore of all the other water bodies.

Fresh water is held in rivers, ponds, and lakes, is stored during the winter months as snow and ice, and is locked up for

---

[1] HUMPHREYS, W. J., "Physics of the Air," 2d ed., pp. 97–101, McGraw-Hill Book Company, Inc., New York, 1929.

[2] HUMPHREYS, W. J., The Atmosphere: Origin and Composition, *National Research Council, Bull.* 79, p. 11, 1931.

[3] CHAMBERLIN, T. C., and R. D. SALISBURY, "Geology," vol. 1, p. 7, Henry Holt & Company, 1909.

many years in the polar ice caps and mountain glaciers. If the surface fresh water were evenly distributed over the continents, it would probably be thinner even than the equivalent of suspended atmospheric moisture. If the water in the polar ice caps is included, however, the water body would be larger than that retained in the soil-moisture reservoir. Surface water, especially that flowing in streams, contributes to ground water, and hence influent stream seepage will be studied in detail.

Soil-moisture Reservoir.—Even in regions blessed by abundant supplies of surface water most plants, and hence man who subsists upon them, could not live if the water stored in the soil zone were not available for plant consumption. Taking the average thickness of the zone penetrated by roots as 5 ft., the moisture held in the soil is equivalent to a little less than 1 ft. of water. Crops consume 1 to 4 ft. of water annually, and therefore the soil moisture must be renewed by frequent rains or by irrigation in order to support a vigorous growth of vegetation.

In arid and semiarid regions rainfall is less than the quantity of water consumed by crops and may not meet the full demand of natural vegetation. The water stored in the soil is attached to the soil particles and is removed in large part by plant transpiration (pages 145–148). This deficit must be fully repaired before water can move downward to the water table through the soil zone. When rainfall is less than the capacity of existing vegetation to consume water, no rainfall can penetrate to the water table through a depleted soil zone, even though the formations of the zone of aeration are pervious. Therefore seepage from rainfall may not be an important source of ground water in arid regions.

The soil is usually the upper portion of the zone of aeration. Below the reach of roots water films attached to the surfaces of openings are not removed by transpiration. After the excess water (*gravity water*) drains away, these residual water films (*pellicular water*[1]) remain fixed and are only very slowly depleted by subsurface evaporation and chemical reaction of the water with rock particles, known as weathering. Therefore the water held suspended between the water table and the soil is not available

[1] From the French word "pellicule" meaning skin (Fourmarier, P., Recherches relatives a l'influence de l'eau sur la migration du petrole dans les roches, *Ann. Soc. Géol. de Belgique*, vol. 47, *Bull.*, 1924).

directly or indirectly to man. The quantity of unavailable water thus stored is generally much larger than that stored as soil moisture.

Ground-water Reservoir.—Van Hise[1] has estimated the quantity of ground water to be equivalent to a layer of water covering the globe to a depth of about 200 to 600 ft. This is based on an estimate of the average porosity of rocks to the depth of 5 to 6 miles. The porosity of crystalline rocks below the superficial fracture zone is very small. The openings are largely of subcapillary size, consisting of intercrystal interstices and closed fracture planes. Therefore crystalline rocks below the zone of open fractures may be neglected as a reservoir for water. The porosity of sedimentary and alluvial material, if not cemented, is large. In thick sequences of sedimentary rock the ground-water body is probably very much thicker than estimated by Van Hise, and much thinner where crystalline rocks come close to the surface.

Water held in clay, silt, shale, cemented sandstone, and crystalline rocks is held in interstices so small that it is either permanently attached to the walls of the openings or moves with extreme slowness (fixed ground water) and is usually not available as a source of water for pumping. Available water is enclosed in openings of capillary and larger sizes principally in sand, gravel, uncemented sandstone, and near-surface fractures and solution openings.

If the present economic limit for deep water wells is taken as 2000 ft., the available water body in saturated pervious alluvial and sedimentary material extending to that depth would fill a surface reservoir, equal in extent to that of the body of pervious material, to a depth of 500 ft. Of course, alluvial materials do not commonly extend to a depth of 2000 ft. and are not usually pervious throughout, and sedimentary formations consist of interstratified pervious and impervious material. However, under favorable conditions, alluvial material and pervious sedimentary formations may constitute reservoirs of great capacity.

Comparison of Surface and Subsurface Storage.—The advantage of ground-water storage is that it largely eliminates evapo-

[1] Van Hise, C. R., Treatise on Metamorphism, *U.S. Geol. Surv. Mon.* 47, pp. 129, 569–571, 1904.

ration which affects surface storage. The natural subsurface reservoirs are large and may hold a reserve supply for use during a cycle of dry years and by artificial recharge may be utilized to their full capacity. They do not call for the investment of large sums of money, as do high dams and large surface reservoirs. Also they are safe. Water pumped from underground reservoirs may be cheaper than water supplied by surface irrigation systems.

Surface storage in the form of snow is important in the western mountain ranges and especially in the Sierra Nevada of California, where it constitutes an enormous reservoir which is filled every winter. Unfortunately, however, the reservoir may break with the first warm rains in spring, causing enormous floods in the rivers draining the high Sierra. Although snow storage is of value, it must be supplemented by artificial storage and the full use of the subsurface reservoirs in the arid Southwest.

THE HYDROLOGIC CYCLE

The *hydrologic cycle* includes all movements of water vapor in the atmosphere, condensation to liquid and solid states in the atmosphere; precipitation of liquid and solid water on the ground surface; evaporation and melting of ice and snow on the ground surface, including partial return to the vapor state in the atmosphere; evaporation and flow of water on the surface, including partial return to the vapor state in the atmosphere, and movement of water toward the ocean; all movements of water underground and back to the surface; and evaporation and transpiration of water on the ground surface and from the surface of the ocean back to the vapor state and to the atmosphere.

Engineers are apt to emphasize only one small part of the hydrologic cycle, that is, the movement of water from waterbearing materials into wells. However, it is necessary to study the entire cycle in order to understand subsurface-water motions. The hydrologic cycle may be long or short. It may be summarized, beginning with the short cyclic movement and ending with the longer and more complicated.

1. Vapor condenses to rain, snow, or fog and vaporizes again before the water reaches the earth's surface.

2. Vapor condenses in the atmosphere into rain or snow which reaches the surface of the earth and is then evaporated before the

water gets underground. This evaporation may be directly from the rain water before it forms runoff, from streams, lakes, or the ocean. The water gets back into the atmosphere without an underground journey.

3. Water vapor condenses and falls as snow or rain on the ground and seeps below the surface. The water which enters the soil may return to the atmosphere by the following methods: (*a*) It may be held as soil moisture and returned directly by transpiration and evaporation; or (*b*) it may become "gravity" or "vadose" water and seep down to the saturated zone. After water reaches the saturated zone, it may percolate as *free-moving* water through pervious material, the openings of which are interconnected (Chap. VIII), or it may move as *confined* water in and through ground-water conduits (Chaps. XI and XII).

Ground water escapes when the water table is close to, or intersects, the surface. Direct discharge from the water table may take place in three ways: (1) by effluent seepage and spring flow, (2) by evaporation from the *capillary fringe* when the latter extends to the ground surface, and (3) by transpiration (pages 84–92). Probably more water is lost by evaporation and transpiration from the capillary fringe than by effluent seepage. When the water table transects the surface, a swamp or spring is produced. The subsurface motions of water are discussed in detail in Chaps. VII to XI.

THE GENERAL GROUND-WATER EQUATION

The general ground-water equation is a mathematical statement of the disposition of rainfall which, on reaching the surface of the earth, is returned to the atmosphere by evaporation and transpiration, collects to form stream flow, or seeps into the subsurface reservoirs. It may be written

$$R = E + S + I$$

where R is rainfall; E, evaporation and transpiration loss; S, water discharged from the area as stream flow; and I, the *ground-water increment*. The ground-water increment (I) is the unknown and desired quantity and could be calculated if the other three factors could be measured.

Measurements of rainfall and stream flow present no great difficulty and are made by the hydraulic engineer in connection with water power, irrigation projects, and flood control. *Rainfall* (*R*) is measured and available data are studied by ground-water hydrologists because it is the ultimate source of all ground water and because the amount entering the underground reservoirs depends in part upon the distribution and intensity of the rains (pages 68–77). *Stream flow* (*S*) is measured carefully because it is one of the factors of the general ground-water equation (pages 80–84), but especially because if stream flow is measured before it passes over a ground-water basin or reservoir and again after it leaves the area, the difference (less corrections for other stream losses or gains) measures the quantity of water seeping underground through the stream bed (pages 473–474). *Evaporation* and *transpiration* (*E*) are the physical processes by which water is transferred into water vapor. Transpiration is the exhalation of water vapor by organisms; as far as the ground-water investigator is concerned, by plants. It is impossible to measure with any satisfactory degree of accuracy the amount of evaporation and transpiration over a large area; for instance, the watershed tributary to, and overlying, a ground-water basin. If these measurements were possible, we could use the general ground-water equation to obtain the ground-water increment by subtracting from total rainfall on the area, stream flow out of the area, and evaporation and transpiration loss in the area. Detailed and fairly satisfactory measurements are made of evaporation from free-water surfaces, of evaporation and transpiration from moist lands, such as swamps, and of transpiration by various types of vegetation (pages 84–92). These may be used to solve a local ground-water equation.

Local Ground-water Equation and Ground-water Inventory.— Detailed estimates of the amount of water added to water-bearing materials of a given area from rainfall, stream flow, and subsurface movement of water into the area (the *ground-water increment*) balanced against estimates of amounts abstracted from the water-bearing materials by evaporation; transpiration; effluent seepage into stream beds, drainage ditches, or swamps; discharge by springs; subsurface movement out of the area; and water withdrawn by pumping wells (*ground-water decrement*) are the factors of the local ground-water equation from which a *ground-water inventory* is made (Chap. XVI).

If water is moving in a confined aquifer, the quantity flowing in the conduit may be determined from the cross-sectional area, porosity (usually effective porosity), and velocity of percolation (pages 470, 489–490). The last may be determined from the coefficient of permeability and the hydraulic gradient, or by direct measurement by means of dyes or by Slichter's electric-conductivity method (pages 215–219).

In special cases one factor may represent all of the water that gets underground or is abstracted from the reservoir, and the measurement of this factor may determine the ground-water increment. For example, all the water abstracted from the ground-water reservoir in an enclosed desert basin may be discharged by transpiration and evaporation in a small area in the center of the basin. Measurement of water transpired and evaporated in this area will also determine the quantity that enters the ground-water basin (ground-water increment) and the amount available for pumping. Pumping in this case salvages water that would be discharged naturally from the basin and wasted. Again, if it is known that all water reaching the water table is supplied by *influent seepage* from stream flow, measurement of stream losses will give the ground-water increment. Additions to and subtractions from ground water can be calculated from changes in level of the water table (not from changes in water level in wells tapping confined water) if the *specific yield* of the water-bearing materials is known (pages 480–485).

GEOLOGIC CONTROL OF GROUND WATER

If water-bearing materials were uniformly pervious and homogeneous, ground-water problems could be solved by hydraulic data; studies of the effect of hydrologic variations and geologic structure of water-bearing materials would be unnecessary. The materials underground, however, are heterogeneous and their hydrologic characteristics are varied. These variations control the quantity and distribution of ground water.

Geologic formations or structures that transmit water in sufficient quantity to supply pumping wells or natural springs are called *aquifers* or water carriers. They are generally separated by aquicludes and aquifuges. *Aquiclude* is a formation which, although porous and capable of absorbing water slowly, will not transmit it fast enough to furnish an appreciable supply for a well or spring.   An aquiclude is porous but not pervious to water moved by gravity.   It contains *fixed ground water*.   For example, practically no percolation of water is induced by gravity in clays, yet they may absorb water up to 50 per cent of their volume.   *Aquifuge*[1] is a rock which is impervious to water. Examples are granite, quartzite, and completely cemented sedi-

Fig. 3.—Cross section of tubular aquifer of coarse gravel confined in dense impervious volcanic tuff in the Mokelumne River Valley, California.

mentary rocks.   An aquifuge is neither porous nor pervious; the enclosed aquifers are shear zones, fissure zones, slatey cleavage, fissures and faults, and porous zones in lavas.

Every geologic body has a geologic structure and a related hydrologic structure.   In sedimentary rocks aquifers are usually formations of great extent, occurring as sheets separated by aquicludes also sheetlike in form (pages 360–364).   In superficial alluvial deposits aquifers vary in shape, size, and inter-

[1] This term was originally suggested by Dr. W. M. Davis.   As defined by him it included both aquifuge and aquiclude.   The term is used in this book in the more restricted sense given above and this modification was approved by him.

connection, depending upon the source material and processes by which they are formed. In alluvial flood-plain deposits and alluvial cones the aquifers are tubular in form; in flood-plain deposits they are sinuous and interconnected, and in alluvial cones the tubes are often divergent and not interconnected below the intake area (pages 367–376). In igneous, metamorphic, and cemented sedimentary rocks the principal aquifers are fractures which may be of either small or large extent; fracturing may be of regular or irregular pattern, and individual fractures may or may not be interconnected (pages 292–296). In soluble rocks solution openings may develop a system of tubular aquifers, the hydrologic characteristics of which are different from the types of aquifers described above (pages 301–309).

The geologic structure and hydrologic characteristics of the stream bottom and underlying materials are especially important because they control influent seepage from streams, which is an important source of ground water. Where underlying materials are uniformly pervious, seepage loss from the stream may be great. Where a relatively impervious formation occurs between the stream bed and the water table, seepage loss may be nil. Instances are known where surface materials are so pervious that water sinks in at rates of 10 to 24 ft. per day (page 181). Soils have a vertical porosity due to root openings and animal burrows and flocculated colloids which give a certain degree of perviousness to material that otherwise might be practically impervious (pages 124–125).

OCCURRENCE AND DISTRIBUTION OF SUBSURFACE WATER[1]

Water occurs underground in two great zones separated by the water table (Fig. 4). The occurrence and movements in these two zones are markedly different. The water table exists only in water-bearing formations which contain openings of sufficient size to permit appreciable movement of water. It is generally considered to be the lower surface of the *zone of suspended water* and the upper boundary of the *zone of saturation*, as defined by Meinzer, which extends down as far as there are interconnected openings. The water table may be defined as the contact plane between free ground water and the capillary fringe, and is located

[1] Subsurface or underground water is here used to include *all water* occurring in liquid form below the ground surface.

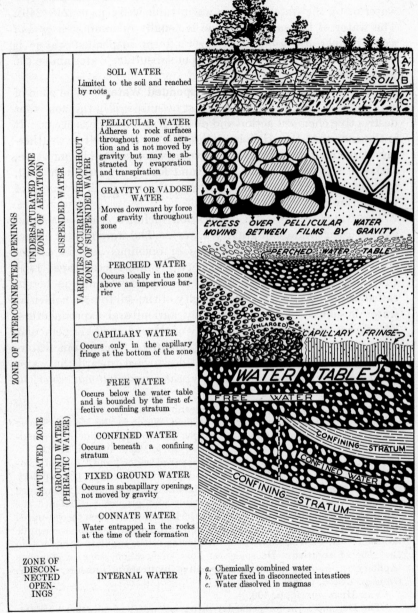

				SOIL WATER Limited to the soil and reached by roots	
ZONE OF INTERCONNECTED OPENINGS	UNDERSATURATED ZONE (ZONE OF AERATION)	SUSPENDED WATER	VARIETIES OCCURRING THROUGHOUT ZONE OF SUSPENDED WATER	PELLICULAR WATER Adheres to rock surfaces throughout zone of aeration and is not moved by gravity but may be abstracted by evaporation and transpiration	
				GRAVITY OR VADOSE WATER Moves downward by force of gravity throughout zone	
				PERCHED WATER Occurs locally in the zone above an impervious barrier	
				CAPILLARY WATER Occurs only in the capillary fringe at the bottom of the zone	
	SATURATED ZONE	GROUND WATER (PHREATIC WATER)		FREE WATER Occurs below the water table and is bounded by the first effective confining stratum	
				CONFINED WATER Occurs beneath a confining stratum	
				FIXED GROUND WATER Occurs in subcapillary openings, not moved by gravity	
				CONNATE WATER Water entrapped in the rocks at the time of their formation	
ZONE OF DISCONNECTED OPENINGS		INTERNAL WATER			*a.* Chemically combined water *b.* Water fixed in disconnected interstices *c.* Water dissolved in magmas

Fig. 4.—Occurrence and distribution of subsurface water.

by the level at which water stands in boreholes tapping free water or by the water levels in water-table wells (pages 248–249). The water of the saturated zone is usually denominated *ground water* or *phreatic water*.[1] Meinzer's term suspended water[2] is used in this text for all occurrences of subsurface water above the water table.

Zone of Aeration or Zone of Suspended Water.[3]—The zone of aeration is of interest to the geologist because it is in this zone that destructive chemical action and disintegration of rocks occur. It is the zone that Van Hise has denominated the "belt of weathering,"[4] in which the oxygen of the atmosphere assisted by moisture, carbonic acid, the organic acids, and locally by sulphuric acid, acts on the rocks and manufactures the manifold products of weathering.

The water of the zone of aeration includes *stored water* and *moving water* (vadose or gravity water). The stored water occurs as attached films on the surfaces of openings and as wedge-shaped bodies at the junctures between interstices (pages 143–144). The stored water above the capillary fringe is herein called *pellicular water*.[5] The capacity of the soil to hold pellicular water is called "*field capacity*" by agricultural experimenters. The excess water over field capacity of the soil and over pellicular water of the entire zone of aeration up to "maximum water-holding capacity" is free to travel downward toward the water table and is referred to as *gravity water, gravitational water,* or

---

[1] From the Greek word φρέαρ, -ατος, meaning well.

[2] MEINZER, O. E., Occurrence of Ground Water in the United States, *U.S. Geol. Surv. Water-Supply Paper* 489, pp. 29–30; Outline of Ground-water Hydrology, *U.S. Geol. Surv. Water-Supply Paper* 494, pp. 21–23.

[3] Meinzer uses the terms "zone of suspended water" and "zone of aeration" as synonymous and his usage is adopted in this text. The capillary openings are generally saturated above the water table and below the warped water-air surface between capillary water and ground air. Hence the arbitrary selection of the water table as the boundary between the saturated and unsaturated zones is based on convenient usage rather than on scientific accuracy. R. F. Walter criticizes the placing of the capillary fringe within the zone of aeration. He suggests: Zone of aeration, zone of complete capillary saturation, and zone of positive hydrostatic pressure. (*Amer. Geophys. Union*, p. 299, 1936.)

[4] VAN HISE, *op. cit.*, p. 409.

[5] The German term for pellicular water is "water of adhesion" (Höfer-Heimhalt, "Grundwasser und Quellen").

vadose water. Water moves freely under the control of gravity only after the grains or rock surfaces have been coated with pellicular water. If these films have been removed by evaporation or transpiration, they must be reformed before seepage can take place.

The *belt of soil water*[1] which constitutes the upper portion of the zone of aeration is limited to the surface layer penetrated by roots. It varies in thickness from a few inches, where solid rock is covered with a thin veneer of soil, to a seldom occurring maximum of 60 ft. (page 125). Active root development occurs chiefly within 10 ft. of the surface. The belt of soil water is the great reservoir of available soil moisture upon which plant life depends. Information as to the occurrence and distribution of water in the soil is derived chiefly from studies of the agricultural scientist and from geological study of the products and processes of weathering. Recent studies of soil moisture, transpiration, and evaporation have greatly modified ideas regarding the occurrence and movements of water in the soil.

Soil moisture is subdivided by the soil scientist according to its availability to plants, depending on the force of attachment to surfaces of soil particles. Water that is held loosely and is easily abstracted by root action may be called *available moisture.* It is limited by *field capacity* on one hand and the *wilting coefficient* on the other. A second portion is unavailable or available with difficulty and is commonly called *unavailable moisture.* Unavailable moisture is divided into two portions: that occasionally available with difficulty, which is limited by the wilting coefficient and the hygroscopic coefficient; and that completely unavailable, which is held in the soil below the hygroscopic point.

The *hygroscopic coefficient* has been variously defined, but may be considered to mark the limit of moisture that can be held at the ground surface in equilibrium with atmospheric water vapor. Residual moisture below the hygroscopic limit may be called *fixed moisture* and probably includes moisture held in colloidal combination by the molecular forces of adhesion and condensation.

The capillary fringe (Fig. 5) lies above the water table and is in contact with it. The water of the fringe is held above the water

[1] *Soil water* includes the gravity water and the pellicular water (soil moisture) of the soil zone.

table by *capillarity*, which is defined as the property of tubes with hairlike openings when immersed in water to raise and hold water above the static level of the water in which they are immersed (pages 148–161). This water may be accurately denominated *capillary water*[1] or *fringe water*.[2]

The capillary fringe is from a fraction of an inch to 10 ft. thick, depending upon the size of the interstices and texture of the material just above the water table. If the depth to the water table is equal or less than the height of capillary lift, the capillary fringe will discharge ground water by evaporation, or if the capillary fringe extends up to the zone penetrated by roots, ground water will be discharged by transpiration. Unlike

CAPILLARY WATER
— WATER TABLE
GROUND WATER

Fig. 5.—The capillary fringe. Capillary interstices near the base of the fringe are saturated; ground air appears in increasing amounts toward the top of fringe.

pellicular water, the capillary fringe has unbalanced surface energy necessary to raise water to the height of capillary lift. The limit of capillary lift varies inversely with the diameter of the capillary openings. Capillary movement is relatively rapid in the larger capillary openings of small lift (1 to 3 ft.) and slow in smaller tubes with higher lift (up to 10 ft.).

Perched Water Table.—Within the zone of aeration an impervious stratum below pervious deposits may support a body of saturated material, the upper limit of which is a *perched water table*. Underlying the saturated pervious material and separating it from the main water table are partly saturated formations of the zone of aeration.

Zone of Saturation.—As all openings in the zone of saturation are fully filled, unbalanced film forces which develop only at air-water surfaces and which are important in the zone of aeration are ineffective. The controlling factors in this zone are geologic

[1] Heretofore both water attached as films to the surfaces of interstices of partly saturated material (pellicular water) and water in the capillary fringe have been denominated "capillary water." In this text the term is restricted to water held in the capillary fringe.

[2] MEINZER, *Water-Supply Paper* 494, *op. cit.*, p. 26.

structure, hydrologic characteristics of water-bearing materials, and hydraulic gradient.

Free, Confined, and Fixed Ground Water.—If water moves through an interconnected body of pervious material unhampered by impervious confining material, it may be denominated *free ground water* moving under the control of the slope of the water table (Chap. IX) as distinguished from *confined water* which moves in strata, conduits, or arteries under the control of the difference in head between the intake and discharge areas of the confined water body (Chap. XI). If water is confined in compressible material (chiefly sand and gravel) and if high artesian pressure in the confined aquifer is reduced by pumping, the aquifer may be compressed by weight of overlying material supported in part by artesian pressure; or if the confining strata are uncompacted, the reduction of pressure in the aquifer may allow water to be pressed out of confining material into the aquifer by the weight of overlying material. These interesting phenomena due to overpumping and resulting compaction are discussed on pages 328–346. *Fixed ground water* is held in small openings (chiefly subcapillary in size) which resist water movement under the usual hydraulic gradients existing underground. It is to be distinguished from pellicular water which exists only in undersaturated material.

Connate Ground Water.—Saline water entrapped in the interstices of sedimentary rock when originally deposited has been discussed (page 28).

MOTIONS OF WATER UNDERGROUND

There are four distinct types of movement of subsurface water, two of which occur exclusively above the water table, one type may occur above or below the water table, and one occurs only in the zone of saturation. Each type has its own particular characteristics and is controlled by laws quite different from the others, and each has been given a distinctive name in this text.

Above the water table the principal movements[1] are: (1) Seepage which takes place chiefly in a downward vertical direction. (2) Capillary rise. (3) Ground-water turbulent flow may

[1] Minor movements of soil moisture are due to subsurface evaporation, molecular attraction of soil particles for moisture, and transfer of moisture by roots (pp. 145–146).

occur in large openings above or at the water table, or below the water table if large openings and free exit and entrance of water exist. (4) Percolation occurs only in the saturated zone in interconnected openings under ordinary hydraulic gradients existing underground.

Seepage from the ground surface to the water table is first a slow, diffuse movement by which the surfaces of all openings are wetted and, second, a downward movement of gravity water on the films coating the openings. The movement is complicated by the presence of ground air which is displaced in part by the downward seeping water and completely by a rising water table. There is no mathematical equation capable of indicating the rate of seepage from the ground surface to the water table because the time necessary to wet the sides of the openings and to drive out ground air is an unknown variable.

Capillary movement is confined to water movement in the capillary fringe. It is discussed in detail in Chap. VI.

Ground-water turbulent flow[1] may occur in openings of large size, such as fractures or tubular openings, and possibly in interstices in very coarse sedimentary and alluvial material under high hydraulic gradients sufficient to develop turbulent movement. However, natural ground-water gradients are usually too small to develop turbulent flow except in large conduits above or at the water table, in conduits below the water table where free escape permits rapid movement, or in the vicinity of intake of a pumping well.

Percolation (laminar flow) is slow movement of water in interconnected pores of saturated granular material under hydraulic gradients commonly developed underground. Resistance to movement developed by friction of the moving water against the surfaces of innumerable grains constituting the water-

[1] Hydraulic engineers recognize two types of flow; namely, turbulent and laminar. Above a definite critical velocity, which varies inversely with the size of the conduit, eddies and whirls characteristic of turbulent flow are developed. Below the critical velocity the particles of water move in straight lines characteristic of laminar flow (pp. 191–200). In this text the term "ground-water turbulent flow" is used to designate the occasional turbulent movement of ground water, and "percolation" is applied to the slow movement of water under relatively low hydraulic gradients occurring underground. It is a type of laminar flow but has peculiar characteristics due to the intricate interconnection of pores which constitute passageways of alternately expanding and contracting cross-sectional area.

bearing material determines the permeability of the material, which is commonly considered to vary roughly as the square of the average diameter of the pores. Much steeper gradients are necessary to force water through fine material than through coarse material and velocity of percolation decreases in fine material until it becomes inappreciable in fine silt and clay.

Summary of Water Movements in Zone of Aeration.—Rain falls on the surface of the earth, a portion runs off, a portion evaporates, and a portion is absorbed by the soil which constitutes a natural sponge or blotter, storing part of the water

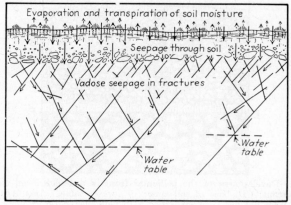

Fig. 6.—Movement of water through soil into fractured rock.

as soil moisture. The excess may seep to the water table. The amount of water absorbed in the zone above the water table from rainfall depends chiefly upon the structure and texture of the surface materials, the degree of wetness of the soil, and the duration and concentration of rainfall. The complex motions of water in this zone due to the interaction of gravity, film forces, and molecular and colloidal attractions, described here as seepage, are treated in detail in Chaps. VI and VII.

In fractured rock the minute and closely spaced fractures opened by weathering at the surface give place to more widely spaced fractures with depth. After the surfaces of fractures are wetted by pellicular water, vadose water seeps down at varying rates and is captured by the larger fractures below. Hence there is a progressive concentration of seeping water in the

large fractures with depth[1] (Fig. 6).　　This is in marked contrast
with the slow, even downward movement in pervious granular
materials.

In granular material temporarily saturated by rainfall, gravity
water drains down to the water table and films of residual
pellicular water remain attached to the surface of each sand grain.
Within the soil zone the pellicular water is removed by transpi-

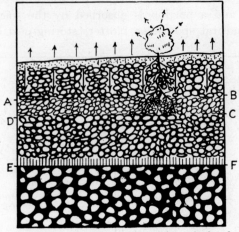

Fig. 7.—Development of the pellicular front in a depleted soil zone.　*AB*,
pellicular front; *CD*, base of soil zone; *EF*, water table.　Area *ABCD* below
pellicular front has not been recharged with pellicular water.

ration and to a less extent by near-surface evaporation.　After
removal of the pellicular water, depleted films must be built up
before further downward seepage can take place.　Progressive
regeneration of pellicular films takes place on an even front,
called here the *pellicular front* (Fig. 7).　Below the soil zone

[1] The result of the intimate penetration of the surface sponge and the
concentration of water in larger fractures at depth can be seen in exposures
of weathered rock.　Complete leaching and alteration occur in the superficial material, but at depth weathering and leaching are confined to the
large fractures and the cores of the larger blocks may be fresh and unaltered.
Observations on weathered rock in foundation excavations, and especially
on oxidized ores, indicate that the chemical processes of rock and ore alteration may fix all available moisture in the hydrous minerals formed by
weathering, and the extremely dry openings will then offer considerable
resistance to the processes of wetting which must precede the movement of
water by gravity.　In this case capillary resistance becomes effective
(pp. 152–153).

transpiration is inactive and evaporation is very slight and except under unusual circumstances pellicular water is not abstracted. Hence, after the pellicular front reaches the base of the zone affected by transpiration (the soil), free passage of gravity water to the water table can take place.

In fine silts, and especially in dense clays, seepage below the surface material penetrated by roots (soil) is extremely slow, or practically nil, on account of the small interstices in these formations. These materials may constitute effective barriers to downward movement of water below the soil zone, thus support-

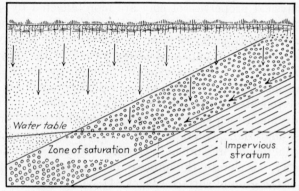

Fig. 8.—Seepage through pervious stratum on impervious formation and overlain by less pervious material.

ing the soil moisture and making it available for plants. Root filaments and animal and insect burrows may develop perviousness in soil. This induced vertical porosity may extend down 10 to 20 ft., to a maximum recorded depth of about 60 ft., and makes possible water movement in material that would otherwise be impervious.

In Coarse Material Underlying Fine Material.—Very commonly above the water table fine clayey soil or fine silt overlies coarse sandy material, or layers of varying permeability occur. Water seeps slowly through the less pervious material until it reaches the more pervious stratum. It then moves rapidly on the water films of the pervious material until it reaches the base of the formation. If the base of the pervious deposit (often sorted sand or gravel) is inclined, the water moves rapidly along the lower contact of the stratum until it reaches the water table

(Fig. 8). If the base is flat or basin-shaped, it may support a
body of perched water. If the pervious material becomes fully
saturated, the water table is raised thereby and percolation probably takes place throughout the entire cross section of the water-
conducting formation.

Solution openings above the water table are not completely
filled by descending water. Water concentrates and flows or
cascades rapidly to the water table, below which the openings are
completely filled with water.

EFFECTS OF WETTING ON CLAYEY MATERIAL

The physical properties of clay are more affected by wetting
than are those of any other type of material. Clay has a maximum absorptive capacity of more than 50 per cent of its volume
and absorption is accompanied by expansion of the clay body.
Water is slowly driven out of clay at depth by the weight of
overlying material. This process is called compaction and is
described repeatedly in this text. Water is also removed by
surface drying, which causes shrinkage, cracking, and hardening
of clayey material. Overpumping of aquifers enclosed in clay
causes reduction of pressure in the aquifer and may assist drainage
of the clay, accelerate the process of compaction, and cause
sinking of the ground surface (pages 341–345).

The important effect of wetting in clayey material is the
increase in plasticity and slipperiness with increase in absorbed
water. As most superficial material contains some clay and
as these deposits are commonly used as construction material
for earth embankments and dams, the study of the physical
properties of near-surface material is undertaken intensively by
engineers.[1] Geologists are also interested in the effect of wetting
as an important factor in producing landslides, solifluction (soil
flow), soil creep, and mudflow, all of which are important
geological processes. Ground-water hydrologists study the effect
of wetting on the physical properties of rocks which may have a
bearing on the suitability of foundation conditions.

Landslides.—Landsliding may be defined as a slipping of the
ground surface. Landslides vary in size from the spectacular

[1] TERZAGHI, CHARLES, *Eng. News-Record*, vol. 95, July–December, 1925;
LEE, C. H., Earth as a Basic Material of Construction, *Civil Eng.*, August,
1931; GILBOY, G., Soil Mechanics Research, *Proc. Amer. Soc. Civ. Eng.*,
vol. 57, No. 8, pp. 1171–1177, 1931; vol. 98, pp. 218–308, 1933.

movement in India[1] to small surface slumps that ordinarily receive little attention. When these small soil slips affect residence property or the business portion of a town, they have been intensively investigated.

Favorable conditions for sliding may occur in various types of formations and on various topographic slopes. If the material is clay and very slippery, the slide may take place on a relatively flat slope. If the formation contains clay intermixed with talus, the required slope may be much steeper. Landslides may occur in sedimentary rocks where certain members, such as shale layers, become softened and slippery, forming gliding planes, and in crystalline rocks containing fractures and joints filled with clay.

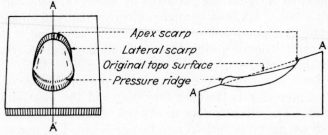

Fig. 9.—Sketch of plan and cross section of a normal land slip, showing the crescent-shaped scarp at apex and upper sides and pressure ridge at toe of slide.

Characteristics of Slides.—Slipping movement may take place on lubricated bedrock or within the superficial portion of a thick deposit of slippery material. In the latter case the movement plane is symmetrical and concave on the upper side. The movement is a rotation, the upper portion of the slide dropping down and forming a scarp in the material above the slide, and uplift at the toe developing a pressure ridge. The moving clayey material is hummocky owing to irregular motion throughout the mass. The scarp on the hillside has the shape of a new moon. These features are illustrated in Fig. 9. If movement takes place on bedrock or on a slippery stratum, such as a shale layer overlain by stronger rock, the slide loses its symmetrical character, but in general the principles that govern the movement in these larger slides are the same as for the smaller soil slips.

[1] GRABAU, A. W., "A Comprehensive Geology," Part I, pp. 398–399, D. C. Heath & Co., 1920.

The force that causes movement of landslides of all types is the component of gravity acting parallel to the surface on which slipping takes place. This component of gravity, however, may be rendered effective under certain definite conditions enumerated as follows:

1. The slide must contain material of a lubricating nature which reduces friction of flow in the direction of slope.

2. A flattening of the slope at the toe increases stability but if the base of the slope is steepened, by either natural or artificial excavations, resistance to sliding is reduced.

3. Addition of material, and hence weight, on a slippery mass ready to move may start a slide. Clayey soils commonly are accumulated in relatively flat areas by rainwash, cloudburst, or stream action. Likewise dumping of clayey material on an area underlain by slippery soil will aid in initiating movement. Buildings or other structures will add weight and may cause movement in unstable material.

4. Wetting is generally considered the principal cause of sliding, and wet clay is the best lubricant and the most slippery material. The other factors mentioned above are usually considered as agencies which are favorable to the movement. Wetting may be due to natural conditions, such as stream flow, rainfall, or underground water; to overirrigation; or, in a town, to wasting of water by inhabitants and to breaking of water and sewer lines.

It will be noted that there are many factors contributory to starting movement in an unstable mass of clayey material. In legal action where the attempt is made to fix the responsibility for sliding it may be extremely difficult or impossible to evaluate the relative importance of each of the contributing factors, some natural and some due to the activities of man.

Hydrologic Conditions.—Of special interest to the student of ground water are the hydrologic conditions which exist in a mass of slippery clay prior to sliding. It has been thought by those not familiar with the hydrologic properties of clay that considerable amounts of water may be contributed to a clay body by percolating ground water. However, no percolation of water can take place in clay, and unless the deposit has interstratified and continuous layers of pervious material (aquifers) there will be no appreciable movement of water through the mass. In such cases it is difficult to drain a mass of clay by drainage ditches.

The clay body may be alternately filled and depleted of water by natural processes. Depletion is by evaporation and transpiration and recharge is by absorption of water applied directly to the dried superficial material. Cracks, which may extend several feet below the surface, develop during the dry season. Observations show that a clay mass saturated in the rainy season by absorption of water may be partly dried to a depth of 10 to 15 ft. below ground surface. Deep cracks in the surface soil are favorable to evaporation during the dry summer season and are also favorable to the penetration of surface water supplied either by rainfall or surface flow. Inasmuch as the clay body may hold water up to 50 per cent of its volume, a deep drying out of clay soil would produce a reservoir capable of absorbing several feet of water. As the annual rainfall in most portions of the semiarid West is small, this reservoir is capable of absorbing not only all rainfall on the overlying area, but also considerable quantities of surface water from other sources. When the quantity of surface water absorbed adds sufficient weight to the mass and develops sufficient slipperiness so that equilibrium conditions are overbalanced, sliding takes place.

Relation to Dikes and Dams.—The importance of studying the effect of wetting on the physical properties of soil materials has been emphasized in recent years by the slumping of such material used in earth-fill dams. For example, the hydraulic-fill Calaveras Dam (Alameda County, California) contained excessive amounts of very slippery material derived from serpentine. On account of the exceedingly slippery character of the fill the heel of the dam slumped back into the deep water when the reservoir was full. Fortunately the apex of the slump did not truncate the crest of the dam and repair was made by addition of broken rock placed against the heel. In another case, the Lafayette Dam, Contra Costa County, California, an earth-fill dam was placed on alluvial material which contained pockets of clay. The weight of the dam caused the compression and movement of these clay pockets and a large landslide occurred in the fill itself, affecting the toe of the dam.

To prevent the failure of earthen dams, either hydraulic fill or dry fill, due to sliding, specifications have been carefully prepared to insure that clayey material in the fill be reduced below the danger point.   A second principle adopted in the construction of earthen dams is to make the fill material progressively coarser in character toward the toe of the dam.   Relatively impervious material is satisfactory for a dam core provided protection against sliding is afforded, but downstream from this core the material should be of increasing permeability in order that the upper surface of the zone of saturation may not intersect the dam above the ground surface.   If the material at the toe of the dam and above the ground surface is allowed to become saturated, resistance to movement is greatly reduced within the mass of the earth fill and displacement of the saturated material and failure of the dam itself may result.

FREE AND CONFINED GROUND WATER
Free Ground Water

Water in interconnected interstices down to the first impervious barrier moves as a single water body which uses up its energy of position by percolation, just as a surface stream converts all head available at every point into flow.   Water will rise to the water table and not above it in a borehole penetrating a free ground-water body.

The Water Table.—The water table in pervious granular material[1] is the upper surface of the zone saturated by free ground water.   It is also a graphic representation of the hydraulic slope of the free water bôdy and is usually a "subdued replica" of the surface topography.   The slope of the water table and its relation to topography and geologic structure are discussed in Chap. IX.

A *water-table map* is made by putting down numerous boreholes to the ground-water level.   The holes are surveyed to determine their location and elevation.   The depth to water is then measured, the elevation of water in each hole is calculated and contours of equal elevation of the water table are drawn (pages 248–249).   A "water level in wells" map may or may not be a water-table map; if the wells tap free water only, the map will be a water-table map.

[1] Discussion of the properties of the water table in fractured impervious rocks and in large tubular openings is not undertaken in this preliminary treatment. The occurrence of ground water in fractures and solution openings is discussed in detail in Chap. X.

Many conclusions can be drawn from a water-table map. By comparing it with a surface topographic map the depths to water at any locality within the area mapped can be determined. The hydrologic character of the material is indicated by the water-table map. If the material is fine, contours will be close together and the slope of the water table will be steep because a steeper hydraulic gradient is required to force a given amount of water through fine material than through coarse material. The water-table slope is adjusted automatically to the velocity of moving water and to the permeability of the material (pages 227–248). The direction of ground-water movement is always down the slope of the water table. The construction and study of water-table maps are an important phase of ground-water investigation.

Confined Ground Water

Confined water is a body of ground water overlain by material sufficiently impervious to sever free hydraulic connection with all overlying ground water except at the upper edge of the confining stratum where the confined water connects with free ground water. If an impervious barrier separates two confined bodies of ground water, motions and resulting equilibrium established in the upper body will not affect the lower body of confined water. The latter will establish an independent hydraulic system, depending upon the difference in head between intake and discharge areas of the confined water and the frictional resistance developed by ground-water motion.

Material separation between free and confined bodies of ground water occurs in sedimentary formations, especially where pervious sandstone is overlain by impervious shale; in the lower portions of alluvial cones and fans in which pervious tubes of sand and gravel may be overlain by, or encased in, less pervious silt and clay; in large fractures; and occasionally in large sub-surface conduits, especially in lava and limestone.

Confinement begins at the upper edge of the confining stratum (*A*, Fig. 11). *B* (*fountain head*) is a point on the water table directly above the upper edge of the confining stratum, and *BD* is the slope of the water table. *BC* is a horizontal line representing the theoretical[1] static level of the confined water under the

[1] The *actual* static level of confined water is indicated by the pressure gradient and pressure surface.

hypothesis that the conduit is encased in material so impervious
that there is no leakage and therefore the confined water body is
completely static. Under these assumed conditions water in a
well piercing the conduit would rise to the level *BC*. However,
leakage of the conduit water through the confining material
probably always occurs, which results in percolation through the

Fig. 10.—Cut on the highway near Clements, California, showing interstratified coarse sand and fine silt. Such structure would develop confined water
systems at depth.

length of the conduit above the point of leakage and friction of
this motion reduces the head on the confined water. Therefore
water in a well piercing the conduit will rise to the line *BC'*
which is the *pressure gradient* (piezometric gradient[1]) of the
confined water and indicates the static level of all wells that may
be drilled on the line of cross section.

[1] The long-used terms *pressure gradient* and *pressure surface* are preferred
to the terms piezometric gradient and piezometric surface suggested by
Meinzer (*Water-Supply Paper* 494) or his later suggested term, pressure-
indicating surface.

Considered in three dimensions, the surface to which confined water will rise in wells piercing a common conduit is called the *pressure surface*. It diverges from the water-table slope at the upper edge of the confining stratum and approaches and often rises above the ground surface in the downslope direction from the intake of the conduit. It usually is flatter than the

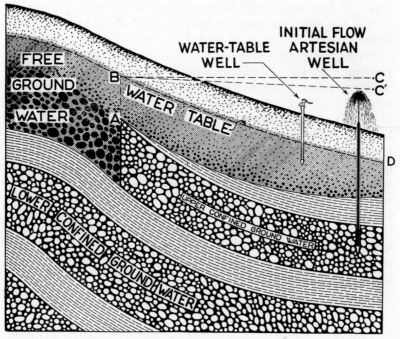

Fig. 11.—Comparison of free and confined ground water. *BC*, theoretical static level of confined water body; *BC'*, pressure gradient, indicates actual static level in wells piercing the conduit.

water-table slope because escape from the confined conduit is generally retarded at the lower end; hence natural percolation in the conduit is slower than percolation of free ground water and the hydraulic slope developed by frictional resistance of the slowly moving confined water is less than the water-table slope. Occasionally, however, the pressure surface of a confined system lies below the water table, in which case it has been called a "negative pressure surface."

When the water in a well tapping confined water rises above the water table, the well is called an *artesian well*. If the water in the well does not rise to the water table, the well is sometimes called an artesian well with "negative artesian head." Popularly a well is artesian only when the water level is above the ground surface. Meinzer[1] limits the term to a well in which the water stands above the water table, and it is used in this sense in this text. If the water level in a well is lowered by overpumping so that the water no longer stands above the water table, the well is not artesian, although, of course, the ground water is confined.

Pressure-surface Map.—The static water levels in wells piercing a confined aquifer determine the pressure surface of the confined water. The map is made in the same way as the water-table map except that care is taken to use only the water levels of those wells that draw on the confined water body. If these levels lie above the ground surface, they are measured by pressure-gage readings on capped wells. A pressure-surface map is a graphic representation of the hydraulic gradients of the confined water body. If there is more than one body of confined water, only the wells that tap the body under investigation can be used to determine the pressure surface. Where wells are perforated in all water-bearing zones, and therefore tap free water and various confined water strata, the water level in those wells represents the composite pressure effect of all water bodies penetrated and may be difficult to interpret.

Comparison of Water-table and Confined-water Wells

As confined ground water may occur below free ground water and may be entirely separated from it and move independently, it is often necessary to determine whether or not wells tap confined or free ground water. This can be determined in various ways. A direct method is to put down small wells or boreholes to the water table near a deep well. If the water levels in the test wells and the deep well correspond, and if pumping the deep well lowers the water level of the test wells, it may be concluded that the deep well draws on "free water." If not, the water tapped by the deep well is confined.[2]

---

[1] MEINZER, *Water-Supply Paper* 494, *op. cit.*, p. 39.

[2] In this discussion it is assumed that the well is perforated only in the deep horizon. If the well is perforated in both the free and confined zones,

Water-table Well.—Pumping a water-table well produces a cone of water-table depression around the well, as shown in Fig. 12. Study of such a cone of depression will tell much

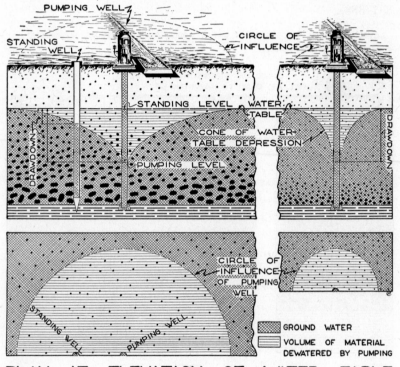

FIG. 12.—Hydraulic features caused by pumping a water-table well. For simplicity the area of influence is bounded by a circle and the popular term circle of influence is used instead of the preferred term area of influence.

regarding the character of the material and the hydraulic conditions of the ground water. A fine or "tight" material will produce a steep cone of depression. If the material is pervious, a very flat cone is produced. The time of recovery also varies with

---

both lowering of the water table and reduction of pressure in the confined aquifers may take place. The confined water will escape into the free-water body if the static level of the confined water is higher than the water table. This movement may be reversed by pumping.

the character of the water-bearing material.   It is rapid in pervious material and slow in less pervious material.   The *cone of depression, area of influence, drawdown, and recovery* compared with the quantity of water pumped and the rate of pumping furnish data for the analysis of the hydraulic behavior of the well (pages 381–388).

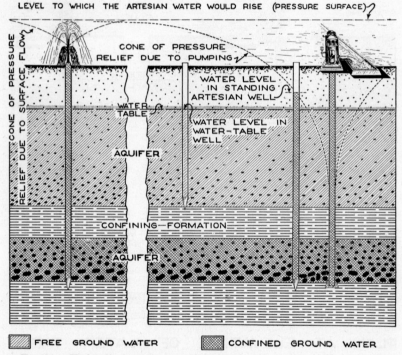

FIG. 13.—Hydraulic features caused by surface flow and by pumping of confined-water well. Initial flow (prior to development of cone of pressure relief) shown by light lines above adjusted flow (dark lines).

Wells Tapping Confined Water.—A well tapping confined water develops no cone of water-table depression because the water is in a conduit and is not connected with the overlying free water except at the intake of the conduit.   Pumping reduces hydraulic pressure in the conduit and if other wells tap the same conduit, the standing level in them will be lowered, the amount of lowering decreasing with distance from the pumping well.   The lowering of water level in the adjacent nonpumping wells during and due to pumping of the well under investigation measures the reduction in pressure in the aquifer caused by pumping. If the lowering of the water level in adjacent wells is plotted, the curved surface thus shown is similar in shape to the cone of water-table depression. It may be defined as an imaginary surface indicating *pressure-relief* conditions in a confined aquifer during well flow. It is not an actual surface showing extent of dewatering during pumping as is the case of the cone of water-table depression. This imaginary surface is called the *cone of pressure relief* (see Fig. 13 and pages 388–391).

A well tapping pressure water with static level above the ground surface and with a valve discharging vertically set in the well cap illustrates the loss in pressure head due to flow at the ground surface. When the valve is first opened, the water column rises approximately to the pressure surface (initial flow) and immediately starts dropping to a constant flow level (adjusted flow, Fig. 13) representing the location of the base of the cone of pressure relief developed by discharge through the valve. The drop due to pressure relief is usually fairly rapid and in one case a pressure drop of 14 ft. to the adjusted level of 2.35 ft. above the ground surface occurred in about 15 sec.

APPLICATION OF GROUND-WATER HYDROLOGY TO GROUND-WATER LITIGATION

The effects of pumping wells on the ground-water supply and on the position of the water table, also when the water table is lowered, the effects of such lowering on the moisture conditions of the soil and especially on natural subirrigation (pages 158–161), are often subject to litigation. An understanding of the differences in behavior between water-table wells and wells drawing on confined water is the essential foundation for any worth while expert opinion in litigation involving the direct or indirect effects of pumping.

The following simple comparison of the pumping effects of water-table wells and confined-water wells may be helpful in cases where the effects of pumping on neighboring properties are in controversy. Such controversies commonly arise where a company or individual is pumping water out of a common "ground-water basin" and exporting the water to points outside the watershed.

Comparison of Pumping Effects

Pumping a water-table well evacuates the materials within the cone of depression of all movable water and therefore lowers the water table and capillary fringe within the area of influence of the well and affects natural subirrigation within the area of influence. Such lowering of the water table may even affect stream flow crossing the area of influence if the stream is supplied from and therefore "supported" by the water table, and may perhaps change the stream from effluent to influent, thereby causing the stream to lose water.

In contrast, a well pumping from confined water does not evacuate the materials within the cone of pressure relief surrounding the well,[1] and may not produce any of the effects noted in connection with pumping a water-table well. A rise in the water level of a confined well does not indicate an addition of water to the water-bearing material surrounding the well, either at the water table or at depth. Pumping from a conduit does not dewater the conduit but merely reduces the pressure head, causing movement of water in the conduit from a source usually at some distance from the well (pages 353–354).

Pressure in a confined aquifer may be affected by other agencies than pumping; for example, external agencies such as loading of the overlying confining strata by tidal rise, flood water pressing down on flexible conduits, or even passage of trains near the well, or by earthquakes (pages 337–338). Therefore variations in the water level of a well may call for detailed analysis to determine the causes of fluctuation. The change of a few inches in the water level of a well distant from a pumping well, both tapping confined water, may indicate the abstraction of less than a bucket of water from within the casing of the standing well and no material dewatering of the aquifer in the vicinity of the wells. A similar lowering of the water level in a water-table well caused by pumping a second well tapping free water may indicate the abstraction of millions of gallons of ground water in the vicinity of the wells.

As depletion of water in a pumped area is usually determined by measurements of water levels in wells, it is important to

---

[1] Unless there is leakage of free water into confined-water strata during pumping, which may be caused by casing perforated in both the free- and confined-water zones.

recognize and evaluate pressure effects as compared with water-table effects. This problem usually arises where overpumping the ground-water supply is claimed. When such claims are made, the static level of the well is measured, not the pumping level, which measures the local drawdown necessary to cause water to move into the well.

The theory that the "natural water table" must be maintained has been advocated in court. In most cases such a claim is absurd and contrary to the purpose of salvaging water by pumping. The natural water table registers an equilibrium between intake and discharge of ground water prior to pumping. If wells are pumped to the limit of ground-water supply, the water table is lowered in the discharge area, thereby eliminating ground-water loss by evaporation, transpiration, and effluent seepage. Also a moderate ground-water lowering or "ground-water hole" around pumping wells is necessary to prevent the escape of water downslope from the wells. A subsurface reservoir is thus created to collect and retain the ground-water supply entering the area.

Artesian Conditions Due to Compressibility of Rock Formations

Artesian conditions may exist in wells tapping water-bearing sand and gravel completely surrounded by relatively impervious materials. Artesian effects may also be due to flexibility and compressibility of aquifers and confining formations, and pumping may draw on water ordinarily fixed in the confining materials. The theory of the functioning of such artesian systems is complex and as far as the writer is informed has not as yet been expounded in court. However, quantitative study of the effects of pumping may force the consideration of such confined water systems and it is hoped discussions in Chaps. XI and XII will remove some of the mystery which to the legal mind seems to befog the subject.

Owens Valley Litigation

Plaintiffs in this litigation claimed that the broad, inter-montane alluvial Owens Valley, California, functions as a "ground-water basin" and that pumping at any point in the valley depletes the supply of the basin. In this litigation the defendants carried on exhaustive geological and engineering studies covering the entire field of ground-water hydrology.

They showed that the pervious water-bearing formations were ancient stream-channel deposits encased in the less pervious body of the great alluvial cones of the Sierra Nevada. The bottom of the valley and the lower portions of the flanking alluvial cones are made up largely of fine silts, too impervious to supply wells.[1] The ground water is supplied to divergent gravel channels buried in the alluvial cones by seepage from streams debouching from the mountains at the apex of the cones. In the original state of nature the ground water in these conduits was forced to the surface by the pinching out of the buried channels near the foot of the cone. This discharge supported large areas of swamp land below the land of the plaintiffs. The defendants showed that pumping draws on confined water, fed far above the lands of the plaintiffs; decreased the volume of water moving down to the fingers of the aquifers; and, by cutting off the supply of water, slowly dried up the swamps below, thereby salvaging water that was wasted prior to pumping.

Effect of Diversion of Stream Water on Pumping Wells

Another set of problems in ground-water hydrology must be investigated in connection with lawsuits involving the effects upon wells caused by dams in the mountain reaches of streams, and diversion of water that otherwise would flow over the water-bearing alluvial deposits in the valley below. There is no answer applicable to all cases because the effect may be slight or very important. The effect on supply for pumping would depend, among other things, upon the relative importance of stream-bed influent seepage and other sources of ground water which are not affected by stream flow, such as seepage from rainfall and irrigation. The amount of stream-bed influent seepage depends not only upon the depth of stream and wetted perimeter of the stream channel (pages 168–173), but also upon the hydrologic and geologic structure of the materials between the stream bed and the water table. The quantity of influent seepage might be materially increased by a moderate lowering of the water table due to pumping, because seepage loss occurs only where the stream level is above the water table, and thus the effect of diminished stream flow might be in part automatically corrected

[1] This does not apply to the "Bishop cases" in Owens Valley, where the geological conditions are different.

by the increased length of the portion of the stream bed feeding water underground.   Measurement of all factors of discharge and recharge of the water-bearing materials is necessary to determine the effect of the diversion of water postulated above.

Parable of the Widow's Meadow

Many examples of investigations made in connection with ground-water litigation are given in the text[1] and possibly the above brief discussion is sufficient to emphasize the necessity of employing all phases of investigation of ground-water hydrology in connection with litigation over ground water.   This chapter is closed with an account of the first problem investigated by the writer in connection with ground-water litigation.   He has related this experience in his lectures for nearly twenty years and the tale has been dubbed by his students "the parable of the widow's wilting meadow."

The widow's name is Mrs. Mary Monroe and her meadow is in the Tehachapi Mountains, on the Tehachapi highway between Bakersfield and Mojave, just south of Monolith, California. The meadow was originally carpeted with grass, supported considerable livestock, and was the main livelihood of the large family.   It occupies the lower portion of the broad, flat valley of Cash Creek, just above the head of a sharply incised canyon.

The Southern Pacific Company purchased a right of way through the meadow on which it sank wells which tapped artesian water with static level a few feet above ground surface, furnishing large yields under the pump.   Water was exported from the watershed to supply the railroad shops at Mojave.   Suit was filed by Mrs. Monroe against the railroad company for damages due to the drying up of the springs and the meadow, which she claimed was the direct result of the pumping operations of the company.

The existence of an ancient lake was shown by logs of wells drilled by the Southern Pacific Company and obtained at the start of the trial.   These logs show 10 to 15 ft. of fine material— meadow silt—at the surface, then 80 to 100 ft. of clay, and at the bottom 10 ft. of coarse, water-bearing sand and gravel overlying the granitic bedrock.   Coarse detrital material washed down from the hills is exposed at the margin of the meadow,

[1] See page references under Litigation in index.

grading into the central body of meadow silt at distances of 10 to 20 ft. from the hillslopes. Springs are located around the margin of the meadow in the coarse detrital material just above the contact with the fine meadow silt.

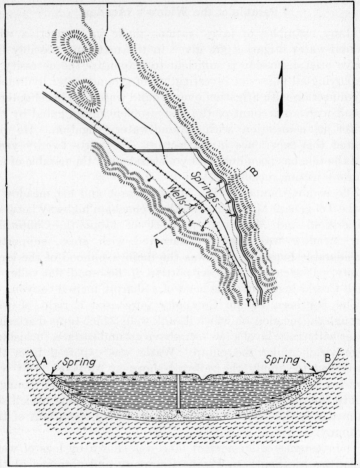

Fig. 14.—Map and cross section of Monroe meadow.

These data formed the basis for the cross section in Fig. 14. The thick clays were interpreted as lake deposits and the sorted, water-bearing sands underneath the clays as stream deposits laid down by the ancestral Cash Creek prior to the faulting which dammed the creek and formed the lake in which the clays were deposited. This occurred, of course, before the last elevation of the Tehachapi Mountains which furnished the grade that has revived the cutting action of the streams which are eating back into the range and destroying the ancient topographic surface, still well preserved in the central portion of the range.

The occurrence of moderate artesian head suggests that the lake clays extend up ancient Cash Creek valley at least as far as the dotted line on the map, and the upper edge of these clays locates the "fountain head" of artesian water in the basal stratum of sand and gravel. The existence of pervious hillwash from the ground surface down to the buried water-bearing sand and gravel was deduced from a knowledge of geologic processes; the detritus is now being deposited and must of necessity have accumulated as long as slope conditions were similar. Experts for the defense attempted to break down this conclusion and introduced many photographs of polished cliffs above glacial lakes at the base of which no considerable deposits of detrital material were visible. However, it was easy to show that geologic conditions at the margins of glacial lakes were quite different from those at the shore of the former lake in the meadow.

The natural circulation of artesian water is shown in the sketch by arrows in solid lines. Spring discharge was concentrated along the sides of the meadow where the pervious hillwash accumulated and is now exposed. Artesian pressure forced water up to the springs on each side of the meadow, overflow of which originally supported heavy growth of vegetation. Pumping from the basal aquifer in the center of the meadow reduced the artesian pressure, thus reversed the natural ground-water circulation, as shown by dotted arrows in the sketch, and dried up the springs. This theory was expounded by the plaintiff at the beginning of the trial before the results of hydrologic study were available.

Numerous boreholes and pits were dug below the water table and the fluctuations of water level in them measured. From these data a series of water-table maps and cross sections were constructed, and the effect of pumping on the water table was studied by means of graphs showing the fluctuation of the water table compared with the period during which the pumps were operated.

The water level in pits on the margins of the meadow near the springs fluctuated strongly following pumping, while the lowering of water level in test holes toward the center of the meadow was slight. The pumps were operated from about 8 A.M. to 2 P.M. The midday and afternoon lowering of water levels was explained by the defendant as due to evaporation and transpiration and to daily barometric fluctuations. Since the amount of lowering was slight except near the margins of the meadow, small fluctuations might plausibly be explained as the effect of evaporation and transpiration and diurnal barometric fluctuations.

The drying up of the meadow was explained by the defendant as due (1) to the dry season and (2) to the excavation of a gully by floods a few years previous. This gully, 10 to 15 ft. deep, was in the center of the meadow. The plaintiff maintained that the fine meadow silts were of low permeability and developed a very narrow trench of water-table depression which caused drying of the meadow only in a strip a few feet wide on each side of the gully.

Near the close of the trial, after the pumpman supposed all observers had left the area, the wells were pumped continuously for three days. Measurements taken by the plaintiff showed progressive lowering of water levels in the test holes throughout this period, maximum lowering as usual occurring in the coarse material in the vicinity of the springs. Recovery occurred only after pumping ceased. Thus were the facts furnished that verified the contentions of the plaintiff and dissipated the pseudo-scientific smoke screen laid down by the defendant to obscure the clear relation between pumping, consequent reduction of artesian head, and drying up of artesian springs.

References

BAKER H. and D. M. CONKLING, "Water Supply and Utilization," John Wiley & Sons, Inc., New York, 1930.

DIXEY, FRANK, "A Practical Handbook of Water Supply," Thos. Murby Company, London, 1931.

HÖFER-HEIMHALT, H., "Grundwasser und Quellen," Friedr. Vieweg & Sohn, 2d ed., Braunschweig, Germany, 1920.

KEILHACK, K., "Lehrbuch der Grundwasser- und Quellenkunde," Gebrüder Borntraeger, 3d ed., Berlin, 1935.

KING, F. H., Principles and Conditions of the Movements of Ground Water, *U.S. Geol. Surv. 19th Ann. Rept.*, pt. 2, 1899.

LACEY, J. M., "Hydrology and Ground Water," C. Lockwood, London, 1926.

MASON, W. P., "Water-supply," John Wiley & Sons, Inc., New York, 1916.

MEAD, DANIEL W., "Hydrology," McGraw-Hill Book Company, Inc., 1919.

MEINZER, O. E., Ground Water in the United States, *U.S. Geol. Surv. Water-Supply Paper* 489, 1923.

———, Outline of Ground-water Hydrology, *U.S. Geol. Surv. Water-Supply Paper* 494, 1923.

PRINZ, E., "Handbuch der Hydrologie," Berlin, 2d ed., 1923.

REDLICH, K. A., K. TERZAGHI, R. KAMPE, and OTHERS, "Ingenieursgeologie," Julius Springer, Wien and Berlin, 1929.

SLICHTER, C. S., Theoretical Investigation of the Motions of Ground Waters, *U.S. Geol. Surv.* 19th, *Ann. Rept.* pt. 2, pp. 295–384, 1899.

——— The Motions of Underground Waters, *U.S. Geol. Surv. Water-supply and Irrigation Papers* 67, 1902.

TURNEAURE, F. E. and H. L. RUSSELL, "Public Water Supplies," 3d ed., John Wiley & Sons, Inc., New York, 1924.

CHAPTER III

BRIEF REVIEW OF RAINFALL, RUNOFF, EVAPORATION, AND TRANSPIRATION

IMPORTANCE OF METEOROLOGY IN HYDROLOGIC INVESTIGATIONS

Meteorology is the branch of applied physics that investigates meteorological phenomena. The physical properties of the air, particularly temperature, barometric pressure, and humidity; and certain terrestrial phenomena, such as topography and rotation of the earth, interact to produce winds and rainfall, weather and climate.

Meteorological data, especially those compiled by the United States Weather Bureau, are used as a basis for the study of rainfall, runoff, transpiration, and evaporation, and hence the ground-water investigator must be familiar not only with the science of meteorology but also with the available published data.

Weather forecasting is of interest to those dealing with water supply and the newly developed methods based upon the principles of "air-mass analysis" now used successfully by the United States Navy and air transport companies should be understood, as well as the empirical methods used by the United States Weather Bureau. In his teaching experience the writer has found that the science of meteorology is so important as a foundation for certain phases of hydrologic work that a chapter on the elements of meteorology, including a section on air-mass analysis by N. E. Bradbury, Assistant Professor of Physics at Stanford University, appears in the last mimeographed edition of this text. It is with regret that the chapter is eliminated from the published edition because of limitation of space. The student is referred to the publications listed at the end of this chapter for information on meteorology.

RAINFALL

Rainfall is usually expressed in depth of precipitated water in inches, measured by rain gages for selected periods of time.

The period desired depends upon the interest of the investigator. If he wishes to know the intensity of rainfall during storms, the records must express the quantity of rainfall for short periods of time. *Maximum intensity* is shown by rainfall measured during the period of heaviest downpour. Intensity may be expressed

Fig. 15.—Mudflow, Owens Valley, Aug. 23, 1925. The large boulders were brought down in the early stages of the flood when the mud had the consistency of fresh cement mixture. Later flow cleared and washed the channels shown in center ground and right foreground.

as the number of inches of rainfall during the selected period; e.g., 1.5 inches in 10 minutes, or as the equivalent rate per minute, per hour, or (for moderate intensities) per day.

Intensity of rainfall is of interest to the geologist because the direct action of rains and of flood flows created thereby increases enormously with intensity.[1] A single cloudburst may erode a

[1] TOLMAN, C. F., Erosion and Deposition in the Southern Arizona Bolson Region, *Jour. Geol.*, vol. 17, pp. 136–163, 1909.

system of gullies and develop mudflows which may bury large areas of land with several feet of mixed boulders and mud. Rainfall intensity is of primary importance to engineers interested in surface-water storage because of its relation to maximum flood flow, which must be taken into account in building dams and bridges. Therefore intensity of rainfall and flood flow are treated in detail in textbooks of hydrology and water supply. Yarnell[1] has summarized the United States Weather Bureau

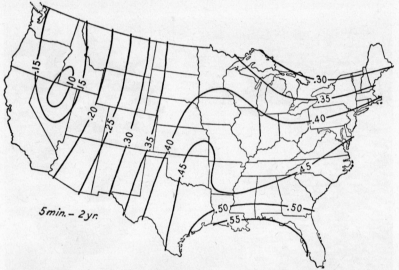

Fig. 16.—Map of the United States showing maximum rainfall in inches for periods of five minutes to be expected once in two years. (*After Yarnell.*)

records in respect to rainfall intensity-frequency and presented a method of estimating runoff. Two maps are reproduced in this text from a large number showing maximum rainfall to be expected in the United States for intervals from 5 min. to 24 hr. and for periods from 1 to 100 years (Figs. 16 and 17).

Although intensity of rainfall is of less interest to the ground-water investigator than seasonal or annual rainfall, it has a decided influence upon influent seepage from rainfall and stream flow. Torrential rainfall of short duration is usually accompanied by rapid runoff and both are unfavorable to influent

[1] YARNELL, D. L., Rainfall Intensity-Frequency Data, *U.S. Dept. Agr. Misc. Publ.* 204, August, 1935.

seepage. Modifying factors are topography, vegetation, and surface geology which affect the quantity of water that gets underground. All the water precipitated by a cloudburst may be absorbed in a flat sand-dune area. Similarly the resulting flood flow may be absorbed if the stream channel is extremely pervious. Usually, however, a much larger proportion of runoff escapes absorption during flood flow than in the lower stages of stream flow. Vegetation holds back runoff from torrential rainfall and reduces destructive erosion by flood flow. The writer has

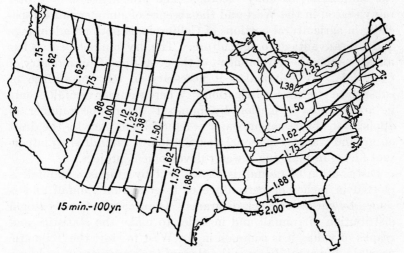

Fig. 17.—Map showing maximum rainfall in inches during a 15-min. period to be expected once in 100 years. (*After Yarnell.*)

witnessed cloudbursts in Cuba precipitating 5 in. of rain per hour which caused little destructive erosion even in hilly country on account of the thick cover of vegetation.

Rainfall per day is usually recorded by weather observers because it forms a convenient basis for compiling the total rainfall per season or per year. *Rainfall per storm* is of interest to the ground-water investigator because the duration of rainfall affects the percentage of rain absorbed and also the quantity of runoff resulting from the storm. The relation, however, is not a simple one. If rain falls slowly, nearly all may be absorbed but may not necessarily be delivered to the saturated zone. Rain must first bring the soil moisture up to field capacity before water can penetrate to the water table. If, after a continuous gentle rain of three or four days during which the soil has been fully charged with pellicular water, it rains heavily, the percentage of runoff may be high because subsurface movement of gravity water can take care of only a small part of the heavy precipitation. Nevertheless the quantity of influent seepage reaching the water table is probably at a maximum during long-continued heavy rainfall.

Seasonal distribution of rainfall is, of course, brought out by the summation of daily records. The prevalence of a winter rainy season in the West and the absence of summer rains, especially in agricultural portions of California, is both an advantage and a disadvantage to agriculture. The dry summer season has made possible the development of the great dried fruit industry of California. It also makes it necessary to rely on surface or subsurface storage for irrigation. Where summer rainfall occurs in areas under irrigation by pumped water, the number of applications of irrigation water is reduced and likewise the draft on ground water. Seasonal distribution of rainfall is an important factor in planning a water-development project.

Distribution of rainfall is shown best by graphs. Rainfall is plotted in inches or percentage of total annual rainfall and is shown by curves or block diagrams. On account of the seasonal distribution of rainfall and in order to make the statistics and graphs of value, it is common in the West to start the "climatic year" in June or July after the close of the rainy season and near the beginning of the season of high temperature and intense evaporation.

Comparison of Rainfall with Runoff.—Comparison of the stream hydrograph (showing runoff) with the rainfall graph shows their interrelation. The late spring or early summer peak flow is characteristic of streams draining mountain areas with heavy snowfall. The hydrographs of such streams usually show a single peak flow which occurs with advance of warm weather, especially after a warm rain. Precipitation is usually distributed over the rainy season (Fig. 18, *A* and *B*). Where the soil of the drainage basin is absorptive, runoff will be much more regularly distributed than rainfall (Fig. 18, *C* and *D*). In semiarid regions the early rains are usually absorbed and runoff starts after heavy rains in the middle of the rainy season (Fig. 18, *E* and *F*).

Estimates of Seasonal or Annual Rainfall.—Annual rainfall gives the total quantity of rain available during the year and is a

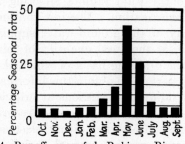

A. Runoff snow-fed Rubicon River, near Quinttette, California.

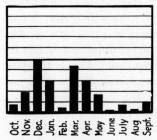

B. Precipitation at Summit, California. (In watershed of Rubicon River.)

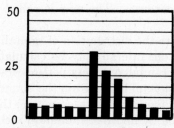

C. Runoff San Gabriel River, near Azusa, California. Snow only in high altitudes; rainfall absorbed and delivered slowly to stream.

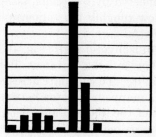

D. Precipitation at Azusa, California.

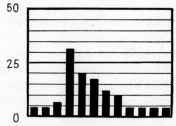

E. Runoff San Diego River, near Lakeside, California. Early rainfall absorbed without appreciable effect on runoff.

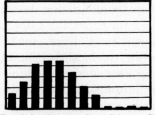

F. Precipitation at San Diego, California.

Fig. 18.—Comparison of stream hydrograph with rainfall graph. (*After Baker and Conkling.*)

yardstick by which the total water available for all purposes in different areas can be compared. It is fundamental information desired by those interested in surface and underground water. The rainfall at any one point in an area of varied topography furnishes little information as to the total rainfall affecting a large area which may be under investigation. The information desired in making a general study of the ground-water supply of an alluvial cone, for example, is the total quantity of rain precipitated during the year on the drainage basin of which the water-bearing alluvial deposit is a part. To obtain this information the investigator establishes rain-gaging stations at critical points throughout the area under investigation and keeps a record for each station. The office work consists of plotting seasonal or annual rainfall in inches on a topographic map of the area. Locations of rain gages are plotted and points of equal rainfall are connected by *isohyetose, isohyetal,* or rainfall contour lines, which follow roughly the topographic contours. The map is called an *isohyetal map.*

An isohyetal map (Fig. 19) shows the distribution of rainfall in inches and the water available from rainfall may be calculated from it. To calculate acre-feet of rainfall over any portion of the area mapped, the area between isohyetal lines within the boundaries of the selected area should be measured by planimeter; then the area between lines is multiplied by depth of rainfall in inches obtained by averaging the inches represented by the two bounding isohyetal lines. Acre-inches of rainfall calculated for each area between isohyetal lines may then be added and converted to acre-feet.

Usually all existing data on rainfall are collected before undertaking the expensive and long-continued measurements described above. In addition to the data published by the Weather Bureau, the local weather observer may supply information, and water companies and municipal water districts often have pertinent information if their studies have been carried on in a similar near-by area.

A rough estimate of the amount of rainfall can be made occasionally from the type and distribution of vegetation in the area. For example, in the central Coast ranges of California the redwood forests indicate an average annual rainfall in excess of 40 in. Plants as indicators of rainfall, however, usually give merely a general comparison of the rainfall in the area under investigation with a near-by area similarly situated topographi-

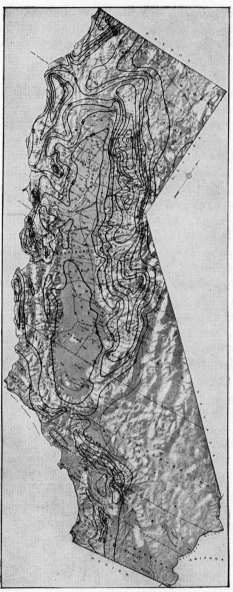

Fig. 19.—Distribution of rainfall in California shown by rainfall contours. (*After map published in 1922 by State Department of Public Works, Division of Engineering and Irrigation, State of California.*)

cally where satisfactory measurements have been made.	Living-
ston and Shreve[1] found that the most important factor affecting
the amount of vegetation is the ratio between precipitation and
evaporation.	However, temperature, amount of sunlight, and
relative humidity also are important factors.

Average rainfall is important in investigations of surface and
subsurface water supply and is computed from the rainfall records
available; hence it varies with the length of time the records
cover.	In California, Sacramento rainfall records date back to
1849 and comprehensive rainfall and runoff records are available
since 1871.[2]	Averages computed from short-term records have
been appreciably lowered by the inclusion of the rainfall figures
for the recent dry cycle in California (from 1916 to 1934).	Past
averages, however, do not indicate with certainty the future
average rainfall.	What is desired is not the average of the past,
but what may be expected in the future, the next 10 or 100 years.

Regional variation in rainfall is a striking feature of the semiarid
western United States.	Even within a small area the rainfall
may be heavy in the mountains surrounding a small valley and
very low in the center of the valley.	In the high Sierra Nevada
and along the coast of Oregon and Washington the rainfall may
reach 100 in., and in Death Valley, California, the annual rainfall
at times is less than 1 in.	The isohyetal map of the state of
California brings out at a glance the distribution of excess and
deficient rainfall (Fig. 19).

Rainfall provinces of the United States are areas characterized
by similarity in distribution and seasonal concentration of
precipitation and by a similar wind system.[3]	There are similar-
ities also in the surface and ground-water problems within each
province.

Droughts.—Drought caused by the reduction of normal rainfall during the crop-growing season, often accompanied by
unseasonably high temperatures, has occurred four times in the
last six years in the United States and has brought financial

---

[1] LIVINGSTON, B. E., and F. SHREVE, The Distribution of Vegetation in
the United States as Related to Climatic Conditions, *Carnegie Inst. Wash.
Publ.* 284, 1921.

[2] Flow in California Streams, *State of California, Dept. Pub. Works Bull.* 5,
1923.

[3] HENRY, A. J., Climatology of the United States, *U. S. Dept. Agr. Weather
Bureau Bull. Q*, pp. 48–51, 1906.

disaster to the agricultural industry in central and midwestern states.[1] Secondary effects, such as lowered water table, destruction of soil moisture and soil covering, have resulted in the removal of soil by wind and later by flood erosion over large areas. Soil conservation has been taken up by governmental agencies and the importance of ground water as an auxiliary supply to surface water in times of drought and the necessity of conserving ground water for domestic and industrial uses are being emphasized. As a result ground water is receiving far more attention in regions normally blessed with abundant rainfall than in former years.

CLIMATIC CYCLES

It is generally believed that climate fluctuates periodically, that these fluctuations are most pronounced in semiarid and arid regions, that there is a periodic swing from a series of wet years to a series of dry years, and that from examination of past records some idea of future rainfall can be gained. Engineers have developed mass curves showing excess or deficit of annual rainfall[2] and definite periods of wet and dry cycles of 7, 15, 30, etc., years have been deduced therefrom. However, correlation between the mass curve showing deficiencies and excesses in rainfall and a simple periodic rainfall curve is more or less imaginary. Available rainfall records in general indicate an *irregular* periodic change from years of rainfall in excess of the average to a group of years with a net average deficiency of rainfall. Available rainfall records are usually too short and in some cases too incomplete to establish the periodicity, if any, of these changes.

An interesting study of rainfall and stream runoff in southern California since 1769 includes investigation of available rainfall and stream-flow data supplemented by hydraulic interpretation of the writings of the mission padres and explorers. The contribution is not only of value for conclusions regarding past climatic conditions in southern California, but also as an example of how the accounts of the traveler, the husbandman, and tiller

[1] HOYT, J. C., Droughts of 1930–34, *U.S. Geol. Surv. Water-Supply Paper* 680, 1936.

[2] Flow in California Streams, *State of California, Dept. Pub. Works Bull.* 5, pp. 29–44, 1923.

of the soil can be interpreted with relation to rainfall and stream flow. Two conclusions reached are: (1) There has been no material change in the mean climatic conditions of southern California in the past 162 years. (2) There have been earlier fluctuations from average rainfall conditions, however, both excesses and deficiencies, of greater magnitude than any which have occurred in the past forty years.[1]

Long-period Climatic Cycles Determined from Tree Rings.—
A. E. Douglass, of the University of Arizona, has made a study of tree rings as indicating climatic cycles.[2] The theory he advances is that thick annual growth rings indicate favorable climatic conditions and thin rings unfavorable conditions. Presumably heavy rainfall is the most important of the "favorable conditions," hence thick rings are believed to indicate wet years.

In 1911 and 1912 Douglass, under the auspices of the Carnegie Institution of Washington, made measurements on the stumps of 450 sequoia trees in California and the results have been analyzed by Huntington.[3] The ages varied from 250 to 3250 years, which gave an accurate record for 2000 years and an approximate record for 1000 years more (Fig. 20). Since rainfall records are not available where the sequoias grow, data obtained from measurement of the tree rings are correlated with rainfall records of the nearest station. Correlation with records at Sacramento from 1863 to 1910 shows that there is no appreciable relation between the rainfall of a given season and tree growth during the following spring and summer. Because of the great depths reached by roots and the slow effect of variation in rainfall on water-table fluctuation, it takes from four to ten years of wet seasons to affect the growth of trees in this area. If rainfall records were available for the area in which the trees grow, correlation between growth rings and rainfall would probably be closer.

The sequoia record was checked with rainfall records at Jerusalem because (1) the historical record of that city is long, (2)

[1] LYNCH, H. B., Rainfall and Stream Run-off in Southern California since 1769, Metropolitan Water District of Southern California, Los Angeles, August, 1931.

[2] DOUGLASS, A. E., Climatic Cycles and Tree Growth, *Carnegie Inst.*, 1919; also chapter in "The Climatic Factor," by Ellsworth Huntington, 1914.

[3] HUNTINGTON, *op. cit.*, pp. 139–174; see also E. HUNTINGTON, and S. VISHER, "Climatic Changes," pp. 74–78, Yale University Press, 1922.

it is located approximately in the same latitude as the sequoia area, (3) the climates are similar—wet winters and dry summers, (4) it lies back from the sea and at an elevation of 2500 ft. The two areas show a close correlation, which, according to Huntington, indicates that climatic conditions are world-wide. The correlation coefficient between the rainfall in Jerusalem and in the sequoia region of California is larger than that between the rainfall of Sacramento and of San Bernardino, 400 miles apart. This indicates that tree growth rings may be a more accurate long-time rain gage than local, short-term records kept by man. Similar work which indicates more or less definite climatic cycles

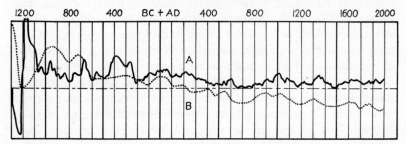

Fig. 20.—Climatic variations in California and Central Asia. Curve *A*, as determined by measurement of annual rings of California sequoia trees; curve *B*, as inferred from study of ruins and ancient history. (*After Huntington and Visher, "Climatic Changes—Their Nature and Causes."*)

is now being carried on in Europe. This work also shows long cycles, from 200 to 500 years, indicating that there has been considerable change in the amount of precipitation throughout long periods of time.

Davis and Sampson[1] criticize the correlation of tree rings with rainfall records. They conclude that in the area investigated by them the annual precipitation and the growth of trees as measured by their annual rings are not related. The variation in growth in pine trees could not be correlated with the precipitation curve. They state that, although the causes of fluctuation in growth are indicated to be fundamentally climatic, the complexity of interaction of trees to environment obscures the relationship when the moisture values are expressed as net annual precipitation.

[1] Davis, W. E., and A. W. Sampson, Experiment in Correlation of Tree-growth Rings and Precipitation-cycles, *Trans. Amer. Geophys. Union*, pp. 495–496, 1936.

The engineer usually adopts the close-up viewpoint that there is no slow progressive change in climate. The geologist, however, recognizes that there have been great and progressive changes in climate in the past. The steady retreat of the Alaskan glaciers ever since the time of the first Russian explorers may be cited as a concrete example of progressive change in climate. The geologist, therefore, is not quite sure of the "return to normalcy" as far as climate is concerned.

STREAM RUNOFF

Stream runoff is a function of quantity, distribution, and especially of concentration of rainfall; of vegetal covering of the ground surface; topography; and hydrologic properties of the formations at the ground surface. The effect of concentration of rainfall on stream runoff has been mentioned and is studied in detail by the hydraulic engineer, as maximum flood flow must be handled by the structures he builds. Cloudbursts occur occasionally in all portions of the United States, although of more frequent occurrence in the semiarid West. Fortunately, however, the area affected by such heavy precipitation is small and destruction is usually limited to culverts and small bridges.

The protection of mountain vegetation against destruction by fire is a major flood-control and soil-conservation problem in the West. In the Los Angeles area debris-laden floods debouch from burned-over mountain areas and deposit their load on the upper portions of the alluvial cones, occasionally causing great destruction and loss of life, as, for example, the Montrose flood in southern California, Dec. 31, 1933 (Fig. 21).

Measurement of Stream Flow.—Measurement of flood flow is difficult and usually is no better than an approximation unless suitable weirs are constructed to handle the large flows. Measurement of flow of a large variable stream is also unsatisfactory. The accuracy of measurement of flow of the Mokelumne River, California, by gaging and measurement of stream cross sections was less than 5 per cent of the total runoff, which was greater than the seepage loss of the stream (page 169). The fundamental data regarding stream seepage loss can be collected only by measurements above and below the area affected by influent seepage from the stream.

Weir and other measurements of stream flow, estimation of stream losses other than by influent seepage, and the effect of bank storage on stream flow are described in textbooks of

Fig. 21.—Destruction of highway-maintenance station, near La Crescenta, California, caused by flood from burned-over mountain area, Dec. 31, 1933.

hydraulic engineering. Details of a refined investigation are given in a report by Paul Bailey.[1] Ordinary methods of stream

[1] Engineering Investigation of Percolation from Alameda Creek and Ground-Water Studies in Niles Cone, Calif.; *Calif. State Water Comm.*, *3d Biennial Rept.*, pp. 97–101, 1920.

gaging are described in *Water-Supply Paper* 371,[1] and a good popular discussion appears in a bulletin by J. E. Christiansen.[2] Unfortunately space forbids a résumé of details and refinements in measuring and estimating small flows of water which are made in detailed investigations of influent seepage.

Comparative Study of Hydrographs.—Runoff is closely interrelated with amount and concentration of rainfall, with evaporation and transpiration, with bank storage, and with influent and effluent seepage. Its relation to the above-mentioned factors is studied by comparison of hydrographs of each factor. For example, the relation of runoff to rainfall is studied by constructing a hydrograph of stream flow and comparing it with the rainfall curve (Fig. 18, page 73). The relation of runoff to rainfall has also been expressed by empirical formulas, such as those of Grunsky,[3] Horton,[4] Bernard,[5] and others. The relation of runoff from rainfall and from bank storage has been studied by comparative graph methods.[6] Bank storage is an important factor in studying surface and ground-water supplies. It is a reserve storage in local stream gravels supplied by influent seepage at high-water stages and drained out at lower stages, thus regulating stream flow. The flow of streams includes direct or surface runoff and effluent seepage from bank storage and from the general water table beyond the stream-bed gravels. Channel storage is the quantity of surface water between stream banks. It is calculated from gage heights taken at surveyed stream cross sections. Graphs and empirical equations have been developed for studying bank and channel storage and their relation to stream runoff and effluent seepage.[7] The interrelation of

[1] LYON, G. J., Equipment for Current Meter Gauging Stations, *U.S. Geol. Surv. Water-Supply Paper* 371, 1915.

[2] Measuring Water for Irrigation, *Univ. Calif. Agr. Exp. Sta. Bull.* 588, March, 1935.

[3] GRUNSKY, C. E., Rain and Runoff near San Francisco, *Trans. Amer. Soc. Civ. Eng.*, vol. 61, p. 496, 1908.

[4] HORTON, R. E., Surface Runoff Phenomena, *Horton Hydrologic Lab. Publ.* 101, 1935.

[5] BERNARD, M. M., An Approach to Determine Stream Flow, *Proc. Amer. Soc. Civ. Eng.*, vol. 60, pp. 3–18, 1934.

[6] SHERMAN, L. K., Stream-flow from Rainfall by Unit-graph Method, *Eng. News-Record*, Apr. 7, 1932.

[7] HORTON, R. E., Natural Stream Channel-storage, *Trans. Amer. Geophys. Union*, pp. 446–460, 1933; 1936, pp. 406–415; O. E. Meinzer, and others,

rainfall, surface runoff, stream flow, infiltration loss, and bank
storage has been outlined by Horton.[1]   He estimates infiltration

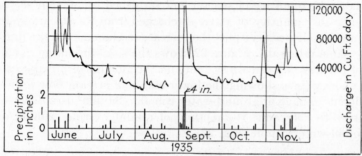

Fig. 22.—Rainfall, total stream flow, and effluent seepage, headwater-basin
of Difficult Run.   Total discharge of stream shown by light lines and effluent
seepage by heavy lines.   Rain gage situated about 25 ft. above stream at weir.
(*After Meinzer.*)

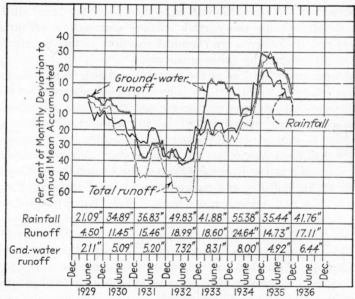

Fig. 23.—Comparison of rainfall, runoff, and ground-water runoff, Nepaug River
watershed.   (*After Saville.*)

and other losses during the storm period on a drainage basin from
a study of stream-flow and rainfall hydrographs.

The Channel-Storage Method of Determining Effluent Seepage, *ibid.*,
pp. 415–418.

[1] Horton, *op. cit.*

Meinzer[1] has developed graphical methods for estimating effluent seepage. When stream flow is not derived from surface runoff, the quantity of stream flow furnished by effluent seepage equals the quantity of water discharged from the stream system minus the decrease or plus the increase in channel storage during the same interval. Figure 22 shows the total discharge in cubic feet per day of a stream system and the amount of precipitation; the heavy lines showing the lower stages of stream flow indicate effluent seepage or ground-water runoff. Saville[2] uses deficiency curves to determine the relation of rainfall, surface runoff, and ground-water runoff (Fig. 23).

EVAPORATION AND TRANSPIRATION

Evaporation and transpiration are the only physical processes by which water is transformed into water vapor. All water that falls on the ocean or is discharged to it from the land and all that is precipitated on the earth's surface and enters subsurface reservoirs, if not fixed by chemical reaction, is finally returned to the atmosphere by these processes.

Measurement by Use of Evaporation and Soil Pans.—Evaporation from free water surfaces is measured by experimental work with evaporation pans or ascertained from data collected in connection with reservoirs, where the amount of inflow and outflow is measured. Experimental measurement of transpiration has been carried on by various state and governmental bureaus, such as the Bureau of Soils of the United States Department of Agriculture, and various experimental stations of state universities and agricultural schools. Soils pans are filled with soil and buried in the area to be investigated and various types of plants are grown therein. Water is kept at a constant level in the soil pan and the amount added to keep it at that level is measured. Water lost by transpiration is then determined under various conditions of growth, spacing of plants, and temperature. However, these determinations lack accuracy on account of the complex conditions which control the rate of plant growth in the natural environment. Literature on the subject is largely

[1] Meinzer, O. E., The Channel-storage Method of Determining Effluent Seepage, *op. cit.*

[2] Saville, C. M., The Underground Water-index, Its Relation to Surface Runoff, *Trans. Amer. Geophys. Union*, pp. 382–386, 1936.

in the bulletins of the United States Department of Agriculture, the various state colleges of agriculture, and technical agricultural societies.[1]

Methods of Estimating Evaporation and Transpiration Losses. Usually it is not possible to determine even approximately the amount of evaporation and transpiration over an entire watershed and therefore the general ground-water equation is of little value in determining the ground-water increment. For example, assume that an investigation is being made to determine the quantity of water available in an alluvial cone built by a stream draining a mountain area. Rain falls over the entire watershed of the stream and can be measured if a sufficient number of rain gages are placed to control the area. Evaporation and transpiration also take place over the entire area, which includes mountain slopes with variable vegetation and soil conditions and the surface of the alluvial cone. The quantity of water discharged by evaporation and transpiration under such variable conditions cannot be measured. In an alluvial cone the water table is usually below the surface except at the foot of the cone. Evaporation from the ground surface above the reach of the capillary fringe and transpiration where roots do not reach the capillary fringe do not draw directly on ground water. In such areas these processes draw on soil moisture fed by rainfall and when the soil moisture is used up, evaporation and transpiration cease. The water table and capillary fringe may reach ground surface in a limited area at the foot of the cone and roots may reach the capillary fringe over a somewhat larger area. Discharge from the water table in this limited area may be determined satisfactorily by experimental work and may be an important factor in the local ground-water equation.

If all additions to ground water are returned to the atmosphere by evaporation and transpiration, a measurement of these losses will also be a measurement of the water entering the ground-water basin from all sources, and as pumping will draw down the water table and salvage evaporation and transpiration losses caused by the near-surface water table, it measures also the safe yield of the well field that can be supported in the valley. Two methods for measuring evaporation and transpiration loss under these conditions have been used.

[1] See references at end of chapter.

Investigation in Owens Valley.—A method for measuring evaporation and transpiration was developed and described by C. H. Lee in his paper entitled "An Intensive Study of the Water Resources of a Part of Owens Valley, California."[1] Owens Valley is an enclosed basin and ground-water discharge is chiefly by evaporation from swamps and ponds and transpiration from natural vegetation supplied with water by the capillary fringe. Estimates of evaporation were based on experimental work with evaporation pans, and transpiration of existing groups of natural vegetation was measured by cutting the plants and determining the transpiration for the first 15 min. by weighing, during which time the rate of transpiration was assumed not to be affected by cutting.

Studies in Escalante Valley.—A second method was first suggested by G. E. P. Smith[2] and carried out and described by W. N. White.[3] Daily ground-water fluctuations in numerous test holes and wells bored in the small transpiration and evaporation area in the center of Escalante Valley, Utah, were measured, and graphic records of these fluctuations were obtained from water-stage registers placed in test wells. On account of the importance of these studies, portions of the report are quoted.

Escalante Valley has an area of about 1000 square miles, a length of about 90 miles, and a width ranging from 5 to 25 miles. It lies between two series of roughly parallel mountains and hills 6000 to 10,000 feet high; the valley floor ranges in altitude from 4800 to 5500 feet. Ground-water recharge in this valley is derived chiefly from stream seepage on the outwash slopes at the mouths of mountain canyons. Nearly all the streams are intermittent or ephemeral. Under natural conditions the average annual recharge is balanced by an equal average annual discharge, most of which occurs by evaporation and transpiration within an area of about 200 square miles forming a strip of irregular width in the lowlands along the trough of the valley. The lands in some parts of this area are bare, but most of the area supports a growth of varying density of ground-water plants such as salt grass, tussock grass, rabbit brush, greasewood, shad scale, pickleweed, seep weed, sedges, and

[1] *U.S. Geol. Surv. Water-Supply Paper* 294, pp. 48–63, 1912.

[2] Described in an unpublished paper read before the Geological Society of Washington, Nov. 22, 1922.

[3] WHITE, WALTER N., A Method of Estimating Ground-water Supplies Based on Discharge by Plants and Evaporation from Soil, *U.S. Geol. Surv. Water-Supply Paper* 659-A, 1932.

willows. Some sagebrush is also found. Cultivated crops, chiefly alfalfa, are raised on about 3500 acres of the area, of which a part is irrigated from wells and a part is supplied by natural subirrigation. . . . [1]

. . . The records obtained from observation wells show that during the growing season there is a marked daily fluctuation of the water table nearly everywhere in fields of ground-water plants. Usually the water starts down at 9 to 11 A.M. and reaches its lowest stage at 6 to 7 P.M. At 7 to 9 P.M. the water begins to rise and continues to rise until 7 to 9 the following morning. The maximum daily drawdown observed during the investigation amounted to about $1\frac{1}{2}$ inches in greasewood and shad scale, $2\frac{1}{2}$ inches in alfalfa, $3\frac{3}{4}$ inches in salt grass, and $4\frac{1}{2}$ inches in sedges and associated marsh grasses. The fluctuations do not occur in plowed fields, cleared lands, tracts of sagebrush, and tracts where the water table is far below the surface. In general they begin with the appearance of foliage in the spring and cease after killing frosts. They cease or are materially reduced after the plants are cut. The water table rises sharply almost immediately after a rain in fields of ground-water plants during the growing season, even though the rain is light and affords no ground-water recharge. There is little or no rise of the water table after rains in clear lands at any time or in fields of ground-water plants when plant life is dormant.

. . . Cylinders were driven near observation wells so as to inclose columns of undisturbed soil in the zone in which the fluctuations take place, and the rise and fall of the water table in the inclosed columns after the addition or subtraction of measured amounts of water were carefully noted. From these experiments the specific yield of the soils was determined. The amount of ground water discharged daily by the plants was then computed by the formula $q = y(24r \pm s)$, in which q is the depth of ground water withdrawn, in inches, y is the specific yield of the soil in which the daily fluctuation of the water table takes place, r is the hourly rate of rise of the water table, in inches, from midnight to 4 A.M., (when it was determined that transpiration and evaporation were practically nil) and s is the net fall or rise of the water during the 24-hour period in inches. In field experiments the quantities on the right-hand side of the formula except the specific yield can be readily determined from the automatic records of water-table fluctuations. . . .

By means of these studies the amount of ground water discharged in fields of different kinds of ground-water plants was computed. As a final step the districts in the valley in which conditions are favorable for salvage of ground water by means of wells were mapped, and the areas of different kinds of ground-water plants were outlined. The

[1] WHITE, *op. cit.*, p. 2.

computed coefficients of discharge were then applied to the different
areas, and thereby estimates were reached as to the safe pumping yield
in these districts.[1]

In Escalante Valley and in all desert playas surrounded by
alluvial cones the hydraulic system is a type of confined water,
the escape area of which is the playa. The water is forced
upward near or to the surface by the hydraulic pressure in the
aquifers of the surrounding alluvial cones. White's studies were
based on the assumption that the upward percolation of water
in the playa is constant. Troxell[2] criticizes this assumption,
stating that during the day when transpiration is active, the discharge level is reduced and the hydraulic gradient is increased,
and upward percolation is more rapid than at night when the
water level rises, the hydraulic gradient is reduced and discharge
is decreased. Troxell offers interesting graphical methods for
estimating ground-water discharge from diurnal fluctuations of
water level.

Pomperaug Basin Investigation.—In humid regions under
favorable conditions it has been found possible to evaluate all
additions to and subtractions from the ground-water body.
Evaporation and transpiration from the ground surface and
from the water table are important agencies of discharge.
Meinzer and Stearns'[3] investigations in the Pomperaug Basin,
Connecticut, show that practically all water that falls on the
basin as rain or snow either evaporates or discharges out of
the basin through Pomperaug River. During any given period,
however, some of the water may be stored as snow or ice, as
surface water in ponds and streams, as soil moisture, or as ground
water. On the other hand, water may be drawn from storage
in the melting of snow and ice, shrinkage of ponds and dwindling
of streams, drying out of the soil, or lowering of the water table.
Obviously therefore for any month, year, or other period the total
evaporation is about equal to the precipitation minus the total

[1] WHITE, *op. cit.*, pp. 2–3.

[2] TROXELL, H. C., The Diurnal Fluctuations in the Ground Water and
Flow of the Santa Ana River and its Meaning, *Trans. Amer. Geophys. Union*,
pp. 498–501, 1936.

[3] MEINZER, O. E., and N. D. STEARNS, A Study of Ground Water in the
Pomperaug Basin, Conn., with special reference to intake and discharge,
U.S. Geol. Surv. Water-Supply Paper 597-B, 1929.

runoff and minus the net increase in storage or plus the net decrease in storage.

Detailed inventories of rainfall, runoff, and changes in storage, therefore, furnish data bearing on total discharge by evaporation and transpiration for each month of the year. *Evaporativity* is the evaporation that would occur from a free-water surface. *Evaporation*[1] *opportunity* is the actual evaporation and transpiration from the ground surface expressed as a percentage of evaporativity. The authors found that evaporation opportunity of the basin was 59 per cent of evaporativity during a period of three years' measurements. During July evaporation opportunity is not far from 100 per cent on account of high transpiration which takes place during the season of plant growth, from about April to October. The total annual evaporation was about 23 in. during the three years covered by the investigation, distributed as follows: transpiration, 9 in.; evaporation from soil moisture, rain and snow intercepted by plants, rain and snow on the ground surface, and water in ponds and streams, 14 in.

Evaporation and transpiration from the water table were computed for the period from May to October from the monthly ground-water recharge, change in ground-water storage during the month, and monthly ground-water runoff (effluent seepage into streams). From November to April the temperature is low, plant life nearly dormant, the ground frozen much of the time, and hence ground-water evaporation was considered negligible. The average annual computed ground-water evaporation for the three years was 6.21 in., or about 27 per cent of the total evaporation. This includes transpiration of trees and other plants that feed upon ground water and also evaporation from soil in low places kept moist by rising ground water. It also includes evaporation from springs, areas of effluent seepage and streams.

Investigation in Connection with Proposed Salt-water Barrier.— A report by Lee on "Evaporation and Transpiration with Special Reference to a Salt-water Barrier"[2] illustrates the importance of the principles of meteorology and data collected by the Weather Bureau as a basis for detailed study of both evaporation and transpiration within a particular area.

[1] The authors include transpiration under evaporation.

[2] *State of California, Div. Water Res. Bull.* 28, Appendix *C*, pp. 247–307, 1931.

The "salt-water barrier" is a proposed embankment or low dam across the Sacramento River, California, to prevent the encroachment of salt water up the river into the "Delta region" which is located on the lower reaches of the Sacramento and San Joaquin rivers. Normal saline contamination of the two rivers during dry seasons has been intensified during the last two decades of deficient rainfall and increase in consumption of irrigation water. The Delta region is by far the most productive large area in California and possibly in the United States. It has been converted from a worthless marsh by dikes built along the banks of the distributary channels of the rivers and around the land lying at or a little below sea level. The diked areas are known locally as islands. The islands are drained by large ditches 10 to 15 ft. deep, the drainage water of which is pumped into the river, and are irrigated by shallow ditches fed by river water syphoned over the embankments. Satisfactory irrigation water is not available during the period of contamination.

The height of the proposed barrier above sea level is limited by the height of the present dike system in the Delta region, as the cost of raising the dikes to permit a higher barrier is prohibitive. A low barrier would impond a shallow lake of great extent, covering areas differing in meteorological characteristics and types of marginal vegetation. The areas considered in Lee's report are

. . . those from which evaporation and transpiration would occur with construction of a salt water barrier, the source of which would be fresh water from the Sacramento and San Joaquin rivers and their tributaries. It was assumed that average water surface behind a barrier would be at elevation 2.5 feet above U.S. Geological Survey mean sea level datum. The areas would consist primarily of fresh-water surfaces in the two bays, open sloughs, and sloughs, drains, ponds, etc., within levees. Surrounding and adjoining these water surfaces would be large areas of natural vegetation. . . . [1]

The acreage of the proposed barrier lake was classified according to areas with different types of vegetation and varying conditions of transpiration and evaporation. This classification appears in Table *C*-1, page 279, of Lee's report. In his study of evaporation Lee compiled all data collected by the Weather Bureau on daily relative humidity, mean temperature, wind

[1] *Op. cit.*, p. 255.

movement, evaporation, and precipitation within the general region to be occupied by the barrier lake, and by analysis of these data subdivided the area into meteorological districts. From the meteorological data and from observations on the temperature of present bays and experimental study of evaporation in the different districts he deduced the following depths of annual evaporation to be expected from the fresh-water lake in each of the meteorological districts.[1]

San Pablo Bay........................ 40.61 in. (3.38 ft.)
Carquinez Strait..................... 46.35 in. (3.86 ft.)
Suisun Bay........................... 49.33 in. (4.11 ft.)
Delta................................ 58.98 in. (4.92 ft.)

His investigation of transpiration loss from areas adjacent to the proposed lake was even more complicated. Existing vegeta-

TABLE 1.—ESTIMATED MONTHLY DEPTH OF EVAPORATION AND TRANSPIRATION FROM NATURAL FRESH-WATER VEGETATION GROWING IN AREA ABOVE A SALT-WATER BARRIER*

Month	Tule and cat-tail, ft.	Salt grass,† ft.	Willows, ft.	
			In large groves	Isolated trees
January..................	0.16	0.06	0.04	0.09
February................	0.09	0.08	0.03	0.05
March...................	0.30	0.12	0.08	0.16
April....................	0.74	0.24	0.20	0.41
May.....................	1.10	0.36	0.30	0.60
June....................	1.28	0.43	0.35	0.70
July....................	1.53	0.56	0.42	0.84
August....	1.32	0.58	0.36	0.73
September..............	1.18	0.39	0.33	0.65
October................	0.98	0.29	0.27	0.54
November..............	0.59	0.22	0.16	0.32
December..............	0.36	0.14	0.10	0.20
Year..................	9.63	3.47	2.64	5.29

* LEE, *op. cit.*, p. 307.
† Values for average annual depth to water table of 2 ft.

tion was mapped and plant assemblages were redistributed according to the change in environment caused by the fresh-

[1] LEE, C. H., *op. cit.*, p. 269.

water lake.   He collected and analyzed all transpiration data
available in the literature and compared them with experimental
data obtained in the Delta region.   As a result of these studies
he estimated the annual evaporation and transpiration from the
tule and cat-tail areas,[1] the salt-grass areas, and the willows as
shown in Table 1.

Applying the evaporation and transpiration data to the areas
classified according to types of vegetation and different conditions
of evaporation and transpiration, above referred to, it was
concluded that sufficient water would not be available to supply
the fresh-water lake.   It may be said that the tule and salt grass
killed the Salt-water Barrier project.

References

Rainfall and Runoff

BAKER, D. M., and H. CONKLING, "Water Supply and Utilization," pp. 34–
    217, John Wiley & Son, Inc., 1930.
DAVIS, W. E., and A. W. SAMPSON, Experiments in Correlation of Tree-
    growth Rings and Precipitation-cycles, *Trans. Amer. Geophys. Union*,
    pp. 493–496, 1936.
DOUGLASS, A. E., Climatic Cycles and Tree Growth, Carnegie Inst., 1919.
GROVER, N. C., and J. C. HOYT, Accuracy of Stream Flow Data, *U.S. Geol.
    Surv. Water-Supply Paper* 400, 1916.
GRUNSKY, C. E., Rainfall and Runoff Studies, *Trans. Amer. Soc. Civ.
    Eng.*, vol. 79, p. 1165, 1915; vol. 85, p. 66, 1921; *Amer. Soc. Civ. Eng.
    Proc.*, vol. 47, pp. 203–242, 1921; Simplified Rain Intensity Formulas,
    Monthly Weather Rev., *U.S. Dept. Agr.*, October, 1930.
HARDMAN, GEORGE, The Relationship between Tree-Growths and Stream
    Runoff in the Truckee River Basin, California-Nevada, *Trans. Amer.
    Geophys. Union*, pp. 491–493, 1936.
HORTON, R. E., Natural Stream Channel-storage, *Trans. Amer. Geophys.
    Union*, pp. 406–415, 1936.
——— Surface Runoff Phenomena, *Horton Hydrologic Lab. Bull.* 101,
    Edwards Bros. Publ., Ann Arbor, Mich., 1935.
——— Accuracy of Areal Rainfall Estimates, *Monthly Weather Rev.*, *U.S.
    Dept. Agr.*, vol. 51, pp. 348–353, July, 1923.
——— Determining the Mean Precipitation on a Drainage Basin, *Jour.
    Amer. Water Works Assn.*, vol. 38, March, 1924.

[1] Lee found that experimental determination of transpiration from tule
tanks was much higher than for natural tule fields.   The reason is that in
the tule fields the humidity becomes high and there is less opportunity for
transpiration from individual plants than is made available to plants in
tanks by moving air.

HOYT, W. G., and OTHERS, Studies of Relations of Rainfall and Runoff in the United States, *U.S. Geol. Surv. Water-Supply Paper* 772, 1936. Contains comprehensive bibliography on rainfall and runoff.

HUNTINGTON, E., and S. VISHER, "Climatic Changes, Their Nature and Causes," Yale University Press, Chap. V, 1922.

LIDDELL, W. A., "Stream Gaging," McGraw-Hill Book Company, Inc., 1927.

MEAD, D. W., "Hydrology," pp. 112–308, McGraw-Hill Book Company, Inc., 1919.

MEYER, A. F., Computing Runoff from Rainfall and other Physical Data, *Trans. Amer. Soc. Civ. Eng.*, vol. 79, p. 1056, 1915.

—— "The Elements of Hydrology," pp. 64*ff.*, John Wiley & Sons, Inc., 1917.

SAVILLE, C. M., The Underground Water-Index, Its Relation to Surface Runoff, *Trans. Amer. Geophys. Union*, pp. 382–386, 1936.

SHERMAN, L. K., Stream-flow from Rainfall by Unit-graph Method, *Eng. News-Record*, vol. 108, pp. 501–505, April, 1932.

SHERMAN, L. K., and R. E. HORTON, Rainfall, Runoff and Evaporation, *Assn. Intern. d'Hydrol. Sci.*, May, 1933. Review of literature on rainfall and runoff published in the United States, with comprehensive bibliographies.

YARNELL, D. L., Rainfall Intensity-Frequency Data, *U.S. Dept. Agr., Misc. Publ.* 204, August, 1935.

Flood Flow

BAKER and CONKLING, *op. cit.*, pp. 190–216.

Flood Problems, A Symposium, *Trans. Amer. Soc. Civ. Eng.*, vol. 85, 1922.

HAZEN, ALLEN, "Flood Flows," John Wiley & Sons, Inc., 1930.

JARVIS, C. S., Flood Flow Characteristics, *Trans. Amer. Soc. Civ. Eng.*, vol. 89, p. 985, 1926.

JARVIS, C. S., and OTHERS, Floods in the United States, *U.S. Geol. Surv. Water-Supply Paper* 771, 1936.

MEAD, D. W., "Hydrology," pp. 544–596.

TURNEAURE and RUSSELL, "Public Water Supplies," John Wiley & Sons, Inc., pp. 65–86, 1924.

Evaporation and Transpiration

BIGELOW, F. H., "Evaporation Observations and Formulae—A Manual for Observers in Climatology and Evaporation," U.S. Weather Bureau, 1909.

BLANEY, H. F., Consumptive Use of Water by Native Plants Growing in Moist Areas in Southern California, *State of Calif., Div. Water Res. Bull.* 44, pp. 1–26, 1933.

BLANEY, H. F. and OTHERS, Rainfall Penetration and Consumptive Use of Water in Santa Ana River Valley and Coastal Plain, *State of Calif., Div. Water Res. Bull.* 33, pt. II, pp. 107–158, 1930.

BRIGGS, L. J., Losses through Transpiration, *U.S. Dept. Agr. Bur. Plant Industry Bull.* 230, 1912.

————, and H. L. Shantz, Daily Transpiration during the Normal Growth Period and its Correlation with Weather, *Jour. Agr. Res.*, vol. 7, no. 4, Oct. 23, 1916.

Buckingham, E., Studies on the Movement of Soil Moisture, *U.S. Dept. Agr., Bur. Soils Bull.* 38, 1907.

Folse, J. A., A New Method of Estimating Stream-Flow Based upon a New Evaporation Formula; Part I, A New Evaporation Formula, *Carnegie Inst. Wash. Publ.* 400, 1929.

Fortier, S., and S. H. Beckett, Evaporation from Irrigated Soils, *U.S. Dept. Agr., Off. Exp. Sta. Bull.* 248, 1912.

Lee, C. H., Absorption and Transpiration, *Trans. Amer. Geophys. Union*, pp. 293–296 (see bibliography pp. 296–298), 1932.

———— Water Resources of a Part of Owens Valley, Calif., *U.S. Geol. Surv. Water-Supply Paper* 294, pp. 48–63, 1912.

———— Evaporation and Transpiration with Special Reference to a Salt Water Barrier, *State of Calif., Div. Water Res. Bull.* 28, *Appendix C*, pp. 247–307, 1931.

Meinzer, O. E., Plants as Indicators of Ground Water, *U.S. Geol. Surv. Water-Supply Paper* 577, 1927.

————, and N. D. Stearns, A Study of Ground Water in the Pomperaug Basin, Conn., with special reference to intake and discharge, *U.S. Geol. Surv. Water-Supply Paper* 597-B, 1929.

Stearns, H. L., and L. L. Byron, Geology and Water Resources of the Mud Lake Basin, Idaho, *U.S. Geol. Surv. Water-Supply Paper* 560-D, pp. 97–102, 1926.

Veihmeyer, F. J., Some Factors Affecting the Irrigation Requirements of Deciduous Orchards, *Hilgardia*, vol. 2, no. 6, pp. 187–280, January, 1927.

White, W. N., A Method of Estimating Ground-water Supplies Based on Discharge by Plants and Evaporation from Soil, *U.S. Geol. Surv. Water-Supply Paper* 659-A, 1932.

General References on Meteorology

Bigelow, F. H., A Manual for Observers in Climatology and Evaporation, 1909.

Blair, T. A. "Weather Elements," Prentice-Hall, Inc., 1937.

Brunt, David, "Meteorology: The World's Manuals," Oxford University Press, 1928.

Hann, J., "Handbook of Climatology," Trans. by R. DeC. Ward, The Macmillan Company, 1903.

Henry, A. J., Climatology of the United States, *U.S. Weather Bur. Bull.* Q, 1906.

Hobbs, W. H., "Earth Features and their Meaning," The Macmillan Company, pp. 446–476, 1931.

Humphreys, W. J., "Physics of the Air," 2d ed., McGraw-Hill Book Company Inc., 1929.

Shaw, Sir N., "Manual of Meteorology," The Macmillan Company, (in four volumes).

Weather Forecasting

BLISS, G. S., Weather Forecasting, *U.S. Weather Bur. Bull.* 42, 5th ed., 1929.

BOWIE, E. H., Weather Forecasting in the United States, U.S. Weather Bur.

BROOKS, C. E., "Why the Weather," Harcourt Brace & Company, 1924.

CHAPMAN, E. H., "The Study of the Weather," Cambridge University Press.

HENRY, A. J., and OTHERS, Weather Forecasting in the United States, U.S. Weather Bureau, 1916.

McEWEN, G. F., Problems of Long-range Weather-forecasting for the Pacific Coast, *Trans. Amer. Geophys. Union*, pp. 486–491, 1936.

Mass Analysis

BYERS, H. R., Characteristic Weather Phenomena of California, *Mass. Inst. Tech., Meteorol. Papers*, vol. 1, no. 2, 1931.

—— The Air Masses of the North Pacific, Scripps Inst. of Oceanography, 1934.

NAMIAS, J., An Introduction to the Study of Air Mass Analysis, *Bull. Amer. Met. Soc.*, 3d ed., vol. 17, nos. 6–7, June-July, 1936.

Nat. Res. Council, Meteorol. Bull. 79, chap. V, 1931.

WILLETT, H. C., American Air Mass Properties, *Mass. Inst. Tech., Papers in Phys. Oceanogr. Meteorology*, vol. 2, no. 2, 1933.

CHAPTER IV

HYDROLOGIC PROPERTIES OF WATER-BEARING MATERIALS, EXCEPT SOIL

The principal hydrologic properties of rocks are porosity, effective porosity or specific yield, specific retention, permeability, and direction of maximum ease of percolation. These properties control the entrance of water into water-bearing formations or rocks; their capacity to hold, transmit, and deliver water; and confinement and concentration of percolation to the direction of maximum ease of movement. Hydrologic properties depend chiefly on porosity, size of openings or interstices and their shape, arrangement, interconnection, and continuity. This chapter discusses the openings in rocks, especially in sedimentary and alluvial formations, processes by which the openings are formed, and relation of openings to hydrologic properties. Laboratory investigations of hydrologic properties are discussed in Chap. VIII, and field methods are discussed especially in Chap. XVI. Soil is given separate treatment on account of unique hydrologic characteristics (Chaps. V and VI).

Rock formations and the openings therein are the results of primary geologic processes which form the rocks and secondary processes that modify them, either increasing or decreasing their porosity and permeability. Geologic processes acting on rocks may change or induce entirely new hydrologic structure which controls the motions of underground water. Ground-water geology deals chiefly with hydrologic properties of rocks, their control over the motions of subsurface water, and the geologic processes which develop hydrologic properties. The hydrologic characteristics of sedimentary or alluvial deposits may be inherited from the parent formation. For instance, weathering of sandstone or granite may produce abundant sand which, under the classifying processes of nature, may be redeposited as aquifers. Weathering of lava rocks, such as basalt, and of shale, slate, and many types of schists, may produce no

96

sand grains and the resultant product may be largely impervious clay (aquiclude).

OPENINGS IN ROCKS

Meinzer has given an excellent discussion of openings in rocks and the types of pore space which hold water. Inasmuch as the author of this text cannot improve on Meinzer's[1] treatment of this subject, it is incorporated as an introduction to the more detailed discussion which follows, although its insertion involves some repetition.

The rocks that form the crust of the earth are in few places, if anywhere, solid throughout. They contain numerous open spaces, called voids or interstices, and these spaces are the receptacles that hold the water that is found below the surface of the land and is recovered in part through springs and wells. There are many kinds of rocks, and they differ greatly in the number, size, shape, and arrangement of their interstices and hence in their properties as containers of water. The occurrence of water in the rocks of any region is therefore determined by the character, distribution, and structure of the rocks it contains—that is, by the geology of the region. Most rocks have numerous interstices of very small size, but some are characterized by a few large openings, such as joints or caverns. In most rocks the interstices are connected, so that the water can move through the rocks by percolating from one interstice to another; but in some rocks the interstices are largely isolated, and there is little opportunity for the water to percolate. The interstices are generally irregular in shape, but different types of irregularities are characteristic of different kinds of rocks. The differences in rocks with respect to their interstices result from the differences in the minerals of which they are composed and from the great diversity of geologic processes by which they were produced or later modified.

The porosity of a rock is its property of containing interstices. Some authors have used the term to refer only to minute interstices, which they call pores, but in comparison with the size of the earth itself even the largest openings are no more than pores, and the term "porosity" is much more useful if it is made to apply to all openings, instead of only to openings having an arbitrary limit of size. Porosity is expressed quantitatively as the percentage of the total volume of the rock that is occupied by interstices or that is not occupied by solid rock material. A rock is said to be saturated when all its interstices are filled with water. In a saturated rock the porosity is practically the percentage of the total volume of the rock that is occupied by water.

[1] MEINZER, O. E., The Occurrence of Ground Water in the United States, *U.S. Geol. Surv. Water-Supply Paper* 489, p. 2, 1923.

The porosity of a sedimentary deposit depends chiefly on (1) the shape and arrangement of its constituent particles, (2) the degree of assortment of its particles, (3) the cementation and compacting to which it has been subjected since its deposition, (4) the removal of mineral matter through solution by percolating waters, and (5) the fracturing of the rock, resulting in joints and other openings. Well-sorted deposits of uncemented gravel, sand, or silt have a high porosity, regardless of whether they consist of large or small grains. If, however, the material is poorly sorted small particles occupy the spaces between the larger ones, still smaller ones occupy the spaces between these small particles, and so on, with the result that the porosity is greatly reduced (Fig. 24, A and B). Boulder clay, which is an unassorted mixture of glacial drift

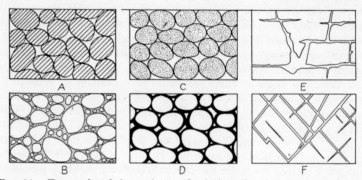

Fig. 24.—Types of rock interstices and relation of rock texture to porosity. *A*, well-sorted alluvial material, high porosity; *B*, poorly sorted alluvial material, low porosity; *C*, well-sorted deposit of porous pebbles, very high porosity; *D*, well-sorted deposit, porosity decreased by cementation; *E*, rock rendered porous by solution; *F*, rock rendered porous by fracturing. (*After Meinzer.*)

containing particles of great variety in size, may have a very low porosity, whereas outwash gravel and sand, derived from the same source but assorted by running water, may be highly porous. Well-sorted uncemented gravel may be composed of pebbles that are themselves porous, so that the deposit as a whole has a very high porosity (Fig. 24, *C*). Well-sorted porous gravel, sand, or silt may gradually have its interstices filled with mineral matter deposited out of solution from percolating waters, and under extreme conditions it may become a practically impervious conglomerate or quartzite of very low porosity (Fig. 24, *D*). On the other hand, relatively soluble rock, such as limestone, though originally dense, may become cavernous as a result of the removal of part of its substance through the solvent action of percolating water (Fig. 24, *E*). Furthermore hard, brittle rock, such as limestone, hard sandstone, or most igneous and metamorphic rocks, may acquire large interstices through fracturing that results from shrinkage or deformation of the rocks or through other agencies (Fig. 24, *F*). Solution channels and fractures may be large and of great practical importance, but they are rarely abundant enough to give an otherwise dense rock a high porosity.

Types of Openings

Openings in lavas include gas cavities, porous flow textures and structures, openings between included rock fragments, and interstices in tuffs and breccias. Principal openings in soluble rocks, such as limestone and gypsum, are solution cavities which often control water storage and movement. Fractures are the principal openings in crystalline rocks. Large fractures, usually few in number, are produced by deep-seated earth stresses and may extend to great depth, and small near-surface fractures may occur in great numbers. In sedimentary rocks, using the term to include marine, lacustrine, eolian sediments, and alluvial materials, the openings are pores between grains, the size, shape, and interconnection of which may be modified by compaction and cementation. Fractures also constitute an important type of opening if the sedimentary rock is cemented or otherwise consolidated. In general inter-grain pore space is the most important subsurface receptable for liquids and gases. The most important and abundant fluid underground is water, but liquid hydrocarbons occur occasionally in large quantities. Gases present include air, water vapor, carbon dioxide, hydrogen sulphide, and hydrocarbon gases.

Openings are produced by a number of processes. These processes and the openings produced by them may be classified as *primary* and *secondary*.

Primary Openings.—In *sedimentary rocks* primary openings are produced by the process of sedimentation, and their arrangement determines the original fabric of the rock and controls its hydrologic properties.

Amygdaloidal or *gas cavities* in lava are occasionally important in volcanic regions. Amygdaloidal cavities differ from cavities in sedimentary rocks in that they are not originally interconnected but each opening is enclosed in dense lava. Unless some later process opens connections between cavities, there can be no movement of water between them. For example, certain amygdaloidal lavas have 80 per cent pore space but nevertheless water cannot be extracted unless the rock is broken. Breakage of the walls of pores, thereby producing the necessary interconnection, is often caused by flow of lava under a solid crust or by fracture due to earth movement or weathering.

Other Openings in Lavas.—Lavas may be impervious if the flows are dense and unbroken, or exceedingly pervious if broken or drawn out by flow movement, inflated by gas, or mixed with material picked up and partly cemented by flowing lava. Agglomerate and tuff intermixed or interstratified with lava may be porous. Discussion of the ground-water province of the Hawaiian Islands by R. G. Sohlberg (pages 539–552) describes the control of structure and texture of volcanic rocks on ground water.

Interstices occur *between crystals* in crystalline rocks but the pores are usually of subcapillary size and are not interconnected. Crystalline rocks do not permit water movement except in fractures.

Secondary Openings.—Earth stresses occasionally produce large open fractures extending to great depth. The most important of these are faults along which dislocation of the rock mass on either side has occurred. However, "incipient" or tightly closed fractures are more common. These are opened up in the belt of weathering where they may control water movements (Chap. X).

Solution cavities are common in limestone. Their development is controlled by intersecting fracture systems and impervious insoluble layers. The tubular openings converge toward a discharge exit, often located in a deep valley. Although solution openings usually perforate limestone above the main exit, the writer believes that large tubular conduits are dissolved below the water table. Some of the largest springs result from the emergence of underground rivers flowing in subwater-table solution channels.

Openings are produced by weathering, especially in crystalline and cemented sedimentary rocks. These may be the result of solution or occasionally of mechanical action, such as frost and temperature changes. The chief function of weathering is not rock fracture, but the opening up of all closed or incipient fractures and other planes of weakness. The weathered zone may be open and porous down to the contact between the weathered and the fresh material. This contact is often located at the water table because weathering does not take place in the saturated zone. However, large fractures often extend below the water table and in that case are aquifers. Earth movements and other geological agencies may lower or raise the water table, and if raised, the drowned portion of the weathered zone may constitute a capacious reservoir.

List of Agencies That Produce Openings

1. Processes of sedimentation.
2. Expansion of included gases, forming cavities in lava and in mudflows.
3. Drying out or desiccation, especially in clays, producing mud cracks and other secondary fractures.
4. Crystallization of igneous rocks producing intercrystal interstices.
5. Fracturing or mechanical disruption.
6. Chemical action, solution.
7. Colloidal processes, flocculation.
8. Combination of chemical and mechanical action known as weathering.
9. Vital processes: (*a*) Root openings; (*b*) animal and insect borings.

Agencies That Destroy Openings

Many formations would be pervious were it not for the various processes of nature which destroy or fill openings.

Compaction.—As soon as sedimentary material is deposited, compacting and hardening begin owing to the weight of the overlying materials. In the Mississippi delta fresh deposits of clay have 80 to 90 per cent porosity, but after more material is laid over them, they become compacted and porosity drops to about 40 per cent. This process continues after burial until the porosity of shale (compacted clay) may be reduced from more than 30 per cent to less than 3 per cent. In Kay County, Oklahoma, shales from shallow core holes have an average porosity of 20 per cent, but at depths of 4500 ft. their porosity is about 4 per cent.[1]

[1] ATHY, L. F., Compaction and Its Effect on Local Structure: "Problems of Petroleum Geology," A Symposium, Amer. Assoc. Pet. Geol., p. 815, 1934.

Deflocculation of Clays.—Clayey soils may be pervious owing to the aggregate grain structure (pages 124, 127) induced by flocculated colloidal material. Such soil may be puddled (deflocculated) by tillage when the soil is too wet for cultivation or by the trampling of animals and thus become impervious. Clay may also be deflocculated by chemical reaction with the soil solution, and is always deflocculated at moderate depths (10 to 50 ft.) by the weight of the overlying material.

Slumping of material, especially on the banks of a river, may destroy a direct connection between aquifers and the source of water supply.

Cementation.—Another important agency which destroys openings, sometimes beginning at the ground surface but more commonly and more important below the water table, is precipitation of materials such as calcium carbonate, silica, and other natural cements. In general, porosity of sedimentary rocks is reduced from 30 per cent to 5 per cent and sometimes even to less than 1 per cent as a result of cementation.

Metamorphism.—Openings left in cemented rock are sometimes further reduced and for all practical purposes destroyed by metamorphism. When metamorphic rocks with schistose or slaty cleavage are exposed at the surface by denudation, weathering may open the planes of schistosity and slaty cleavage and produce fairly pervious rock.

Weathering.—The processes of weathering usually produce openings, especially weathering of crystalline and cemented sedimentary rocks. However, weathering may destroy openings and disintegrate rock particles into clayey material and hence decrease porosity, especially of alluvial materials. R. Eckis has described the decrease in porosity near the apices of alluvial cones of the South Coastal basin, California,[1] due to weathering of the alluvium above the water table, with the result that the coarse gravel deposits and boulder beds have been converted into clayey gravels and in extreme cases largely into clay. Farther from the mountains the alluvial cones contain much sorted sand and the water table is closer to the ground surface, so the material has been protected against weathering. Hence the central por-

[1] ECKIS, R., South Coastal Basin Investigation: Geology and Ground Water Storage Capacity of Valley Fill, *State Calif. Div. Water Res. Bull.* 45, p. 99, 1934.

tions of the cones in this region are more porous and pervious than the upper portions near the mountains.

Long-continued action of soil-forming processes, which involves weathering, develops an impervious horizon *B* (pages 126–127) and thus greatly decreases the porosity of soil.

Geometry of Spherical Aggregates

As defined by Meinzer, "The porosity of a rock is its property of containing interstices." The interconnected pores of sedimentary and alluvial materials are by far the most important reservoirs and transmitting media for ground water. The shape of the interstices and the pattern of the interconnected openings are extremely complex and in order to lay the foundation for a mental picture of the interstitial fabric of water-bearing materials, one should start with the geometry of aggregates of spheres of the same diameter. Of course no water-bearing materials consist exclusively of spheres of one size, but some well-sorted sand aquifers probably develop pore-space patterns similar to those developed by packing of spheres, and the theoretical treatment of such aggregates is perhaps worth while if we bear in mind the profound modifications of pore pattern caused by irregularity in shape of grains and in degree of assortment of natural water-bearing material.

Slichter's treatment[1] of space relations of spherical aggregates has been the foundation on which most students of ground water have based their concepts of arrangement of pore space and size of individual pores. Recently Graton and Fraser[2] have published an exhaustive treatise on the geometry of aggregates of spheres.[3] The illustrations accompanying their articles are the most complete set of pictures of shape of pores and pattern of their

[1] SLICHTER, C. S., Theoretical Investigation of the Motions of Ground Water, *U.S. Geol. Surv. 19th Ann. Rept.*, pp. 305–328, 1899.

[2] GRATON, L. C., and H. J. FRASER, Systematic Packing of Spheres—With particular relation to porosity and permeability; H. J. Fraser, Experimental Study of the Porosity and Permeability of Clastic Sediments: *Jour. Geol.*, vol. 43, no. 8, November–December, 1935.

[3] Their paper "deals with the geometry of various ideal and near-ideal assemblages of discrete, ideal spheres. It treats them primarily from the abstract geometrical standpoint as if it made no difference whether the units were marbles, atoms, or planets, or whether they were assembled by man, machine, or nature."

interconnection and many of them are reproduced[1] in the following pages of this text. The authors show that packing of spheres may be disorderly or geometrically systematic. The latter arrangement consists of sets of "rows" (the centers of tangent

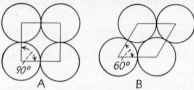

Fig. 25.—Types of layers. *A*, Square layer; *B*, "simple" rhombic layer.

spheres arranged along a straight line) arranged in parallel direction. A parallel group of rows constitutes a layer. The two simple types of layers are illustrated in Fig. 25. The simple rhombic layer represents the most compact arrangement for a

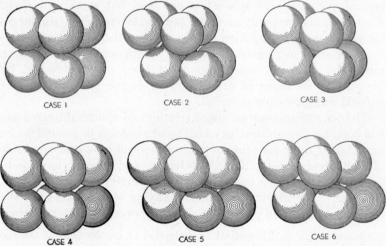

Fig. 26.—Type sphere groups of six arrangements. (*After Graton and Fraser.*)

single layer and the square layer is the most open aggregate. These two arrangements only were considered by Slichter,[2] but Graton and Fraser go further and show that the two simple types

---

[1] Reproduced by courtesy of Journal of Geology, Rollin T. Chamberlin, Editor.

[2] Slichter, *op. cit.*

of layers may be "stacked" in three ways, giving the six arrangements shown in Fig. 26. The "unit cells" of each system of packing are shown in Fig. 27. The voids are illustrated in

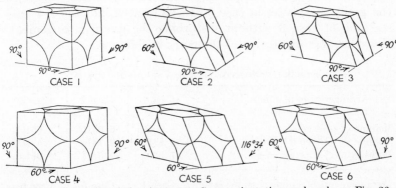

FIG. 27.—Unit cells of the six cases. Same orientation and scale as Fig. 26. (*After Graton and Fraser.*)

Fig. 28. The "throat planes" or smallest cross sections of the voids are shown in white.

The porosities of the six arrangements are shown in Table 2.

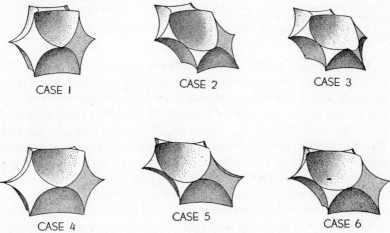

FIG. 28.—Unit voids of the six arrangements. Same orientation and scale as Figs. 26 and 27. (*After Graton and Fraser.*)

The arrangements of cases 3 and 6 give minimum porosity, although case 3 starts with a basal cubic row and the upper row offset so that the upper spheres rest on the openings between spheres of the lower layer. Two rhombic layers cannot be arranged so that the openings of the lower layer are all capped by spheres; nevertheless the packing is identical with case 3 because the group of spheres in case 6 can be rotated into the row and stacking of case 3 without disturbing the group arrangement. However, the orientation of the pores is different.

TABLE 2.—POROSITIES OF THE VARIOUS PACKINGS*

Arrangements of square layers	Case 1	Case 2	Case 3
Volume of unit cell†	$8.00R^3$	$6.93R^3$	$5.66R^3$
Volume of unit void†	$3.81R^3$	$2.74R^3$	$1.47R^3$‡
Porosity	47.64%	39.54%	25.95%
Arrangements of simple rhombic layers	**Case 4**	**Case 5**	**Case 6**
Volume of unit cell†	$6.93R^3$	$6.00R^3$	$5.66R^3$
Volume of unit void†	$2.74R^3$	$1.81R^3$	$1.47R^3$‡
Porosity	39.54%	30.19%	25.95%

* GRATON and FRASER *op. cit.*, p. 805.

† The volume of the complete cell and of the corresponding void is given for each case. The volume of the unit void is in each case derived by subtracting the volume of the unit sphere $4.19R^3$, from the volume of the unit cell.

‡ The void of cases 3 and 6 is composite and the volume of the composite void is given here.

Arrangements 3 and 6 are completely stable. Further classification changes arrangements 2 and 5 into 3 and 6, and arrangements 1 and 4 are completely unstable and the spheres tend to roll into 3 and 6 directly or through the intermediary arrangements of cases 2 and 5. However, if the spheres are packed within retaining walls in the square row pattern, this arrangement will be repeated in all overlying rows and this unstable arrangement of case 1 is the only possible symmetrical arrangement. The change from less stable to the stable arrangement calls for spreading and consequent decrease in thickness of the aggregate.

The unit void of case 1 has eight spherical rectangular surfaces and six throat planes that are concave squares. It is designated as a concave octahedron (see Fig. 28, case 1). The voids of cases 2 and 4 are identical and are bounded by eight spherical triangular surfaces terminating in four concave square throat planes and two spherical triangular throat planes point to point. The unit void of case 5 is a peculiar double wedge-shaped form bounded by four large and four small spherical triangles, with two concave-rectangle throat planes and four of double triangle shape. The unit void of cases 3 and 6, the most compact and stable arrangements, appears unexpectedly complex. It consists of a central large opening of the shape of a concave cube with two smaller openings attached as wings on each side, which are hollow concave-tetrahedrons (Fig. 29, *C* and *D*). The large concave cube accounts for 18.58 per cent porosity and the two small concave tetrahedrons 3.68 per cent each of the total porosity of

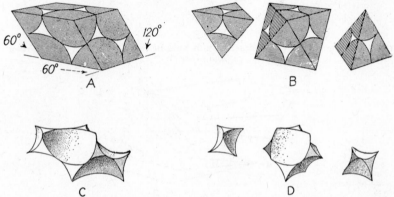

Fig. 29.—Elements of unit cell and unit void of case 6. *A*, unit cell; *B*, elements of unit cell; *C*, unit void; *D*, elements of unit void. (*After Graton and Fraser.*)

25.95 per cent. Successive cross sections through unit void of cases 3 and 6 and key to sections across unit voids are shown in Fig. 30.

The throat entrance represents the minimum cross section of the pore. It is a concave figure and its size can best be represented by the ratio of the diameter of the largest sphere that can pass through the throat to the diameter of the spheres constituting the aggregate. Fraser[1] designates this as the critical ratio of entrance, and uses the term "critical ratio of occupancy" for the ratio of the diameter of the largest sphere that can occupy the pore without disturbing the packing to the diameter of the spheres of the aggregate. The critical ratio of entrance is 0.154D for the tightest packing and 0.414D for the loosest pack-

[1] FRASER, *op. cit.*, p. 919.

ing. The critical ratio of occupancy for the tightest packing is 0.414D (for the large void) and 0.225D (for the small void), and

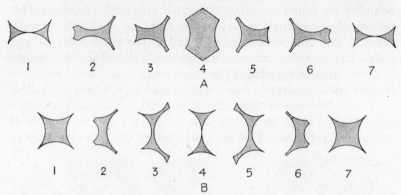

Fig. 30.—Successive sections across unit void of cases 3 and 6. (*After Graton and Fraser.*)

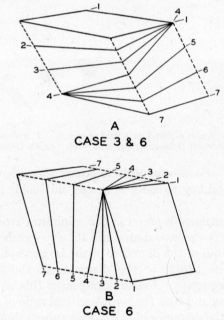

Fig. 30. (*Continued*)—Key to sections across unit void of cases 3 and 6. Outlined forms are those of unit cells in Fig. 27; solid lines show positions of sections.

for the loosest packing the ratio is 0.732D. These figures constitute the first worth-while estimate of the size of throat entrance and void.

Graton and Fraser discuss "twinning" in development of symmetrical packing and development of colonies of regularly packed spheres set in aggregates of haphazard arrangement.

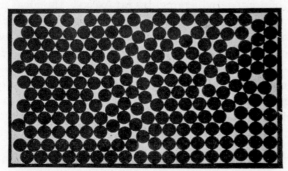

Fig. 31.—Haphazard packing of spheres in rectangular container. (*After Graton and Fraser.*)

The haphazard arrangement is best developed at the walls of the container (Figs. 31 and 32). The authors conclude after investigation of probabilities of arrangement of spheres that the

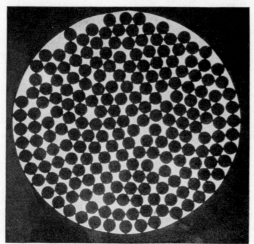

Fig. 32.—Haphazard packing of spheres in round container. (*After Graton and Fraser.*)

resulting assemblage is most likely to consist of colonies of tightest packing (case 6) with intervening zones or surrounding shells of haphazard arrangement.[1]

[1] GRATON and FRASER, *op. cit.*, p. 882.

Porosities of compacted aggregates of spheres obtained by Fraser[1] exceed the calculated porosities of case 6 (porosity 25.95 per cent) by approximately 50 per cent. The fact that the porosity of compacted aggregates far exceeds the ideal minimum porosity of case 6 suggests that the most compact arrangement may never be obtained under the classifying processes of nature. However, on account of intermixed sizes, porosities of natural water-bearing materials are usually less than that of case 6.

Further consideration of disorderly arrangements or mixed groupings is of academic interest only, as irregularities due to variation in shape of grain and degree of sorting characteristic of the natural formations far exceed the effects mentioned.

Pore Pattern in Alluvial and Sedimentary Material

The principal factors that develop pore-space patterns in natural alluvial material different from those of ideal assemblages of spheres are variability in shape and size of grains, orientation of grains due to settling and compacting, alternation of coarse and fine material and of sorted and unsorted material (sedimentary textures and structures). Some of these factors are mentioned in the quotation from Meinzer (pages 97–99). Hydrologic properties of sedimentary and alluvial materials are discussed in this chapter, in Chaps. VIII and XVI, and elsewhere in this text.

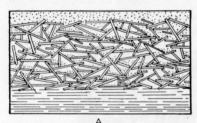

FIG. 33.—*A*, Irregular arrangement of mica flakes, high porosity; *B*, oriented mica flakes, low porosity.

Shape of grain varies from round grains of marine and dune sand to flat flakes of mica. Angular grains predominate in subaerial deposits (except wind-blown sand), especially those formed in arid regions. Mica often predominates in clayey and silty sediments. Interstices between mica flakes or in material containing mica may be either larger or smaller than interstices

[1] FRASER, *op. cit.*, pp. 941–946.

between round grains of similar size, and likewise porosity and permeability may be either larger or smaller. Freshly deposited silt made up of mica flakes in random orientation may have large porosity and relatively large interstices (Fig. 33*A*), and compacted silts with oriented mica flakes (Fig. 33*B*) may have low porosity and small interstices compared with the size of the mica flakes. Silty and clayey sediments settle and compact as more material is deposited upon them and high porosity is soon reduced. Slow compaction continues with increase in pressure and water is slowly freed thereby.

Effect of Pore Pattern.—Certain laws governing the relation of pore pattern to porosity and to direction of maximum ease of percolation are summarized below.

1. *Percentage of pore space does not increase with the size of material.* A deposit of boulders is popularly considered more porous than sand but, as a matter of fact, boulder deposits are generally less porous because the spaces between boulders are usually filled, at least in part, with finer material and the boulders interrupt the pore space that would occur in deposits made up of fine material alone.

2. From the foregoing discussion it follows that *heterogeneity reduces pore space.* Usually the larger the number of grain sizes in a formation, the less the pore space.

It may be noted, however, that the mixing of grains of nearly equal size does not materially reduce pore space over that of either group of one size because the smaller grains cannot be placed in the interstices between the larger grains without disturbing them. But the mixing of two sizes, one of which is small enough to form an aggregate which fills interstices between the larger grains, reduces the percentage of pore space of the mixture below that of the smaller material. From this we conclude that:

3. *The size of the finest interstitial material which occurs in sufficient amount to surround the grains of coarser material controls the velocity of percolation in heterogeneous material.*[1]

[1] From porosity determinations and mechanical analyses of several hundred samples from the South Coastal basin it was concluded that porosity of natural coarse sediments does not depend upon the size of material, as coarser materials have more grade sizes (poorer sorting) and hence lower porosity. (R. Eckis, South Coastal Basin Investigation, *State of Calif., Div. of Water Res. Bull.* 45, pp. 85–96, 1934.)

4. *The larger the proportion of large grains enclosed in fine material, the greater the reduction in average porosity of the formation.*

5. Slichter states that percolation of water in a pervious formation will occupy the entire cross section of the aquifer.[1] This conclusion, although not accepted by some German writers,[2] is probably correct under the assumptions underlying his mathematical treatment. However texture and structure of water-bearing materials interfere with freedom of movement of water and *maximum ease of movement is always parallel to stratification, except in soils* in which direction of maximum ease of movement is usually at right angles to the ground surface and to the soil horizons.

Average Porosity in Nature

Much information regarding porosity of various types of material appears in the literature. However, unless summarized, it is apt to be confusing to the student. The purpose of the following brief summary is to give a concrete idea of the average porosity of water-bearing materials.

The highest porosity known is 80 to 90 per cent which has been reported for freshly deposited alluvium of the Mississippi delta.[3] Possibly equally porous are the mudflows deposited by cloudbursts, which occur as aerated mud. However, no measurement has been made of the porosity of these materials. Porosity of more than 45 per cent is very rare except in soils and recent river deposits. Porosity of 5 per cent is considered small, 5 to 15 per cent medium, and over 15 per cent large. *Uncemented alluvial material* may have porosity as high as 50 per cent. *Uniform loose sand*, especially quicksand, may have porosity as high as 45 per cent. *Gravel* varies greatly in porosity on account of variation in interstitial material. Twenty-five per cent is probably the average maximum porosity of gravel, although more than 45 per cent has been reported. A mixture of sand, gravel, and some silt may have as high as 15 per cent porosity.

In fractured rocks porosity and perviousness decrease markedly with depth. For example, open fissures near the surface are

[1] SLICHTER, C. S., The Motions of Underground Waters, *U.S. Geol. Surv. Water-Supply Paper* 67, p. 17, 1902.

[2] HÖFER-HEIMHALT, H., "Grundwasser und Quellen," Druck and Verlag von Friedr. Vieweg & Sohn, Braunschweig, pp. 69, 81, 1920.

[3] MEINZER, *Water-Supply Paper* 489, *op. cit.*, p. 8.

closed at depth, and rocks decomposed at the surface are unweathered and solid below the water table. Large supplies of water are tapped at depth only under an uncommon combination of conditions, such as open fissures in mines or uncemented pervious sandstone in deep oil wells. The saturated zone may not extend down to the bottom of the zone of interconnected openings. Water may be used up by chemical action before it penetrates far below the surface. Many deep mines are dry and deep boreholes often encounter dry pervious formations.[1]

PRINCIPAL HYDROLOGIC PROPERTIES OF WATER-BEARING MATERIALS

Porosity equals percentage of pore space to total volume of formation; it determines total water-holding capacity of forma-

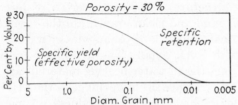

Fig. 34.—Relation of porosity, specific yield, and specific retention to grain size for sorted material.

tion; it does not vary with size of constituent grains but varies with degree of assortment; it is maximum with complete assortment (one grain size); decreases with compaction, consolidation, cementation, and metamorphism.

Porosity (water-holding capacity) = specific yield
+ specific retention (Fig. 34).

Specific yield[2] (effective porosity) measures water moved by gravity; increases with size of grain and assortment.

Specific retention[2] measures field capacity or content of pellicular water; decreases with increase in size of grain and assortment.

[1] FULLER, M. L., Total Amount of Free Water in Earth's Crust, *U.S. Geol. Surv. Water-Supply Paper* 160, pp. 64–67, 1906.

[2] Pumping abstracts from the ground-water reservoir water that can be moved by gravity and lowers the water table, producing movements of

Specific absorption measures the capacity of water-bearing material to absorb water after gravity water has been removed. It is commonly supposed to equal specific yield which is often determined by measurement of specific absorption. However specific absorption does not equal specific yield if the water-bearing material either suffers compaction or dries out and is rendered more porous during a period of over-pumping (pages 471–472).

Permeability is measured by the quantity of water passing through a unit cross section in a unit time under 100 per cent hydraulic gradient, and therefore measures velocity of percolation if porosity is known. Permeability is supposed to vary approximately as the square of the diameter of grain of water-bearing material. It varies with degree of assortment or percentage of fine material and arrangement of grains of coarse and fine material (sedimentary structure). Sorted materials of large grain size, such as sorted sand and clean gravel, are the formations of high permeability that deliver large quantities of water.

Variation with Rock Type.—The hydrologic properties of the innumerable varieties of water-bearing materials are the result of size, shape, and arrangement of openings in the material. A like combination of geologic processes produces a type of formation with characteristic hydrologic properties. Often the rock has been worked upon successively by a series of different geologic processes which have progressively changed the hydrologic properties. Limitation of space makes it impossible to review the hydrologic properties of all varieties of rocks or the results of all possible combinations of geologic processes. Such a discussion would cover the science of geology as applied to ground-water

---

water in the material thus dewatered characteristic of the zone of suspended water. The terms water-holding capacity, specific yield, and specific retention used by the soil scientist in relation to soil moisture are also used by the ground-water investigator in connection with pumping wells. *Specific yield* measures pumped water which is abstracted from a unit volume of material by pumping or drainage. The yield increases with size and assortment of grains. It is measured by the ground-water hydrologist in percentage of volume of water pumped to volume of water-bearing material dewatered. *Specific retention* represents field capacity or content of pellicular water retained against the force of gravity during pumping. It decreases with increase in size of grain and assortment and is measured as percentage of water retained to total volume of material dewatered. See pages 146–148 for definition of terms used by the soil scientist.

hydrology.   The hydrology and description of types of aquifers are discussed in later chapters.[1]

Summary for Alluvial Materials

Sorted Sand with Small Variation of Grain Size.

Porosity.—Large, 25 to 40 per cent.   Effective porosity large, specific retention small.

Permeability.—Varies approximately as square of average diameter of grain, therefore permeability increases greatly with grain size.

Direction of Maximum Ease of Water Motion.—Equal in all directions extending only as far as the material is homogeneous and of the same grain size.   Sedimentary processes produce alternation of different materials, which results in a direction of maximum ease of movement parallel to sedimentary texture and structure, such as stratification, lamination and inclination of strata.

Clean Sand Containing Several Grain Sizes.

Porosity.—Medium, reduced by interstitial grains.   Effective porosity appreciably less than porosity, and specific retention noticeable.

Permeability.—Governed chiefly by that of the material of smallest grain size.

Direction of Maximum Ease of Water Motion.—In the direction of stratification and geologic structure.

Clean Gravel.

Porosity.—Usually greatly reduced by interstitial material because the cleanest of gravel usually contains interstitial grains.   Effective porosity but little smaller than porosity.   Specific retention small.

Permeability.—If interstitial material is lacking or in minor amount, the gravel is so permeable that water may move according to the laws which govern turbulent flow (pages 191–200) provided suitable entrance and exit for water exist.

Direction of Maximum Ease of Water Motion.—Controlled by stratification and geologic structure.

The above-mentioned types of water-bearing materials constitute the chief aquifers of sedimentary and alluvial formations. Decreasing grain size and increasing fineness and proportion of interstitial material gradually change the character of the formation from an aquifer to an aquiclude.   The important aquicludes are silt and clay and their extent and structure control water movement in aquifers.   The coarser and slightly pervious aquicludes, especially coarse silts, may act in part at least as aquifers

[1] See also Meinzer's detailed descriptions of water-bearing formations of the United States in *Water-Supply Paper* 489, *op. cit.*, pp. 193–314.

in replenishing slowly the more pervious formations during long continued pumping. The slow drainage of fine material by pumping often makes it difficult to determine the specific yield of a well field.

Crystalline and Metamorphic Rocks

Geological interpretation of observed data, and knowledge of the occurrence of underground water are essential in the search for water in crystalline and metamorphic rocks. In general the water supply in granitic or metamorphic rocks is controlled by minor geologic features, such as faults, fractures, and contacts, and these features are located by geological mapping. Water-bearing fractures and contacts are occasionally indicated by the presence of *phreatophytes;* that is, plants the roots of which obtain moisture directly from the water table via the capillary fringe.[1]

For example, in the beautiful rolling plateau on either side of the Santa Margarita River, San Diego County, California, the bedrock is granite. The westward sloping plateau is an uplifted and tilted peneplain covered with residual soil which overlies deeply weathered and highly fractured granite (locally called gray granite). Surface water supply is not sufficient for irrigation and ground water is concentrated in cracks in the weathered granite, the water table lying a little above the contact between the weathered and the unweathered, dense granite (called blue granite). The contact is sharp and can be recognized when penetrated by the drill and the larger water-bearing fractures extend into the blue granite. More water was needed and it was suggested to a driller that he drill deep into solid granite to get additional supply. The writer advised, however, that the driller side-drill from the dug wells a little below the contact between the gray and the blue granite. This was done and whenever a fractured zone was encountered, the water supply of the well was greatly increased.

Laboratory and Field Tests of Hydrologic Properties

Laboratory investigation of hydrologic properties, the most important of which are effective porosity (specific yield) and permeability, is discussed in Chap. VIII, and by Meinzer in *Water-Supply Paper* 489, by Norah D. Stearns in *Water-Supply*

[1] Meinzer, *op. cit.*, pp. 95–96.

A

B

FIG. 35.—*A*, coarse sand aquifer of Mokelumne River region. Transparent grains are quartz, dull white fragments feldspar. Average diameter of grain approximately 1 mm. (see scale); *B*, extremely fine, compacted silt of Mokelumne River region. Grain size approximately .01 mm. (Magnification $\times$ 10.)

Paper 596-*F*, and by various other authors.   Hydrologic properties are also investigated by oil-field engineers[1] and sedimentationists.[2]

Heterogeneity of superficial materials usually makes tests on small samples of little value for ground-water study.   Special technique for taking large undisturbed samples has been developed.   However, this sampling has been limited to near-surface materials.   When a core sampler is designed to take undisturbed samples of unconsolidated material at depth, laboratory and geological study of samples will make possible quantitative study of hydrologic properties.

Microscopic examination shows size and arrangement of grains and the resulting hydrologic character of water-bearing materials. The average size of grain can be determined by micrometer measurements, according to accepted technique.   Photomicrographs of the surface of natural samples have proved more satisfactory than study of thin sections.   Figure 35 is an example of this method of determining hydrologic characteristics in an extensive investigation of the water-bearing materials of the Mokelumne River region.[3]   Figure 35*A* shows a typical river sand which, of course, is extremely pervious.   Figure 35*B* shows fine, compacted, light gray silt which acts as an aquiclude.

Field investigations have been undertaken and developed chiefly by soil scientists who are more interested in the movement of soil moisture than in seepage or percolation or capacity of subsurface reservoirs.   Engineers have adopted some of their methods but unfortunately without full appreciation of the problem at hand.   For example, effective porosity has been studied by ground-water hydrologists for the purpose of calibrating ground-water fluctuations in terms of additions to or subtractions from the available water supply.   Investigation of material above the highest water table, however, does not furnish data bearing on the determination of effective porosity of the underlying ground-water reservoir.   If ground water is confined in aquifers, additional storage occurs chiefly at the fountain head of the water-bearing strata, and determination of specific yield of

[1] TICKELL, F. G., "The Examination of Fragmental Rocks," Stanford University Press, 1931.

[2] TWENHOFEL, W. H., "Treatise on Sedimentation," Williams & Wilkins Company, 1926.

[3] TOLMAN, C. F., "Report on Geology of Mokelumne Region," pt. I, Plate III, Unpublished report, 1930.

formations near and below the water level in wells may have no bearing on capacity and yield of the subsurface reservoir.

References

Geological Processes Affecting Openings in Rocks (see pp. 356–357 for references on compaction).

ATHY, L. F., Compaction and Its Effect on Local Structure, "Problems of Petroleum Geology," Sidney Powers Memorial Volume, Published by Amer. Assoc. Pet. Geol., pp. 811–823, 1934.

BLACKWELDER, E., Cavernous Weatherings in Arid Regions, *Pan-Amer. Geologist*, vol. 49, no. 4, p. 311, May, 1928.

CHAMBERLIN and SALISBURY, "Geology," rev. ed., Work of Ground Water—Weathering, Solution, Cementation, etc., pp. 75–89, Henry Holt & Company, 1927.

CLARKE, F. W., The Data of Geochemistry, *U.S. Geol. Surv. Bull.* 770, 1924; Decomposition of Rocks, pp. 479–542; Sedimentary and Detrital Rocks, pp. 543–593.

DAVIS, W. M., Origin of Limestone Caverns, *Bull. Geol. Soc. Amer.*, vol. 41, pp. 475–628, 1930.

LEITH, C. K., "Structural Geology," Fractures and Faults, pp. 29–112, Henry Holt & Company, 1923.

MEINZER, O. E., *Water-Supply Paper* 489, *op. cit.*, Structural Influence on Ground Water, pp. 149–192.

POSNJAK, E., and G. TUNNELL, "Studies of Weathering and Sedimentation," Carnegie Inst. Wash., Yearbook no. 27, pp. 71–76, December, 1928.

VAN HISE, C. R., A Treatise on Metamorphism, *U.S. Geol. Surv. Mon.* 47 Weathering and Cementation, pp. 409–556, 1904.

WALLACE, R. C., The Distribution of Colloidal Products of Weathering: *Roy. Soc. Canada Proc. and Trans.*, 3d ser., vol. 17, sec. 4 pp. 69–77, 1923.

WILLIS, B., and R. WILLIS, "Geologic Structure," 2d ed., Description of Faults, pp. 59–124, McGraw-Hill Book Co., Inc., 1929.

Hydrologic Properties.

BAKER and CONKLING, "Water Supply and Utilization," pp. 291–305, John Wiley & Sons, Inc., 1930.

ECKIS, ROLLIN, South Coastal Basin Investigation: Geology and Ground Water Storage Capacity of Valley Fill, *State of Calif., Div. Water Res. Bull.* 45, pp. 84–114, 226–260, 1934.

GRATON, L. C., and H. J. FRASER, Systematic Packing of Spheres, with Particular Relation to Porosity and Permeability; H. J. Fraser, Experimental Study of the Porosity and Permeability of Clastic Sediments, *Jour. Geol.*, vol. 43, no. 8, November-December, 1935.

HAZEN, ALLEN, Some Physical Properties of Sands and Gravels, *Mass. State Board of Health*, 24th *Ann. Rept.* for 1892, 1893.

MEINZER, O. E., *Water-Supply Paper* 489, *op. cit.*, pp. 1–22, 102–148.

MELCHER, A. F., Texture of Oil Sands with Relation to the Production of Oil, *Amer. Assoc. Pet. Geol. Bull.*, vol. 8, pp. 716–774, November to December, 1924.

RUSSELL, W. L., A Quick Method for Determining Porosity, *Bull. Amer. Assoc. Pet. Geol.*, vol. 10, no. 10, p. 931, 1926.

SLICHTER, C. S., Theoretical Investigation of the Motions of Ground Water, *U.S. Geol. Surv.* 19th *Ann. Rept.*, pp. 305–328, 1899.

STEARNS, N. D., Laboratory Tests on Physical Properties of Water-bearing Materials, *U.S. Geol. Surv. Water-Supply Paper* 596-F, 1927.

TICKELL, F. G., "The Examination of Fragmental Rocks," Stanford University Press, pp. 24–34, 1931.

VAN HISE, *op. cit.*, pp. 123–158.

CHAPTER V

THE SOIL

Soil may be defined as the layer or mantle of mixed mineral and organic material penetrated by roots.[1] The action of soil-forming processes within the superficial zone penetrated by roots produces the textures and structures characteristic of the soil which affect particularly the permeability and direction of maximum ease of water movement through the soil. The soil structures and textures are imposed upon all types of superficial fragmental material produced by weathering of underlying solid rock or transported and deposited by geologic processes.

Soil structure is more important as affecting hydrologic properties than soil composition and the concept of the ground-water hydrologist is that the soil is a definite geologic formation, the characteristics of which are produced largely by reaction of plant growth and decay on the parent material and by solution and precipitation of mineral and organic material within the soil zone.

The soil was probably the earliest observed of geological formations and the earliest experimented with in a practical way by mankind. It is a fundamental natural resource, and only water can challenge soil for the designation "our most important mineral resource." It is a curious anomaly that the soil is a rock body distinct from all other geological formations with characteristic texture, structure, layering or development of "horizons," chemical composition, and hydrologic properties; but nevertheless geologists have neither recognized and described its important characteristics, nor have they made important contributions to soil science in recent years.[2]

[1] Many workers are still thinking of soil in the fragmental state, forgetting that plant roots must explore the various horizons of the soil. The older and commoner definition of soil is "a mass of more or less decomposed and disintegrated rock fragments . . . with organic matter." (C. F. Shaw, A Definition of the Terms Used in Soil Literature, 1st International Congress of Soil Science, vol. 4, comm. V, p. 39, 1928.)

[2] The writer has examined about 100 textbooks on geology, going back as far as the year 1800, in order to discover the early geological ideas regarding

The earliest view was that the soil consisted chiefly of vegetable mould,[1] but cursory examination of soil and rubbing it in the hand showed that the organic portion was small, and soil was recognized as the ultimate decomposition product of weathering mixed with variable amounts of organic debris.   It was also early recognized that this product of rock decay might either be the residuum left in place or transported and redeposited.[2]   From this came the classification of the two main types of soils as residual and transported.   Merrill's textbook[3] is probably the best contribution of the geologist to soil science in general and to classification of soil in particular.

The zonal character of soil was mentioned by De Beaumont (1845),[4] but no elaboration of this important feature of the soil is found in the textbooks or in the four important American treatises on soil,[5] and geologists generally overlooked the horizon development which follows root penetration.

The prevalent geological idea that soil is merely the finely comminuted end product of disintegration without particular form or recognizable characteristics probably accounts for the fact that more than half of the geological textbooks do not describe "soil."

The geologist's lack of interest in soil may be drawn from the following translations: "These operations (soil formation) are so simple and we so often see them in operation that it is useless to enter into much detail in regard to them."[6]   "The soil often hinders geological research by covering the rocks in place."[7]

---

soil and the advance made in the past 130 years.   A textbook study seemed to be the best line of approach because the texts reflect the geological opinion of the time and show the general views regarding soil and the attention given to its study by geologists.

[1] LYELL, SIR CHARLES, "Manual of Elementary Geology," London, 1852.

[2] D'OMALIUS D'HALLOY, J. J., "Eléments de Géologie," Paris, 1835; Playfair, John, "Illustrations of the Huttonian Theory of the Earth," Edinburgh, 1802.

[3] MERRILL, G. P., "Rocks, Rockweathering and Soils," The Macmillan Company, 1906.

[4] DE BEAUMONT, L. E., "Leçons de Géologie Pratique," Paris, 1845.

[5] HILGARD, E. W., "Soils"; G. P. MERRILL, "Rocks, Rockweathering and Soils"; F. H. KING, "The Soil"; and N. S. SHALER, "Origin and Nature of Soils."

[6] D'OMALIUS D'HALLOY, J., *op. cit.*, free translation.

[7] DE BEAUMONT, L. E., *op. cit.*, free translation.

Soil is here defined as the layer or mantle of mixed mineral and organic material penetrated by roots. As previously stated, the first geological viewpoint was that the organic material was the important and characteristic constituent. Subsequently geologists have repeatedly emphasized the importance of root growth. A typical definition of soil appears in Blackwelder and Barrows, "Elements of Geology," "The Mantle Rock: Loose material covers the land. When capable of supporting plant life, this is called soil."[1]

Considered from the viewpoint of the ground-water scientist, the root zone properly delimits the soil zone because the vertical perviousness produced by roots is one of the important hydrologic characteristics of the soil zone. This view might well be adopted by the soil scientists not only because it defines accurately the zone in which soil-forming processes are active, but also because it furnishes an easily applied criterion for placing the boundary between the substratum of the soil and the parent material. The root content of the substratum can easily be separated from the other material by washing. The only difficulty to be apprehended in the application of this criterion would be in the case of those soils to which material is being added during soil formation. Young alluvial soils of the river flood plain may receive large contributions of alluvium which may drown the deeper roots. It might then be difficult to differentiate the present substratum and the substratum of the past.

A summary of some of the features that the geologist has not considered would include the following: (1) Soil horizons as a characteristic feature of the soil; (2) classification of soils as youthful, mature, and senile according to the stage of development; (3) texture and structure of soils and their development according to the age of the soil; (4) soil and colloidal chemistry and bacteriology of the soil; (5) soil physics; and (6) soil hydrology.

LOCATION, GENERAL CHARACTERISTICS, AND PROPERTIES OF SOIL

The soil covers at least 95 per cent of the land surface.[2] It lies at the contact of the atmosphere and the land surface and is

[1] BLACKWELDER, E., and H. H. BARROWS, "Elements of Geology," p. 16, American Book Company, 1911.

[2] SHALER, N. S., Origin and Nature of Soils, *U.S. Geol. Surv.*, 12*th Ann. Rept.*, pt. II, p. 226, 1891.

subject to repeated wetting and partial drying, to leaching by organic and mineral solutions especially at or near the surface, and to precipitation and cementation in the intermediate and lower soil horizons. Shaw[1] defines soil as "a natural body occupying the surface portion of the Earth, composed of mineral and organic materials and having more or less definitely developed horizons of eluviation (leaching) and illuviation (deposition)." Marbut[2] states that profiles of mature soils consist of two main horizons: (1) the upper horizon in which material has been removed, a horizon of extraction; and (2) a lower horizon to which material has been added, a horizon of concentration.

The unique chemical environment of the soil results in the development of soil colloids of complex chemical composition and varied physical texture. The texture of the colloids in the soil zone affects the physical characteristics of the soil profile (cross section of the soil horizons).[3] Colloidal material derived from the intermixture of rock and organic debris may develop in the surface soil (horizon A) a multiple-grain or aggregate structure of great porosity and perviousness.[4] The openness of this structure may be increased by tillage and by the upturning of soil on the roots of fallen trees and shrubs.

The penetration of the soil zone by roots, the preservation of the root openings by compaction and by the precipitation of cementing material around the roots, and the opening of root passages by the decay of the organic material encased therein produce in the soil a "vertical perviousness" at right angles to the direction of maximum permeability of undisturbed alluvial and other sedimentary formations.

This vertical perviousness may be increased by cracks opened up by drying out of the colloidal material of the soil. Hilgard[5]

[1] Shaw, C. F., A Definition of the Terms Used in Soil Literature, 1st International Congress of Soil Science, vol. 4, comm. V, p. 44, 1928.

[2] Marbut, C. F., Classification, Nomenclature and Mapping of Soils in the Americas, Rept., Subcommission II of Commission V, 1st International Congress of Soil Science, vol. 1, pt. I, pp. 248–268, 1927.

[3] Anderson, M. S., and H. G. Byers, Character of the Colloidal Materials in the Profiles of Certain Major Soil Groups; U.S. Dept. Agr., Bur. Soils, Tech. Bull. 228, p. 1, 1931.

[4] Davis, R. O. E., The Nature of Soil Components and Their Relations to Sedimentation, Rept. of Comm. on Sedimentation, Natl. Research Council, Ann. Meeting, Apr. 30, 1927; and R. C. Wells, Flocculation of Colloids, ibid., pp. 50–52, 1923.

[5] Hilgard, E. W., "Soils," The Macmillan Company, p. 113, 1906.

states that contraction of several heavy clay soils was found to range from 28 to 40 per cent of the original bulk. The vertical perviousness is further increased by burrowing animals and insects, such as ground squirrels, gophers, ants, beetles, and earthworms. In thickness soil varies from a thin film of a fraction of an inch to a maximum thickness of 60 ft. It averages between 2 and 4 ft., and rarely exceeds 10 ft. in thickness.[1]

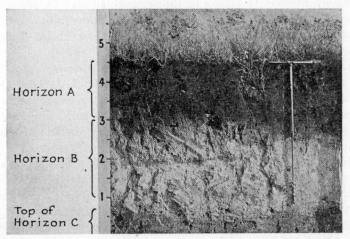

Fig. 36.—Exposure of Barnes loam, Cass County, North Dakota, showing well-developed profile with leached horizon *A*, horizon *B* largely calcareous hardpan, and upper portion of horizon *C*. (*Courtesy of Charles E. Kellogg, Chief, U.S. Bureau of Soils.*)

Soil Horizons.[2]—The soil is made up of horizons *A*, *B*, and *C*. Horizon *A* is the surface soil subject to leaching and decomposition. Horizon *B* is the subsoil. It is the intermediate horizon subject to compaction and cementation. The substratum or

[1] Shaler states that decaying roots leave open channels through the soil sometimes extending for distances of 30 ft., and taproots leave open channels in a vertical direction of 10 to 15 ft. (Shaler, *op. cit.*, p. 272.)

Ordinary grasses and field crops do not penetrate to depths of more than a few feet; in semiarid regions they may extend to 6 ft. Roots of corn, oats, wheat, and barley extend to depths of 4 to 5 ft. and winter wheat from 6 to 7 ft. Alfalfa roots penetrate as deep as 20 to 30 ft., and certain types of mesquite and other deep-rooted desert plants send roots from 50 to 60 ft. (Meinzer, *Water-Supply Paper* 489, *op. cit.*, p. 82–83.)

[2] Owing to the numerous subhorizons developed, especially in mature soils, the soil profile is frequently described without reference to the primary horizons *A*, *B*, and *C*.

horizon C is here defined as the zone of root growth below horizon B. The three horizons constitute the soil profile.[1]

Horizon A is characterized by mineral decomposition, transformation of the mineral constituents and organic debris into colloids, the solution and abstraction of the soluble compounds, and the development of the pervious aggregate structure due largely to flocculated colloids and enclosed mineral aggregates. Horizon A rarely exceeds 18 inches in thickness.[2] It may be absent or have a thickness of a few feet. It may be divided into a number of subhorizons, A_0, A_1, and A_2. A_0 is the superficial litter of leaves and vegetable material.

Under partial drying the soil of horizon A assumes a granular[3] or powdery texture. Clayey soils, especially if deflocculated, shrink and crack in drying. This horizon often has a prismatic structure and occasionally a columnar structure. In general it is both pervious and absorbent and delivers water to the underlying horizon.

Horizon B is the subsoil. It is the horizon of precipitation and accretion of materials dissolved in the horizon above. Accumulations of calcium carbonate or clayey material containing aluminum and ferric hydroxides are known as hardpans.[4]

Pan formation in soils rich in humus is caused by the accumulation of salts of iron, calcium, magnesium, and other bases where there is no free drainage through the soil. Hardpans may be formed by precipitation of dissolved material such as calcium carbonate or silica at a certain depth year after year. When this accumulation takes place, the subsoil is more or less firmly cemented and limits downward movement of roots and water. The claypan is an accumulation of stiff, compact, and relatively impervious clay. It is not cemented and, if immersed in water, can be worked into a soft mass.

---

[1] SHAW, *op. cit.*, pp. 48–49.

[2] BALDWIN, M., The Gray-Brown Podsolic Soils of the Eastern U.S., 1st Intern. Congress of Soil Science, vol. 4, p. 277, 1927.

[3] In a moist condition granular sediments, in the absence of clay, flocculate sufficiently to produce a fair tilth, but on drying they collapse into close arrangement resulting from single-grain structure. They are apt to form closely packed masses. (Hilgard, *op. cit.*, pp. 102–103.)

[4] SHAW, *op. cit.*, pp. 46–47; R. H. RASTALL, "Agricultural Geology," pp. 140–143, Cambridge, 1916.

Horizon *B* may be pervious owing to aggregate grain structure, flocculated colloidal material, vertical parting, or columnar structure which may be more pronounced than in horizon *A*; but as horizon *B* is richer in clayey material and calcareous cements than horizon *A*, it is usually less pervious. The clayey material may give it a large absorptive capacity (field capacity). The feeding roots are usually vertical and develop a pronounced perviousness in a vertical direction. Horizon *B* is usually less than 3 ft. thick.[1]

Horizon C, the substratum, is that portion of the underlying or parent material which has been penetrated by roots. The parent formation may be decomposed rock in place or freshly deposited and nonindurated alluvium or other sedimentary material. Weathered material in place is known as regolith.[2] Horizon *C* is commonly not more than 6 ft. in thickness but may extend to 50 ft.[3] It is a portion, but usually not all, of the regolith.

LIFE HISTORY OF SOILS

The development of horizons in soil may be weak or strong. It is usually a slow process even geologically considered. The rate of zonation is affected by the processes of degradation and aggradation. If the removal of soil material by wind, rainwash, and running water is slow, thick horizons *A* and *B*, especially horizon *B*, may develop. If degradation is rapid, horizon *A* may be removed as fast as formed and horizon *B* may be exposed at the surface. In extreme cases both horizons *A* and *B* may be removed.

A deep water table offers favorable opportunities for leaching and redeposition near the surface. Alternate wetting and partial drying are also conducive to development of thick soil horizons. Hence soils are usually much thicker in semiarid regions than in regions of high and well-distributed rainfall.[4] If material deposited by rainwash, running water, or wind is incorporated

[1] MARBUT, C. F., A Scheme for Soil Classification, 1st Intern. Congress of Soil Science, vol. 4, comm. V, p. 26, 1928.

[2] MERRILL, G. P., "Rocks, Rockweathering and Soils," p. 288, The Macmillan Company, 1906.

[3] MEINZER, *op. cit.*, pp. 82–83.

[4] MARBUT, Classification, Nomenclature, and Mapping of Soils in the Americas, *op. cit.*, pp. 263–264.

in the soil, horizon A may be diluted with this material and therefore may be only slightly leached, and horizon B may be drowned out by rapid accumulation of material at the surface. Soils of aggradation, therefore, are apt to have poorly developed horizons.

The degree of horizon development may be described in terms of age, a terminology often used by geologists. Soils with weak zonation may be described as youthful, those with pronounced zonation as mature, and those ruined by hardpans may be called senile. Soils of aggradation are usually youthful and deep. Flood-plain soils are built up so rapidly that they actually "drown out" deep root systems. They are usually pervious. Old soils, on the other hand, especially if not subject to aggradation, are often impervious. The older alluvium of California and the cemented "red soils" and "hog wallow" soils are extremely impervious.[1]

THE SOIL AS A RESERVOIR OF SOIL MOISTURE AND A GROUND-WATER CONTROL

The soil is a distinct and separate body to be distinguished from the parent material which is below the root zone. The soil has its own peculiar hydrologic characteristics due to root growth and the chemical and biological activities which occur at the contact between the atmosphere and the land surface.

The soil is a sponge which first absorbs rain water and, if conditions permit, delivers a portion of it to the underlying formations and thence to the water table. It is the first great reservoir which retains the soil moisture and delivers it to plants. It is the first "control" governing the passage of water from the surface to the water table. If the soil is pervious and the reservoir is full (technically if the field capacity of the soil is satisfied), delivery of water to the underlying formations may take place. The importance of the soil as a ground-water control justifies its somewhat detailed treatment.

Seepage and Percolation Rates in Soils.—The soil is the first formation through which influent seepage from rainfall and from water flowing over or standing on soil passes to reach the water table. Hence the rate of seepage through the soil is of primary importance in estimating ground-water recharge. Moreover the

[1] HILGARD, *op. cit.*, p. 114.

practice of water spreading has emphasized the importance of measurement of these rates. It is probable that in the future flood flow of streams will be deflected in increasing amounts onto pervious areas; certain experiments (pages 179–180) suggest that pervious flat areas covered with soil may need no preparation for spreading operations except the construction of low earth embankments around them. The soil must be brought up to field capacity before water will move through it to the water table and the problem is to determine the rate of seepage after field capacity is reached.

Seepage is defined as the downward movement of gravity water toward the water table. If the water-bearing material becomes saturated, the movement is called percolation, and the rate of seepage can approach but not equal the rate of percolation. Soil has been sampled by soil augers and the rate of movement through the samples determined experimentally.[1] In these experiments seepage and percolation have not been differentiated. The rate determined probably is in excess of the average seepage rate under natural conditions. Irregularities of soil composition and especially of root penetration may render it impossible to obtain representative cores for the determination of rate of seepage under natural conditions; hence field tests are of more value than tests on cores.

COMPOSITION OF SOILS

The soil consists of three principal constituents, mineral grains, soil colloids, and soil solutions. Some of the minerals constituting the grains are quite resistant, others are attacked slowly by the soil solutions, but the important chemical reactions are those between the colloids and the soil solutions.

Soil Colloids.—The soil colloids include organic colloids rich in humus material and the clay colloid. The latter is by far the most important and is considered the fundamental constituent of the soil. It may be separated by the supercentrifuge and is called "ultraclay." It is a compound of Ca(H, Mg, Na, K, etc.) with a variable radical $[SiO_2, n(Al_2O_3, Fe_2O_3)]$.[2] It is supposed to be a definite colloidal compound which reacts as a salt with interchangeable basic radicals. The metallic radicals, especially

[1] SLATER, C. S., and H. G. BYERS, A Laboratory Study of the Field Percolation Rates of Soils, *U.S. Dept. Agr. Tech. Bull.* 232, pp. 3–7, 1931.

[2] Encyclopaedia Britannica, 1929, vol. 20, p. 927, Soil.

calcium, are easily lost and when they are gone, the clay has a strong acid reaction. The bases are interchanged or removed by reaction with the soil solution and are made available to plants.

The physical character of soils is largely due to the state of flocculation of the fundamental colloid. The lime-rich colloid is well flocculated and maintains the flocculated state under considerable variation of physical conditions, including wetting and drying, and temperature changes. The loss of lime and substitution of other ions, especially Na, may cause deflocculation of the clay colloid which produces sticky and impervious soils. Hence soils rich in the calcium colloid are usually fertile, as, for example, the lime-rich soils of the semiarid regions.[1] The deleterious effect of Na_2CO_3 (black alkali) on soils is due in large part to the deflocculation caused by the reaction of sodium salts on the clay colloid, resulting in the interchange of sodium and calcium.

Importance of $CaCO_3$.—Soil chemistry explains the importance of calcium salts in the soil, especially of $CaCO_3$. The importance of $CaCO_3$ was discovered by the Russian soil scientists[2] who found that in continental Europe certain soil types were formed under the control of climate, which in turn controls chemical environment. Arctic moist conditions and tundra growth, as well as cold climate, much moisture and forest cover, produce an acid environment and a soil colloid rich in Al_2O_3 and Fe_2O_3. Calcium is leached out of the soil and hence $CaCO_3$ is absent in the upper horizons of the soil profile. In the humid warm conditions of the tropics and under the abundant tropical vegetation and the acid environment produced thereby, laterite is formed. It is a residual deposit rich in Al_2O_3 and Fe_2O_3 and deficient in SiO_2.[3] Under drier climatic conditions and absence of forest cover and tropical vegetation neutral or alkaline soil solution conditions produce the great group of $CaCO_3$-rich soils.[4]

[1] Marbut, C. F., Classification, Nomenclature and Mapping of Soils in the Americas, *op. cit.*, pp. 263–264.

[2] Glinka, K. D., A Brief History of Russian Soil Science, 1st International Congress of Soil Science, vol. I, pt. 1, pp. 116–136, 1927.

[3] Marbut, A Scheme for Soil Classification, *op. cit.*, pp. 21–23.

[4] Marbut speaks of the two great groups of soils in the United States in his paper, A Scheme for Soil Classification, *op. cit.*:

Group I: Pedalfers: Soils in whose maturely developed profiles no higher percentage of lime carbonate is found than in the parent material, and in

Chemical reactions control the composition of the soil horizons regardless of the characteristics of the underlying parent material. An example of this is the thick layer of caliche, consisting largely of $CaCO_3$, which occurs in horizon B (the sub soil) of the piedmont alluvial deposits underlying a portion of the City of Tucson, Arizona. A dense impervious layer from 2 ft. to a maximum thickness of 6 ft. occurs below the surface soil, and underlying this crust are gravels many hundreds of feet thick consisting largely of granitic rocks. In this case the soil-forming processes have concentrated $CaCO_3$ in the form of a thick and massive hardpan, although the parent material is not rich in $CaCO_3$.

SOIL CLASSIFICATION

The purpose of any classification may be practical or scientific. A classification of soils may be evolved for the purpose of (1) producing groups and subgroups into which may be fitted all the natural occurrences of soil observed by the field student and the laboratory investigator, or (2) arranging and classifying the soil-forming processes and resulting products so that they may be studied efficiently.

The purpose of the following review of soil classification is to discover the main groups with respect to soil-forming processes and the resulting products for the better understanding of the hydrologic properties of the soil. The writer is not a soil expert and would not presume to formulate a scheme that would be used by those engaged in scientific or practical study of soil. Perusal of the literature and study of the character of the geologic

---

which either a shifting or accumulation of sesquioxides, and in many cases both, has taken place.

Group II: Pedocals: Soils with fully developed profiles in which lime carbonate is found on some horizon in the solum in higher percentage than in the parent geological formation.

With reference to the occurrence of these two groups the United States is bisected. East of the line there are no well developed soils in which $CaCO_3$ has accumulated in any part of the solum. The two groups do not occur within the same region of the United States except in those regions which are mountainous. East of the Rocky Mountains each occupies a region of its own. The pedalfers cover eastern United States up to and one hundred miles west of the Mississippi River, and the pedocals extend westward to the foot of the Rocky Mountains.

See also Marbut's paper, Classification, Nomenclature and Mapping of Soils in the Americas, *op. cit.*, pp. 262–268.

processes involved in the classification of soils suggest the following features that should be considered in soil classification. These are taken up in the order of their importance.

1. Classification According to Development of CaCO₃-rich or CaCO₃-free Soils.—These two types of soil are produced by different chemical environments which are, in turn, the consequence of climatic conditions, vegetal cover, and soil saturation. This results in a well-defined geographical distribution of soils. Hence this grouping is of primary importance in defining the controlling factors in soil formation. It is therefore placed first in the scheme of classification.

A. Group I, pedocals or soils rich in $CaCO_3$.

B. Group II, pedalfers or soils rich in Al_2O_3 and Fe_2O_3.

Numerous subclassifications of these two major groups appear in the literature and various equivalents for the main soil groups are used apparently without regard to priority of usage.

The characteristic hydrologic property of mature soils of these two types is low permeability due to precipitation of $CaCO_3$ in the pedocals and to concentration of impervious aluminum and iron-rich clays in the pedalfers. The pedocal is usually deeper than the pedalfer. It is more pervious in horizon *A* because the clay colloid is flocculated and hence the soil has multiple-grain structure. Horizon *B* of the pedocal is also usually more pervious except in the senile stage when the precipitated lime cement may be as impervious as the clay hardpan of the pedalfer.

2. Classification of the Stages of Soil Formation.—This classification is based on the percentage of completion of the soil-forming processes or the age of the soil.

These stages may be classified as (1) youthful (immature), (2) mature, and (3) senile. The terms youthful, immature, and mature are in common use. Senile is a graphic term and aptly describes the condition of the soil when its strength, productivity, and permeability have been ruined by pan formation.

Porosity and permeability decrease with the age of the soil. Senile soils with well-developed hardpans are impervious. Youthful soils have no impervious horizon *B* and therefore are decidedly more pervious than the underlying material on account of added porosity due to weathering and breaking up of the surface soil and to the presence of roots and animal and insect burrows.

3. Special Classification of Youthful Soils.—Youthful soils may be further classified according to parent material, as they inherit the properties of the latter. For example, we might use the term regolith soil for immature soil formed on any well-developed regolith, granitic soil for soil formed on granite or on granitic regolith, glacial soil for soil formed on glacial material, eolian soil for soil formed on wind-deposited material, and alluvial soil for soil formed on material deposited by alluviation.

4. Classification According to Principal Geologic Processes Active during Soil Formation.—The geologic processes active during soil formation may be degradational or aggradational. The degradational soil is a residuum left in place in spite of transporting processes, such as wind, rainwash, or running water. It covers a far larger proportion of the earth's surface than the aggradational soil. Material may be added to the soil during its formation, in which case the soil is aggradational. Inasmuch as soils classified according to parent material may in some cases be soils of either aggradation or degradation, the phrase "of aggradation" or "of degradation" may be added whenever necessary.

Soils of degradation may reach full maturity or old age. Foreign material is not added to the soils as they are formed and is not incorporated in the soil horizons.

Soils of Aggradation.—Under this group the depositing processes are active during soil formation. Material is being incorporated in the soil as it is worked upon by the zoning processes which may be suppressed by the rapid addition of new material. In all cases soils of aggradation are immature.

Subgroups of Soils of Aggradation.—The principal subgroups of soils of aggradation are:

1. Colluvial soils: These contain material contributed by rainwash and are concentrated usually at the foot of declivities.[1]

2. Eolian soils of aggradation: Wind materials are deposited either in moist places or in localities covered by close vegetation. The building up of such soils may be very rapid in semiarid regions.

3. Alluvial soils of aggradation: The best examples of these soils are found in flood-plain deposits. Deposition of alluvial material by floods may be very rapid and soil zoning may be completely suppressed. Roots may penetrate to great depths in

[1] HILGARD, *op. cit.*, p. 12.

these soils provided the water table is deep.   A zone of dead roots may exist underneath the living material.

The hydrologic properties of alluvial soils of aggradation are of great importance to the ground-water investigator because the floods which cover the bottom lands may be the chief contributors to ground water.   The permeability of the portions of alluvium penetrated by roots may be much larger than portions that have not been perforated in this manner, but in general is much less than that of river sands and gravels which may underlie the flood-plain soils.

5. Classification by Mechanical Analysis.—A nomenclature dependent upon mechanical composition has long been in existence.   The classification which appears in Page's book on geology published in 1844[1] is very similar to present classification of surface soil.   Classification of soils according to grain size differs from the classification of the geologist for sedimentary formations which are usually more uniform in composition and are classified according to the predominant material present.   The terms founded on size of constituent grains used by the geologist are gravel, sand, silt, particle clay, and colloidal clay.   If the materials are mixed, the component material present in minor quantities is used as an adjective, as sandy clay or clayey silt. Soil classification includes gravel, sand, loam, and silt; three of which may be compounded, as, for example, sandy clay loam; and other special terms, such as chalk and gumbo.

The present scheme of classification of soil materials according to particle size as determined by mechanical analysis has been outlined in the *U.S. Department of Agriculture Department Circular* 419 by Davis and Bennett.   This classification is important and a condensed summary of the circular follows:

There are 15 to 50 soil classes based on mechanical composition now in common usage, and an effort has been made by the Bureau of Soils to devise a system whereby a soil might be put in one of the ten main classes as shown in Table 3.

[1] PAGE, DAVID, "Rudiments of Geology," Edinburgh, p. 195, 1844:
Sandy soil less than 10 per cent clay.
Sandy loam 10 to 40 per cent clay.
Loam 40 to 70 per cent clay.
Clay loam 70 to 85 per cent clay.
Strong clay 85 to 95 per cent clay.
Agricultural clay, no sand.

TABLE 3.—MECHANICAL COMPOSITION OF THE PRINCIPAL SOIL CLASSES*

Soil classes	Per cent sand	Per cent silt	Per cent clay	Soil classes	Per cent sand	Per cent silt	Per cent clay
Sand.........	80–100	0– 20	0–20	Sandy clay loam.........	50–80	0–30	20– 30
Sandy loam...	50– 80	0– 50	0–20	Clay loam.....	20–50	20–50	20– 30
Silt loam.....	0– 50	50–100	0–20	Silty clay.....	0–20	50–70	30– 50
Loam.........	30– 50	30– 50	0–20	Sandy clay....	50–70	0–20	30– 50
Silty clay loam.......	0– 30	50– 80	20–30	Clay.........	0–50	0–50	30–100

* DAVIS, R. E., and H. H. BENNETT, Grouping of Soils on the Basis of Mechanical Analysis, *U.S. Dept. Agr., Dept. Circ.* 419, p. 4, Table 1, 1927.

Davis and Bennett have devised an equilateral triangle diagram on which the physical composition of soils may be indicated diagrammatically. On this diagram the sides represent zero proportions of sand, silt, or clay and the apices 100 per cent proportions of these three soil constituents (Fig. 37). This is an improvement over earlier diagrams of the Bureau of Soils, as it gives directly not only the limiting proportions of silt and clay, but also those of sand for each soil class.

The use of the equilateral triangle to determine the classes from mechanical analyses may be illustrated by the following examples: If a soil is composed of 28 per cent sand, 33 per cent silt, and 39 per cent clay, the point defined by these percentages is plotted on the diagram, as *A* in the figure, and the soil would be classed as clay. Similarly point *B* is plotted for a soil material composed of 62 per cent sand, 22 per cent silt, and 16 per cent clay.

FIELD MAPPING OF SOILS

The field man mapping for the United States Bureau of Soils first samples and investigates in detail the surface soil (horizon *A*) and classifies this exposed soil material according to its composition determined by mechanical analysis. He also examines by sampling or by observation of natural and artificial cuts each horizon of the soil profile. By this study the similarity of any individual soil body to other soil groups can be recognized in spite of differences which appear in the surface soil.

Locality names are given to soil types in the course of the field mapping. The name is chosen from the locality which has been completely investigated, and this soil becomes the type for all soils of the same character in the general region mapped.[1] For example, Madera loam was first mapped in Madera County,

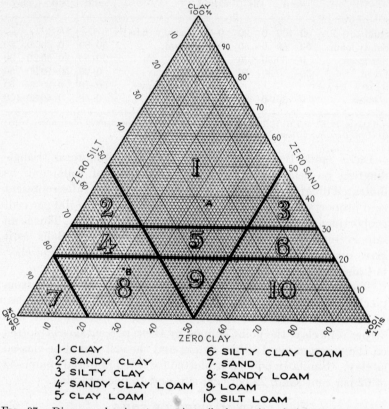

Fig. 37.—Diagram showing ten main soil classes in relation to percentage composition of sand, silt, and clay. (*After Davis and Bennett.*)

1- CLAY	6- SILTY CLAY LOAM
2- SANDY CLAY	7- SAND
3- SILTY CLAY	8- SANDY LOAM
4- SANDY CLAY LOAM	9- LOAM
5- CLAY LOAM	10- SILT LOAM

DIRECTIONS: Plot percentage of sand on left diagonal, clay on right diagonal, and silt on base of triangle. Extend line from sand percentage parallel to "zero sand," silt percentage on line parallel to "zero silt," and clay percentage parallel to "zero clay." The intersection of any two of these lines places the sample in the soil group indicated by the diagram.

California, but this type of soil is found to be widely spread throughout the Sacramento Valley region of California. The character of the surface soil is usually attached to the locality name; for example, "Madera clayey loam."

[1] SHAW, C. F., The Basis of Classification and Key to the Soils of California, 1st Intern. Congress Soil Science, vol. 4, comm. V, p. 76, 1928.

Soil maps show the extent of each of the soil groups, and the Bureau of Soils also publishes a detailed description of the soils delineated on the map. From this description the hydrologic character of the soil members can be deduced. These deductions can then be checked by observation and by digging and sampling the soil horizons. Usually mere inspection will show the impervious character of hardpan soils and by noting the extent of this type of soil on the map, the area in which no material contribution to ground water is being made from rainfall may be determined. The soil maps, therefore, may be of great value to the student of ground water, especially where a ground-water inventory is being made.

References

General

COMBER, N. M., "An Introduction to the Scientific Study of the Soil," 2d ed., Edw. Arnold and Company, London, 1932.

GLINKA, K. D., "Die Typen der Bodenbildung," Berlin, 1914. Translated by C. F. Marbut, The Great Soil Groups of the World and their Development, Mimeographed by Edwards Bros., Ann Arbor, Mich., 1927.

HALL, A. D. "The Soil," London, John Murray, 4th ed., 1931.

HILGARD, E. W., "Soils," The Macmillan Company, 1906.

KEEN, B. A., "The Physical Properties of the Soil," Longmans, Green & Company, London, 1931.

KING, G. H., "The Soil, Rural Science Series," The Macmillan Company, 1907.

MERRILL, G. P., "Rocks, Rockweathering and Soils," The Macmillan Company, 1906.

RASTALL, R. H., "Agricultural Geology," Cambridge, Chap. VI, 1916.

ROBINSON, G. W., "Soils, Their Origin, Constitution and Classification," 2d ed., D. Van Nostrand Company, Inc., 1936.

SHALER, N. S., Origin and Nature of Soils, *U.S. Geol. Surv. 12th Ann. Rept.*, pt. 2, 1891.

SHAW, C. F., A Definition of Terms Used in Soil Literature, 1st Internat. Cong. of Soil Sci., vol. 4, comm. V, 1928.

Soil Classification and Mapping

DAVIS, R. O. E., and H. H. BENNETT, Grouping of Soils on the Basis of Mechanical Analysis, *U.S. Dept. Agr. Dept. Circ.* 419, 1927.

GLINKA, K. D., *op. cit.*

MARBUT, C. F., Classification, Nomenclature and Mapping of Soils in the Americas, Rept. Subcomm. II, comm. V, vol. 1, pt. 1, 1st Internat. Cong. Soil Sci., pp. 248–268, 1928.

———— A Scheme of Soil Classification, 1st Internat. Cong. Soil Sci., vol. 4, 1928.

——— Soils of the United States, pt. III, Atlas of American Agric., Washington, D. C., July 1935.

MILNE, G., Some Suggested Units of Classification and Mapping, Particularly for East African Soils, Soil Research (Berlin), vol. 4, no. 3, pp. 183–198, 1935.

SHAW, C. F., *op. cit.*, pp. 53–54.

——— The Basis of Classification and Key to Soils of California, 1st Internat. Cong. Soil Sci., vol. 4, comm. V, pp. 65–103, 1928.

——— Field Textures and Physical Composition Determined by Two Methods of Mechanical Analysis, *Trans. 3d Internat. Soil Cong.*, vol. 1, pp. 42–46, 1935.

VILENSKY, D. G., A Classification of Soils on the Basis of Analogous Series in Soil Formation, *Proc. 1st Internat. Soc. Soil Sci.*, New Series, vol. 1, pp. 224–241, 1927.

——— Concerning the Principles of a Genetic Soil Classification, Contrib. Study of Soils of Ukrainia, vol. 6, pp. 129–151, 1927.

WHITNEY, M., The Use of Soils East of the Great Plains Region, *U.S. Dept. Agr., Bur. Soils, Bull.* 78, 1911.

——— Soils of the United States, *U.S. Dept. Agr., Bur. Soils, Bull.* 55, 1909.

WRIGHT, C. H., "Soil Analysis, A Handbook of Physical and Chemical Methods," Thos. Murby, London, 1934.

Soil Composition

ANDERSON, M. S., and H. G. BYERS, Character of the Colloidal Materials in the Soil Profiles of Certain Major Soil Groups, *U.S. Dept. Agr. Tech. Bull.* 228, 1931.

ANDERSON, M. S., and others, Absorption by Colloidal and Noncolloidal Soil Constituents, *U.S. Dept. Agr. Prof. Paper, Bull.* 1122, 1922.

DAVIS, R. O. E., The Nature of Soil Components and their Relations to Sedimentation, Researches in Sedimentation in 1924, Report of the Committee on Sedimentation, pp. 43–45, 1925.

DENISON, I. A., The Chemical Composition of Colloidal Materials Isolated from the Horizons of Various Soil Profiles, *Jour Agr. Res.*, vol. 40, no. 5, pp. 469–483, Mar. 1, 1930.

HENDRICK, J., and W. G. OGG, The Composition of the Soil and of the Mineral Particles Which Compose It, *Jour. Agr. Sci.*, vol. 7, pp. 458–469, 1916.

ROBINSON, W. O., and R. S. HOLMES, The Chemical Composition of Soil Colloids, *U.S. Dept. Agr., Dept. Bull.* 1311, 1924.

Soil Development

ANDERSON, M. S., and H. G. BYERS, *op. cit.*

CROWTHER, E. M., The Relation of Climatic and Geological Factors to the Composition of the Clay and the Distribution of Soil Types, *Proc. Roy. Soc. Bull.*, vol. 107, pp. 10–30, 1930.

KELLOGG, C. E., Development and Significance of the Great Soil Groups of the United States, *U.S. Dept. Agr. Misc. Publ.* 229, 1936.

MARBUT, C. F., Classification, Nomenclature and Mapping of Soils in the Americas, *op. cit.*, pp. 261–268, 1928.

MOHR, E. C. J., "Tropical Soil Forming Processes and the Development of Tropical Soils," Trans. by R. C. Pendleton, Coll. Agr. Univ. of Philippines, 1930.

ROBINSON, G. W., *op. cit.*, pp. 37–71.

SHAW, C. F., The Basis of Classification and Key to the Soils of California, *op. cit.*, pp. 65–68, 1928.

STAUFFER, R. S., Influence of Parent Materials on Soil Character in a Humid Temperate Climate, *Amer. Soc. Agr., Jour.* 27 (II), pp. 885–893, 1935.

Soil Structure

DAVIS, R. O. E., *op. cit.*, pp. 44–48.

FREE, E. E., Studies in Soil Physics, *Plant World*, vol. 14, nos. 2, 3, 5, 7, 8, 1912.

HILGARD, E. W., *op. cit.*, pp. 102–110, 180–185.

MARBUT, C. F., Classification, Nomenclature, and Mapping of Soils in the Americas, pp. 252–253, 1927.

SHAW, C. F., A Definition of Terms, *op. cit.*, pp. 56–57.

SOKOLOVSKY, N. A., Le problème de la structure du sol, "Physique du sol," pp. 89–95, 1934. A review of Russian work on soil structure.

Texture of Some Important Soil Formations, *U.S. Dept. Agr., Div. Agr. Soils, Bull.* 5, 1896.

Percolation and Seepage Rates in Soils

Lysimeter Experiments—III, Records for Tanks 3 to 12 during Years 1910–1924: *Cornell Univ. Agr. Exp. Sta.*, Mem. 134, pp. 13–15, November, 1930.

SLATER, C. S., and H. G. BYERS, A Laboratory Study of the Field Percolation Rates of Soils, *U.S. Dept. Agr. Tech. Bull.* 232, 1931.

CHAPTER VI

OCCURRENCE OF WATER AND FORCES ACTING IN THE ZONE OF AERATION

The materials above the water table are in the unsaturated zone of aeration. The driving forces which cause water movements in this zone are gravity, unbalanced film force, transpiration and evaporation, and chemical and physicochemical forces. The forces resisting movement of water are chiefly attractions between water and surfaces of mineral particles, rock masses, and colloidal materials. The force of gravity quickly removes the gravity water from the zone of suspended water and interaction of unbalanced film forces and transpiration and evaporation results in movements that are not in evidence in the saturated zone below the water table. The zone of suspended water, therefore, needs a different descriptive treatment of occurrence and motions of water than that accorded the zone below the water table.

Hydrologic Characteristics.—The hydrologic characteristics and water movements of the soil zone have been investigated by soil scientists. Water movements in the saturated zone below the water table have been studied by ground-water scientists and are fairly well understood. The intermediate belt between the soil and the capillary fringe has been called the "no man's land" of ground-water hydrology by Meinzer who appreciates the importance of this zone and regrets that more attention has not been given it. The importance of artificial feeding of water to the water table is forcing attention upon this little investigated region between the soil and the water table.

The hydrologic properties of the formations between the water table and the ground surface may be summarized as follows:

Soil is subdivided into surface soil (horizon *A*), subsoil (horizon *B*), and substratum (horizon *C*). The structures and textures of soil have been described in detail in the previous chapter. The important hydrologic characteristics of the soil may be enumerated as follows:

1. Because of multiple-grain structure, perviousness of the soil is not usually a function of the size of mineral grains as is the case for ordinary sedimentary materials.

2. The chief hydraulic pathways through the soil are cracks, vertical partings, clod, prismatic, and columnar structure of horizons *A* and *B*, and root casts and animal borings of all three horizons.

3. Horizon *B*, the subsoil, controls movement of water toward the water table because of great decrease in permeability with the development of soil horizons and age of the soil.

4. Horizon *C*, the substratum, has the original hydrologic characteristics of the parent material on which have been superimposed an additional porosity and perviousness due chiefly, if not wholly, to root casts and animal borings.

The soil is underlain either by regolith or by fairly fresh, unweathered material. For example, fresh glacial till underlies large areas of soil in North Central United States, and recently deposited alluvium fills practically every important river valley. On these sediments a weakly zoned (immature) soil has been developed. The hydrologic character of regolith depends upon the character of the fresh rock from which it is derived and the processes of weathering. If weathering has been largely mechanical and the rock has broken down into angular material, the regolith as a whole will be pervious. If weathering has been intense and has developed clayey material, the regolith will have low permeability.

Clayey Soil Functioning as Aquifer.—An interesting occurrence of clayey soil functioning as an aquifer due to root perforations was observed in a pit 10 miles north of Livermore, California.[1] When the water level was lowered by pumping, innumerable jets of water spurting a maximum distance of 2 ft. discharged into the pit through a network of circular holes, the diameter of which ranged from a pinpoint to about 0.25 in. Dark-gray to black organic material was visible in some of the holes, which were preserved by rapid burial and hardening of the deposit, precipitation of calcareous cementing material around roots, and destruction of plant material by weathering. Holes were visible on four sides of large samples and the constant yield of water from the pit indicated that interconnected openings persisted over a fairly

[1] SMITH, M. B., personal communication dated October, 1935.

large area adjoining the pit. Water did not enter the pit through clay which had slumped against the casing, destroying the holes.

OCCURRENCE OF WATER ABOVE THE WATER TABLE
Water of Dilation

Water of dilation[1] is the excess water held by sedimentary materials in an inflated state, and occurs chiefly at or near the ground surface. Water of dilation is driven out of freshly deposited colloidal clays, silts, and quicksand by drying or by compaction, which reduces flocculated clay to dense, deflocculated clay, presses the particles of silt together into an orderly arrangement in place of random orientation, and drives excess water out of quicksand. Freshly deposited clay swells with the addition of water and shrinks with extraction of water owing to drying or application of pressure. After such shrinkage occurs, clay absorbs less than the original amount of water of dilation with a second addition of water or with relief of pressure.[2] Each grain of sand in quicksand is separated by a water film from every other film-coated grain and the mineral particles do not touch each other. From the physicochemical viewpoint quicksand may be considered as sand dispersed in water.[3] Quicksand occurs at the ground surface, especially under turbulent water, and is occasionally developed by overpumping in subsurface conduits the walls of which support the load of overlying formations and in which the water and sand mixture moves as a liquid.

Further compaction by increasing load drives out water from clay and silt, gradually transforming them into shale. All water thus extracted may be designated *water of compaction.* The

---

[1] The term "water of supersaturation" suggested by C. H. Lee is the equivalent of water of dilation. Lee defines the former as "that which is in excess of the water of saturation . . . in quicksand, plastic clay, or flowing mud whose particles have lost contact and are more or less separated by water." (*Trans. Amer. Geophys. Union*, p. 399, 1935.)

[2] See references on compaction at end of Chap. XI.

[3] One type of quicksand is a loosely packed system containing a large amount of fluid which will flow on shaking but returns to a firm, pastelike condition when at rest. Mixtures with this property are called thixotropic and are commonly fine powders (average diameter of grain about 1μ or 0.001 mm.), such as bentonite and fine volcanic ash. Quicksand of grain size up to 10μ in diameter has this property which is due to a mixture of 2.1 per cent clay. (H. Freundlich, and F. Juliusburger, Quicksand as a Thixotropic System, *Trans. Faraday Soc.*, vol. 31, no. 168, pt. 5, May, 1935.)

first portion derived when near-surface sediments are transformed from the expanded to the dense stage represents water of dilation. Water subsequently extracted by compaction of dense clay and silt into shale is freed at depth, usually far below the water table.

Shale is finally recrystallized into slate by heat and pressure, and the water driven out by metamorphism is designated *water of metamorphism* or *metamorphic water* (page 28).

Water of Saturation

Water of saturation is the total water that can be absorbed by water-bearing materials without dilation of the sediments, or the total water held by water-bearing materials (except quicksand) below the water table.

Gravity Water

Above the water table the portion of water that is moved down toward the water table by the force of gravity has been variously denominated as *gravity water, gravitational water, vadose water,* or by the agricultural scientist as "free water." The ground-water student should not use the last term in this sense because of prior usage which differentiates free-moving ground water below the water table from confined, pressure, or artesian water.

Pellicular Water

In harmony with the definition of capillarity as the property of hairlike tubes to raise water above the level of the water in which they are immersed, the term "capillary water" should be restricted to water held in capillary openings above a water surface (the water table). The film or skin of water left around each grain of water-bearing material after gravity water has drained off has been included by most writers under the term capillary water. This film water should not be so included according to the definition given above. For this film water the author has adopted the name *pellicular water* (Fig. 38).

In addition to films which completely surround each particle, the smaller portions of interstices may have small segments of water bounded by two opposed capillary films as shown in Fig. 38*D*. These two films balance each other and therefore cannot move the water once it is lodged in the smallest portion of the capillary opening. The fundamental difference between capillary water and pellicular water as here defined is that *the single energy surface of capillary water is unbalanced by an opposing film* and is connected with the water table by a column of water and

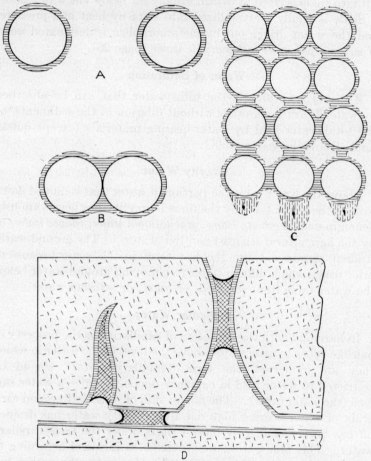

Fig. 38.—Pellicular water. *A*, two separate spherical grains surrounded by film of water; *B*, two spherical grains in contact; *C*, water films surrounding grains; gravity water moves over films and drains off at bottom; *D*, water held in fractures by balanced film force.

hence increases the hydraulic head in the tube and produces capillary rise; while the *opposed films of pellicular water are generally balanced dynamically*, and even when partially unbalanced by transpiration, produce only minor movement of water.

Soil Moisture.—Residual water left in the soil after gravity water has drained off is denominated *soil moisture*. It is the portion of pellicular water in the soil and therefore within reach of plant roots. The amount of water retained by the soil varies from the maximum left after gravity water has drained out to the amount left after evaporation and transpiration have removed all "available" soil moisture.

The water films around soil particles are in contact with the film enclosing a growing plant root. The "suction force" of the root is a constant of about 7 to 8 atmospheres, and the "adhesive force" of the soil for water varies from zero in a saturated soil to 250,000 or more atmospheres in a nearly dry soil. In an ordinary air-dried soil the pull is about 1000 atmospheres.[1] The balance is in favor of the plant in a saturated soil down to the wilting point where the forces are equal and the plant can no longer abstract water from the soil. If evaporation further reduces soil moisture, water will move from the plant to the soil. Drought-resisting plants may supply this draft from water stored in plant tissue, as, for example, the cactus, or may absorb water from moister portions of the soil and exude it in the drier portions in contact with feeding roots. The special mechanism developed is a long taproot reaching deep moisture. The plant, therefore, is able to transport moisture from one soil horizon and add it to another, but the amount thus moved is small.

Movement of soil moisture to a zone depleted by transpiration from adjacent regions has been postulated. Briggs[2] shows diagrammatically the stresses that would cause water movement from a fully saturated film area to a depleted area. However, recent studies[3] of the movement of soil moisture show positively that when water is applied to the soil by irrigation or rainfall it moves directly downward repairing depleted films only as far as the supply is sufficient to completely restore pellicular water (pages 46–47). Only after all film deficiencies have been supplied is there movement of water to the water table. These recent

[1] BREAZEALE, J. F., and F. J. CRIDER, Plant Association and Survival, and the Build-up of Moisture in Semi-arid Soils, *Univ. Ariz., Agr. Exp. Sta. Tech. Bull.* 53, p. 96, June 1934.

[2] BRIGGS, L. J., The Mechanics of Soil Moisture, *U.S. Dept. Agr., Div. Soils Bull.* 10, p. 19, 1897.

[3] SHAW, C. F., The Normal Moisture Capacity of Soils, *Soil Sci.*, vol. 23, no. 4, pp. 305–314, April, 1927.

experiments indicate that the *film force due to partly depleted films is not sufficient to move appreciable water to plant roots.*

Although films depleted by transpiration do not possess energy to move substantial amounts of water from undepleted films, it must not be assumed that wet material will not part with a portion of its moisture to dry material in contact with it. Materials such as clay and fine silt, which do not permit gravity movement of water, are charged with water by unbalanced film force and by colloidal and other physicochemical forces. The complex processes involved in the condensation and retention of gases and liquids on solid surfaces have been included under the broad term "sorption" by J. W. McBain.[1]

Field Capacity.—Shaw's experiments[2] indicate that when water is added to uniform soil and allowed to seep downward, a condition of distribution is reached at which the moisture content at all depths is approximately the same. He proposed the term *normal moisture capacity* for this condition, but usage favors the equivalent term *field capacity*. Field capacity may be defined as the percentage of volume of water retained against gravity to total volume of material, or, as defined by the soil scientist, the percentage by weight of water retained against gravity to the weight of the sample when dry.

In experiments conducted on deciduous orchards in California by Veihmeyer[3] it was found impossible to bring about uniform moisture content in the soil of less than maximum field capacity. When irrigation water was applied to loam soils, the moisture content was raised to field capacity and this content was established throughout the entire depth of soil penetrated by water and there seemed to be little subsequent movement of moisture. Veihmeyer concludes from these experiments that soil moisture must be completely built up to field capacity before movement of gravity water takes place.

Available Moisture.—A portion only of soil moisture is available for plant growth, and therefore pellicular water is further subdivided by the agricultural scientist into *available moisture* (available to plants) and *unavailable moisture*. Available mois-

[1] McBain, J. W., "The Sorption of Gases and Vapours by Solids," pp. 1–17, G. Routledge & Sons, Ltd., 1932.

[2] Shaw, *op. cit.*

[3] Veihmeyer, F. J., Some Factors Affecting Irrigation Requirements of Deciduous Orchards, *Hilgardia*, vol. 2, no. 6, 1927.

ture equals field capacity less the amount of water held in the soil at the *wilting point*. The *wilting coefficient* of a soil is the ratio of the weight of water in the soil when the leaves of plants undergo permanent wilting to the weight of the soil when dry. Residual pellicular water in excess of the wilting coefficient represents available moisture. However, Batchelor and Reed[1] have shown experimentally that plants can function for a time under soil-moisture conditions below the wilting point and even with reduction to the hygroscopic limit if not too prolonged.

Hygroscopic Water.—The usage of the term "hygroscopic water" has been variable, but the definition now generally accepted corresponds closely to that given by Meinzer: "Hygroscopic water is the water in the soil that is in equilibrium with atmospheric water vapor."[2]

The work of Briggs and Shantz[3] suggests that there is an empirical relation between the various types of water mentioned above measured in ratios of weight of water to dry weight of sample; that is, field capacity, wilting coefficient, hygroscopic coefficient, and moisture equivalent. The *moisture equivalent* has been defined as the ratio between the water a soil will retain against a centrifugal force 1000 times the force of gravity and the weight of the soil when dry.[4] The chief use of this factor is for determining the hygroscopic coefficient, wilting coefficient and for estimating field capacity. These relations are shown in the following equations.[5]

Moisture equivalent = approximately field capacity[6]
= wilting coefficient × (1.8 to 2)
= hygroscopic coefficient × 2.7

Recent investigations, however, have shown that empirical

[1] BATCHELOR, L. D., and H. S. REED, Seasonal Variation of Soil Moisture in a Walnut Grove in Relation to Hygroscopic Coefficient, *Univ. Calif. Publ., Agr. Exp. Sta., Tech. Paper* 1, September, 1923.

[2] MEINZER, *Water-Supply Paper* 494, op. cit., p. 24.

[3] BRIGGS, L. J., and H. L. SHANTZ, The Wilting Coefficient for Different Plants and Its Indirect Determination, *U.S. Dept. Agr., Bur. Plant Ind. Bull.* 230, 1912.

[4] MEINZER, *Water-Supply Paper* 494, op. cit., p. 25.

[5] MEINZER, *Water-Supply Paper* 489, op. cit., p. 92.

[6] All expressed in percentage of dry weight of sample. Field capacity expressed in percentage of volume of water held against the pull of gravity

determination of moisture equivalent does not give a satisfactory basis for calculating the wilting coefficient or field capacity.

Unavailable Water.—Water is retained in the soil against the force of surface evaporation and against the absorptive power of plant roots. As indicated in the foregoing discussion there is no accord as to the exact point where water becomes "unavailable" to plants. Unavailable water probably includes water held by complex physical and physicochemical forces which need not be discussed in further detail in this book.

Capillary or Fringe Water

Fringe water is held above the water table or a perched water table in capillary openings by the force of capillarity (page 42, Fig. 5).

CAPILLARY ACTION

Capillarity is the property of small tubes immersed in a liquid which causes the liquid in the tube to rise above the static level of the liquid in which the tube is immersed. Capillarity is produced by the surface tension of the "film" or *meniscus* at the liquid-air contact in the tube.

Surface tension is developed at the contact between a liquid and air and is due largely to unbalanced attraction of the molecules of the liquid for each other. Each molecule is attracted by adjacent molecules equally in all directions except those at the surface which are attracted only by the molecules beneath. If the surface layer of molecules is turned up or down at the edge of the water container, tension is developed parallel to the surface, which acts, in a fashion, like a flexible and contracting skin between the liquid and the air.[1] Modern investigations indicate

---

to volume of sample becomes specific retention. For a recent excellent discussion of moisture equivalent and specific retention see paper by A. N. Piper, Notes on the Relation between the Moisture Equivalent and the Specific Retention of Water-bearing Materials, *Amer. Geophys. Union Trans.,* pp. 481–487, 1933.

[1] ADAM, N. K., "The Physics and Chemistry of Surfaces," Clarendon Press, p. 3, 1930. "The fact that a liquid surface contracts spontaneously shows that there is free energy associated with it, that work must be done to extend the surface. This free energy in the surface is of fundamental importance; a vast number of problems relating to the equilibrium of surfaces can be solved without knowing more than the magnitude of

that this surface energy is concentrated in a layer one to two molecules thick.[1] There is no actual skin at the surface, but the resolution of the molecular attractions at the air-liquid surface shows that they strive to produce a surface of the smallest possible area. This is the *fundamental property of liquid surfaces.* The attractions acting on molecules at the surface of a liquid compared with those acting on molecules at depth are shown in Fig. 39. A small body of water in the air or floating in an immiscible liquid assumes a spherical form because the stresses

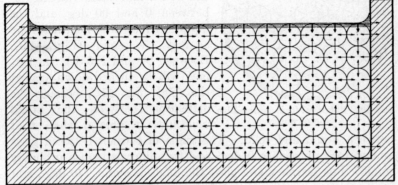

Fig. 39.—Attractions acting on molecules at the surface of a liquid and on those at depth.

developed by the air-liquid surface or the two-liquid surface act inward along the radii of a sphere (Fig. 40). The sphere has the smallest possible surface area for any given volume. Mathematically the surface layer may be treated as a contractile skin.

The *angle of contact* between a liquid-air surface and a solid surface depends upon the relative strength of the attractions of the molecules of the liquid for each other and of the molecules

---

this free energy. In the solution of such problems a mathematical device is almost invariably employed to simplify the calculations; it is to substitute for the surface free energy a hypothetical tension, acting in all directions parallel to the surface, equal to the free energy. This is what is generally known as the *surface tension.*"

[1] This conclusion was based on studies of oil films on water but is not universally accepted and is not fully reconcilable with evidence from lubrication, adhesion, X-ray and electron-beam examination of surfaces or even with the existence of pellicular water. (Personal communication from J. W. McBain, Professor of Chemistry, Stanford University.)

of the liquid for the solid.   This also governs the surface "wetting capacity" of the liquid.

If the attraction of molecules of the liquid for each other is not the same as the attraction of molecules of the liquid for the solid, the angle of contact between the solid and the liquid surface will

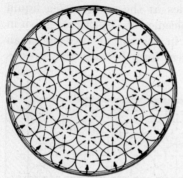

be modified at and near the contact (Fig. 41).   If the intermolecular attraction in the liquid is less than the attraction between the liquid and solid, the angle is between 0 and 90 deg. and the liquid surface will be turned up against the solid (Fig. 41*B*). Between 90 and 180 deg. the surface will be turned down against the solid (Fig. 41*C*) because the attraction   between   the   liquid molecules   is   greater   than   that

FIG. 40.—Spherical form assumed by a drop of water.

between liquid and solid.   The angle of contact between glass and water approaches 0 deg. and for minerals is also probably small.   For mercury and glass the angle is about 140 deg., and for water and paraffin it is 105 deg.   For oily or greasy surfaces it is larger than 90 deg.   For each fluid there is a characteristic angle of contact with each solid substance.

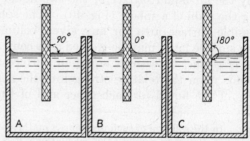

FIG. 41.—Angles of contact between liquid and solid surfaces.

If two parallel plates inserted in a container partly filled with water (Fig. 42) are placed near enough to each other to eliminate the horizontal portion of the water-air surface between them, or in other words, when this surface becomes curved throughout the distance between plates, the water surface will rise or fall, depending upon whether the contact angle is less or greater than 90 deg.

(movement is in the direction faced by the concave side of the air-water surface). The amount of displacement increases as the space between plates is diminished. If the contact angle is 90 deg., there is no displacement of the liquid surface as the plates are brought together.

A *capillary tube* shows a slightly greater elevation or depression of the liquid surface in the tube above or below the static level of the liquid in which it is immersed than occurs between plates discussed above. In the curved water-air surface in the capillary tube the resolution of attractive forces between molecules of the liquid shows that there is a residual force acting upward for

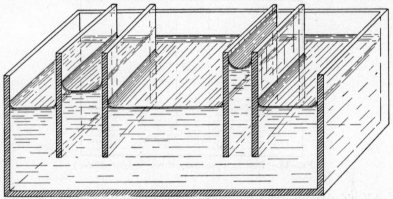

FIG. 42.—Capillary rise between parallel plates.

concave surfaces and downward for convex surfaces. An illustration of this is a rubber band; if under tension and pulled down (representing a concave meniscus), when released it will snap upward. If pulled up, it will snap down when released. Hydrostatic equilibrium between the liquid in the tube and outside it is disturbed by the warping of the meniscus, and the liquid in the tube rises if the pressure difference of the meniscus is upward or drops if it is downward. "The well-known rise of a liquid in a capillary tube is simply an automatic recording of the pressure difference across the meniscus of the liquid in the tube, the curvature of the meniscus being determined by the radius of the tube and the angle of contact between the solid and the liquid."[1]

[1] ADAM, *op. cit.*, p. 15: "Let *r* (Fig. 43) be the radius of a cylindrical tube, so small that the liquid meniscus does not depart sensibly from the spherical

As previously mentioned water has an attraction for most surfaces (contact angle less than 90 deg.) and a repulsion (contact angle greater than 90 deg.) for others, such as oiled or greased surfaces or extremely dry, fine powder.[1]   The repulsion between

---

form, and θ the contact angle between the liquid and the glass (this is generally zero).   Then the radius of curvature of the meniscus is $r/\cos \theta$ (or r for water in a glass tube) and the pressure under the meniscus becomes less than that at the same height in a liquid with a plane surface. . . . This produces a driving pressure, tending to force the liquid up the tube, and the meniscus will rise to a height h, such that the weight of the column

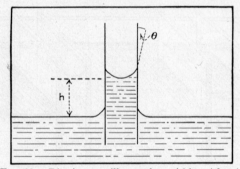

FIG. 43.—Rise in a capillary tube.   (*After Adam.*)

of liquid elevated above the plane surface outside the tube just balances the pressure deficiency under the curved meniscus.

"The liquid is not pulled up the tube by a hypothetical surface tension pulling on the walls, as is suggested by the explanation found in so many elementary text-books—it has never been clear to the author what is the hook on the wall to which this surface tension attaches itself, nor how the hook contrives to move up the tube in advance of the rising meniscus. Nor is it driven up by the squeezing action of the attractions exerted by the walls of the tube on the layers of molecules remote from the walls . . . The energy relations determine what is the stable contact angle; the fluidity of the liquid permits the molecules to move about till they rest at this stable contact angle; the contact angle and the curvature of the tube curve the liquid surface; the pressure difference follows from the free energy resident in the surface, and the liquid then flows up the tube under the hydrostatic pressure.

"When the contact angle is greater than 90 degrees, $\cos \theta$ is negative, and the liquid falls in the tube.   This occurs with mercury and glass, as a general rule, and with water in tubes coated with paraffin wax internally."

[1] A curious phenomenon, of no particular importance in regard to water movements but affecting the physical character of certain types of soils,

water and dry soils may be important in controlling the rate of rainfall penetration, especially in silts and clays, when the surface material has been dried out by long exposure as is common in arid regions. The surface of each particle must be coated with water before water can move on the water films to the next underlying particle. If the particles are thoroughly dry, the contact angle resists spreading of water over the surface of the solid and regeneration of pellicular water is slow (Fig. 44).

Movement of Water in Capillary Fringe.—Water adjusts its position in a capillary tube to the equilibrium between hydrostatic pressure outside the tube and hydrostatic pressure ± film pressure inside the tube. This difference in head is called *capillary lift*. Continuous movement takes place only while the equilibrium is unbalanced by abstraction of water from the tube by evaporation and transpiration.

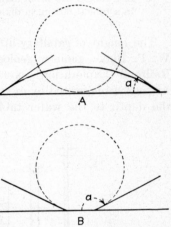

Fig. 44.—*A*, spreading of a drop of water on moist surface; contact angle α less than 90 deg.; *B*, drop of water on dry surface which resists spreading of the drop; contact angle α greater than 90 deg.

Capillary lift varies inversely as the diameter of the tube (Fig. 45). In an opening of 1 mm. diameter the capillary lift equals 1.2 in., hence there is a distinct capillary lift in an opening

---

has been denominated by the writer "capillary disruption." If a dry fragment of fine silt or any alluvial material with a silt binder is immersed in water, it is apt to crack and even to explode into small pieces. The disruption is due to compression of air entrapped in the interstices of the sample, caused by the penetration of capillary water from every point on the wetted surface. This phenomenon does not indicate that the sample has little strength or that the formation will not bear considerable load, as was suggested to the jury passing on the St. Francis dam disaster in southern California. If such samples are wetted from one side only, capillary water drives out the air, and the strength of the thoroughly moistened material can be tested. This process may be important in breaking up the coarser clods of poorly tilled and cultivated soil. In clays capillary disruption is not usually important. Swelling of clay is due to absorption of water by colloidal material.

of that size.[1]   The amount of capillary rise is calculated by King as follows:[2]

In a tube 1.00   in. in diameter................. 0.054 in.
In a tube 0.10   in. in diameter................. 0.545 in.
In a tube 0.010 in. in diameter................. 5.456 in.
In a tube 0.001 in. in diameter................. 54.560 in.

The height of capillary lift has been exaggerated by geologists. W. P. Blake, pioneer geologist with the United States Pacific Railroad Exploration, explained surface crusts of caliche in Arizona as deposited by evaporation of capillary water, although the depth to the water table is as much as 100 ft. below the

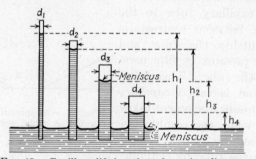

Fig. 45.—Capillary lift in tubes of varying diameter.

ground surface.[3]   Hall,[4] in 1903, estimated the maximum capillary lift in certain soils at 200 ft., and McGee,[5] in 1913, estimated lift with favorable subsoil conditions at 30 to 35 ft. Actual measurements of capillary lift do not substantiate these estimates.   Meinzer's summary of experimental data collected by various investigators appears in Table 4.[6]

---

[1] A good discussion of the mathematical treatment of capillarity and movement of soil moisture appears in B. A. Keen, "Physical Properties of Soil," pp. 89–99, Longmans, Green & Company, London, 1931.

[2] KING, F. H., "The Soil," p. 138, The Macmillan Company, 1907.

[3] BLAKE, W. P., The Caliche in Southern Arizona, *Trans. A.I.M.E.*, vol. 31, p. 225, 1902.

[4] HALL, A. D., "The Soil," p. 94, John Murray, London, 1903.

[5] McGEE, W. J., Wells and Subsoil Water, *U.S. Dept. Agr., Bur. Soils Bull.* 92, p. 11, 1913.

[6] MEINZER, O. E., *Water-Supply Paper* 489, pp. 34–35.

TABLE 4.—MAXIMUM CAPILLARY LIFT IN VARIOUS TYPES OF MATERIAL

Observer	Date of observa- tion	Type of material	Estimated maximum capillary lift
Mitscherlich......	1905	Varied soils	1.5 meters (4.9 ft.)
Tulaikow.........	1907	Fine textured soil	60–70 cm. (1.9–2.3 ft.)
Leather..........	1908	Pusa soil	7 ft.
Retmistrov.......	1913	Soil in boxes	3 ft.
Lee..............	1912	Coarse sandy soil	4 ft.
Lee..............	1912	Fine sandy or clayey soil	8 ft.
Slichter..........	1906	Sandy loam	3 ft.
Meinzer..........	1917	Nevada soil—gyp- siferous silt	3–8.1 ft.

The majority of modern authorities give the maximum capillary lift, and consequently the maximum thickness of the capillary fringe, as 10± ft. The limit of capillary lift as deduced from experimental work is given by Briggs as 165 cm., or 5.4 ft.[1] Capillary rise in dry soils reaches 1.18 ft. Rise in moist soils is 4.5 times as great as that in dry soils.

Rate of Capillary Rise.—Hilgard[2] illustrates by diagram capillary rise in soil sediments of different grain size, giving the length of time required for water to reach the limit of capillary lift in each sediment. In his figure clay shows capillary rise markedly below that of the finest granular sediment, which suggests that the physical nature of colloidal clay is unlike that of granular sediments or that friction of movement in the small interstices of clay so reduces velocity under the diminished head toward the limit of capillary lift that water does not ascend to full capillary height in a reasonable time. A table derived from Hilgard's diagram is shown on page 156.

It is to be noted in general that experimental determination of capillary rise in soil sediments is less than that observed in the field or calculated from the size of the interstices. Figure 46 shows the rate and extent of capillary rise observed by W. A. Packard in six soils of California.[3]

[1] BRIGGS, L. J., and M. H. LAPHAM, Capillary Studies and Filtration of Clay from Soil Solutions, *U.S. Bur. Soils Bull.* 19, p. 26, 1902.

[2] HILGARD, E. W., "The Soil." p. 206, The Macmillan Company, 1906.

[3] Private unpublished investigation by W. A. Packard.

TABLE 5.—CAPILLARY RISE OF WATER IN SOIL SEDIMENTS OF DIFFERENT
PARTICLE SIZE

Diameter, mm.	Time required to reach limit, days	Extent of lift, in.
Clay..............	350	60.5
Silts:		
0.016..............	475	122
0.025..............	300	105
0.036..............	147	52 (incomplete)
Sands:		
0.047..............	160	53.25
0.072..............	144	34.75
0.12..............	158	26.25
0.16..............	171	19.25
0.30..............	188	13
0.5..............	138	11
Grits:		
1..............	100	9.5
2..............	80	4.5
Sandy loam soil........	144	52

As shown in the tables, it takes a long time for water to reach the limit of capillary lift. The reason for this is that the driving force is the difference between ultimate capillary lift and the actual position to which the water has been raised at any particular time. This difference may be designated as *capillary head.* When capillary water first starts rising, capillary head is full. When the lift is approaching the limit, the driving force is approaching zero. Applying this to the consideration of rate of rise in the capillary fringe when acted upon by evaporation and transpiration, it would seem that theoretically at least the rate of movement might be determined by measuring the reduction in capillary lift (capillary head) due to transpiration and evaporation. As far as known by the author this has not been attempted.[1]

Capillary Fringe above a Sinking and a Rising Water Table.— The height at which water can be held by capillarity is independent of the shape and size of the tube below the meniscus.

[1] MEINZER, O. E., Outline of Methods for Estimating Ground-water Supplies, *U.S. Geol. Surv. Water-Supply Paper* 638-C, pp. 106–107, 1932.

This is illustrated by Meinzer in *Water-Supply Paper* 489, Fig. 11, page 23. Water is held above a subsiding water table in tubes of supercapillary size if there is a restriction of capillary size at or below the height of capillary lift (Fig. 47*A*). Water can be drawn

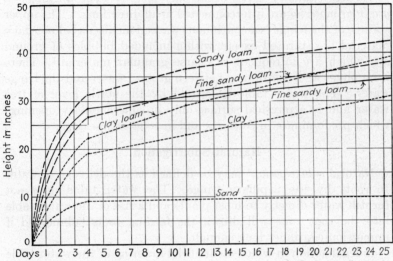

Fig. 46.—Rate and extent of capillary rise in six California soils. (*After Packard.*)

up above a water table, however, only by a continuous capillary opening without supercapillary enlargements (Fig. 47*B*). Hence more water is held in the capillary fringe above a sinking water table than above a rising water table.

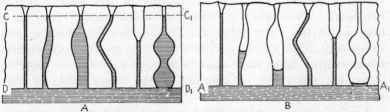

Fig. 47.—Capillary fringe above a subsiding and a rising water table. *A*, water table dropped from C-C_1 to D-D_1; *B*, water table rose to A-A_1.

Capillary Fringe in Natural Material.—Emphasis on the properties of individual capillary tubes has developed an erroneous concept that the capillary fringe is a bundle of innumerable vertical capillary tubes, each tube holding a separate meniscus. In the larger openings the overlying ground air is close to the water table; hence the capillary fringe has been considered the basal portion of the zone of aeration (footnote, page 40).

Vertical capillary tubes occur only in *soil*. The openings *in granular material* are interconnected in all directions. The upper surface of the fringe is a continuous warped meniscus below which material is saturated except within included bubbles of ground air, which are infrequent in coarse granular material.[1] There is no physical discontinuity between ground water and the fringe water. The water table is located by the static level of free water and is a physical surface only in supercapillary openings which predominate in *fractures* and in *solution openings*.

Natural Subirrigation

Natural *subirrigation*[1] may be defined as the delivery of water to roots by the capillary fringe. The water table does not furnish water directly to most plants and a rise of the water table into the root zone will drown the feeding roots submerged if immersion continues long enough.

In legal action in which an artificial lowering of the water table by pumping, stream diversion, or drainage ditches is claimed to be prejudicial to plaintiffs, the effect on subirrigation is usually set forth as one of the principal damages. To evaluate the effect of water-table lowering in a given area, the part actually beneficially subirrigated under natural conditions must be determined. In cases where the water table stands too close to the surface to permit vigorous root growth, lowering of the water table is beneficial. Even when subirrigation which existed prior to a lowering of the water table was of some benefit, drainage and subsequent irrigation of a deeper zone of root growth may produce larger crops. Each area must be studied in detail in order to determine the effect of lowering of the water table in that particular area.

The efficiency of subirrigation is directly dependent upon the relation between root development and available moisture delivered by the capillary fringe. If roots are submerged by a rise in water table, they are probably rendered ineffective during

[1] Inclusions of ground air below the water-air contact of the capillary fringe are being studied experimentally in the Stanford Hydrologic Laboratory.

the period of submergence, and if the water remains in the root zone for a sufficient time, the submerged roots will drown.   Hence fluctuations of the water table may completely destroy possible beneficial effects of subirrigation.   When the water table is lowered, the percentage of moisture in the zone wetted by the capillary fringe before water-table lowering is reduced to field capacity.   When roots reduce the field capacity to the wilting point, this zone becomes of no further crop-producing value until again supplied with water by the capillary fringe above a rising water table, or by rainfall or irrigation.

Figure 48, *A* to *F*, illustrates the method used by Packard[1] to determine the relation of root development and distribution to ground-water fluctuations.   The fluctuating water table and overlying capillary fringe are shown by differently lined areas. Distribution of feeding roots was determined by screening, separating the feeding roots (0.5 to 1 mm. in diameter) from the larger roots by hand, and weighing them for successive 6-in. layers of soil.   The weight of feeding roots in grams for each 6 in. in depth is plotted.

Growth and productivity of plants are shown approximately by the number of feeding roots.   Therefore it was assumed that the weight of feeding roots in each zone indicates favorable or unfavorable conditions to plant growth, which are the result of the distribution of soil moisture and position of the water table. Figures *A* and *B* show root distribution of cereals with shallow roots in a normal year and in an abnormally wet year, with the water table fluctuating from 13 to 19 ft. below the surface. Fluctuations of the water table have no effect on this crop, for roots do not extend to the capillary fringe and must depend entirely upon rains and irrigation.   Figures *C*, *D*, and *E* show distribution of alfalfa roots in relation to varying ground-water conditions, with the water table fluctuating from 8 to 17 ft. below the surface.   The deeply penetrating roots of alfalfa reach ground water at its lowest level and any appreciable fluctuation of the water table will affect growth of the plants.   In *C* there is a normal fluctuation of 4 ft. and ground water and the capillary fringe supply moisture to 30 per cent of roots.   In *D*, an abnormally wet year, the added rise of 5 ft. in the water table results in wetting 13 ft. above the lowest water table.   *E* represents an

[1] PACKARD, W. A., unpublished report.

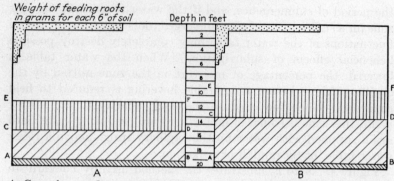

A. Ground-water fluctuations and distribution of cereal roots in a normal
year.

B. Ground-water fluctuations and
cereal root distribution in wet year.

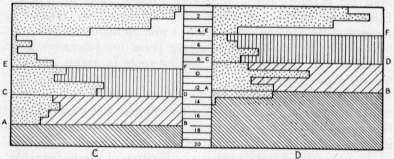

C. Ground-water fluctuations and alfalfa root distribution in normal
year.

D. Ground-water fluctuations and alfalfa root distribution with high
water table.

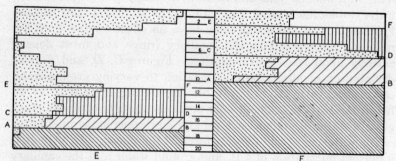

E. Ground-water fluctuations and alfalfa root distribution with low
water table.

F. Normal alfalfa root development
under irrigation.

FIG. 48.—Relation of ground-water fluctuations to distribution of feeding
roots. A–B, lowest water table; C–D, highest water table; E–F, upper limit of
capillary fringe. (After Packard.)

abnormally dry year, when only 5½ ft. are wetted above the lowest water table. In this case normal rainfall penetration does not reach the capillary fringe and as a result there is a depleted zone between the zone moistened by influent seepage from rainfall and that supplied with water from the capillary fringe, which results in an irregular distribution of roots. Figure *F* illustrates normal root development under irrigation.

The above summary illustrates one method of investigating the effects of fluctuating ground water on natural subirrigation.

References

General

ADAM, N. K., "The Physics and Chemistry of Surfaces," Clarendon Press, Oxford, 1930.

HAZEN, ALLEN, Some Physical Properties of Sands and Gravels, *Mass. State Board Health*, *24th Ann. Rept.* for 1892, pp. 551 *et seq.*

MEINZER, O. E., The Occurrence of Ground Water in the United States, *Water-Supply Paper* 489, pp. 22–38, 1923.

Capillarity

ADAM, N. K., *op. cit.*, pp. 1–24.

BRIGGS, L. J., and M. H. LAPHAM, Capillary Studies and Filtration of Clay from Soil Solutions, *U.S. Dept. Agr. Bur. Soils Bull.* 19, 1902.

HILGARD, E. W., "The Soil," The Macmillan Company, New York, pp. 201–211, 1906.

KEEN, B. A., "Physical Properties of Soil," Longmans, Green & Company, London, pp. 89–99, 1931.

KING, F. H., Movements of Ground Water, *U.S. Geol. Surv. 19th Ann. Rep.*, pp. 85–93, 168–178, 1898.

MEINZER, O. E., *op. cit.*, pp. 22–25; 31–38.

SHAW, C. F., and A. SMITH, Maximum Height of Capillary Rise Starting with Soil at Capillary Saturation, *Hilgardia*, vol. 2, no. 11, pp. 399–409, February, 1927.

VAN HISE, C. R., Treatise on Metamorphism, *U.S. Geol. Surv. Monog.* 47, pp. 138–143, 1904.

WARINGTON, R., "Physical Properties of Soils," Clarendon Press, Oxford, pp. 92–100, 1900.

Pellicular Water

ALWAY, F. J., and G. R. McDOLE, Relation of the Water-retaining Capacity of a Soil to its Hygroscopic Coefficient, *Jour. Agr. Res.*, vol. 9, pp. 65–66, 1917.

BATCHELOR, L. D., and H. S. REED, Seasonal Variation of Soil Moisture in a Walnut Grove in Relation to Hygroscopic Coefficient, *Univ. Calif. Publ., Agr. Exp. Sta., Tech. Paper* 1, September, 1923.

BECKETT, S. H., and OTHERS, Irrigation-water-requirement Studies of Citrus and Avocado Trees in San Diego County, Calif., 1926 and 1927, *Univ. Calif. Publ., Agr. Exp. Sta. Bull.* 489, pp. 14–44, 1930.

BRIGGS, L. J., The Mechanics of Soil Moisture, *U.S. Dept. Agr., Div. Soils Bull.* 10.

BRIGGS, L. J., and J. McLANE, The Moisture Equivalent of Soils, *U.S. Dept. Agr. Bull.* 45, 1907.

BRIGGS, L. J., and H. L. SHANTZ, The Wilting Coefficient for Different Plants and Its Indirect Determinations, *U.S. Dept. Agr., Bur. Plant Ind. Bull.* 230, 1912.

BUCKINGHAM, E., Studies on the Movement of Soil Moisture, *U.S. Bur. Soils Bull.* 38, 1907.

FREE, E. E., Studies in Soil Physics, *Plant World*, vol. 14, nos. 2, 3, 5, 7, 8, 1912.

PIPER, A. M., Notes on the Relation between the Moisture-equivalent and the Specific Retention of Water-bearing Materials, *Trans. Amer. Geophys. Union*, pp. 481–487, 1933.

SHAW, C. E., The Normal Moisture Capacity of Soils, *Soil Science*, vol. 23, no. 4, pp. 303–317, April, 1927.

VEIHMEYER, F. J., Some Factors Affecting Irrigation Requirements of Deciduous Orchards, *Hilgardia*, vol. 2, no. 6, 1927.

VEIHMEYER, F. J., and A. H. HENDRICKSON, The Moisture Equivalent as a Measure of the Field Capacity of Soils, *Soil Sci.*, vol. 32, pp. 181–194, 1931.

VEIHMEYER, F. J. and OTHERS, Some Factors Affecting the Moisture Equivalent of Soils, 1st Internat. Cong. Soil Sci., vol. 1, pp. 512–534, 1928.

WILSDON, B. H., Studies in Soil Moisture, pt. I, *Mem. Dept. Agr. India, Chem. Ser.*, vol. 6, pp. 154–186, 1921.

Surface Tension

ADAM, N. K., *op. cit.*, pp. 146–165, 293–324.

KING, F. H., "The Soil," *Rural Science Series by L. H. Bailey*, pp. 136–142, The Macmillan Company, New York, 1907.

MEINZER, O. E., *op. cit.*, pp. 21–22.

CHAPTER VII

INFLUENT SEEPAGE INCLUDING WATER SPREADING

According to generally accepted usage, *seepage* is the movement of water into or out of the ground. Movement of water into the ground from the surface down to the water table is called *influent seepage* and discharge of ground water to the surface is *effluent seepage*. The terms influent and effluent are also used with reference to streams, ground water, and the water table. An *influent* or *losing stream* is feeding water underground and an *effluent or gaining stream* is receiving water from underground sources. *Influent ground water* or an *influent water table* is receiving water from the surface and *effluent ground water* or *water table* is discharging water to the ground surface.

The term seepage has been used heretofore with reference chiefly to the appearance or disappearance of water at the ground surface and not to the type or character of movement of water below the ground surface. Indeed, water movement in the unsaturated zone caused by seepage from the surface has unfortunately been designated as "percolation." For several years the author has searched for a commonly used term that could be aptly applied to the complex movements of water from the ground surface to the water table and has finally selected the term seepage for these movements, in spite of the fact that some slight confusion might arise from the dual meaning, namely, appearance and disappearance of water at the ground surface, and the complex motions of water from ground surface to water table. It should be noted further that only *influent* seepage into the ground through the unsaturated zone to the water table is controlled by the laws of seepage, while *effluent* seepage occurs only in saturated materials where the water table intersects the ground surface and such effluent discharge moves according to the laws of percolation. Influent seepage from a body of surface water, such as a stream or lake, will move by percolation if the water table is in contact with and slopes away from the bed of lake or stream, so that no undersaturated zone occurs between surface water and ground water.

In this chapter discussion is limited to the motions of influent seepage. The effect of influent seepage on the slope of the water table and effluent seepage are taken up in Chap. IX, The Water Table in Granular Pervious Materials.

Influent Seepage from Rainfall

A portion or occasionally all of rainfall sinks into the ground, a portion may run off, and a portion or all may be evaporated. Influent seepage from rainfall which reaches the water table is called the ground-water increment from rainfall. Rainfall is usually of short duration and between storms field capacity may be so reduced that rain cannot completely replenish pellicular water depleted by transpiration and evaporation, and wherever such a deficiency exists, there will be no contribution to ground water. Under these conditions even pervious materials will not conduct rain water to the water table. Rainfall penetration to the water table may also be prevented by an impervious stratum between ground surface and water table.

Investigation of Rainfall Increment.—Prior to examination of moisture conditions following rainfall much can be learned from a study of structure of the soil, especially the thickness and character of horizon *B* (page 126). After a storm, water continues to stand for some time where impervious hardpan exists and such areas permit little influent seepage. If the investigator has sufficient familiarity with the region to interpret the soil maps, published by the United States Bureau of Soils, in relation to hydrologic characteristics of the soil, they may be used to delimit areas that will absorb and transmit water readily from areas that are impervious to influent seepage.

Penetration of rain water into clayey or silty soils can be recognized easily in pits or boreholes or in natural cliffs and banks, as the moist condition becomes apparent when the material reaches field capacity. In sand, however, moisture conditions are not so easily recognized, but if overlying material is moist, it may be assumed that rainfall has penetrated the immediately underlying sand. Delivery of water by sand to the water table depends upon the existence of pervious connections with the water table. If there are no good connections, *perched water bodies,*[1] overlain by *perched water tables,* may be developed.

In order to investigate the continuity of pervious material from the surface to the water table, the geologic and hydrologic structure of intervening formations are studied by examination of materials encountered in wells or test holes, by testing hydrologic properties of samples, and by construction of geologic cross sections from surface to water table.

Measurement of rainfall increment can be made only after the materials through which water seeps have been charged to field capacity down to the water table. Inasmuch as pellicular water is not depleted by transpiration below the zone reached by roots (the soil), it may be assumed that after the soil is charged to field capacity, influent seepage will pass through the zone charged with pellicular water and will reach the water table, and downward movement will cease as soon as excess water over field capacity has drained out. The quantity of influent seepage has been measured in soil columns and lysimeters and by catching drip water in tunnels.

Soil Columns.—Large pipes or tanks are cemented around a column of undisturbed soil and experimental determination is made of hydrologic properties of the enclosed section of soil. Measured quantities of water are applied and compared with the amount which drains from the soil column and porosity, specific yield, permeability, and rate of influent seepage can be studied. If natural vegetation is allowed to grow on the surface of the soil column and the sample extends through the soil zone into underlying material, the quantity of water retained in the column

[1] Examples of perched water tables are found in Sulphur Spring Valley, Arizona, where saturated material is supported by calcareous hardpan, sometimes far above the true water table; and in part of the Tintic mining district of Utah where decomposed igneous rocks are underlain by quartzite and limestone. Wells and springs in the Tintic district obtain water from decomposed igneous rocks, but deeper wells entering the underlying limestone and quartzite strike a second zone of aeration. In the Hawaiian Islands perched water tables are common in strata of permeable lava which occur interbedded with volcanic ash. Here the study of perched water tables has become an important phase of hydraulic engineering and groundwater geology. Another example of a perched water body in Long Island, New York, is described by Veatch (A. C. Veatch, *et al.,* Underground Water Resources of Long Island, N. Y., *U.S. Geol. Surv. Prof. Paper* 44, pp. 57–58, 1906).

represents the amount of water necessary to bring the soil up to field capacity, and the amount passing out through the bottom of the tank measures the amount of influent seepage. Unfortunately, early experimenters with soil columns did not appreciate the necessity of bringing the soil up to field capacity before influent seepage can reach the water table.[1]

Soil-column tests determine the hydrologic characteristics of materials near the surface and rate of influent seepage, but these characteristics should not be taken as indicating the hydrologic characteristics of materials below the water table.

Lysimeters and Tunnels.—Measurements of influent seepage have been made by American and European investigators with *lysimeters,* or vessels placed above the water table to intercept seepage. These may be buried in the ground or placed in tunnels. Earliest records date back to tests made in England from 1796 to 1798. The longest record extended over a period of 49 years and others have extended over 20 to 30 years.[2]

Various types of lysimeters and methods of burial have been used. Unless the vessel is placed without disturbing the material through which seepage passes, results do not represent natural conditions. Taylor[3] describes tests made by driving open cylinders into the roof of a tunnel driven a short distance from a shallow shaft. A collecting pan was placed below the cylinder. Another method used in these tests was to drive a trough-shaped intercepting vessel into the side wall of a pit. However, only a very small drip was obtained from these tests, and from further

---

[1] Pioneer and extensive experiments with soil columns were carried on by Paul Bailey, who dug around an undisturbed column of soil and sunk a pipe several feet in diameter around the column. Asphalt was poured around the enclosed column to prevent leakage, the column raised, and a bottom with a valve put on. Various tests were then made on the column of soil, and it was found that water did not penetrate to the bottom. These experiments demonstrated that influent seepage from rainfall during the season in which the tests were made did not deliver water to the water table in that type of soil. (Paul Bailey, Engineering Investigation of Percolation from Alameda Creek and Ground Water Studies in Niles Cone, Calif., *Calif. State Water Comm., 3d Biennial Rept.,* 1919–1920.)

[2] MEINZER, O. E., Outline of Methods for Estimating Ground-water Supplies, *U.S. Geol. Surv. Water-Supply Paper* 638-C, p. 102, 1932.

[3] TAYLOR, G. H., Investigations Relating to the Absorption of Precipitation and Its Penetration to the Zone of Saturation; *Trans. Amer. Geophys. Union,* pp. 206–207, June, 1931.

experimentation it was determined that after material in the vessel becomes saturated, capillary rise discharges water above and over the sides of the lysimeter unless the sides exceed the height of capillary lift.

Drip from tunnels was measured to determine the approximate amount and rate of influent seepage in investigations in Owens Valley, California. Tunnels were driven under Oak and Lone Pine creeks and the quantity of influent seepage dripping from the roof of the tunnels was estimated. In order to catch all vadose water from the overlying materials, the writer suggested that strips of tin be inserted at the sides of the tunnel and bent to form a drain to catch water seeping from the sides. It was decided, however, that a quantitative estimate was not needed and this refinement was not carried out.

W. N. White[1] conducted tests with watertight cylindrical lysimeters with open tops placed against the roof of short tunnels and held there tightly by jacks. Lysimeters were packed and weighed before placing in the tunnels and weighed again after six weeks with considerable rainfall. One lysimeter placed 10 ft. below the surface gained weight to indicate an addition of 4 in. of water and another placed 6 ft. below the surface gained a similar amount. This method is more satisfactory than the methods used by Taylor because it is possible by weighing to obtain the amount of moisture that has entered the vessel even though the material has not been brought up to field capacity, as it is not necessary with this method for influent seepage to pass through the lysimeter. The lysimeter may be removed at any time before the material becomes saturated and before water is lost over the sides by capillary rise. Where influent seepage is large, the lysimeter must be removed and weighed frequently. Lysimeters have been used also by soil scientists to determine soluble salts removed from the soil by drainage water.[2]

In recent years results obtained from tests with lysimeters have been critized as not representing natural conditions. Meinzer states:

Many of the lysimeter tests have been made with disturbed materials and under other artificial conditions. . . . Moreover, even if tests are

---

[1] TAYLOR, *op. cit.* pp. 210–211.

[2] LYON, T. L., and J. A. BIZZEL, Lysimeter Experiments: Records for Tanks 1 to 12 During the Years 1910–14: *Mem.* 12, *Cornell Univ. Agr. Exp. Sta.*, June, 1918.

made under natural conditions, the fundamental difficulty will still be encountered that downward percolation is irregularly distributed, and it is difficult or impossible to find a place for the test that is even approximately representative of average conditions.[1]

Water-level Measurements.—Measurement of rise in water table over a large area following rainfall might furnish valuable data regarding quantity of influent seepage reaching the water table. The total volume of material saturated by influent seepage from a storm or group of storms as indicated by rise in the water table multiplied by specific yield will give the quantity of available water added to ground water.

Effect of Pervious Cover.—If an area is mantled with pervious surface material and no running water crosses the area, the entire ground-water supply may be derived from rainfall.[2] In semiarid regions the basal sands of a sand-dune area may contain the only potable water and a large percentage of the total rainfall may be conserved in the sand.

Effect of Duration of Surface Saturation.—Materials underlying a perennial stream or lake are usually saturated and *continuously* delivering water to the water table unless the surface water body is supported by an effluent water table, or unless the materials between the stream or lake bed and water table are impervious. If, on the other hand water is delivered from rainfall or temporary streams, the period of delivery of water by influent seepage *is limited* as discussed in preceding paragraphs.

Influent Seepage from Streams

Influent seepage from stream flow is the second important source of ground water. It is fairly easy to measure except for

[1] MEINZER, *Water-Supply Paper* 638-C, *op. cit.*, pp. 102–103.

[2] An example of ground-water increment from direct rainfall is found in Long Island, New York, described by Veatch. The geologic and topographic conditions in this area are such that it may be affirmed that the underground water is derived wholly from rainfall. Geologically the island is a series of relatively porous gravel and sand strata, containing irregular and discontinuous clay masses, the whole limited below by the peneplaned surface of a mass of highly disturbed and metamorphosed Paleozoic and pre-Paleozoic rocks which form a more or less complete barrier to downward percolation. (A. C. Veatch, Fluctuations of Water Level in Wells, with special reference to Long Island, N. Y., *U.S. Geol. Surv. Water-Supply Paper* 155, pp. 9–10, 1906.)

streams subject to flood flow. Stream flow is gaged above and below the area under investigation and the difference, less evaporation loss from the stream and "bank storage" which may be returned to the stream, is influent seepage to the water table. Rates of seepage and percolation from influent streams are discussed under the subject of ground-water mounds (pages 240–245). Seepage and percolation from stream beds are controlled by hydrologic properties of materials in and underlying the stream bed and the geologic structure between the stream bed and water table.

Mokelumne River Valley.—This area affords a good example of the control of influent seepage by geologic structure underlying the area covered by high-water flow. Seepage loss from this river is less than 5 per cent of the total flow. This loss is less than the unavoidable error in ordinary stream gaging; therefore influent seepage cannot be determined in this area by measurement of stream flow. The small proportion of influent seepage to total flow indicates that the underlying geologic structure is an inefficient mechanism for delivery of influent seepage to the water table.

Figure 49 shows the present channel of the Mokelumne River (1), the bottom lands (2), and the older alluvial material (3) containing lenticular bodies of sand deposited in ancient buried stream channels (4). Wells situated on the upper mesa penetrate the gravel channels encased in older alluvium. The structure underlying the bottom lands was determined by drilling from rafts floated in the river and by boreholes drilled in the bottom lands. This exploration showed that the Mokelumne River valley, which is bounded by cliffs on either side of the bottom lands, was formerly much deeper. The old valley is floored by pervious sands and gravels (2B) upon which lie fine alluvial soils of considerable permeability near the surface but with permeability decreasing markedly with depth. The sands underlying the present river extend down to the basal sand and gravel stratum and are in contact with it throughout the length of the valley.

In order to reach aquifers supplying wells, influent seepage from the stream must move through the stream-bed gravels (1), into the basal gravel stratum (2B), and through the contact (5) between the basal gravel stratum and the old buried channels tapped by wells. This area of contact (represented by 5 in plan at elevation AB) acts as a control gate upon stream contribution to wells. High water merely increases the head on influent seepage, and spreading of flood flow over the mile-wide bottom lands does not affect the area of contact between the gravel stratum

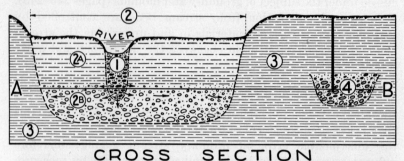

CROSS SECTION

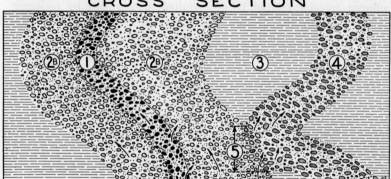

PLAN AT ELEVATION AB - CONTACT OF GRAVELS

Fig. 49.—Generalized structure of alluvial materials of Mokelumne River region. 1, gravel of present stream channel; 2A, impervious silt and clay of bottom land; 2B, sand and gravel flooring old valley excavated by Mokelumne River; 3, impervious "old alluvium;" 4, pervious gravel of old channels encased in old alluvium; 5, contact between gravel of ancient valley floor and abandoned channel. Direction of percolation shown by arrows.

at the bottom of the buried valley of the river and the ancient stream gravels in the old alluvium.

If pervious material extended without break from the bottom lands to wells, high floods would greatly increase the wetted area capable of absorbing and delivering water. In that case preventing high floods by dams would considerably decrease influent seepage. Under the control of this particular geological structure, however, controlled flow and sustained head throughout the year regulated by dams in the mountains are more effective in putting water underground than uncontrolled high floods of short duration.

It was claimed by plaintiffs in litigation that dams in the foot-hill region and in the Sierra Nevada caused increased deposition of silt in the channel of the Mokelumne River opposite wells of the plaintiffs because flood flow and consequent erosion were reduced. This view was adopted by the judge, whose ruling required certain releases of stored water which he thought necessary to clear the channel of silt. He apparently did not appreciate the force of the geological testimony of the defendants—that the river water percolates freely into the river gravels (1) and thence into the basal gravel stratum (2B), through the contact area (5) and into the old buried channels (4), from which it is drawn into wells, *regardless* of silt deposited in the lower reaches of the river. Furthermore, a deposit of silt in the neighborhood of wells would actually increase the hydraulic pressure on the "contact areas" feeding wells because the intake, the elevation of which determines the head, would be moved upstream beyond the margin of the deposit of impervious silt to the point where free contact exists between river water and pervious river gravels.

Mimbres River Seepage Losses.—White[1] found that seepage losses from the Mimbres River, New Mexico, for moderate velocities of flow were as great as 4.5 per cent of the total flow to the mile. Average figures taken during floods when water was heavily laden with sand and silt are as follows: In the first 2 miles the volume decreased to 65 per cent of its amount at the upper gaging station. In the next 10 miles it had decreased to 49 per cent (or an additional 25 per cent decrease). In the next 12 miles it decreased to 36 per cent of its original volume (another 25 per cent drop). One set of measurements made of fairly clear water showed that a discharge of 40 sec.-ft. disappeared entirely in the first 13 miles.

Seepage Reduction by Silt and Natural Precipitates.—Stream seepage may be greatly reduced by deposits of fine silt and by chemical precipitation, especially calcium carbonate and mag-

---

[1] WHITE, W. N., Preliminary Report on the Ground-water Supply of Mimbres Valley, New Mexico, *U.S. Geol. Surv. Water-Supply Paper* 637, p. 79, 1930.

nesium carbonate. For example, in the Coast ranges of California where serpentine forms the bedrock, ground water is often charged with $MgCO_3$ and in low-water periods the stream water also becomes highly mineralized with this substance, which is precipitated in the stream beds and cements stream gravels to such an extent that the cemented formation becomes impervious to water and even resists mechanical erosion.

Relative Importance of Influent Seepage from Various Sources

Neglecting possible replenishment by subsurface percolation through conduits into the water-bearing formations, influent seepage from rainfall, from streams, from irrigation ditches, and heavy surface irrigation is usually the only important source of replenishment of ground water, although leakage from reservoirs and lakes may supply small amounts.

Direct rainfall may be an important source, especially during unusually wet seasons and long continued storms in areas in which geologic and hydrologic structure favor influent seepage. Hence rainy cycles are effective periods of ground-water recharge in semiarid regions.

Influent seepage from streams is usually important, but by no means is it always the most important source of replenishment. Influent seepage from streams continues as long as flow continues if subsurface conditions are favorable. Under unfavorable geological conditions, however, the quantity of influent seepage from streams may be small and the length of channel subject to large seepage loss may be short.

In general, rainfall contributions increase in importance with increase in humidity of climate, and influent seepage from streams increases in relative importance to rainfall increment with increase in aridity.

Summary of Factors Controlling Influent Seepage

Influent seepage, from whatever source, must pass through the zone of suspended water, including the capillary fringe, unless the water table stands at the ground surface, in which case the saturated zone forms a natural barrier to influx of water from the surface.

Increment from rainfall must pass through the soil and underlying materials above the water table. Hence hydrologic characteristics of the soil and underlying material control influent seepage from rainfall.

Stream beds are usually cut below the soil zone, hence seepage rate usually depends upon the hydrologic characteristics and geologic structure of formations in place between the stream bed and the water table, and not upon those of the soil. Detailed study of the character and geologic structure of near-surface materials, especially materials underlying stream beds, is becoming an important phase of ground-water investigations.

Influent seepage in cracks and fractures and in flocculated clay soil is more erratic than seepage through granular material. Above the water table fissured rocks, especially those containing sulphide minerals, are subject to intense oxidation along the surfaces of cracks and pellicular water is used up rapidly by the chemical processes of weathering. Rewetting is necessary before seepage can take place and this may be rendered difficult owing to intense drying. Movement of gravity water on film-coated surfaces of fractures may take place if fractures are open, but tight fractures (closed or nearly closed) are more common than open fractures. Vadose water quickly fills the narrow portions, developing water-air films across the fracture above the narrow portions, enclosing ground air in the larger portions. These conditions cause extreme variability in the rate of seepage.

Dense (deflocculated) clay is practically impervious to seepage of water, but flocculated clayey soils may be appreciably permeable to gravity water.

ARTIFICIAL RECHARGE OF GROUND-WATER RESERVOIRS

Influent seepage produced artificially for the purpose of recharging ground-water reservoirs has been practiced in the United States on a steadily increasing scale since 1889, and for the purpose of water purification on a small scale in Europe. At the present time (1936) preparations are being made for several large spreading operations in California.

The term "water spreading" is applied to all operations by which water is distributed over permeable formations or supplied to temporary streams during the dry period. Recently experimental feeding of water down wells and shafts has been practiced and these operations also have been included under the term " water spreading."

History of Development.—In the United States one of the earliest spreading projects planned to increase ground-water storage was started by the Denver Water Company, Colorado, in 1889.[1] In 1906 the Irvine Ranch built spreading works on Santiago Creek, California, and shortly thereafter the first spreading grounds on the Santa Ana River were prepared.[2] In 1915 the Pomona Valley Protective Association diverted water from San Antonio Creek and spread it over 600 acres. Since that time spreading of more or less temporary character has been conducted at numerous localities in California, such as Niles cone and Santa Clara Valley, Santa Clara County, in Ventura County, and elsewhere.

Important spreading projects in operation or in preparation in California include the following:

The *Tri-County Water Conservation Association's* pioneer operations were conducted on the alluvial cones of Santa Ana River, Plunge and City creeks above the city of San Bernardino, California. Water is diverted from the above-mentioned streams in periods of clear water following flood stages, in order to avoid clogging of spreading ditches with silt. The operations, therefore, do not include salvaging of flood flow. Diversion ditches conduct water when available to a system of contour ditches well up toward the apex of the cones and leakage from these ditches feeds water into the alluvial cones and replenishes both the water table and the large San Bernardino artesian basin, which is fed by free ground water in the upper portion of the Santa Ana River cone. Five hundred second-feet are diverted by crude boulder diversion dams from the Santa Ana River and fed underground. Graphs (Fig. 50) show the relation of quantities of water fed underground to water levels in artesian and non-artesian wells. It will be noted that the effect of heavy spreading in the year 1921–1922 was not reflected in water levels in artesian wells until the latter part of the water year 1923–1924 and the year 1924–1925.

The *Santa Clara Valley Water Conservation District's* plans for conservation of flood flow and spreading include construction of

[1] MICHELSON, A. T., Underground Storage by Spreading, *Trans. Amer. Geophys. Union*, pt. II, p. 52, 1934.

[2] BOGART, E. L., Water Problems in Southern California, *Univ. Ill. Studies in Social Sci.*, vol. 19, no. 4, 1934.

five dams and other improvements designed to retard and spread
flood water over the bottom lands. All these dams were under
construction in 1936 and were finished in time to conserve

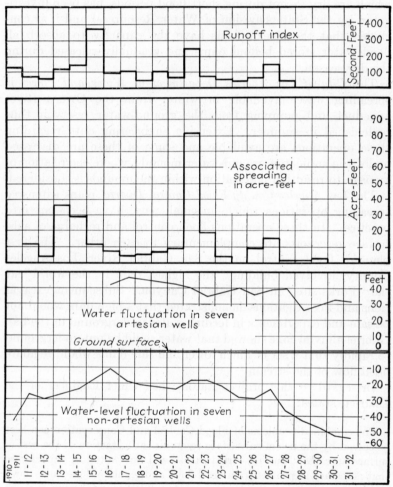

Fig. 50.—Relation of spreading and influent seepage from rainfall on water levels
in artesian and nonartesian wells. (*After G. A. Elliott.*)

the 1935–1936 water crop. This district embraces most of the
productive Santa Clara Valley, Santa Clara County, where overpumping has reduced the water level more than 100 ft. over part
of the valley. The increased pumping cost from the present

water level over that from the 1915 water level is estimated at $800,000 a year, or approximately a third the cost of construction of the project. The absorptive capacity of the stream beds, which are dry except during short flood periods, has been investigated by the State Division of Water Resources[1] and it is concluded that the stream beds have the capacity to absorb all flood water stored behind dams and gradually released during the dry season.

The *City of Los Angeles Department of Water and Power* is spreading water available in winter from the Owens River aqueduct and pumping from the ground-water reservoir thus replenished in summer. Extensive engineering data regarding these operations are available and some of these are discussed under the subject of ground-water mounds, where the relation of seepage to resulting percolation within the mounds is considered.

The *Los Angeles County Flood Control District* plans extensive spreading operations which, in small part, have been put into practice. In these operations flood control and recharge of subsurface reservoirs are complementary to each other. The first plan for flood control on the San Gabriel River, Los Angeles County, involved building "the highest dam in the world" at the "Forks site" in San Gabriel Canyon. Subsequent excavations and investigations demonstrated that a high dam would not be safe and experiments in feeding water underground in the San Gabriel alluvial cone showed that water could be put underground so rapidly that a set of much lower and safe dams would regulate flood flow of the stream.[2]

In regard to this project Eaton, then Chief Engineer of the District, states:

The combined problems of Flood Control and Conservation can best be solved by the use of subsurface reservoirs at a fraction of the cost of surface storages. Surface structures should be limited in capacity to that necessary to protect from flood flows and regulate these flows down to a rate permitting their passage into underground basins through spreading grounds and shafts.[3]

[1] *State of Calif., Div. Water Res. Bull.* 42, 1933.
[2] Los Angeles County Flood Control District, San Gabriel Project. Progress Report of Consulting Board, Oct. 27, 1931.
[3] EATON, E. C., "Los Angeles County Flood Control District Comprehensive Plan for Flood Control and Conservation," p. 3, September, 1931.

Los Angeles County's present underground storage basins number at least 26 covering an area of 700,000 acres with a storage capacity now capable of replenishment between present and 1914 water levels of 2,300,000 acre feet. This figure is 50 times the combined capacity of the District's surface reservoirs and one-third the combined surface reservoir capacity of all California's 800 surface storages.[1]

Twelve dams have been completed in this project and the large San Gabriel Dam 1 is partly constructed. Prior to construction of the San Gabriel project, only 11.5 per cent of mountain runoff was controlled by reservoirs and one per cent of valley runoff. The comprehensive plan contemplates the construction of six additional mountain reservoirs and three for control of valley runoff. These will control and conserve 44 per cent of runoff from the mountain watershed and 45 per cent from the valley watershed.

Advantages of Ground-water Storage.—Water stored underground is not subject to evaporation or surface pollution except when the reservoir is filled to within capillary reach of the ground surface. The subsurface reservoir is usually of large capacity. In place of costly dams required to hold water at the surface, smaller and safer structures may suffice to hold back flood flow until it can be put underground. Water may be stored underground for use during a series of years of subnormal rainfall. Subsurface storage is especially valuable in a region like that tributary to the City of Los Angeles, where few safe damsites for large structures are available on account of the weakness and instability of foundation conditions and the high seismicity of the region, and where the alluvial deposits are generally pervious.

The quantity of available storage room underground depends upon the volume of porous material between the "seasonal high" position of the water table for the year in which storage operations are conducted and the water table which develops an undue effluent seepage. If pumping plants are so arranged that they draw down the water table throughout the area of effluent seepage, injuries due to a high water table may be overcome and a larger available storage space maintained throughout the year and throughout a wet cycle than under natural conditions. A

[1] EATON, *op. cit.*, p. 8.

coordinated plan of water storage, therefore, involves installation and operation of pumping plants.

From the legal standpoint, land owners have cause for action if their properties are injured by a high water table due to artificial storage of ground water. It has been suggested that the water table at the end of a wet cycle of years ("cyclic high") is the upper boundary of the ground-water reservoir[1] and filling the reservoir to this level is permissible. Whether or not the "cyclic high" position of the water table will be adopted by the courts remains to be seen. One can foresee numerous lawsuits from spreading operations now contemplated in southern California, and it would be advisable to study the probable effluent seepage at various water-table stages before spreading operations are initiated.

Methods of Water Spreading

Maintaining Continuous Flow in Stream Channels.—If a stream is not perennial, flow may be maintained by releases from a detention reservoir sufficient to supply flow equal to the absorptive capacity of the stream bed. This method if available is economical because no ground need be purchased and prepared for spreading.

All spreading operations in California are conducted on alluvial cones or fans and these deposits vary greatly in permeability one from another. In most cones maximum perviousness occurs at the apex and decreases down the slope of the cone. In other cases, especially in the Los Angeles basin,[2] boulder and gravel deposits near the apex are only moderately pervious, and sandy portions some distance down slope are the most pervious deposits of the cones. In many alluvial cones the pervious portions are old stream channels buried in the body of the alluvial deposit and encased in impervious silts and clays. In such cones influent seepage is large where the surface stream channel intersects the buried aquifers and is small elsewhere.

As a result of the geologic and hydrologic structure of the cone, the pervious portion of the stream bed may be long or short, or the

[1] EATON, *op. cit.*, p. 3.
[2] ECKIS, R., South Coastal Basin Investigation: Geology and Ground Water Storage Capacity of Valley Fill, *State Div. Water Res. Bull.* 45, p. 99, 1934.

channel may be relatively impervious throughout its course. In the latter case maintenance of natural flow will not put much water underground. As a preliminary step to extensive spreading operations the Los Angeles County Flood Control District measured the absorptive capacity of all the stream beds in the county[1] in order to govern releases from dams.

Check Dams and Other Stream-bed Improvements.—Check dams have been used to retard flood flow, partially desilt water, and maintain small reservoirs back of the dams. These are usually of no value in streams subject to heavy flood flow and are of doubtful value in putting water underground unless the stream bottom is very pervious. Silt accumulation back of the dams retards influent seepage. Where broad valleys are pervious and stream flow is confined to narrow incised channels, flood flow may be spread out over the valley and influent seepage increased.

Spreading through Ditches.—The common practice in California is to carry water in ditches to prepared plots of grounds. These plots are furrowed and water is distributed as in ordinary irrigation practice and water may also be allowed to spread over the area between furrows. If the water carries sediment, both the ditch and furrow systems must be given sufficient grade to prevent deposition of sediment, which may be discharged over settling areas below the feeding grounds. Water is usually at least partly desilted in storage reservoirs and the smaller the quantity of silt in suspension, the cheaper and more satisfactory the spreading operations. Desilting tanks are planned for a portion of the water to be spread in the San Gabriel project.

Basin Method.—Areas are surrounded by retaining dikes, are either harrowed or natural vegetation is not disturbed, and a shallow sheet of water is maintained over the diked area or "basin." Experiments conducted for a period of 155 days by the Division of Irrigation of the Bureau of Agricultural Engineering showed that in areas of the same soil-type, basins with vegetation undisturbed absorbed 1.7 times more water than furrowed plots and 1.3 times more water than basins cleared of

[1] Los Angeles County Flood Control District, Report Showing Typical Percolation Measurements on Various Streams in Los Angeles County, December, 1932.

vegetation and harrowed.[1,2] The more rapid seepage in the untilled area treated by the basin method is somewhat surprising and is probably due in part to the fact that root holes furnish passageways for influent seepage.

The basin method has been used by the Department of Water and Power of the City of Los Angeles in the eastern portion of the San Fernando valley in which the alluvial deposits consist largely of coarse granitic sand and gravel. An area of 186 acres in Big Tujunga wash has been selected for this purpose and the basin method has been adopted, as it allows better control of the water as well as larger net spreading area. From studies of the first year's operations made at test basins, influent seepage varies from 3 to 10 acre-feet per acre per day. Over a period of 33 days the average seepage rate was 6 acre-feet per acre per day, and for a 53-day period, 4 acre-feet per day. A depth of water is maintained in the basins sufficient to cover the bottom. In the season 1931–1932 approximately 35 acres were under water with a mean flow of 100 cu. ft. per second. By this method of spreading a total of 120,000 acre-feet of water could be stored in four years.

In these basins as now operated repeated harrowings are necessary to break up algal deposits. Important data are being

---

[1] Azusa spreading basins:

Vegetated plot, all-time average seepage rate....... 5.55 acre-feet per day
Denuded plot, all-time average seepage rate........ 3.84 acre-feet per day

Difference in favor of vegetated plot............... 1.71 acre-feet per day

Consumptive use by vegetation during the spreading season is 0.2 acre-feet per day greater than evaporation from the denuded plot. Seepage rates on the denuded plot varied from 8 acre-feet to slightly more than 1 acre-foot per day and the rate of decrease was uniform, reaching the minimum in three to four weeks after spreading started. Removal of ½ in. of top soil reestablished the original rate. A more consistently high rate was recorded on the vegetated plot. When a ground-water mound was built up to the ground surface, percolation became a little over 3 acre-feet per acre per day. This decrease is explained by reduction in head due to the lateral component of movement generated by the ground-water mound. (D. G. Muckel, Jr., Some Factors Affecting the Rate of Percolation on Water-spreading Areas, *Conservation Activities*, Cons. Assn. Los Angeles Co., vol. 4, no. 4, pp. 8–9, April, 1936.)

[2] MICHELSON, A. T., Underground Storage by Spreading Water, *Trans. Amer. Geophys. Union*, p. 522, 1934.

obtained regarding rate of seepage to the water table, of percolation down the slope of the water table, and the effect of spreading on the water table. These will be discussed in connection with ground-water mounds (pages 240–245). Rise of the water table at the foot of an alluvial cone and resulting waterlogging of valuable land are prevented by a battery of wells below the spreading area.

In addition to spreading basins in this area, water is being fed into gravel pits located in the eastern portion of the San Fernando Valley. Rates of influent seepage in some of these pits reach as much as 24 ft. per day.[1] The results of these operations are to store Owens River aqueduct water in winter when there is excess, allow water to percolate down the water-table slope until it is brought close to the ground surface, and pump out the excess water from the areas of high water table in summer when it is needed. After two years of experimental work the final site for the spreading grounds was so located that it would take six months for water to percolate from spreading basins (intake) to the pumping plant. This is important because excess aqueduct water is available in winter and the greatest demand is in summer.

The Santa Clara Water Conservation District operates three spreading grounds near the apices of large oversteepened alluvial cones on the northern edge of the Santa Clara River valley, Ventura County, California. The following brief summary of operations from a report by Freeman[2] indicates that the valley fill at the spreading grounds is unusually pervious and operations have been successful. During the 1934–1935 season 13,000 acre-feet were spread in the 33 basins of the Saticoy unit, raising the water table from 80 ft. to 10 ft. below the surface. These basins have not been cultivated, cleaned, or subsoiled since construction in 1929 and there has been no noticeable reduction in seepage rate at the start of spreading seasons. The yearly capacity of the basins is 200 acre-feet per acre of wetted area. Hydrographs of six wells adjacent to the area are shown in Fig. 51.

The Santa Paula Creek spreading grounds consist of 97 small basins constructed in overflow channels of the creek near the apex

[1] LANE, D. A., Increasing Storage by Water Spreading, *Jour. Amer. Water Works Assn.*, vol. 26, no. 4.

[2] FREEMAN, V. M., Water Spreading as Practiced by the Santa Clara Water Conservation District, Ventura Co., Calif.; *Trans. Amer. Geophys. Union*, pp. 465–471, 1936.

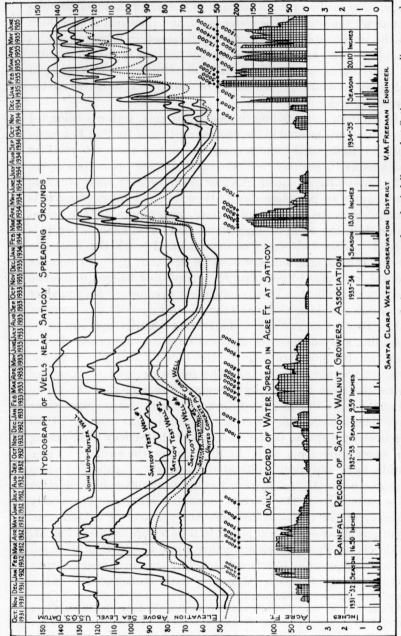

FIG. 51.—Comparison of fluctuation of water level in wells, record of water spread, and rainfall record at Saticoy spreading grounds Ventura County, California, November 1931 to July 1935. Dots below well hydrographs represent accumulated total quantity of water spread in acre-feet since beginning of season. (*After Freeman.*)

of an alluvial cone with the water table 100 ft. below the surface; in the Piru unit the water table is from 130 to 160 ft. deep. Flood water is not diverted into the basins until silt is reduced to 20 cu. ft. of suspended matter per acre-foot of water. This point is reached 2 to 10 days after peak flow. After two years the upper basins were cleaned of silt accumulation 2 to 4 in. thick.

Another method of spreading used in this area is scarifying the stream channel of the river after each flood. The estimated induced seepage was 1272 acre-feet for the period March 8 to April 11, 1933, and 1520 acre-feet from December 21, 1933 to February 22, 1934.

Feeding Water Down Shafts and Wells.—In California spreading operations have been practiced chiefly in the upper or intermediate portions of alluvial cones, which are normally more pervious than the silty or clayey downstream portions. However, some alluvial cones are of low permeability over much of their surface and, if influent seepage from streams passing over the cones is small and satisfactory spreading areas are not available, the only method of subsurface recharge is by feeding water down wells or shafts.

Pioneer attempts to feed water down wells have not been uniformly successful. Experimentation has chiefly been limited to feeding water in individual wells and hence no comprehensive data are available as yet. In one case[1] water was fed down a well which pierced a confined aquifer in an alluvial cone. Over-pumping had depleted ground-water supply so that the water level in the aquifer stood just above the bottom of the well. Feeding was not sufficient to halt depletion and in spite of added water the water level in the conduit continued to drop until it stood below the well (Fig. 52).

Experimental spreading of water was conducted in a group of wells in San Fernando Valley, California, but, after a week of feeding, absorption through the wells decreased so rapidly that the experiment was abandoned.[2] In order to put these wells in operation again as pumping plants, it was necessary to redevelop them in much the same way as a new well is brought in. An experiment in feeding water underground through wells in the

---

[1] This attempt was on the San Francisquito alluvial cone on which Stanford University and the city of Palo Alto are located.

[2] LANE, Increasing Storage by Water Spreading, *op. cit.*

Los Angeles industrial area was fairly successful, one well absorbing 47.53 acre-feet in three months.[1] Eaton reports that tests made by the Los Angeles County Flood Control District on recharging deep aquifers by shafts and wells have shown this method to be entirely feasible, provided water is desilted before charging down wells.[2]

It is, of course, essential that clear water be fed down wells, as the water-bearing materials opposite perforations in the well casing would otherwise be quickly sealed by filling of interstices

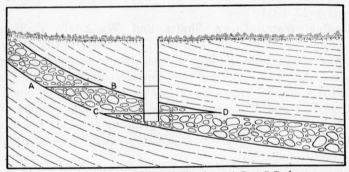

Fig. 52.—Drawdown of water level in aquifer, from *A-B* to *C-D*, due to overpumping by wells tapping the aquifer downslope from the standing well.

with suspended silt. No experiments have been made to determine whether or not algal growth might develop and hinder influent percolation from wells. In addition to sealing of water-bearing material with introduced foreign sediment, reversal of flow in the well due to water additions prevents removal of loose material surrounding the well, which would be taken out by pumping. Lane concludes that salient factors to be considered in spreading by means of wells are:

Water must be clear and free from matter that would promote growth of bacteria; the rates of percolation will be affected by the head applied above the natural water table, whether the perforations are into a dry stratum or one containing water. Frequent surging of wells by

[1] Lane, D. A., Surface Spreading Operations by Basin Method and Tests on Underground Spreading by Means of Wells, *Trans. Amer. Geophys. Union*, p. 525, 1934.

[2] Eaton, *op. cit.*, p. 9.

blowing with an air-compressor will materially increase percolation rate.[1]

Theoretically the capacity of a well to yield water should indicate roughly its capacity to absorb water. The condition of the well and the tendency of formations encountered to "run" are important factors controlling the suitability of the well for recharging purposes. If trouble was encountered during drilling in stabilizing flow of material into the well, especially quicksand, it probably is not advisable to attempt feeding operations. An "envelope well" (pages 403–406) is especially suitable for recharging.

There is no question but that an important phase of future development of water resources will be to store water underground through wells if impervious strata occur above the water table and if pervious absorptive strata occur below. Subsurface recharge of deep aquifers through wells piercing interbedded impervious strata and pervious aquifers is described on pages 169–171. The ancient Mokelumne Valley is floored with pervious river sands and gravels but is excavated in impervious formations encasing deep pervious aquifers. Deep wells connecting the upper and lower pervious deposits are continuously feeding water into the deep aquifers depleted by pumping.

Purification by Spreading

Spreading operations have been carried on in Europe for the purpose of water purification. At Frankfort, Germany, river water badly polluted by sewage and industrial waste has been put underground in order to replenish ground water depleted by pumping. In 1908 an experimental purification plant was built about 1600 ft. from the pumping station. Polluted river water was first passed through a scrubber, then through open sand filters, and to the infiltration gallery. The scrubber was later replaced by a clarifying pond and water applied to the ground in shallow ditches, the method popular in southern California. Water seeps through 43 ft. of sandy soil (in 14 days) before reaching the water table, allowing ample time for oxidation of organic impurities. Test wells located along the slope of the water table show the progress of seepage water after reaching the water table

[1] LANE, D. A., Surface Spreading Operations by Basin Method, etc., *op. cit.*, p. 526.

as indicated by chemical tests of samples (based on the higher alkalinity of river water compared with ground water). The velocity of percolation was found to be 1.6 ft. per day, the first infiltrate reaching the pumping plant in about three years. A rise in ground-water level was noticeable after the first few weeks of water application (Fig. 53).

Filtration decreased organic pollution only slightly, but percolation had an immediately noticeable effect. A marked

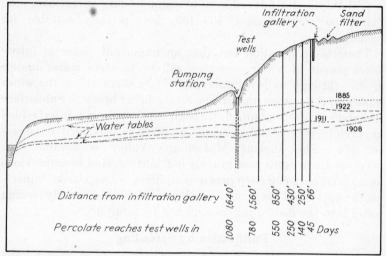

Fig. 53.—Spreading operations, for water purification at Frankfort, Germany. (*After Scheelhaase.*)

reduction in organic material in solution was noted in samples from the first test well 66 ft. from the point of application. The Federal Institute of Water Hygiene in Berlin checked the results for purity of water and stated that the percolate could not be distinguished from the best ground water at a distance of 500 ft. from infiltration point, in either taste, temperature, odor, color, or chemical composition. No operating difficulties have been experienced and the two infiltration areas have not clogged in 12 years. The water table has been raised 6.5 ft. (1924) and infiltration continued throughout the year has resulted in doubling summer pumping output.[1]

[1] SCHEELHAASE, DR., Producing Artificial Ground Water at Frankfort, Germany, *Eng. News-Record*, p. 174, July 31, 1924.

At Dresden, Germany, water spreading is also practiced for purification. Water is pumped from the Elbe River into open concrete settling basins where it remains 4 to 6 hr., resulting in deposition of 30 to 60 per cent of suspended matter. It is then run through a sand filter and then into sanded spreading basins by means of sprinklers. The pumping plant is about 120 ft. from the infiltration basins. After pumping, water is treated for lime and manganese and is then ready for use.[1]

Experiments in feeding sewage water underground have been carried on in southern California, but no data are available as yet on results of these attempts at purification.

References

Influent Seepage and Methods of Determining Amounts

BAILEY, PAUL, Engineering Investigation of Percolation from Alameda Creek and Ground-water Studies on Niles Cone, *Calif. State Water Comm. 3d Bienn. Rept.*, pp. 95–131, 1921.

BARK, D. H., Duty of Water Investigations, Experiments, and Results, *Idaho State Eng. 9th Bienn. Rept.*, pp. 302–309, 1911–1912.

———— Experiments on the Economical Use of Irrigation Water in Idaho, *U.S. Dept. Agr. Bull.* 339, pp. 37–39, 1916.

CONKLING, HAROLD, San Gabriel Investigation, *Calif. Div. Water Rights Bull.* 5, pp. 52–72, 1927.

HILL, R. A., and N. D. WHITMAN, Percolation from Surface Streams, *Trans. Amer. Geophys. Union*, pp. 477–479, 1936.

HORTON, R. E., The Role of Infiltration in the Hydrologic Cycle, *Trans. Amer. Geophys. Union*, pp. 446–460, 1933.

LEE, C. H., Water Resources of a Part of Owens Valley, Calif., *U.S. Geol. Surv. Water-Supply Paper* 294, pp. 64–85, 1912.

LYON, T. L., and J. A. BIZZELL, Lysimeter Experiments, *Cornell Univ. Agr. Exp. Sta. Mem.* 12, pp. 9–30, 1918.

MEINZER, O. E., Outline of Methods for Estimating Ground-Water Supplies, *U.S. Geol. Surv. Water-Supply Paper* 638-C, pp. 100–105, 1931.

POST, W. S., Santa Ana Investigation, Flood Control and Conservation, *Calif. State Eng. Irrig. Bull.* 19, pp. 165–179, 1929.

SMITH, G. E. P., Ground-Water Supply and Irrigation in the Rillito Valley, *Univ. Arizona Agr. Exp. Sta. Bull.* 64, pp. 118–119, 1910.

San Gabriel Investigation, Analysis and Conclusions, *Calif. State Div. Water Rights Bull.* 7, pp. 52–69, 1929.

STEARNS, ROBINSON, and TAYLOR, Geology and Water Resources of the Mokelumne Area, Calif., *U.S. Geol. Surv. Water-Supply Paper* 619, pp. 172–274, 1930.

[1] RIEDEL, C. M., River Water Used at Dresden to Increase Ground-water Supply, *Eng. News*, vol. 112, pp. 569–570, May 3, 1934.

TAYLOR, G. H., Investigations Relating to the Absorption of Precipitation and Its Penetration to the Zone of Saturation, *Amer. Geophys. Union Trans.*, pp. 206–211, 1931.

VEATCH, A. C., Fluctuations of Water Level in Wells, *U.S. Geol. Surv. Water-Supply Paper* 155, pp. 32–34, 44–49, 60–61, 1906.

Ventura County Investigation, *State Calif., Div. Water Res. Bull.* 46, pp. 82–90, 1933.

WHITE, W. N., Preliminary Report on Ground-Water Supply of Mimbres Valley, New Mexico, *U.S. Geol. Surv. Water-Supply Paper* 637-B, pp. 77–80, 1930.

Spreading Operations

BAKER and CONKLING, "Water Supply and Utilization," pp. 362–365, John Wiley & Sons, Inc., 1930.

BOGART, E. L., Water Problems in Southern California, *Univ. Ill. Studies in Social Sciences*, vol. 19, no. 4, 1934.

EATON, E. C., Los Angeles County Flood Control District Comprehensive Plan for Flood Control and Conservation, September, 1931.

FLINN, WESTON, and BOGERT, "Waterworks Handbook," pp. 74, 260–265, McGraw-Hill Book Company, Inc., New York, 1927.

FULLER, M. L., Drainage by Wells, *U.S. Geol. Surv. Water-Supply Paper* 258, pp. 6–22, 1911.

HILGARD, E. W., Subterranean Water Supply of San Bernardino Valley, *U.S. Dept. Agr. Bull.* 119, pp. 133–134, 1902.

HORTON, R. E., Drainage of Ponds into Drilled Wells, *U.S. Geol. Surv. Water-Supply Paper* 145, pp. 30–39, 1905.

KING, F. H., The Movements of Ground Water, *U.S. Geol. Surv. 19th, Ann. Rept.* pt. II, pp. 260–276, 1898.

LANE, D. A., Increasing Storage by Water Spreading, *Jour. Amer. Water Works*, vol. 26, no. 4.

——— Surface Spreading by Basin Method and Tests on Underground Spreading by Wells, *Trans. Amer. Geophys. Union*, pt. II, pp. 523–527, 1934.

LEE, C. H., Subterranean Storage of Flood Water by Artificial Methods in San Bernardino Valley, Calif., Report of Conservation Comm. of California, pp. 335–400, 1913.

MEINZER, O. E., B. C. RENICK, and KIRK BRYAN, Geology of No. 3 Reservoir Site of the Carlsbad Irrigation Project, N. Mex., with Respect to Water-tightness: *U.S. Geol. Surv. Water-Supply Paper* 580, pp. 21–25, 1927.

MITCHELSON, A. T., Storage of Water Underground by Spreading over Absorptive Areas, *State Calif., Div. Water Res. Bull.* 32, South Coastal Basin, pp. 49–56, 1930.

——— Underground Storage by Spreading Water, *Trans. Amer. Geophys. Union*, pp. 522–523, 1934.

POST, W. S., Santa Ana Investigation, *op. cit.*

RIEDEL, C. M., River Water Used at Dresden to Increase Ground-water Supply, *Eng. News-Record*, vol. 112, pp. 569–570, May 3, 1934.

SCHEELHAASE, DR., Producing Artificial Ground Water at Frankfort, Germany, *Eng. News-Record*, p. 174, July 31, 1924.

STEARNS, H. T., and W. O. CLARK, Geology and Water Resources of the Kau District, Hawaii, *U.S. Geol. Surv. Water-Supply Paper* 616, p. 21, 1930.

Symposium on Contribution to Ground Water Supplies, *Trans. Amer. Geophys. Union*, pp. 456–481, 1936.

TATE, C. E., Spreading Water for Flood Control, *Amer. Soc. Civ. Eng. Bull.*, vol 1, no. 4, pp. 76–86, 1919.

THOMPSON, D. G., Ground-water Supplies for Rice Irrigation in the Grand Prairie Region, Ark., *U.S. Dept. Int. Press Mem.* 49844, Jan. 26, 1931.

TIBBETTS, F. H., Report on Waste Water Salvage Project: Santa Clara Valley Water Cons. Distr., Oct. 2, 1931.

——— 1934 Well Replenishment Project, May 8, 1934.

VOLK, K. G., Maintenance and Operating Problems of Water Spreading-grounds, Southern California, *Trans. Amer. Geophys. Union*, pp. 527–530, 1934.

CHAPTER VIII

PERCOLATION, GROUND-WATER TURBULENT FLOW,[1] AND PERMEABILITY

By C. F. Tolman and J. F. Poland

This chapter deals chiefly with percolation, the most important type of movement of ground water, and various laboratory methods for its measurement. The development of laws expressed in mathematical equations governing the relation of rate of percolation to permeability, ground-water gradient, size of interstices, and diameter of constituent grains of water-bearing materials, and the value of these laws in ground-water investigations are discussed. Turbulent and laminar flow in pipes are considered briefly as an introduction to the discussion of similar types of subsurface movement here described as subsurface turbulent flow and percolation.

Legal Terminology.—Before presentation of the subject matter of this chapter, attention is called to the curious legal terminology in respect to ground-water "flow" and "percolation." In legal usage the term "subsurface stream flow" is applied to ground water moving in a "definite and determinable subsurface channel" with known geologic boundaries (subsurface "bed and banks"). Water moving in a definite channel of this type is classified in law books as a "subsurface stream" and the doctrine of riparian rights has been applied thereto. "Diffuse" ground-water movement, the direction and quantity of which have been supposed by legal authorities to be undeterminable, has been classified as "percolation." In other words, "subsurface stream flow" is

---

[1] Engineers use the term flow to describe all types of motion of surface water, the most common of which is turbulent flow. Ground-water flow is chiefly laminar and this type of movement is designated consistently in this text as percolation. Under unusual conditions ground water may develop turbulent flow. The general term flow as applied to ground-water movement is avoided as far as possible in this text.

limited to a definite and determinable subsurface course, and in contrast "percolating water moveth where it listeth."

It is perhaps unnecessary to state that the legal usage is not in accord with the scientific terminology. "Subsurface stream flow" takes place usually by percolation and rarely by turbulent flow, which occurs chiefly in solution conduits. If the necessary observations can be made, the quantity of water percolating and the direction of movement are as easily determinable for a general body of ground water as for ground water moving within subsurface "beds and banks."

TURBULENT AND LAMINAR FLOW

Flow of water was first observed in stream channels, in canals and ditches, and later in pipes. Casual observation showed that stream flow generates eddies and complex cross currents, and similar flow conditions were noted in pipes in which water movement is rapid. For stream flow and flow in pipes it has long been considered that velocity varies approximately as the square root of the frictional resistance expressed as loss in head or hydraulic gradient.

Flow of water in capillary tubes was first studied by Hagen[1] and Poiseuille[2] who found that in capillary tubes the relation of loss of head to flow is different from that in large pipes and that velocity varies directly with the head consumed or hydraulic gradient. Darcy[3] discovered that the same relation of velocity to head governs water movement in water-bearing sands, and this type of flow in water-bearing formations has generally been designated as percolation.

The fact that the second type of flow was first recognized as a characteristic of capillary tubes and that the openings of most granular water-conducting materials are chiefly of "capillary" size led to the tacit assumption that this type of motion is characteristic of water-bearing materials, except the rare types in which the openings are of "supercapillary" size, such as solution openings, large fractures, and possibly open conglomerate and gravel, and coarse, sorted sand.

[1] HAGEN, G., Ueber die Bewegung des Wassers in engen cylindrischen Röhren, *Poggendorff Annalen*, vol. 46, pp. 423–442, 1839.

[2] POISEUILLE, J., Recherches expérimentales sur le mouvement des liquides dans les tubes de très petit diamètre, *Mém. Savants Étrange*, vol. 9, 1846.

[3] DARCY, H., "Les fontaines publiques de la ville de Dijon," Paris, 1856.

In 1883, Osborne Reynolds[1] demonstrated that at low velocities water particles move through tubes in straight parallel lines, but with increasing velocity a rate is reached when eddies are developed. This was given visual demonstration by injecting a fine jet of dye-colored water into the center of the water stream in the tube. At low velocities the colored water passed through the

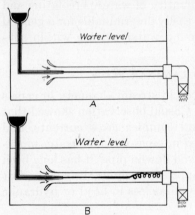

FIG. 54.—Development of eddies with increase in velocity. *A*, jet of dye-colored water passed through center of water stream as an undisturbed column at low velocity; *B*, with increase in velocity eddies develop toward end of column. (*After A. H. Gibson.*)

tube as an undisturbed column. With increase in velocity eddies developed at the far end of the tube, and as velocity was further increased, eddies filled the tube and the dye was dissipated throughout the stream (Fig. 54).

In Reynolds' experiments with increasing pipe flow the velocity at which eddying commenced is called the *higher critical velocity*. He also demonstrated that turbulent flow could be changed to laminar flow by gradually reducing the velocity. This change always occurs at a lower velocity than does the change from laminar to turbulent flow. This second critical velocity at which eddies die out is known as the *lower critical velocity*. Below the lower critical velocity the motion is always laminar and above the higher critical velocity it is always turbulent. With velocities between the two critical points the motion is unstable and may be either laminar or turbulent, depending upon the initial condition of flow (Fig. 58, page 198). Reynolds concluded from his experiments that *the critical velocity is inversely proportional to the diameter of the pipe and the temperature of the water*. Critical velocities in feet per second and in feet per day calculated at a temperature of 10°C. (50°F.) for pipes of various diameters are shown in Table 6.

The rectilinear motion at lower velocities is designated as *straight-line, streamline, laminar*, or *viscous flow*. In pipes water

[1] REYNOLDS, OSBORNE, *Trans. Royal Soc. London*, 1882–1895.

moves at low velocities in concentric cylinders with maximum velocity in the central, smallest cylinder and minimum velocity at the walls. Laminar flow in a V-shaped trough consists of V-shaped layers parallel to the sides of the trough. In slow-

TABLE 6.—CRITICAL VELOCITIES IN PIPES
[Calculated at 50°F. (10°C.)]

Pipe diameter, inches	Higher critical velocity		Lower critical velocity	
	Feet per second*	Feet per day	Feet per second*	Feet per day
½	4.37	377,568	0.70	60,480
1	2.18	188,352	0.35	30,240
2	1.09	94,176	0.17	14,688
4	0.55	47,520	0.09	7,776
6	0.36	31,104	0.06	5,184
12	0.18	15,552	0.03	2,592

* After table of Russell, p. 163.

moving stream flow sheets of water move approximately parallel to the stream bed.

Turbulent or *sinuous flow* occurs in all types of containers at higher velocities than laminar flow, and development of this type

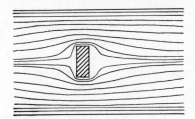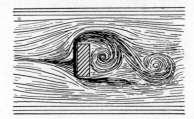

FIG. 55.—Development of turbulence with increase in velocity due to obstruction in line of flow. (*After Meinzer.*)

of flow is accelerated by roughness of sides of container or obstructions in the line of flow (Fig. 55) which develop cross currents and eddies. In pipes each particle of water has two components to its velocity, one parallel and the other normal to the pipe axis. The forward component reaches its maximum when the particle is at or near the center of the pipe and its minimum value when at the side of the pipe.[1] Frictional resistance in pipes varies with the nth power of the velocity, where n varies between 1.7 and 2, depending upon the roughness of the pipe walls.

Percolation may be considered as a type of laminar flow because no head is consumed in the development of eddies and therefore frictional resistance and velocity vary directly as head loss or hydraulic gradient. However, water motion in intricately interconnected openings of water-bearing materials is curvilinear, following the sinuosities of the pore walls. For this type of laminar flow the term percolation is applied consistently in this text.

Percolation is described by Slichter[2] as follows:

In the slow motion of a viscous liquid the bounding layer sticks fast to the walls of the vessel containing the liquid, so that motion nearly ceases in the neighborhood of the boundary. This is not the case, however, in the movements of ground waters, as the frictional resistance which the water meets is present in each individual pore between the soil particles, and is not transmitted from layer to layer through the water itself, as in the case of a viscous liquid. If the material is no finer near the impervious layer or boundary, the resistance to motion per unit length is no greater at the boundary of the region than in its interior. This uniform distribution of the resistance to motion throughout the mass of the ground water, and the separation of each individual stream in a capillary pore from every other similar stream in the neighboring pores makes the character of the motion difficult to understand.

Ground-water turbulent flow may take place under *high velocities* in large openings. Turbulent flow in large tubular openings has been called cavern flow. The flowing body of subsurface water has been designated a subsurface stream which, if above the water table, is a perched subsurface stream and if at the water table, is a water-table stream (pages 304–305). Ground-water movement in large conduits, either solution openings or fractures, below the water table is turbulent if the hydraulic gradient and outlet are large enough to produce rapid movement.

Example of Subsurface Reservoir Discharged by Turbulent Spring Flow

Fish Springs, Owens Valley, California, once flowed at the rate of 30 to 40 sec.-ft. and was an important source of water for the Los Angeles aque-

[1] RUSSELL, GEORGE E., "Text-Book on Hydraulics," 4th ed., pp. 161–162, Henry Holt and Company, 1934.

[2] SLICHTER, C. S., The Motions of Underground Waters, *U.S. Geol. Surv. Water-Supply Paper* 67, pp. 35–37, 1902.

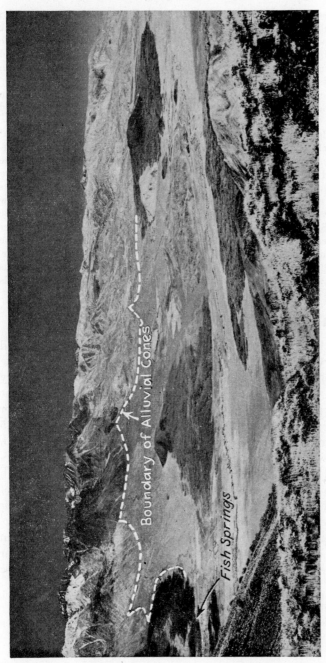

FIG. 56.—Owens Valley region south of Bishop, California, taken from the Inyo Mountains. Three lava fields are shown: Goodale Creek field on the left, at the base of which is Fish Springs; Red Mountain cone and lava field in the center; and Crater Mountain at the right. The piedmont alluvial cones covering the entire center-ground overlap the Goodale and Red Mountain flows and supply ground water to the porous lava below the water table. Owens Valley earthquake fault truncates the lower portion of the lava flows and the two cracks formed by the earthquake of 1873 are shown in the photograph cutting the lower portion of the Crater Mountain flow.

duct. A protracted period of dry years reduced the general water supply, and in a well-drilling campaign which followed, a well was put down in the lava flows north of Fish Springs. In testing the well the largest available pump was operated at full capacity and produced very little drawdown and it was thought that an "unlimited" supply of ground water had been encountered.

Thirty wells were put down at large expense and as soon as they began pumping, the water level in all the wells was lowered and Fish Springs ceased to flow.

The freedom of flow shown by the small drawdown and the horizontal surface to which all wells recovered when pumping ceased should have suggested an impounded body of water in large openings overflowing at the Springs and functioning like an underground lake. The geology of the water-bearing formations showed this to be the case. A group of lava flows containing much scoriaceous material, beds of cinders, and open "flow tunnels" or galleries formed as the flowing lava solidified extends from the foot of the Sierra Nevada nearly to the center of Owens Valley. The upper or western edge of the flows is covered in part by alluvial material from the Sierra Nevada and the lava receives an abundant supply of ground water. On the south a fault cuts the lava which abuts against relatively impervious silts and clays. The fault dams the ground water back in the open channels and caverns of the lava and the overflow spills out at Fish Springs.

Effect of Size of Opening and Velocity on Type of Flow

Under the assumption that percolation (laminar flow) is limited to capillary openings, attempts have been made to define the size limits of openings in which this type of flow occurs. Capillary openings, however, can only be properly defined as tubular openings producing capillary rise. Tubes 1 in. in diameter produce a rise of 0.054 in. and 0.1 in. in diameter, a rise of 0.545 inch (page 154). Daniell[1] defines capillary tubes as those in which flow of water follows Poiseuille's law. He states categorically that "for water (a capillary tube) is a tube under $\frac{1}{50}$th of an inch in diameter." The idea that there is a limiting size of tube which determines the type of flow is incorrect. *Laminar flow takes place in tubes of any size provided velocity is sufficiently slow.*

A criterion known as Reynolds number[2] is often used in hydraulic analysis to determine whether flow in a pipe is laminar or turbulent for any particular relationship of velocity, pipe

---

[1] DANIELL, A., "Textbook of the Principles of Physics," 3d ed., p. 316, The Macmillan Company, 1895.

[2] Reynolds number $R = Vd\rho/\mu$; where V is velocity; d, pipe diameter; ρ density; and μ, viscosity.

diameter, and density and viscosity of water. Various investigators have shown that flow of fluids in pipes is completely laminar below a Reynolds number of 2000 (log 2000 = 3.3) (Fig. 58, page 198). Turbulent flow usually occurs when R is greater than 3000. Between limiting values of 2000 and 3000 the flow may be either turbulent or laminar, depending upon the initial condition of flow. [See change in slope between log 2000 (3.3) and log 3000 (3.48).]

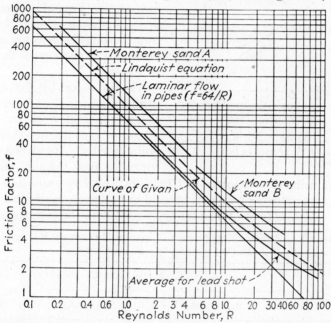

Fig. 57.—Results of experimental work on flow of water through uniform granular materials expressed by correlation of Reynolds number with friction factor. Materials tested: Lead shot, 3.05 mm., 2.54 mm., 2.03 mm., 1.52 mm., 1.27 mm., 1.00 mm.; Monterey sand, *A*, 0.63 mm. average diameter; *B*, 1.41 mm, average diameter. Turbulence causes change in slope. (*Dashed line after Hickox.*)

Reynolds number has recently been applied to determine the character of flow of water through granular material by several investigators. This method was followed by J. F. Poland who carried on experimental work with shot of various sizes and with uniform sand in order to determine the critical velocity or transition point at which turbulent flow begins to develop in granular materials. The detailed discussion of experimental results has not yet been published, but the curves plotted in Fig. 57 summarize the data.

The curve for laminar flow in pipes plots as a straight line curve on log-log paper. The three curves for flow through granular material (the Poland curves for flow through Monterey sand and lead shot, and the Givan curve for flow through lead shot) show a change in slope at a Reynolds number approximating 10.

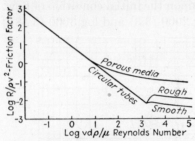

This change in slope is caused by the inception of turbulent flow at this Reynolds number. With increasing velocity, losses from turbulence become more marked and the curves flatten to the right.

A recent report by McCurdy[1] contains an excellent summary of experimental work on flow of gases and liquids through porous media. He plots a type curve for flow through porous media, using data reported by Chalmers, Taliaferro, and Rawlins[1] from experiments on flow of natural gas through sands and lead shot. McCurdy combined the type curve with the corresponding

Fig. 58.—General comparison of flow through pipes and through porous media by plotting log of Reynolds number against log of friction factor. (*After McCurdy.*)

TABLE 7.—CRITICAL VELOCITIES IN UNIFORM GRANULAR MATERIALS
(In Feet per Day* to Nearest 100)[2]

Porosity, per cent	Grain size, in mm.							
	0.1	0.2	0.5	1.0	2.0	4.0	10.0	20.0
25	130,900	65,400	26,200	13,100	6,500	3,300	1,300	700
30	101,700	50,800	20,300	10,200	5,200	2,600	1,000	500
35	81,000	40,500	16,200	8,100	4,100	2,000	800	400
40	65,400	32,700	13,100	6,500	3,300	1,600	700	300

* Calculated at 68°F. (20°C.).

curve for flow through empty tubes. The resulting figure is of such general interest that it is reproduced as Fig. 58. The change from straight line to turbulent flow in the McCurdy curve

[1] See references at end of chapter.
[2] Laboratory tests check calculated velocities for 35 per cent to 40 per cent porosity. No laboratory data are available to check calculated critical velocities for 25 to 35 per cent porosities.

(log 10 = 1) is in agreement with the experimental results plotted in Fig. 57.

The results of all experimental work discussed are in sufficient agreement to warrant adoption of a Reynolds number of 10 as indicating the inception of turbulent flow through granular materials. This number is the basis for calculating critical velocities in uniform granular materials as shown in Table 7.

If these critical velocities which indicate the inception of turbulence are compared with the average field velocities (effective velocities) in various materials, as shown in Table 8, the comparison will furnish a criterion of the type of flow to be expected at a known hydraulic gradient in any given uniform unconsolidated granular material.

TABLE 8.—AVERAGE FIELD VELOCITIES IN NATURAL GRANULAR MATERIALS
(In Feet per Day)

Type of material	Grain size, mm.	Average field velocity	
		At hydraulic gradient 1 %	100 %
Silt, fine sand, loess...........	0.005 to 0.25	0.065	6.5
Sandstone, medium sand......	0.25 to 0.5	1.16	116.0
Coarse sand, sandy gravel.....	0.5 to 2.0	6.33	633.0
Gravel.....................	2.0 to 10.0	30.00	3,000.0
Maximum velocity in gravel*..	1.85 eff. size	110.00	11,000.0

* Sample 99 of Stearns. See *Water-Supply Paper* 596-*F*, p. 165; 74 per cent of sample was larger than 5 mm.

A comparison of the two tables shows that the average field velocity in natural granular materials, with hydraulic gradient as high as 100 per cent, does not approach the critical velocity until the size of gravel is 2 to 10 mm. in diameter. In any finer granular material turbulent flow probably never occurs under natural subsurface gradients. Table 8 shows an average field velocity of 3000 feet per day for 2 to 10 mm. gravel with 100 per cent gradient. Table 7 indicates a critical velocity of 3300 feet per day for 2 mm. uniform material with 40 per cent porosity. In other words, turbulent flow is not likely to occur in materials with grain size smaller than 3 to 4 mm. even with 100 per cent hydraulic gradient.

An obvious criticism of comparing the two sets of velocities lies in the fact that the critical velocities in Table 7 are computed for uniform granular materials, while the field velocities are averaged values for nonuniform materials. Experimental work will be necessary to determine whether effective size furnishes an accurate factor for calculating critical velocities in nonuniform materials and for correlating these velocities with movement in uniform materials. However the tables should furnish a general basis for determining approximate critical velocity in sands and gravels with low uniformity coefficients. It is concluded that *at normal ground-water gradients*, which seldom exceed 1 per cent (53 ft. per mile), *turbulent flow in sand and gravels is virtually nonexistent*. The hydraulic gradient of the cone of depression of a pumping well may reach a maximum of 100 per cent, however, and turbulent flow undoubtedly occurs in many cases in the water-bearing material contiguous to the well.

Comparison of Critical Velocity in Tubes and in Granular Materials.—The calculated lower critical velocity in a tube of 1 mm. diameter is of the order of 500,000 ft. per day. Uniform granular material of 4-mm. diameter contains many channels approaching 1 mm. in average cross section.[1] Table 7 indicates a critical velocity of approximately 1600 ft. per day for uniform granular material of 4-mm. grain size with porosity of 40 per cent. This great difference in the lower critical velocity for tubes and for interconnected pore openings of the same approximate average diameter in granular material is partially explained by the physical difference in wall shape and the alternate rapid contraction and expansion of void-channel cross section in granular material which tends to induce turbulence at relatively low velocities. It has not been appreciated until recently that the change from complete laminar flow (percolation) to partial turbulence occurs at much lower velocities in granular materials than in tubes equivalent in size to the average diameter of pore ducts.

DEVELOPMENT OF DARCY'S LAW

Darcy's law governs the relation between velocity of percolation, permeability of water-bearing materials, and water-table

---

[1] For tightest packing of uniform spheres the throat cross section equals 0.15 diameter and the void cross section equals 0.41 diameter, or an average channel of 0.28 diameter of the uniform grains.

slope of free water or hydraulic gradient of confined water. It is used principally in calculating yield of water moving under a known hydraulic gradient. Various equations have been evolved in which permeability calculated from factors determined by mechanical analysis of granular materials has been substituted for the direct measurement of permeability. The development of these equations is discussed in the following pages.

The movement of fluids through capillary tubes was first investigated by Hagen[1] in 1839 and by Poiseuille[2] a few years later. The relation discovered is that rate of flow in capillary tubes varies directly as the hydraulic gradient and this has been called the Hagen-Poiseuille law. Hagen also investigated the effect of temperature on the viscosity of water. Darcy[3] conducted a series of experiments on water sands in 1856, verified this relation of velocity to gradient for water-bearing sands, and suggested the application of this relation to problems of water movement through water-bearing materials.

Darcy's conclusions are expressed in the following formula:

$$V = \frac{kh}{l} \quad \text{or} \quad V = k \sin \theta[4]$$

in which V is the velocity of moving water; h, the difference in head at the two ends of the column of material through which movement takes place; l, the length of the column; and θ, the angle of water-table slope or slope of the pressure surface of confined water; k is a constant depending upon the character of the material and must be determined experimentally for each different type of material.

Darcy did not attempt to determine and segregate the factors that control k, as did later experimenters, but used the method favored at the present time of experimental measurement of k for different types of materials. This factor measures the permeability of the water-transporting material, now generally indicated by ground-water hydrologists in the United States

[1] HAGEN, *op. cit.*

[2] POISEUILLE, *op. cit.*

[3] DARCY, *op. cit.*

[4] V in both Darcy's and Hazen's equations represents the velocity of a solid column of water of the same size as that containing the sand tested. To convert into average or effective velocity, divide by average or effective porosity (pages 215–217).

by the letter P, representing a standardized coefficient (page 208).

Between 1880 and 1892 Allen Hazen[1] made experiments on river sands and gravels at Lawrence, Massachusetts. He went farther than Darcy in that he differentiated the effect of grain size of water-bearing material on the coefficient of permeability, and took into consideration the effect of temperature on the viscosity of water. In short, he partially split k into its component parts. His experiments on homogeneous materials indicated that velocity varies as the square of the diameter of grain of the water-bearing material. Water-bearing material usually consists of grains of many sizes, but for sorted materials on which he experimented, varying in diameter from 0.1 to 3 mm., he found the "effective diameter" of grain could be used. This has been defined in two ways: (1) Effective size (diameter of grain) is the grain size of a theoretical body of homogeneous material of one grain size that would transmit water at the same rate as the material under consideration, and (2) effective size is the grain size which mechanical analysis shows to be smaller than the grain size of 90 per cent of the material under consideration and larger than the grain size of 10 per cent of the material. Although these two assumptions appear to be fairly compatible as applied to the materials Hazen used, they must not be extended to more heterogeneous material. Moreover, as the experimental determinations of the permeability coefficient of a great variety of materials are now available,[2] the Darcy equation has become far more valuable than Hazen's equation or those of Slichter, discussed below, for the calculation of velocity of percolation in any given type of material.

The apparatus used by Hazen is sketched in Fig. 59. The modern permeameters now used in American hydrologic laboratories are similar in principle and differ chiefly in refinement for ease of manipulation and accurate measurement of head and velocity of discharge. Hazen's formula reads:

$$V = C \times \frac{h}{l} \times d^2(0.70 + 0.03t)$$

[1] HAZEN, A., Some Physical Properties of Sands and Gravels, *Mass. State Board of Health*, 24*th Ann. Rept.* for 1892, 1893.

[2] STEARNS, N. D., Laboratory Tests on Physical Properties of Water-bearing Materials, *U.S. Geol. Surv. Water-Supply Paper* 596-F, pp. 160–166, 1927.

where V is velocity in meters per day in a solid column of the same area as that of the sand; C, a constant, about 1000; d, effective size in millimeters; h, head (measured in any unit); l, distance of percolation (in same unit as head); t, temperature in degrees centigrade (viscosity of water varies with temperature).

In 1899 King[1] published a review of the laboratory studies that had been made on the movement of water through permeable materials. F. H. Newell was cited as publishing the earliest experimental data (1885) on the relation of pressure to movement of fluids through rock. Newell forced water, kerosene, and crude oil through cores of Bradford sandstone. ‘The work of Graham and Meyer, who demonstrated that Darcy's law holds for gases, was also reviewed by King.

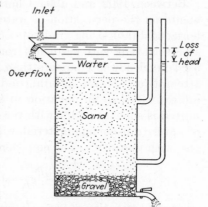

King himself experimented with the movement of water and air through various materials. He discusses evidence

Fig. 59.—Hazen's apparatus for determining laws of percolation through sand.

indicating that velocity of percolation through fractured rock or sand increases faster than the pressure difference, and suggests that the layer of stationary fluid adhering to the walls of the openings (*attached ground water*) may become thinner as pressure is increased, tending to increase slightly the effective diameter of the openings.[2]

The validity of Darcy's law at very low and very high gradients has been questioned by many investigators. Recent experimental work at the hydrologic laboratory in Washington, D. C., proves that the Darcy law holds for gradients as low as 2 or 3 in. to the mile. Experimental work has shown that Darcy's law holds for all gradients up to the critical velocity and the inception of turbulence. The critical velocity varies inversely as the grain size in uniform granular materials and roughly should vary

[1] KING, F. H., Principles and Conditions of the Movements of Ground Water, *U.S. Geol. Surv. 19th Ann. Rept.*, pt. 2, pp. 59–294, 1899.
[2] *Ibid.*, pp. 140*ff.*

inversely as the effective size in heterogeneous permeable material. In lead shot of 1.27 mm. diameter complete laminar flow is maintained until a gradient of approximately 56 per cent is applied, when minor turbulence develops.[1]   On the other hand, flow through granular material with a permeability of 243, a porosity of 42 per cent, and an effective size of 0.1 mm.[2] will follow Darcy's law to a gradient of many thousand per cent.

Between 1902 and 1904 Charles Slichter[3] conducted experiments on the percolation of water through sand and gravel in a horizontal tank using gradients of 17 to 108 ft. to the mile and in a vertical tank with gradients from 53 to 650 ft. to the mile.   He used much lower gradients than had earlier investigators in an attempt to approach natural conditions.   The results of his work are expressed in an equation in which quantity of water transmitted is shown to vary with the square of effective size of grain of water-transporting material, with the temperature of the water, and with porosity.   The equation is

$$q = 0.2012\frac{pd^2s}{\mu h K} \text{ cu. ft. per minute}[4]$$

where q is quantity of water in cubic feet per minute; p, pressure loss in feet of water; s, area of cross section in square feet; h, distance through which water moves in feet; d, effective size of grains in millimeters; μ, coefficient of viscosity; and K a constant, depending upon the porosity.

In *Water-Supply Papers* 67 and 140[5] Slichter gives tables which assist calculation of average velocity if porosity is used, or effective velocity if effective porosity is used (pages 215–217). Results obtained with these tables, however, are not in agreement with results using Darcy's law and permeability coefficients determined experimentally.   It is concluded that Slichter's equations apply only to the types of materials he studied and are not of general application to nonuniform materials.

[1] At 20°C.

[2] Sample No. 23, p. 166, *Water-Supply Paper* 596-F, *op. cit.*

[3] SLICHTER, C. S., Field Measurements of Rate of Movement of Underground Waters, *U.S. Geol. Surv. Water-Supply Paper* 140, 1905.

[4] SLICHTER, C. S., Theoretical Investigation of the Motion of Ground Water, *U.S. Geol. Surv. 19th Ann. Rept.*, pt. II, p. 301, 1899.

[5] *Water-Supply Paper* 67, *op. cit.*, pp. 24–25; *Water-Supply Paper* 140, *op. cit.*, p. 12

In general Hazen's formula seems to hold over a somewhat larger range of hydrologic conditions than Slichter's. Both the Hazen and Slichter formulas are modifications of Darcy's law. Practical tests of these formulas, however, indicate that effective size determined by mechanical analysis is not a satisfactory basis for estimates of permeability coefficient or velocity of percolation.

Terzaghi[1] developed the following formula for the permeability of sands, in which permeability is expressed as K.[2]

$$K = (800 \text{ to } 600)\frac{V_0}{V_t}\left[\frac{N - 0.13}{\sqrt[3]{1 - N}}\right]^2 d_w{}^2$$

in which d_w is effective size of grain in centimeters; N, void volume (voids divided by total volume); V_0, coefficient of viscosity at 10°C.; and V_t, coefficient of viscosity at t°C.

The basic assumption in this equation is that in the void channels the widest part of the channel is at least five times the diameter of the narrowest part. The loss in head in the latter would be 25 times that in the widest part of the channel.

Fair and Hatch[3] recently derived a formula for the calculation of permeability which is

$$K = \frac{1}{C_H t F\left[\dfrac{S}{100} \text{ sum of } \dfrac{W}{d}\right]^2}$$

where K is the coefficient of permeability; C_H, a filtration constant determined as 5/gravity; t, temperature correction taken as viscosity/density; F, porosity factor, $(1 - p)^2/p^3$, where p is porosity; S, shape factor, varying from 6 for spheres to 7.7 for angular sands; W, percentage by weight of material of a given diameter; and d, diameter (for sands it is taken as the geometric mean of the adjacent screen sizes).

In this equation, unlike previous equations, the size, proportion, and distribution of the voids are expressed in terms of

[1] TERZAGHI, C., Principles of Soil Mechanics, *Eng. News-Record*, vol. 95, p. 31, 1925.

[2] K in the following two equations is measured in different units from Meinzer's coefficient of permeability P.

[3] FAIR, G. M., and L. P. HATCH, Fundamental Factors Governing Stream-line Flow of Water through Sands, *Jour. Amer. Water Works Assn.*, vol. 25, no. 11, pp. 1551–1565, 1933.

hydraulic radius and porosity.   Fair and Hatch have found that the permeability of any assemblage of spheres of the same diameter varies directly as $p^3/(1 - p)^2$, where p is porosity.

The following table of Fraser[1] shows a comparison of experimental determination of permeability with permeability as computed by equations of Slichter, Terzaghi, and Fair and Hatch.   The first three samples are single-sized spheres and the second three are a mixture of two sphere sizes in the proportion 1:1 by volume.

TABLE 9.—PERMEABILITY OF COLUMNS OF SPHERES
(After Fraser)

Measured diameter, cm.	Computed diameter d_w, cm.	Void ratio	Experimental coefficient K	K_S Slichter	Variation from K, per cent	K_T Terzaghi	Variation from K, per cent	K_F Fair and Hatch	Ratio to K
0.31	0.324	0.4329	5.00	4.43	−11.4	5.29	+5.7	10.36	2.06:1
0.21	0.216	0.4310	2.24	1.97	−11.6	2.17	−3.2	4.32	1.92:1
0.16	0.162	0.3898	0.88	0.83	− 8.0	0.90	+2.4	1.58	1.84:1
0.31 + 0.81	0.375	0.3808	4.83	....	......	4.51	+0.5	11.65	2.60:1
0.21 + 0.81	0.346	0.3154	2.01	....	......	1.96	−2.3	3.00	1.40:1
0.16 + 0.81	0.240	0.3106	0.92	....	......	0.86	−5.4	1.73	1.88:1

Fraser,[1] commenting on values calculated by the Fair and Hatch formula, which are nearly double the experimental values, states:

Their equation . . . is based on the streamline flow, whereas it seems reasonably certain that in pores whose average cross section is as large and variable as in these columns of spheres, turbulent flow is inevitable. Consequently, it would appear that in order to satisfy the experimental data the percolation constant should be increased from 5 to about 9.7.

The above discussion of available formulas indicates no lack of reasonably accurate equations for the determination of permeability of graded, relatively uniform sands.   However, there is as yet no accurate formula for calculating permeability of nonuniform sands or gravels with a large uniformity coefficient.   The derivation of such a formula must rest on a more accurate evalua-

[1] FRASER, *op. cit.*, p. 957.

tion of the effective size and of the effect of size variation as measured by the uniformity coefficient.

LABORATORY DETERMINATION OF PERMEABILITY

In 1923, in connection with an investigation of the ground-water supplies of New Jersey, an hydrologic laboratory was established at Washington, D. C., by the United States Geological Survey, under the direction of O. E. Meinzer, in order to examine

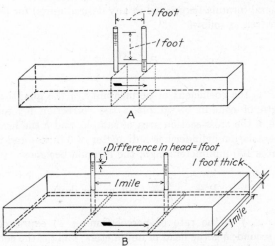

FIG. 60.—Diagrammatic representation of the coefficient of permeability. *A*, as defined for use in the laboratory; *B*, as defined in field terms. (*After Meinzer.*)

samples taken during field investigations under consistent laboratory conditions. The apparatus most frequently used in this laboratory is a modification of Hazen's permeameter (Fig. 59, page 203) allowing inflow of water at the bottom of a column of material of known height and outflow at the top (Fig. 61, page 209). Measurement by permeameter has been standardized. The methods adopted and some types of apparatus used are described by Stearns in *Water-Supply Paper* 596-*F*. This paper is probably the best laboratory guide available dealing with the experimental determination of hydrologic properties. Quoting from Stearns,[1]

The results of the test are expressed as a coefficient of permeability, which is based on Darcy's law that the rate of flow varies in direct

[1] STEARNS, *op. cit.*, pp. 148–149.

proportion as the hydraulic gradient. The coefficient of permeability of a material is the rate of flow, in gallons a day, through a square foot of its cross section, under a hydraulic gradient of 100 per cent, at a temperature of 60°F. (Fig. 60A). In field terms the coefficient of permeability may be expressed as the number of gallons of water a day, at 60°F., that is conducted laterally through each mile of the water-bearing bed under investigation (measured at right angles to the direction of percolation) for each foot of thickness of the bed and for each foot per mile of hydraulic gradient (Fig. 60B).[1]

The general formula (expressed in any desired units) for permeability may be written as follows:

$$P = \frac{qlt}{Tah}$$

in which P is the coefficient of permeability, q the quantity of water, l the length of column of sample, t the correction for temperature, T the time, a the cross-section area of sample, and h the head.

If the percolation cylinder has a diameter of 3 inches and the column of material is 100 millimeters high, the formula becomes

$$P = \frac{46.56\ tf}{h} \text{ (gallons per day)}$$

in which . . . f is the rate of percolation (q/T) expressed in milligrams per second; h is the head in millimeters; and t is the correction for temperature which gives the rate of percolation at 60°F., based on the viscosity of water as given in . . . *Water-Supply Paper* 140 (page 13).

Description of Apparatus

Constant-head Permeameter.—In the constant-head or discharging permeameter (Fig. 61) the water level in the receiving reservoir remains constant and the overflow, which is measured or weighed, represents the quantity of water that has passed through the material in any given period. The water level in the supply reservoir is raised or lowered from time to time but is maintained at a given level long enough to determine the rate of

[1] The unit of permeability adopted by petroleum engineers, but not by ground-water hydrologists, is *the darcy*, which is expressed in cu. cm. per sec. flowing through one sq. cm. of cross section with a pressure differential of one atmosphere per cm. of length. (Wyckoff, F. L., and others. Measurement of Permeability of Porous Media, *Amer. Assn. Pet. Geol. Bull.*, vol. 18, no. 2, p. 166.)

percolation under the resulting head.[1] A constant-head permeameter was used for most of the tests recorded in *Water-Supply
Paper 596-F*.   The formula

$$P = \frac{qlt}{Tah}$$

is used in solving for permeability.

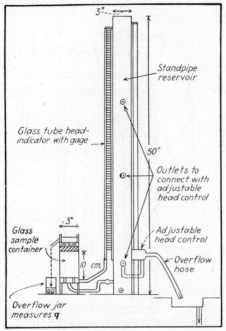

Fig. 61.—Constant-head permeameter.

Nondischarging Permeameter.—The nondischarging apparatus
(Fig. 62) is used by the Hydrologic Laboratory for tests at very
low gradients. Satisfactory results have been obtained at
gradients of two inches to the mile, equal to 0.003 per cent.   The
permeability of any material tested in this apparatus can be
computed by the formula

$$P = \left(\frac{K}{T}\right) \log_{10} \left(\frac{h_1}{h_2}\right)$$

in which K is a constant, depending upon the apparatus and the

[1] MEINZER, O. E., and V. C. FISHEL, Tests of Permeability with Low
Hydraulic Gradients, *Trans. Amer. Geophys. Union*, pt. II, p. 405, 1934.

units used.[1]   The only observations required are the changes in water level in the two reservoirs during a measured time interval. The quantity of water passing through the sample is computed from the changes in water level and the cross-sectional area of the reservoirs.   Substituting the value of the constant K for the apparatus figured, length of sample 2 meters, T expressed in minutes, with 6-in. reservoirs and 1-cm. pressure tubes, the equation becomes

$$P = \left(\frac{6{,}333{,}000}{T}\right) \log_{10}\left(\frac{h_1}{h_2}\right).$$

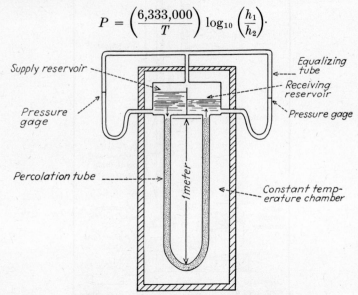

Supply reservoir

Equalizing tube

Receiving reservoir

Pressure gage

Pressure gage

Percolation tube

1 meter

Constant temperature chamber

Fig. 62.—Nondischarging permeameter.

Variable-head Permeameter.—The variable-head permeameter was developed by soil research technologists for use with materials of low permeability.   In this apparatus the feed water is contained in a standpipe of known area.   As water percolates through the sample the water level in the standpipe drops.   A single observation on the length of time required for the head to drop a certain distance is sufficient for the determination of the coefficient of permeability.[2]

[1] Fishel, V. C., Further Tests of Permeability with Low Hydraulic Gradients, *Trans. Amer. Geophys. Union*, pt. II, pp. 499–503, 1935.

[2] Gilboy, Glennon, Soil Mechanics Research, *Proc. Amer. Soc. Civ. Eng.*, vol. 98, p. 223, 1933.

A permeameter is in use at the Stanford University Hydrologic Laboratory which is a modification of the apparatus used at the Massachusetts Institute of Technology in which the water moves downward through the sample. The principal change is a reversal in the direction of movement through the sample. Figure 63 shows a section of the modified apparatus. The supply reservoir is convenient for filling the glass standpipes of small cross-sectional area.

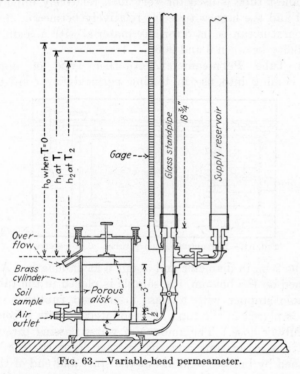

FIG. 63.—Variable-head permeameter.

The equation used is

$$K = \frac{al}{AT} \log_e \frac{h_1}{h_2}$$

If a is the cross-sectional area of the glass standpipe in square inches; l, length of sample in inches; A, area of sample in square inches; T, time of test, and h_1 and h_2, head at start and end of test, respectively, expressed in any unit; K is the result in cubic inches of water per square inch per second. If K is multiplied by

53,860, the result becomes gallons per square foot per day, or the coefficient of permeability as defined by Meinzer.

Three sizes of glass tubes are used in the Stanford University laboratory:

No. 1 small.................. 0.299 sq. cm., 0.035 sq. in.
No. 2 medium................ 0.824 sq. cm., 0.128 sq. in.
No. 3 large.................. 3.410 sq. cm., 0.529 sq. in.

The smallest tube is used for very fine, relatively impermeable material and the largest tube for relatively permeable material. The apparatus can be used for any material with a coefficient of permeability between 0 and 2000.

Glass Tube Permeameter.—Another type of apparatus rapidly coming into use in testing permeability consists of a

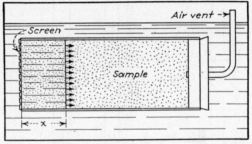

Fig. 64.—Horizontal capillary tube. (*After Gilboy.*)

glass tube 2 in. in diameter and about 6 in. in length. A screen is clamped on the bottom, the sample is placed in the tube, and a one-hole stopper with a glass insert and rubber hose connection is placed in the top. A graduated burette is connected to the rubber hose. The amount of water passing through the sample in a given time and the average head $(h_1 + h_2)/2$ are determined by burette readings at the start and end of the test, and permeability is calculated using the standard formula

$$P = \frac{qlt}{Tah} \text{ (p. 208)}$$

The apparatus is very simple, inexpensive, and convenient for rapid field tests. Several tubes can be filled and a series of tests run with rapidity.

This apparatus without burette attachment has been used to make horizontal capillarity tests. The tube is immersed in a shallow pan of water and the rate of capillary saturation of the dry pulverized soil is measured (Fig. 64). The equation used is

$$l^2 = T\sqrt{kF\frac{1 + e}{e}}$$

in which l is the length of saturated soil column in centimeters; T, time measured in minutes; k, coefficient of permeability expressed in centimeters per second; and e, the void ratio (ratio of volume of voids to volume of solid).[1] The factor F is determined experimentally. The results of experiments on many soil types give a mean value of 100,000 for F, which has proved sufficiently accurate for rapid, approximate determination of permeability.

Several types of apparatus combining consolidation and permeability tests have been developed and used in engineering investigations of damsites and foundations. Detailed discussions of these methods may be found in engineering publications.[2]

FIELD DETERMINATION OF PERMEABILITY

A field method for determining permeability was proposed by G. Thiem[3] in 1906. A detailed field test of the method was made in 1931 by L. K. Wenzel.[4] Such a test is made

by locating two observation wells within the cone of depression of a pumped well and by measuring the distance to the observation wells, the thickness of the water-bearing formation, the discharge of the pumped well, and the drawdowns in the observation wells after pumping has been carried on until the water levels in the observation wells are constant. The coefficient of permeability is then computed from Thiem's formula, which is in modified form

$$P = \frac{527.7Q' \log_{10}\left(\frac{a'}{a}\right)}{m(s - s')}$$

[1] GILBOY, *op. cit.*, p. 225; *ibid.*, vol. 57, pp. 1173–1174.

[2] PROCTER, R. R., Field and Laboratory Verification of Soil Suitability, *Eng. News-Record*, Sept. 21, 1933; CASAGRANDE, A., New Facts in Soil Mechanics from the Research Laboratory, *Eng. News-Record*, pp. 320–323, Sept. 5, 1935.

[3] THIEM, G., "Hydrologische Methoden," Leipzig, 1906.

[4] WENZEL, L. K., The Thiem Method for Determining Permeability of Water-bearing Materials, *U.S. Geol. Surv. Water-Supply Paper 679-A*, 1936.

in which . . . $Q'^* =$ rate of pumping, in gallons a minute; a and $a' =$ respective distances of the two observation wells from the pumped well, in feet; m (water-table conditions) = average thickness (at a and a') of the saturated part of the water-bearing bed in feet; m' (artesian conditions) = thickness of water-bearing bed in feet; s and $s' =$ respective drawdowns at the two observation wells, in feet.[1]

The test was made in the Platte River valley near Grand Island, Nebraska, to determine the permeability of the water-bearing sand and gravel underlying the valley. A central well was pumped continuously for 48 hr. and measurements of the discharge were made every 30 min. During the period of pumping and after pumping stopped about 5000 measurements were made of depth to water level in 80 observation wells located on lines radiating from the pumped well to distances up to 1200 ft. The average coefficient of permeability of the river deposits surrounding the central well was determined to be about 997 for the area lying more than 40 ft. and less than 200 ft. from the pumped well.

This method was developed for water-bearing formations of uniform permeability and thickness. In the Nebraska test it was applied satisfactorily to materials of varying permeability. The alluvial cones of the western states are extremely variable in permeability and the water levels in wells may register the effect of both water-table and pressure-surface conditions. The satisfactory application of Thiem's formula to this type of material is questionable. However, the heterogeneity of alluvial deposits may render this method of permeability determination more reliable than the laboratory method which is limited to one type of material in each test and results are then applied to assumed field conditions.

Field tests of permeability have been made by measuring the amount of water percolating into a pit which intersects the water table. A test of this nature was made by J. F. Poland in 1934 in connection with a study of the permeability of the foundation material of the Stevens Creek damsite in Santa Clara Valley,

---

* Q' is used in place of Q which is used in this text for rate measured in gallons per square foot per day.

[1] WENZEL, L. K., Recent Investigation of Thiem's Method for Determining Permeability of Water-bearing Materials, *Trans. Amer. Geophys. Union*, p. 313, 1932.

Santa Clara County, California.   Tests were made on a series of gravel cores carefully excavated from the foundation material (Santa Clara formation, a conglomeratic gravel).   These cores were cemented into 8-in. casings, 18 in. in length.   Those oriented with bedding parallel to the casing walls gave an average permeability coefficient of 8, and vertical cores, cutting the inclined strata at 60 deg., gave an average permeability coefficient of 0.5.   Subsequently a 26-ft. pit was dug into the conglomeratic gravels and field determinations of the permeability coefficient were made from the quantity of water entering the pit in 12-hr. periods and the cross-sectional area of the gravels exposed below the water table.   The field tests gave an average coefficient of 7, checking closely the results from the oriented cores.[1]

DETERMINATION OF AVERAGE AND EFFECTIVE VELOCITY

The rate of percolation may be expressed as either a volumetric or linear function of time.   The former is expressed in this text by Q, representing gallons per square foot per day, and the latter by V, representing velocity of percolation in feet per day.   The volumetric rate is obtained from permeability determinations and hydraulic gradient according to Darcy's law expressed as

$$Q = PS$$

where S = hydraulic gradient or slope of water table = h/l = $\sin \theta$.

Conversion of volumetric to linear rate of surface flow is simple. For example, a flow of one cubic foot per second (1 sec.-ft.) per square foot evidently equals velocity of 1 ft. per second.   Percolating water, however, occupies only the pore space in a given volume of water-bearing material; therefore to obtain the *average* velocity of percolation, the volume of water passing through a unit cross-sectional area (volumetric rate) must be divided by the porosity.   Using the units adopted,

$$V_a = \frac{Q}{7.5p^*} = \frac{PS}{7.5p}$$

where p is porosity and 7.5 converts gallons into cubic feet.

---

[1] POLAND, J. F., "Report on Permeability of Santa Clara Formation at Stevens Creek Damsite," Appendix to "Geology of the Murphy Damsite on Stevens Creek, Santa Clara Co., Calif.," by C. F. Tolman.   Unpublished private report, 1934.

* In the following formulas porosity is expressed as a decimal fraction.

V_a is average velocity calculated for all the ground water in the pores, only a portion of which is moving, and will not check with experimental measurements of actual velocity of the moving portion of ground water made by electrical conductivity and dye methods. The immovable ground water is assumed to be equal in amount to pellicular water, and percentage of pore space occupied by attached water and by moving water to volume of water-bearing material is assumed to represent, respectively, specific retention and effective porosity. The actual velocity of the moving water is herein denominated effective velocity and may be calculated from permeability measurements by the equation

$$V_e = \frac{PS}{7.5 p_e}$$

where V_e is effective velocity or actual velocity of the portion of water moving, and p_e is effective porosity. The relation of effective velocity to average velocity may be written

$$\frac{V_e}{V_a} = \frac{p}{p_e}$$

Average velocity is determined from permeability measurements or from empirical equations if porosity is used. Effective or true velocity is determined by direct measurements of velocity and by calculated values where effective porosity is used.

In ground-water investigations porosity can be used to determine the capacity of a ground-water reservoir but not its yield, for which the determination of effective porosity is necessary. The measurement of velocity or its determination from the permeability coefficient is usually made for the purpose of estimating the quantity of water (q) transmitted by a conduit. Either average or effective velocity may be used in these calculations. For average velocity the equation employed is

$$q = 7.5 V_a apT$$

where a is cross-sectional area in square feet, and T time in days; and for effective velocity

$$q = 7.5 V_e ap_e T.$$

Velocity determined by permeameter measurements furnishes accurate information if the material has not been disturbed in selection. Methods of sampling for permeameter tests are discussed by Stearns[1] and by Slater and Byers.[2] General conclusions as to ground-water velocities can be obtained only by testing samples which represent the formations carrying the ground water.

Permeability may be calculated if effective velocity, effective porosity, and hydraulic gradient are determined. Here average velocity and porosity cannot be used because there is no direct method of measuring average velocity. The equation is

$$P = \frac{7.5 V_e p_e}{S}$$

The above discussion emphasizes the importance of effective porosity, which may be determined by saturation and drainage methods either in the laboratory or in the field. The time factor in drainage experiments is important and should be given with each determination. King made tests in 1899 one of which (sand No. 20) showed an extraction of 28.26 per cent after nine days of draining and an additional 3.04 per cent after two and a half years of draining.[3] The determination of effective porosity (specific yield) should be standardized as has been the determination of the permeability coefficient.

Field Determination of Effective Velocity

Salt Method.—The earliest method used to measure the velocity of ground-water movement was that of A. Thiem[4] who was active in the development of underground water supplies for German cities in the last half of the nineteenth century. He employed two test wells placed in line with the ground-water movement, introducing ordinary salt (NaCl) in the upstream well. He collected and tested samples from the downstream well. The sample showing the highest chloride concentration was used to determine the mean velocity.

Slichter Method.—Slichter developed the method of determining the velocity and direction of ground-water movement

---

[1] STEARNS, *op. cit.*, pp. 122, 123.

[2] SLATER, C. S., and H. G. BYERS, A Laboratory Study of the Field Percolation Rates of Soils, *U. S. Dept. Agr., Tech. Bull.* 232, 1931.

[3] KING, *op. cit.*, pp. 86–91.

[4] THIEM, A., Verfahren fur Messung natürlicher Grundwassergeschwindigkeiten, *Polyt. Notizblatt*, vol. 42, 1887.

by the use of electrolytes and electrical connections between wells.[1] The conductivity of water is increased by the addition of an electrolyte. Test wells are driven in groups, each group constituting a single station for the measurement of direction and rate of percolation of ground water. If the wells are no deeper than 25 ft., the downstream wells are driven at distances of 4 ft. from the upstream or "salt well." Deeper wells should be located farther apart, but wells should be as close together as possible so as to cut down to a minimum the time required for a single measurement. An electrical connection is made with the casing of each test well by means of a drilling coupling. Each of the downstream wells contains an electrode which communicates with the surface by means of a rubber-covered copper wire, and each of these wells is connected with the upstream well in an electric circuit.

The upstream well is charged with a strong electrolyte, such as common salt or sal ammoniac, which passes downstream, rendering the moving ground water a good conductor of electricity. As the ground water moves in the direction of one of the lower wells, the electric current between that well and the upstream well gradually rises, mounting rapidly when the electrolyte begins to touch the lower well. When the electrolyte finally enters one of the lower wells, it forms a short circuit between the casing of the well and the internal electrode, causing an abrupt rise in the electric current, which is measured by an ordinary ammeter or a recording ammeter.

The time that elapses from the charging of the upper well to the arrival of the electrolyte at the lower well gives the time necessary for the ground water to percolate the distance between the two wells. The distance between the wells divided by the lapse of time gives the velocity of percolation. The electrolyte does not appear in the downstream wells abruptly, but its appearance is gradual. The time required for the electrolyte to reach its maximum strength in one of the downstream wells may vary from a few minutes in the case of high velocity to several hours in the case of low velocity. Detailed description of the installation of this apparatus appears in *Water-Supply Paper* 140.

Use of Dyes.—Dyes were first used in Europe and later in the United States for tracing the movement of ground water to

[1] SLICHTER, C. S., Field Measurement of Rate of Movement of Underground Waters, *U.S. Geol. Surv. Water-Supply Paper* 140, pp. 16–28, 1905.

determine whether the water supply receives contributions from polluted sources.[1] Uranin, which according to Meinzer[2] is the sodium salt of fluorescein and is commonly called fluorescein, has been found to be superior to other substances in tracing the flow of large or small subsurface streams through well-defined channels such as occur in limestone, as diffusion is rapid and the dye can be detected in minute quantities with the naked eye. Uranin is a reddish-orange powder which when dissolved in water appears by reflected light as bright green. With the use of the fluoroscope one part in 10 billion of water can be detected, and one part in 40 million of water can be detected with the naked eye.[3]

The use of a dye is probably the most accurate method of studying the movement of ground water through definite underground channels. Dyes have also been used with success in studying movement in gravels, but reaction with organic material reduces their applicability in many types of alluvial materials. In studying ground-water movement in alluvial deposits or in porous materials with small interstices, the electrolytic method has been found most successful.

Velocity in Various Types of Granular Material

Permeability, porosity, and effective porosity tests recorded in *Water-Supply Paper* 596-F (pages 164–169) are used in calculating the following percolation rates in unconsolidated material.

TABLE 10.—AVERAGE AND EFFECTIVE VELOCITIES IN UNCONSOLIDATED MATERIALS FOR ONE PER CENT HYDRAULIC GRADIENT

Type of material	Average velocity, feet per day*	Effective velocity, feet per day
Black gumbo to clay.............	0 to 0.001	0 to 0.004
Silt, fine sand, loess..............	0.042	0.065
Sand, sandstone to medium sand....	1.03	1.16
Medium to coarse sand, sandy gravel	6.33	Approx. 6.33
Gravel.........................	25.0	29 to 30
Coarse gravel...................	110.0	

* Calculated by C. H. Lee, private report.

[1] STILES, C. W. *et al.*, Experimental Bacterial and Chemical Pollution of Wells via Underground Water, *U.S. Pub. Health Serv., Hyg. Lab. Bull.* 147, 1927.

[2] MEINZER, O. E., Outline of Methods for Estimating Ground-water Supplies, *U.S. Geol. Surv. Water-Supply Paper* 638-C, pp. 126–131, 1932.

[3] DOLE, R. B., Use of Fluorescein in Study of Underground Waters, *U.S. Geol. Surv. Water-Supply Paper* 160, pp. 73–85, 1906.

Table 11 gives a comparison of average and effective velocities calculated from laboratory permeability experiments and from Slichter's and Hazen's formulas. The table shows discrepancies between determination based on permeability measurement and calculated from data based on mechanical analysis.

TABLE 11.—COMPARISON OF CALCULATED AND MEASURED VELOCITIES

Sample number*	Perm. coeff.	Unif. coeff.‡	Velocity in feet per day on 1% slope			
			Average velocity (using porosity)	Effective velocity (using effective porosity)	Average velocity by Hazen formula	Velocity by Slichter formula†
55	132	2.5	0.5	0.7	0.80	0.125
100	504	8.9	2.9	3.41	7.6	0.3
110	661	2.2	2.0	2.3	1.2	0.42
112	2554	3.8	11	11+	....	0.8

* Stearns' samples in *Water-Supply Paper 596-F, op. cit.*, pp. 164–168.
† For table comparing permeability computed by Slichter formula and determined by experimental methods see *Water-Supply Paper 596-F*, p. 163.
‡ See Glossary, p. 564, for definition of uniformity coefficient.

Application of Field and Laboratory Tests

Field and laboratory measurements of permeability, porosity, and velocity of percolation are usually made for the purpose of estimating ground-water supplies or available ground-water storage volume. The application of these data to field problems is fully discussed in Chap. XVI, The Ground-Water Inventory. Briefly, the evaluation of q, whether it be quantity of water available in a ground-water basin or in a conduit aquifer, usually involves the factors of permeability and velocity. If the permeability is the known factor, the formula to be applied is

$$q = \frac{PaTh}{l} \text{ (page 208)}$$

If effective velocity is the known factor, the formula is

$$q = V_e p_e 7.5 aT$$

References

BALDWIN-WISEMAN, W. R., On the Flow of Underground Water, *Proc. Inst. Civ. Eng.*, vol. 165, pt. 3, 1905–1906.

BARNES, D. P., Flow and Percolation Studies Abroad. Current Experiments at the Hydraulic Institute of Technical University of Berlin, *Civ. Eng.*, vol. 3, no. 7, pp. 389–391, 1933.

BOUYOUCOS, G. J., A New Method of Measuring the Comparative Rate of Percolation of Water in Different Soils, *Jour. Amer. Soc. Agron.*, vol. 22, pp. 438–445, 1930.

CASAGRANDE, A., New Facts in Soil Mechanics from the Research Laboratory, *Eng. News-Record*, pp. 320–323, Sept. 5, 1935.

CHALMERS, J., D. B. TALIAFERRO, and E. L. RAWLINS, Flow of Air and Gas through Porous Media, *Pet. Dev. and Tech.*, pp. 375–401, 1932.

DARCY, H., "Les fontaines publiques de la ville de Dijon," Paris, 1856.

DOLE, R. B., Use of Fluorescein in the Study of Underground Waters, *U.S. Geol. Surv. Water-Supply Paper* 160, 1906.

FAIR, G. M. and L. P. HATCH, Fundamental Factors Governing the Streamline Flow of Water through Sand, *Jour. Amer. Water Works Assn.*, vol. 25, no. 11, pp. 1551–1565, 1933.

FANCHER, G. H., and J. A. LEWIS, Flow of Simple Fluids through Porous Materials, *Ind. Eng. Chem.*, vol. 25, no. 10, pp. 1139–1147, 1933.

FISHEL, V. S., Further Tests of Permeability with Low Hydraulic Gradients, *Trans. Amer. Geophys. Union*, pt. II, pp. 499–503, 1935.

FRASER, H. J., Experimental Study of the Porosity and Permeability of Clastic Sediments, *Jour. Geol.*, vol. 43, no. 8, pp. 910–1010, 1935.

FURNAS, C. C., Flow of Gases through Beds of Broken Solids, *U.S. Dept. Commerce, Bur. Mines, Bull.* 307, 1929.

GRATON, L. C. and H. J. FRASER, Systematic Packing of Spheres with Particular Relation to Porosity and Permeability, *Jour. Geol.*, vol. 43, no. 8, pp. 785–909, 1935.

GILBOY, GLENNON, Soil Mechanics Research, *Proc. Amer. Soc. Civ. Eng.*, vol. 57, no. 8, pp. 1171–1177, 1931; vol. 98, pp. 218–308, 1933.

GIVAN, C. V., "Flow of Water through Granular Material," Unpublished Thesis, Stanford University, 1933.

HATCH, H. H., Percolation Tests for Hydraulic Fill Dams, *Amer. Soc. Civ. Eng. Proc.*, vol. 58, no. 8, pp. 1301–1342, 1932.

HAZEN, ALLEN, Some Physical Properties of Sands and Gravels with Special Reference to Their Use in Filtration, *Mass. State Board Health*, 24th *Ann. Rept.*, 1892.

HICKOX, G. H., Flow through Granular Materials, *Trans. Amer. Geophys. Union*, pt. II, pp. 567–572, 1934.

HULBURT, R., and D. FEBEN, Hydraulics of Rapid Filter Sand, *Jour. Amer. Water Works Assn.*, vol. 25, pp. 19–65, 1933.

KING, F. H., Principles and Conditions of the Movement of Ground Water, *U.S. Geol. Surv.* 19th *Ann. Rept.*, pt. 2, pp. 59–294, 1899.

McCURDY, R. C., "A Study of the Petroleum Drainage Problem," Unpublished Thesis, Stanford University, 1933.

MEINZER, O. E., Outline of Methods for Estimating Ground-Water Supplies, *U.S. Geol. Surv. Water-Supply Paper* 638-*C*, pp. 126–140, 1932.

—— and V. C. FISHEL, Tests of Permeability with Low Hydraulic Gradients, *Trans. Amer. Geophys. Union*, pt. II, pp. 405–409, 1934.

MOORE, T. V., *et al.*, The Determination of Permeability from Field Data, *Amer. Pet. Inst.*, vol. 14, no. 4, pp. 4–13, 1933.

POISEUILLE, J., Recherches expérimentales sur le mouvement des liquides dans les tubes de très petit diamètre, *Mém. Sav. Étrang.*, vol. 9, pp. 433–543, 1846.

PROCTER, R. R., Field and Laboratory Verification of Soil Suitability, *Eng. News-Record*, Sept. 21, 1933.

REYNOLDS, OSBORNE, An Experimental Investigation of the Circumstances Which Determine Whether the Motion of Water Shall be Direct or Sinuous and of the Law of Resistance in Parallel Channels, *Trans. Roy. Soc. London*, vol. *A*174, pp. 935–982, 1883; *Scientific Papers*, vol. 2; On the Equations of Motion and the Boundary Conditions for Viscous Fluids, *Brit. Assn. Adv. Sci. Repts.*, 1883; On the Dynamical Theory of an Incompressible Viscous Fluid and the Determination of the Criterion, *Trans. Roy. Soc. London*, vol. *A*186, pp. 123–164, 1896.

RUSSELL, GEORGE E., "Textbook on Hydraulics," 4th ed., pp. 149–226, 421–435, Henry Holt & Company, 1934.

SLATER, C. S., and H. G. BYERS, A Laboratory Study of the Field Percolation Rates of Soils, *U.S. Dept. Agr. Tech. Bull.* 232, 1931.

SLICHTER, C. S., Theoretical Investigation of the Motion of Ground Water, *U.S. Geol. Surv. 19th Ann. Rept.*, pt. II, pp. 295–381, 1899.

—— The Motions of Underground Water, *U.S. Geol. Surv. Water-Supply and Irrigation Paper* 67, 1902.

—— Field Measurements of the Rate of Movement of Underground Waters, *U.S. Geol. Surv. Water-Supply and Irrigation Paper* 140, 1905.

STEARNS, N. D., Laboratory Tests on Physical Properties of Water-bearing Materials, *U.S. Geol. Surv. Water-Supply Paper* 596-*F*, 1927.

STILES, C. W., *et al.*, Experimental Bacterial and Chemical Pollution of Wells via Underground Water, *U.S. Pub. Health Serv., Hyg. Lab. Bull.* 147, 1927.

THIEM, G., "Hydrologische Methoden," Leipzig, 1906.

WENZEL, L. K., Recent Investigation of Thiem's Method for Determining Permeability of Water-bearing Materials, *Trans. Amer. Geophys. Union*, pp. 313–317, 1932; *ibid.*, pp. 475–477, 1933.

—— The Thiem Method for Determining Permeability of Water-bearing Materials, *U.S. Geol. Surv. Water-Supply Paper* 679-*A*, 1936.

WYCKOFF, R. D., and others, Measurement of Permeability of Porous Media, *Amer. Assn. Pet. Geol. Bull.*, vol. 18, no. 2, pp. 161–190, February, 1934.

CHAPTER IX

THE WATER TABLE IN GRANULAR PERVIOUS MATERIAL

The occurrence and motions of ground water and the relations of the water table to ground-water movement are quite different in the three principal types of openings occurring underground. Each type of opening is limited to and characteristic of one of three important groups of geologic formations. (1) Pores are the characteristic openings of pervious granular materials, such as sedimentary and alluvial deposits. They are intricately interconnected and chiefly of capillary size. (2) Open fractures occur chiefly in dense crystalline or cemented rocks, the master fractures in which are commonly of supercapillary size fed by tributary fractures that may be in part of capillary size. (3) Large tubular or cavernous openings are characteristic of limestone and also occur in lavas subject to flowage during solidification. Höfer-Heimhalt[1] has aptly named ground water in the first type of openings "pore water," that in the second type "fissure or fault water," and water in solution openings in limestone "cavern or *Karst* water."

The water-table "laws" deduced for ground-water movements in granular materials are not of general application to water in fractures or in large tubular openings. For this reason the water table in these different types of materials is discussed separately (Chaps. IX and X) and conclusions reached with reference to one type of aquifers should not be assumed to apply to the other types.

In granular pervious material the water table separates capillary water from free ground water. In capillary openings the water

---

[1] Höfer-Heimhalt, Hans, "Grundwasser und Quellen," pp. 115–121, Friedr. Vieweg & Sohn, Braunschweig, Germany, 1920.

[2] Confined water has no water table. It may be connected with a body of free ground water at the intake area which, of course, has a water table (Fig. 11, p. 55). Höfer-Heimhalt defines ground water as "bodies of water moving in unconsolidated rocks, generally sands or gravels, with a continuous, nearly horizontal upper surface (water table) down which the water

223

table is not a physical surface because capillary water completely saturates the material just above the water table. The water table in granular pervious material may be defined as a precise surface which is located by the position of the water level in supercapillary openings.

In granular impervious material the openings are of subcapillary size. Such material functions as an aquiclude and contains no free ground water and no water table. If the aquiclude extends up into the zone of aeration, the water content is reduced by evaporation and transpiration and a gradual transition from saturated to partly saturated material occurs but no water table is developed.

In fractures and solution cavities the openings are predominantly supercapillary in size and the water table is commonly a physical surface which forms the boundary between free ground water and ground air.

The term water table is limited to the upper surface of the main body of ground water. Bodies of ground water held above the main zone of saturation by impervious material are designated perched ground water and their upper surfaces are perched water tables (page 42).

Interpretation of Water Level in Shallow Wells and Boreholes.—In practice the water table is located by measuring the depth to water in shallow boreholes or in wells drawing on free ground water. Test holes are, of course, of supercapillary size

---

moves under gravity. Not to be confused with ground water is pressure water, moving in confined aquifers under hydraulic or artesian pressure. Ground water does not move under pressure. . . . The ground-water mantle is that rock material (gravel, sand, etc.) which separates ground water from surface water. It is the zone of infiltering water. Moisture and air, called ground air, fill the pores of the unconsolidated ground-water mantle." (Translation from Höfer-Heimhalt, H., "Grundwasser und Quellen," Friedr. Vieweg & Sohn, 1920.)

[1] Meinzer states, "My concept of the water table is that it is a precise surface that is the locus of the static head of the unconfined water at the top of the zone of saturation—not essentially a physical water surface." (Personal communication.) This concept is open to the criticism that in pervious granular material the water table is not at the top of the body of saturated material.

and the water level in them registers the contact between the free water body and the capillary fringe, in other words, the water table.   Water is delivered to boreholes or water-table wells[1] only by material sufficiently pervious to permit percolation. However, very fine material may permit exceedingly slow percolation, and it may take hours or even days for the water to rise in boreholes to the water table.   In material gradational between aquifer and aquiclude it may be difficult to locate a water table.

Pervious deposits are rarely continuous but may be irregularly distributed in impervious or less pervious material, and near the surface the pervious bodies are commonly interconnected.   If the impervious formation occurs in the water-table horizon, the water table is, of course, discontinuous, as no water table can exist in impervious material.   However, if test holes are drilled through the impervious material and pierce underlying pervious deposits, water will rise in the holes to the water level in the interconnected pervious material.   Because of this, the fact is often overlooked that the water table is limited to pervious material and is a discontinuous surface interrupted by all bodies of impervious material which occur in the water-table horizon.

Water-bearing materials are rarely homogeneous, but usually occur in layers of varying permeability.   If the dip of these strata or laminae is in the direction of the water-table slope, slight artesian pressure may be developed in pervious layers.   However, such pressure effects are usually very small for layers a few feet below the water table and are therefore neglected.   For this reason boreholes used in making water-table maps should not penetrate saturated material more than a few feet, and if the test hole is deeper, the level to which water rises as the hole pierces different types of material should be noted.

---

[1] The fact has been mentioned (p. 56) that the standing level in a well may register (1) the water table; (2) the pressure surface of a body of confined water; or (3) if there are several horizons of confined water, the highest pressure surface modified by leakage into aquifers holding water under less pressure.   The condition of the casing, horizons of perforations, and other factors therefore must be taken into consideration in interpreting the meaning of the water level in a well.   In a gravel-envelope well (pp. 403–406) there is free interaction of all bodies of confined water and free water.   If the confined water has positive (artesian) head, it will feed the water table when the well is not pumping.   When pumping the well will draw on free water and all bodies of confined water intersected by it.

Importance of Water Table.—The fundamental importance of the water table in ground-water investigations may be brought out by the following brief and categorical summary. The explanation of statements herein will appear with further development of the subject.

1. The water table is the boundary between the saturated zone and the zone of suspended water. It records the level to which the subsurface reservoir is filled, the quantity of ground water in storage, and the depth to the water supply in any particular area. From its fluctuations, additions to and subtractions from ground-water storage may be calculated if the specific yield of the formations saturated or dewatered by the change in level is known.

2. The water table separates two regions where the forces acting and the resulting motions of subsurface water are different. Above the water table molecular, colloidal, and film forces are important and the interaction of these forces and the force of gravity produce the complex motions herein denominated seepage and capillary rise. Below the water table the force of gravity is not appreciably affected by other forces, except locally where heat is important, and the resulting movement is usually percolation but occasionally ground-water turbulent flow.

3. The slope or profile of the water table is a graphic representation of the rate of percolation and permeability of water-bearing materials. *The slope varies directly as the velocity and inversely as the permeability.* This is the fundamental law governing the interpretation of water-table slopes. Ground-water movement is always in the downslope direction of the water table and if permeability is constant the fastest motion and largest quantity of water moving are in the direction of maximum slope.

4. The water-table outcrop delimits the surface areas subject to influent and effluent seepage. Influent seepage occurs where the water table is below ground surface and stream influent seepage takes place where the water table is below the level of stream beds. Effluent seepage starts at the intersection of the water table with the ground surface and continues throughout the area in which the water table is at the surface.

5. The outcrop of the water table is marked by the uppermost appearance of effluent seepage, the surface indications of which are springs, the upper limit of permanently moistened areas, occasionally of swamps, and the change in vegetation from non-

phreatophytes to phreatophytes.[1] In an area cut by stream erosion the water table first outcrops where the stream intersects the water table and at that point the stream changes from influent to effluent. The outcrop normally continues downstream near or at the margins of the lowlands bordering the stream and may include large areas of bottom lands. In an undrained desert valley the water-table outcrop delimits the central evaporation and swamp area from the dry desert slopes above. If gullies reach the evaporation area, the water-table outcrop may extend some distance up the gullies.

6. Topography is important in controlling the depth of the water table below the surface, as well as its shape. Under the ground surface the water table is a "subdued replica" of surface topography. A flat area, undissected by streams and without a low point of ground-water discharge, will be saturated to the surface if evaporation and transpiration are not capable of discharging all effluent seepage. A deeply dissected region usually has a deep water table.[2]

7. From the purely geological viewpoint the water table separates the belt of weathering, oxidation, rock decomposition and solution, from the underlying belt of mineral precipitation and rock cementation.[3]

8. Contour maps of the water table are graphic representations of the hydraulic slopes of the water table and are the basis for studies of the direction and rate of motion of free water, of drainage of ground water by pumping or drainage ditches and natural streams, and recharge of ground water from all sources, and indicate changes in velocity of percolation or permeability of formations or both.

PRINCIPLES GOVERNING INTERPRETATION OF WATER-TABLE GRADIENTS

The fundamental law governing the interpretation of water-table slopes is Darcy's law.[4] Using Meinzer's permeability

[1] MEINZER, O. E., Plants as Indicators of Ground Water; *U.S. Geol. Surv. Water-Supply Paper* 577, p. 1, 1927; *Water-Supply Paper* 489, pp. 95–96.

[2] VAN HISE, C. R., Treatise on Metamorphism, *U.S. Geol. Surv. Mono.* 47, pp. 410–411, 1904.

[3] *Ibid.*, p. 562.

[4] DARCY, H., "Les fontaines publiques de la Ville de Dijon," Paris, 1856.

coefficient[1] this may be written

$$S = \frac{Q}{P}$$

where S = water-table slope expressed as h/l or sine θ;
h = difference in elevation of water table at two selected points, and
l = slope distance between two points.
Angle θ = angle of slope measured from a horizontal line.
Q = volumetric rate of percolation measured in gallons per day through one square foot.
P = permeability coefficient as defined by Meinzer.

The rate of percolation may also be expressed as linear velocity in the equations

$$S = \frac{V_a 7.5p}{P} \quad \text{and} \quad S = \frac{V_e 7.5 p_e}{P}$$

where V_a is average velocity; V_e, effective velocity measured in feet per day; the factor 7.5 converts gallons into cubic feet; p, porosity expressed as a decimal fraction; and p_e, effective porosity similarly expressed (pages 215–217).

These equations show that the water-table slope varies directly as the rate of percolation, expressed either volumetrically or as linear velocity, and inversely as the permeability of the water-conducting material. It does not vary directly as the quantity of water moving under water-table conditions, because $q = Qa$ (a = cross-sectional area) and the fundamental equation

$$S = \frac{Q}{P} \text{ becomes } S = \frac{q}{aP}$$

Unfortunately the cross-sectional area of moving ground water is usually unknown or only approximately known, and also changes with each fluctuation in water table. Hence the water-table slope does not vary directly with total quantity of water moving but does indicate accurately volumetric and linear velocity. Large changes in water-table slope are caused by over-pumping and by water spreading, and these result in large changes in cross-sectional area of water-conducting material. Under conduit conditions, however, where cross-sectional area

[1] STEARNS, N. D., Laboratory Tests on Physical Properties of Water-Bearing Materials, *U. S. Geol. Surv. Water-Supply Paper* 596-F, p. 148, 1927. See also pp. 207–208 of this text.

is constant, the hydraulic gradient varies directly as *both Q* and
q.

Water-table profiles at right angles to water-table contours
and hence in the direction of ground-water percolation represent
conditions underneath the line of profile at a particular time
and picture a change in permeability for every change in slope,
provided the cross-sectional area carrying the water is constant and there are no additions to or subtractions from ground
water. If the volumetric rate of percolation or the linear rate
and the effective porosity can be determined by any of the
various methods available (pages 207–220) at any one point on the
profile, the permeability of the materials along the entire line of
profile can be calculated. Calculations of permeability, however,
can rarely be made for the entire profile because changes generally
occur in cross-sectional area and quantity of water moving. The
cross-sectional area at right angles to the direction of percolation
increases down the slope of an alluvial cone and with rise of
water table. Also quantity of ground water added by influent
seepage increases downslope to the boundary of the influent water
table. Due allowance must be made for these variations in
interpreting the water-table profile.

Development of Water-table Profiles

Influent seepage moves straight down until a barrier is encountered. This barrier in most cases is the water table and the water

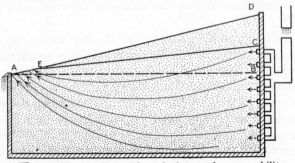

Fig. 65.—Water-table profile with velocity and permeability constant.
AB, horizontal line from lowest point of discharge; *AD*, surface of sand; *AEC*,
water-table profile; *AE*, effluent water table; *EC*, influent water table.

added by seepage modifies the pre-existing water-table slope.
In order to illustrate the development of slopes, beginning with a

theoretical static water body with horizontal water table, a box with glass sides and with left end lower than the right end may be filled with well-sorted sand to the height of the two ends, sloping evenly from the higher to lower end. The even assortment avoids water-table-slope changes due to variations in permeability. If water is introduced through holes in the upper end of the box, the profile will be a straight line and the angle of slope is determined by the ratio Q/P, where both factors are constant (Fig. 65).

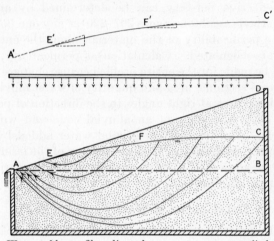

Fig. 66.—Water-table profile adjusted to move water supplied by influent seepage. $A'E'F'C'$ slope required by increasing water supply; AD, surface of sand in box; AE, discharge area; $AEFC$, adjusted water-table profile; AB, discharge level.

If water is sprinkled evenly over the surface of the sand, Q and V increase from zero at the upper end to a maximum at the lower end of the box. The water moves down slowly through the sand, filling the box and developing a horizontal water table as the water rises to the elevation AB of the lower end. When water overtops the lower end, water escapes at this lowest level of discharge, and continued sprinkling develops the water-table slope necessary to move the water supplied by influent seepage. The general character of the curve is shown in Fig. 66. The slope at the lowest discharge point A would be just twice that at the center of the box if all the water could be discharged at the lip of the box. However, an area of discharge is developed above the lip, represented in the figure by AE, capable of discharging all ground water in motion and the slope at E or E' is twice that at F', midway between E' and C'. Within the area of effluent seepage (AE) the ground-water profile is coincident with ground surface and, as discussed below, a water-table profile steeper than ground surface cannot be developed.

If the homogeneous sand is removed and the box is filled with sand the grain size of which decreases toward the discharge end, the experiment will represent the usual effect on water-table slope of decreasing permeability down the slope of an alluvial cone. If water is introduced through perforations in the end of the box (Q and V constant), a profile with increasing slope toward the discharge area is developed similar to that shown in Fig. 66. However, the effect of decreasing permeability on water-table slope is generally more pronounced than that due to additions supplied by influent seepage. In alluvial deposits seepage increment is normally supplied down to the point of effluent seepage and permeability decreases in the same direction, so the actual profile to the right of E and E' usually registers the cumulative effect of these two factors. This combined effect may be reduced by the increase of cross-sectional area toward the periphery of an alluvial cone.

The important conclusion derived from the foregoing simple analysis is that water-table fluctuations and the development of water-table profiles take place through the volume of material above a horizontal plane passing through the lowest level of discharge (AB, Figs. 65–67). The motions of ground water, however, are not limited to this volume but, according to Slichter,[1] extend throughout the total volume of pervious material. Slichter's lines of flow (percolation) to the discharge area are shown in Figs. 65 to 67. Above the lowest point of discharge a zone of effluent seepage develops sufficient in size to discharge the ground water in motion. Above the zone of effluent seepage the water-table slopes are developed directly as the rate of percolation and inversely as the permeability of the water-bearing material.

Effect of Surface Topography.—In the discussion so far uniform surface slope steeper than the water-table gradient has been postulated. The slope of alluvial deposits usually decreases

---

[1] SLICHTER, C. S., The Motions of Underground Waters, *U.S. Geol. Surv. Water-Supply and Irrigation Paper* 67, p, 37, 1902.

from the upper edge to the lower margin of an alluvial cone.   To
illustrate these conditions the sand in the box is given a similar
slope, flattening toward the outlet (Fig. 67). $A'E'D'$ represents
the normal profile of the water table due to decreasing permeability and to increasing influent seepage from rainfall or stream
flow downslope of the alluvial deposit.[1]   The lowest portion of
the water-table profile cannot be developed at the discharge point
A, or at any point above A where the water-table slope is steeper

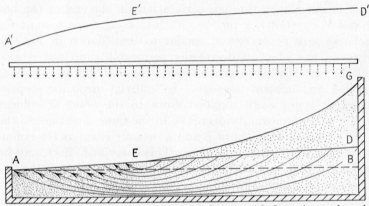

Fig. 67.—Water-table profile in alluvial deposit with flattening surface slope
and decreasing permeability in downslope direction. $A'E'D'$, water-table slope
required by hydrologic properties; AEG, ground surface; AED, adjusted water-
table profile; AE, effluent water table; ED, influent water table.   Surface and
water-table slopes are equal at E.

than the surface slope.   The point where the surface slope equals
the water-table slope marks the change from influent to effluent
seepage and the outcrop of the water table.   Above this point
the water-table profile is developed according to the equation
$S = Q/P$.

The above discussion applies only to a surface slope decreasing
to a flat area, best represented by bolsons and playas of the semi-

[1] In Fig. 67 $A'E'$ (the portion of the required profile underneath the zone
of effluent seepage) is entirely theoretical.   Effluent seepage is decreasing
the quantity of water moving downslope from the point of water-table
outcrop.   Decrease in permeability is increasing the water-table slope in the
same direction.   The relation of the two is unknown.   All that is known
is that the *required slope* is equal to or greater than the ground-surface slope
within the area of effluent seepage.

arid western United States[1] and undissected lower margins of
alluvial cones. If the water table discharges at or near a steep
slope cut in alluvial material, such as a cliff or steep bank of a
stream intersecting the lower portion of an alluvial cone, the
water-table slope may be steeper than the surface slope back of
the cliff and a double discharge area may develop as shown in
Fig. 68.

Curve 1 is the adjusted gradient for more permeable material
and less decrease in permeability to the left than is assumed for

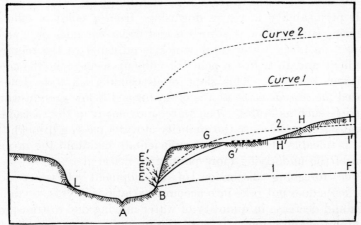

Fig. 68.—Water-table profiles adjusted to discharge on steep slope.

curve 2. Curve 1 is plotted starting at *B*, sufficiently above
A so that *AB* can discharge all effluent seepage, and takes the
position *BF*. It does not intersect ground surface above cliff,
although the slope approaching the discharge point *B* is steeper
than the overlying surface slope.

Curve 2 plotted as *E'GHI*, starting from a higher discharge
point because of assumed lower permeability, cannot be developed
under the topographic conditions shown in the profile. *HI*
assumes position *H'I'*, *H'* being the point where surface and
water-table slopes are equal. Transpiration and evaporation
discharge a portion of the water and *E"G'* is developed, flatter
than *E'G* and with lower discharge because of diminished water
supply. Hanging swamps occurring some distance above a

[1] TOLMAN, C. F., Erosion and Deposition in the Southern Arizona Bolson
Region, *Jour. Geology*, vol. 17, pp. 136–163, 1909.

valley cut in the toe of an alluvial cone are common in western United States.

The water-table slopes discussed so far are the gradients adjusted to carry the quantity of water moving. Every change in water supply requires readjustment of water-table slope. This readjustment of gradient advances far more rapidly than the rate of percolation. Experimental work has shown gradient readjustments 100 times as fast as rate of percolation.[1] The rate of advance of gradient readjustment has been erroneously assumed to represent the rate of percolation (page 241).

If permeability increases downslope from a point of effluent seepage, surface flow is absorbed and water cascades on a steep slope to a lower water table which is adjusted to the required gradient and to a lower point of effluent seepage in the more pervious material. This slope of descending water is denominated *the cascade slope* and is often formed below ground-water barriers such as faults. The water movement in the cascade is usually *seepage* because the quantity of water passing through the less permeable material is not sufficient to maintain the saturation of the underlying more permeable material.

The foregoing discussion of development of water-table gradients does not take into account variations in cross-sectional area and decrease in quantity of water moving due to transpiration and evaporation. Toward the foot of the average alluvial cone gradients are reduced by both these factors. There is no possibility of developing the steep gradient usually required by the low permeability of the distal portions of the cone except when the cone is truncated by a steep slope or cliff, as discussed above. Whenever the required water-table slope is steeper than the topographic slope, ground water piles up above the lowest discharge level in the attempt to reach the required equilibrium slope and the water is discharged by evaporation, transpiration, and effluent seepage.

Effect of varying permeability of formations on the water-table slope and resultant water-table profile may assist in working out geologic structure as illustrated in Fig. 69. The formations shown are coarse gravel overlying less pervious sandstone. Ground-water supply is assumed to be constant and supplied

[1] Experiments performed in the Stanford Hydrologic Laboratory.

from the area to the right of the section. The water-table slopes capable of moving water through the coarse and fine formations are indicated at the top of the figure. The faults are filled with impervious gouge.[1] The water-table profile in equilibrium with the assumed conditions is *ABCDEFGH*. *C*, *E*, and *G* are points of effluent seepage above the fault outcrops. *CB*, *ED*, and *GF* are ground-water cascades. If the geology is

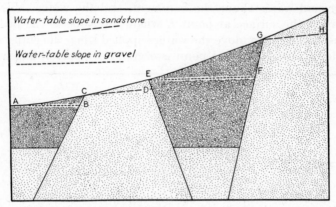

Fig. 69.—Water-table slopes in formations of varying permeability. Faults filled with impervious gouge hold the water table at the surface.

hidden by a superficial deposit, the working out of the geologic structure would be aided by a contour map of the water table, and the faults, if impervious and therefore acting as barriers, would be indicated by closely spaced contours of the ground-water cascades below them and by effluent seepage above them.

Effect of Impervious Basement.—In the preceding discussions pervious material is assumed to be thick and the impervious basement formation at too great a depth to affect appreciably water-table slopes. In thin pervious deposits overlying an impervious basement the configuration and slope of the basement are important controls over water-table slope and movement of ground water. Usually percolation is concentrated in channels cut in the bedrock by stream action and filled with pervious material. However, the surface of the bedrock may be irregular and depressions may be filled with ground-water lakes with

[1] A fault may constitute an impervious member or may be a plane of great perviousness.

subsurface discharge at low points, or an even, thin veneer might conceivably overlie a fairly even basement.

Assume a constant cross section of pervious material deposited in a channel cut in an impervious basement, and assume further that the bedrock slope decreases to the left in the direction of stream flow (Fig. 70). Both the velocity of percolation and the water-table slope are functions of bedrock slope and depth of ground water above the basement, and the water table will intersect the surface at point E where the slope of the bedrock is just sufficient to move the water supplied when the entire cross section of the fill at that point is occupied by percolating water.

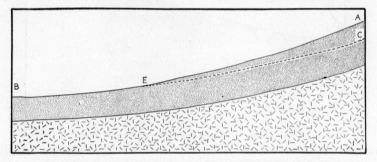

Fig. 70.—Water-table slope developed in thin pervious deposit over impervious basement. EC, water-table slope; E, point of discharge.

With increase in bedrock slope (to the right of point of effluent seepage) the depth to which the pervious formation is filled decreases. The water-table slope is represented by EC.[1]

If the cross-sectional area is variable, as is common in stream channels excavated in impervious material and filled with pervious stream deposits, the narrow portions of the channel (smallest cross-sectional area) have the smallest capacity to transmit water. Hence rising ground water may be forced to the surface at or above the narrow portions of the alluvium-filled excavation, and if the stream bed is dry, running water starts at this point and may be reabsorbed farther down stream if the cross-

[1] The prevailing near-surface position of the water table and relatively thin deposits of alluvial and glacial materials on impervious bedrock in Germany make it difficult for German authorities to think of ground water without reference to the underlying basement. The impermeable substratum is conspicuously present in their discussions and in their illustrative diagrams.

sectional area of the water-bearing material increases.   A surface
stream may be effluent at and a short distance above a narrow
point in the excavated valley and influent below the narrow
portion.   A rise in the bedrock or a fault later than the ancient
bedrock channel by which the downstream section of the channel
is lifted above the upstream portion will also cause a decrease in
cross-sectional area of the stream gravels with rising ground water

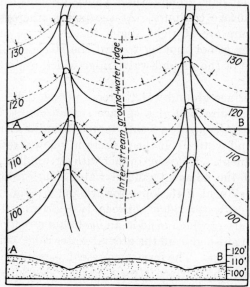

Fig. 71.—Inter-stream ground-water ridge developed between two effluent
surface streams, each maintaining a ground-water trench.   Dashed lines are
water-table contours; solid lines, surface contours.

and effluent seepage.   A fault with reverse movement will drop
the water table in the stream gravels.

Conditions similar to those above described are common in
semiarid regions where the channel cut in bedrock is filled with
gravels.   Springs and desert waterholes occur above narrow portions of the bedrock channels, especially above "dikes" of hard
rock.   Effluent conditions in such streams may indicate covered
faults or dikes.

Ground-water Trench.—A stream gully or valley or a drainage
ditch cut below the general level of ground water will produce a
trench in the water table, which apexes under the stream bed or
drainage ditch but is flatter in cross section than the stream cut or

ditch. Such a stream is effluent and is also called a "making stream." The surface and water-table contours of an effluent stream are shown in Fig. 71.

Ground water percolates in the direction of the steepest water-table slope, or at right angles to the contours. The area within which ground water is moving toward the stream is indicated by the bend in contours in an upstream direction, which also indicates a shallow ground-water valley underneath the valley shown by surface contours. At the points where the ground-water contours are at right angles to the course of the gully, ground water is not moving toward the stream but down the general slope of the ground-water ridge which underlies the surface ridge.

The subsurface ground-water stream percolating beneath and in the general direction of a surface stream course or valley is called a *thalweg* (trough), a term adopted from the German literature on ground water.[1] If the thalweg is below stream flow, the stream is influent. If it is in contact with stream flow, the stream is influent if the adjacent ground water slopes away from the stream and effluent if it slopes toward the stream. The inter-stream ground-water ridge between two streams, the ground-water contours of which bend in an upstream direction (Fig. 71), is to be distinguished from the ground-water ridge built up under an influent stream. The former represents percolation of ground water toward the surface streams which develops a residual ground-water ridge between the two streams. The latter represents additions to ground water from influent stream seepage which builds up a ridge *under the stream*.

Drainage ditches have steep ground-water trenches if they are dug to drain bottom lands or swamp lands which are underlain by fine material. Swamps are usually formed at and below the intersection of the water table with the surface. The line of intersection may be marked by springs (*spring line*), and a swamp

[1] Slichter states that the German term *Thalweg* refers to the drainage line of a valley. Beneath the thalweg there is a *subsurface thalweg* or drainage line for the underground current, in general, coincident in course with the surface thalweg. (*Water-Supply Paper* 67, pp. 32–33, 1902.) The term thalweg is of no value as an equivalent of the English words valley, water course, and stream channel, but is now adopted by general usage for the subsurface "stream" or ground-water current percolating underneath and in the general direction of the stream course or valley.

is maintained down the slope from the springs by the flow of surface water and effluent seepage of ground water. To drain a
swamp a ditch should be placed just below the spring line. The
ditch will then cut off the surface and subsurface movement of
water which is keeping the land below the spring line saturated
(Fig. 72).

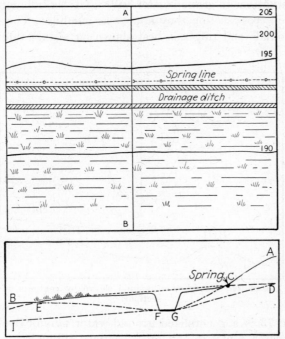

Fig. 72.—Adjustment of water-table slope and development of ground-water
trench by drainage ditch. *EC*, effluent water table before drainage; *EFGC*,
ground-water trench; *IFGD*, final adjustment of water-table profile.

The upper slope *GC* of the ground-water trench developed by
the drainage ditch will be steep at first because both stored and
moving water will be drained, but will decrease in slope as stored
water is removed and will finally assume some such position as
GD, which is steeper than the original slope *CD* before the ditch
was dug, because the discharge point has been lowered and the
cross-sectional area transmitting water reduced. The reversed
water-table slope below the ditch will be steep at first (*EF*), but
will gradually flatten as material above the ditch is drained
and finally may slope away from the ditch (*FI*). The placing

of ditches in inefficient locations, such as the central or lower portions of a swamp, is by no means uncommon.

Ground-water Mounds and Ridges.—The term ground-water mound has been applied not only to mound-shaped additions to ground water built up by influent seepage from small areas such as irrigated fields, spreading grounds, and ponds, but also to ridge-shaped additions to ground water built up under influent streams because in cross section they appear as mounds. The shape of these mounds and ridges is best shown on water-table contour maps.[1]

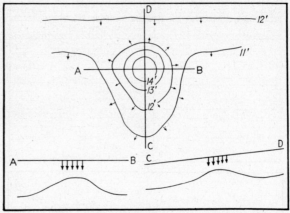

Fig. 73.—Generalized ground-water mound shown by contours and in cross sections.

Figure 73 is a generalized ground-water mound depicted by ground-water contours and cross sections through the mound, constructed after numerous available water-table contour maps. The contours indicate that influent seepage is supplied by a surface area a little smaller than that enclosed by the 14-ft. ground-water contour, because the steep slope shown in the contour map and cross section is at the margin of the area of influent seepage. The slope of the mound is flatter in the direction of water-table slope because alluvial material is usually more permeable in that direction, for it is the direction of flow of the alluvium-depositing stream that formed the cone. The slopes in section *AB*, parallel to the original ground-water contours before development of the mound, are steeper because material is usually

[1] For examples of a mound due to irrigation see Figs. 83, p. 252, and 87. p. 256, and of ground-water ridges, Figs. 82 and 83, pp. 251, 252.

less pervious in the direction at right angles to the flow of the original alluvium-depositing stream. The water-table slopes generated by influent seepage flatten out radially from the feeding area and the mound disappears, because spreading out of the mound water dissipates the velocity of movement with distance from the center of the mound and origin of seepage.

The rate at which the ground-water mound spreads in a horizontal direction is often assumed to represent the rate of

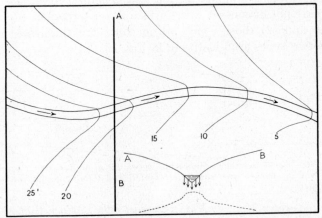

Fig. 74.—Water-table contours showing influent stream. Cross section shows ground-water mound not in contact with stream. (Surface contours not indicated.)

percolation. For example, for spreading operations in the San Fernando Valley, California, Lane gives the rate of vertical downward seepage as 20 ft. per day (100 per cent gradient) and mean velocity of percolation in a horizontal direction, "as indicated by the length of time required for wells to reach their maximum elevation from the time spreading started," as 3.68 miles per year at 0.261 per cent gradient,[1] or recalculated for 100 per cent gradient, 1000 times as fast as vertical seepage. The development of the ground-water mound at rates far greater than possible maximum rate of percolation is a matter of common knowledge and indicates that adjustment of the slope to that necessary to move added water is developed almost contemporaneously with addition of water under the spreading area and does not represent rate of percolation.

[1] Lane, D. A., Increasing Storage by Water Spreading, *Jour. Amer. Water Works Assn.*, vol. 26, no. 4, pp. 421–429, April, 1934.

A ground-water ridge built up beneath an influent stream usually is characterized by a contour pattern as shown in Fig. 74. The ridge is flat-topped. Maximum slope is at the margin of influent seepage below and just beyond the stream banks, and the slope dies out as velocity of percolation decreases with distance from source of seepage and is lost in the body of ground water percolating in a parallel direction to the ridge and the course of the stream.

Ground-water mounds are of two general types: (1) Those which are not in contact with surface water (streams, ditches, or ponds) and (2) those which are in contact with surface water. These two types are illustrated in Fig. 75.

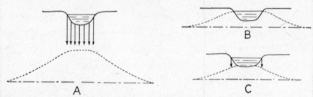

Fig. 75.—Cross sections illustrating types of ground-water mounds. *A*, mound not in contact with surface stream; *B* and *C*, mounds in contact with surface stream.

Ground-water Mounds Not in Contact with Surface Water.—The most interesting feature connected with this type of ground-water mound is the vertical column or *shaft* of *influent seepage* extending from surface water to water table (Fig. 75*A*). The vertical character of seepage was not appreciated until experimental study brought out the dominant vertical movement.[1] As Meinzer has pointed out, information on water movements in the undersaturated zone is sadly lacking, but experimental work in spreading is furnishing data and it is hoped that the results of scientific study of spreading and laboratory experimental work will soon furnish the data necessary for satisfactory treatment of the subject of influent seepage.

Movement of water on pellicular films surrounding the grains of water-transmitting material has been mentioned repeatedly

[1] In material of uniform or decreasing permeability with depth, the column conducting seepage might become saturated, percolation would replace seepage, and Darcy's law would control. Any increase in permeability with depth would increase capacity to transmit water over supply and develop seepage.

in this book. After films are formed around sand grains, subsequent seepage probably slowly drives out ground air. Lane states that "each time a basin (for water-spreading) was shut off and all water allowed to percolate out, if only for an hour, the unit rate of percolation decreased. This proves that intermittent operation of basins, as advocated by some engineers, will not permit the maximum rates of percolation."[1] This suggests that ground air is expelled slowly from the column of influent seepage, a fact that is not surprising to one who has attempted to get rid of air in permeameters. Lane's statement that in "one of the smaller pits observation showed a unit rate of 24 acre-feet per acre per day (and that) this rate continued over a period in excess of 30 days and at the end of the period showed no change, regardless of the height of water in the pit,"[2] is interesting and at first sight remarkable. The extra surface of the sides of the pit exposed to water when the pit was filled might well be supposed to increase the quantity of influent seepage. That it did not, emphasizes the fact that influent seepage moves directly downward. The water table is reported as 100 ft. below the bottom of the 20-ft. pits. The gradient of the water column when the bottom of the pit is covered is 100 per cent and when filled with water, 120 per cent. This difference should affect appreciably the rate of seepage, and that it did not suggests that Darcy's law (page 201) may not control seepage rate as rigidly as percolation rate.

Factors favorable for the development of ground-water mounds not in contact with surface water are:

1. Depth to water table: It is apparent that, if the water table is at considerable depth below the surface, an enormous quantity of influent seepage would be required to bring the level of the ground-water mound in contact with surface water.

2. The presence of a less pervious formation between the water table and surface water has not been discussed in the literature, but it seems probable that a perched body of ground water might be formed and spread out over an area sufficiently large to permit the lower rate of seepage to transmit the available water. The slopes of both the perched and the water-table mounds would be adjusted to the velocity of lateral percolation and permeability of material within the mounds (Fig. 76).

[1] LANE, *op. cit.* (manuscript page 8).
[2] *Ibid.*, p. 9.

3. A uniform *vertical* decrease in permeability would be favorable for complete saturation of material below stream level. If *all ground air is not driven out*, the column of influent seepage would be maintained, possibly spreading a little as it approaches the saturated mound (Fig. 77*A*). If *material is saturated*, a steep mound with cascade slopes would be developed (Fig. 77*B*).

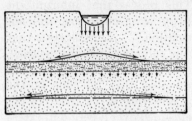

Fig. 76.—Perched ground-water mound developed above less pervious stratum, spreading the water over sufficient area to allow seepage to build up mound on main water table.

4. Greater permeability parallel to geologic structure (bedding and lamination) than across structure is an important factor in the development of ground-water mounds. In this case water percolates in the direction of the slope of the water table with greater ease than it seeps downward from the stream bed. The mound would be flat and could not be built up to surface water (Fig. 78).

Ground-water Mounds in Contact with Surface Water.—In homogeneous material, such as sorted sand, there may be little

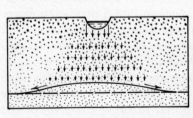 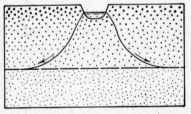

A   B

Fig. 77.—Ground-water mounds developed in material of decreasing permeability. *A*, decreasing permeability spreads shaft of influent seepage and forms wide mound with small slope; *B*, decrease in permeability with depth builds up a steep mound with cascade slopes to the surface stream.

difference in permeability in vertical and horizontal directions. The vertical gradient is capable of supplying water faster than it can spread laterally from under the stream under control of the slope of the ground-water mound. The mound is built up to the source of seepage and makes contact with the water in the stream. It may start at or a little below the water level in the stream or may merely touch the bottom of the stream bed and influent seepage may be developed under the margins of the channel (Fig. 75, *B* and *C*, page 242).

If the ground-water mound is in contact with the surface stream, the relation commonly used by hydraulic engineers, that is, that percolation loss varies as depth of water in the stream multiplied by wetted perimeter and permeability of stream-bottom formations, may hold fairly well. However, this relation does not apply where the mound is not in contact with the stream bed. The author once listened to an amusing discussion in court by an expert who maintained that the rate of seepage depended upon the wetted perimeter and the distance between water level in the stream and the water table, regardless of the fact that the water table was many feet below the stream channel. An opposing witness suggested that, according to the theory advanced, the quantity of water delivered by a shower could be regulated by changing the height of shower above the bathtub.

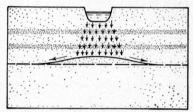

Fig. 78.—Ground-water mound developed in horizontally stratified material.

It has been claimed in litigation and announced without qualification in the decision of a judge that water flowing in a stream is "held up and supported" by the ground water underneath the bed of the stream. The statement holds only for an effluent stream into which ground water is percolating and thus supplying and supporting the stream.

Bodies of Fresh Ground Water Floating on Salt Ground Water

Conditions favorable for the development of a body of fresh ground water floating on salt ground water are illustrated in Fig. 79. Such conditions might exist in an island underlain to considerable depth by pervious sand or lava, with an extension of the pervious material out under the sea. The slope of the water table, built up by influent seepage from rainfall, increases from the center of the island to the sea.

The explanation offered by J. S. Brown of such an occurrence from observed conditions on the East Friesian islands north of Germany; on the coast of Holland; Long Island, New York; and the Hawaiian Islands is condensed from his excellent discussion of the subject.[1]

Where a coast is formed of pervious rocks and ground-water increment is from rainfall, ground water percolates laterally toward the shore and mingles with the salt water of the sea. On small pervious islands fresh water can generally be found at an altitude slightly above mean sea level. Salt water surrounding the island does not penetrate the sand to mean sea level but such islands are found to contain a dome-shaped lens of fresh ground water floating upon a concave surface of salty water. The fresh ground water floats on the salt ground water because its density is lower. This principle was first applied to the hydrology of seacoasts

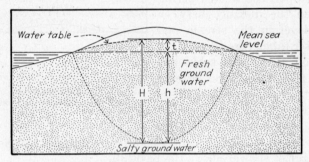

Fig. 79.—Fresh ground water floating on salt ground water. *H*, thickness of fresh-water lens; *h*, depth of fresh water below sea level; *t*, height of fresh water above sea level. Scale of *h* is ⅕ that of *t*.

by Badon Ghyben[2] as the result of investigations in Holland in 1887, but gained little notice from hydrologists at that time. It was also published by Herzberg about 1900,[3] who apparently had no knowledge of the work of Badon Ghyben. Herzberg found in drilling wells on the island of Norderney, one of the East Friesian islands off the coast of Germany, that the depth to salt water was roughly a function of the height of water table above mean sea level and of the density of water of the North Sea. Figure 79 shows the application of his theory.

The column of fresh water *H* is balanced by a column of salt water *h* in order to maintain equilibrium. If *g* is the specific gravity of sea

[1] Brown, John S., A Study of Coastal Ground Water, *U.S. Geol. Surv. Water-Supply Paper* 537, pp. 16–17, 1925.

[2] Ghyben, Badon, Nota in verband met de voorgenomen put boring nabij Amsterdam, *K. Inst. Ing. Tijdschr.*, 1888–1889, p. 21, The Hague, 1889.

[3] Herzberg, Die Wasserversorgung einiger Nordseebäder, *Jour. Gasbeleuchtung Wasserversorg.*, Jahrg. 44, Munich, 1901.

water, and 1 the specific gravity of fresh ground water, then

$$H = h + t = hg,$$

where t = height of water table above sea level, whence

$$h = t/(g - 1).$$

In any case $g - 1$ will be the difference in specific gravity between the fresh water and the salt water. Herzberg gives the specific gravity of the North Sea as 1.027, whence $h = 37t$.

Drilling on Norderney and islands nearby is said to have given results varying but a few meters from those derived from the formula, but it is not clear whether the salt water encountered at the expected depths was of approximately the same composition as sea water or was merely too salty to use.

Although detailed discussion of the cone of depression due to pumping is reserved for a later chapter, it seems advisable to

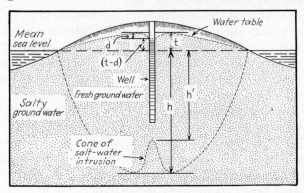

Fig. 80.—Development of cone of salt-water intrusion by pumping fresh-water lens.

mention here that a cone of salt-water intrusion is developed by pumping a body of fresh water floating on salt water. The cone of salt-water intrusion faces and is much steeper than the cone of depression of the pumping well. This is illustrated in Fig. 80 for sea water of specific gravity 1.027. The distance below sea level is one-fifth the scale of the distance above sea level.

If the salt water reaches the well, the well water is contaminated. It is evident that if the water table is drawn down to sea level by pumping, salt water will rise to sea level.

Substituting in the Herzberg equation, $h = t/(g - 1)$; $(t - d)$ for t, where d = drawdown; and h' for h, where h' = depth below sea level of the top of the cone of salt-water intrusion, the equation becomes

$$h' = \frac{t - d}{g - 1}$$

and the depth of fresh water above the intrusion of salt water can be calculated for every foot of drawdown in the well. When h' equals depth of well below sea level, the cone of salt-water intrusion will touch the bottom of the well and the well water will be contaminated.

WATER-TABLE MAPS

A water-table contour map is a map of the upper surface of the saturated zone. It is a graphic plot of the equilibrium relations between velocity, hydrologic properties of the water-bearing materials, and water-table slopes of *free water*.

A water-table map is constructed from measurements of depth to water in boreholes put down to, and a little below, the water table, or from measurements of depth to water in wells.[1] If the wells encounter free water only, the measurements locate the water table. Wells tapping confined water do not locate the water table and hence a contour map of water level in wells may or may not be a water-table map. Usually the most satisfactory measurements of the water table are made in boreholes put down for that purpose. The expense of this work may be prohibitive, however, and measurements of water levels in wells must be interpreted insofar as it is possible to do so. It is emphasized here that in many instances maps of water levels in wells have been erroneously assumed to be maps of the water table.

Methods of Construction.—1. A topographic map of the region investigated is an aid, but not a necessity.

2. The measuring point for each observation well or borehole is marked and its position and elevation determined by survey.

3. A complete set of measurements of depth to water from the measuring point at each well or borehole is made as expeditiously as possible. This furnishes the data for a water-table contour map for the period during which the measurements are made.

---

[1] For detailed directions regarding water-level-in-well measurements see "Report of the Committee on Observation Wells," *U.S. Geol. Surv.*, A Preliminary Manual of Methods, May, 1935. (Mimeographed.)

Usually sets of measurements are made at regular intervals and the water-table fluctuations are recorded in successive maps of the water table. In some carefully investigated localities these measurements have been continued for many years. Where problems of fluctuating water supply and water storage exist, these measurements should be continued indefinitely.

The cost of such maps, including the boring of hundreds and even thousands of boreholes, is large. The preliminary surveying work may cost several hundred to several thousand dollars. Continuous rounds of measurements may occupy the time of many men. Therefore this phase of ground-water study may involve large expenditures.

The position of the water table may also be determined by geophysical methods and maps constructed from geophysical data (pages 259–287).

Interpretation of Water-table Maps

Water-table maps are interpreted according to the principles illustrated in the hypothetical cases outlined in the first part of this chapter. A few selected examples of water-table maps are discussed and interpreted in order to show the application of these principles. The water-table contours show the direction of movement of ground water at right angles to contours, and the slope of the water table is the result of the quantity of water moving and the permeability of the formations. A comparison of maps representing the water table at successive intervals will show changes in water supply.

Rillito River Region.—The accompanying water-table map of a portion of the Tucson quadrangle, Arizona, (Fig. 81) is based on maps published by G. E. P. Smith.[1] The water-table contours are slightly modified to represent the strong ground-water mound of the Rillito River, especially well developed near the close of the winter rainy season.

The bedrock formations of the Santa Catalina and Rincon Mountains to the north and east of Tucson are chiefly granitic in character. As a result the alluvial cone at the foot of the Santa Catalina Mountains (shown in north portion of Fig. 81) is pervious, the Rillito River which crosses the foot of this cone is

[1] SMITH, G. E. P., Groundwater Supply and Irrigation in the Rillito Valley, *Univ. Arizona, Agr. Exp. Sta. Bull.* 64, p. 176, 1910.

influent, and in portions of its course builds up a very pronounced ground-water mound. This mound is shown by the downstream flexure of the contours, which indicates that the Rillito River is feeding water into the alluvial deposits that underlie and are adjacent to it.

In contrast the ground-water contours of the Santa Cruz River (shown in southwest portion of Fig. 81) are flexed in an

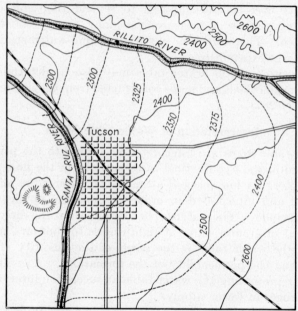

Fig. 81.—Water-table map near junction of Rillito and Santa Cruz Rivers showing ground-water ridge and ground-water trench.

upstream direction, indicating that this river is an effluent or "dewatering" stream. It rises in Arizona, flows into Mexico, and returns again to Arizona. The flood waters occasionally reach the Gila River. It is longer than the Hudson River; nevertheless stream flow, except for occasional flood flow, is derived from effluent seepage from the alluvial cones traversed.

Water pumped from wells in the alluvial cone supplied by seepage from the Rillito River and its tributaries is very slightly mineralized, while water in the cones drained by the Santa Cruz River is highly mineralized due to the character of the bedrock formations of the Santa Rita mountains and resultant composition of the alluvial cone.

Mokelumne River.—Figure 82 is a generalized ground-water contour map of the Mokelumne River region in the Sacramento Valley, California, showing conditions during high- and low-water

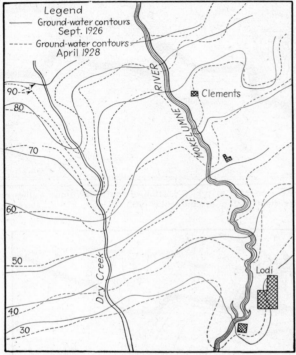

Fig. 82.—Ground-water contours, Mokelumne region, for both high- and low-water stream stages. (*After Stearns, Robinson and Taylor.*)

stages of the streams. Both the Mokelumne River and Dry Creek are influent throughout the year and build up large ground-water mounds after spring floods. Although much smaller, Dry Creek builds up a larger ground-water mound than the Mokelumne River. The generalized cross section of the Mokelumne Valley (Fig. 49, page 170) illustrates the unusual hydrologic structure of the water-bearing formations underlying the river which causes the development of a relatively small ground-water mound.

Figures 83 and 84 are ground-water maps of a portion of the bottom lands of the Mokelumne River valley west of Clements, California. Figure 83 shows a ground-water hole and ground-

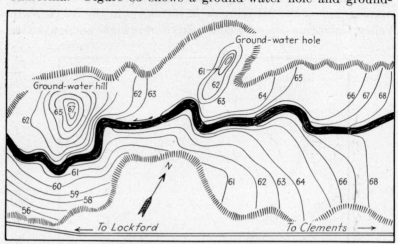

Fig. 83.—Water-table map of a portion of the Mokelumne Valley showing a ground-water hole and a ground-water hill. (*After W. A. Packard*, *private report*.)

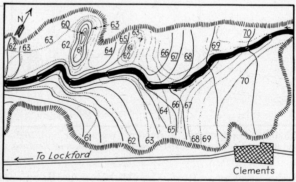

Fig. 84.—Water-table map of a portion of the Mokelumne River Valley showing high-water contours (solid lines) and low-water contours (dotted lines). Effluent contours at low-water stage are due to release of bank storage. (*After W. A. Packard*, *private report*.)

water hill. The ground-water hill is produced by heavy irrigation at that locality. The hole is formed around a well which pierces the "basal gravel stratum" of the valley and continues through the less pervious basal formations and several aquifers encased therein. The well is old and no information as to its perforations is available, but evidently there is some connection between the great basal aquifer underlying the bottom lands and the deeper aquifers, the levels of which have been reduced by pumping on the mesa land above the river valley.

This condition suggests that more effective feeding of the underlying aquifers in this region might be obtained by wells drilled in the bottom lands and perforated in the basal gravel stratum and in the underlying aquifers. Such a procedure would furnish clear water from the basal stratum to the underlying aquifers and overcome the chief difficulty encountered in feeding water down wells, that is, desilting the water.

Figure 84 shows the high-water (spring) contours in solid lines and the low-water (fall) contours in dotted lines. The high-water contours show influent conditions and feeding water into the bottom lands during flood flow. The low-water contours show effluent conditions and draining of water stored in times of high water. This is an example of "bank storage and release" on a large scale. Figure 84 also shows the ground-water hole around the well pictured in Fig. 83 registered in both high and low water-table conditions, and a smaller hole around a second well registered only by the low water-table contours.

The Niles Alluvial Cone.—The Niles alluvial cone lies east of the southern portion of San Francisco Bay in Alameda County, California. This region is well known on account of long-continued study of its surface and subsurface water supply. These studies have been carried on by investigators employed by litigants regarding the ownership of the surface and ground water,[1] by the United States Geological Survey,[2] and by an umpire committee[3] authorized to pass upon the hydraulic and hydrologic questions in controversy. The detailed report of Bailey for this committee contains not only valuable data in regard to engineering phases, such as stream gaging, evaporation, and influent seepage, but also probably the best description of the structure of an alluvial cone that has appeared in literature.

---

[1] BRANNER, J. C., Private unpublished report.

[2] CLARK, WILLIAM O., Ground Water in Santa Clara Valley, Calif., *U.S. Geol. Surv. Water-Supply Paper* 519, pp. 16–18, 74–75, 93–94, 1924.

[3] BAILEY, PAUL, Summary of report in Third Biennial Report, Calif. State Water Commission, Appendix E, 1921, complete report on file, Division of Water Resources, State of California.

Two maps have been selected to illustrate ground-water conditions in Niles cone: (1) A contour map of the water table at the high ground-water stage (after Clark)[1] on which are drawn contours showing the extent of annual ground-water fluctuation (Fig. 85). (2) The second map, after Bailey and Hyatt[2] shows by contours the rate of advance of the ground-water mound built up by flood stages at five-day intervals after the flood (Fig. 86).

1. *Map Showing High and Fluctuating Water Table.*—Figure 85 shows by the position and shape of contours for the stage of high

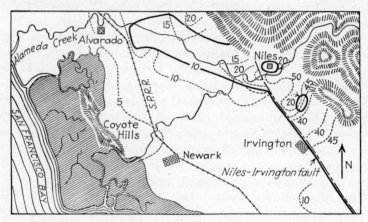

Fig. 85.—Map of the water-table conditions of Niles cone, California. Heavy solid lines are annual fluctuation contours; dashed lines high water-table contours. (*After Clark.*)

water table a pronounced ground-water ridge extending westerly from the apex of the cone and following the present course of Alameda Creek. A separate ground-water mound forms on the northeast side of the Niles-Irvington fault and spreads southeasterly along the course of the fault, which was located by surface exposure, by outcropping effluent seepage, and by the truncation of ground-water contours along its course. It is a strong ground-water barrier as shown by the contours. A ground-water cascade 20 ft. high plunges down the southwest side of the fault.[3] This map also indicates that the water table is held back by the

[1] CLARK, *op. cit.*, Plate X, p. 24.

[2] BAILEY, PAUL and EDWARD HYATT, "The Precise Determination of Replenishment and Draught from the Niles Cone Aquifer," Master's Thesis, Stanford University, p. 142, 1920.

[3] CLARK, *op. cit.*, pp. 60–67.

isolated Coyote Hills which may be described as a ridge of
impervious rock nearly covered or "drowned" by the Niles
alluvial cone. The ground-water fluctuation contours show the
usual small fluctuation toward the foot of the cone and large
fluctuation toward the apex.

2. *Map of Advance of Ground-water Mound or Ground-water
Wave.*—This (Fig. 86) is contoured for periods of five-day

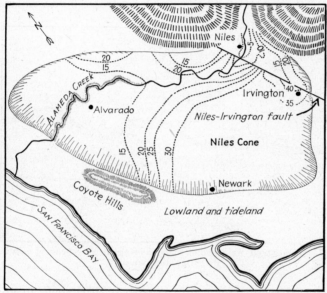

Fig. 86.—Progress of a ground-water wave on Niles cone and the effect of
faulting on the water table. Contours show five-day cyclic advance of ground
water through the cone, as shown by well hydrographs. (Time referred to
fluctuation cycle of a well at head of cone.) (*After Bailey and Hyatt.*)

intervals. Fifteen days after flood flow the ground-water mound
was advancing southeasterly along the northern base of the
Coyote Hills. The rapid movement of the mound along the
margin of the hills may be due to the presence of coarse material
washed down from the hills or by the damming effect and consequent turning of the movement to the east of the hills. After
40 days the mound has occupied the entire eastern portion of the
alluvial cone and has moved northeasterly and up the topographic
slope to the Niles-Irvington fault.

Above the fault the mound moved southeasterly along the
course of the fault, taking only 20 days to reach the same point

on the fault reached by the mound below the fault in 40 days by a circuitous path.

Displacement of Contours by Irrigation and Pumping.— Examples have been shown (Figs. 83 and 84) of displacement of ground-water contours by irrigation and by pumping wells. The sketch, Fig. 87, is presented and discussed in order to emphasize that contour maps must be interpreted not only with reference to natural conditions such as stream flow, evaporation,

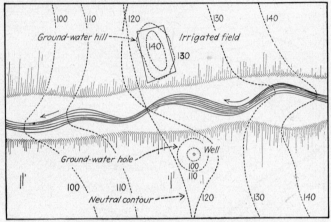

Fig. 87.—Theoretical water-table map showing displacement of contours by irrigation and pumping.

and transpiration, but also in regard to all changes in ground-water conditions produced by man.

In Fig. 87 the influent mound (left) and the effluent trench (right) are separated by the so-called neutral contour. Opposite the irrigated area the neutral contour is displaced in the down-stream direction bending back toward the stream in an upstream direction. This effluent upstream bend *at the creek* correctly indicates that the stream is receiving a portion of the ground water supplied by irrigation. If the fields were irrigated on both sides of the stream, a ground-water trench between two ground-water hills would be developed.

On the other side of the stream a pumping well has drawn the contour back into an influent shape; if wells were pumped on both sides of the stream, the contour near the stream would assume the influent shape of the ground-water ridge. The contours would correctly indicate that pumped ground water was being supplied by the stream.

FLUCTUATIONS OF GROUND WATER

The early ground-water literature up to about 1906 contains many references to fluctuations of ground water. These contributions are not of great value because the change of water level in the well was considered solely in relation to the physical conditions and controlling factors *at that well*. Fluctuation at a

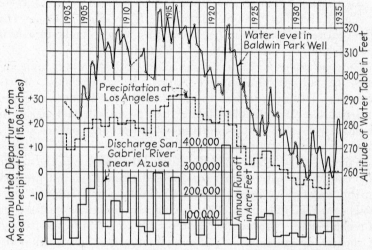

Fɪɢ. 88.—Comparison of ground-water fluctuations with rainfall and runoff.
(*After Ebert.*)

particular locality is not only due to additions to and subtractions from the water table *at that point*, but also to the response of the water table to changes in effluent and influent seepage *over its entire surface*. Water-table slopes are adjusted slowly, and, within the limits imposed by topography, steeper slopes are developed in materials of low permeability than in those of large permeability.

Modern engineering studies of fluctuations of ground-water levels involve a comparison of hydrographs of water levels in wells, rainfall graphs, and other factors affecting ground-water fluctuations. Ebert[1] plots fluctuation of water level in a Baldwin

[1] EBERT, F. C., An Interpretation of Water-table Fluctuations at Four Wells in Southern California, *Trans. Amer. Geophys. Union*, p. 372, 1936.

Park well, accumulated departure curve for mean precipitation, and discharge of the San Gabriel River (Fig. 88). The best general discussion of methods of studying fluctuations of ground-water levels by comparison of graphs is by Wenzel.[1] Fluctuations in water table due to recent severe droughts in central and midwestern United States have been discussed recently in several valuable papers, and interesting graphs showing variations in ground-water surface over long periods of years have been presented.[2]

An excellent review and summary of the older literature on ground-water fluctuations appear in *Water-Supply Paper* 155, Fluctuations of the Water Level in Wells, with special reference to Long Island, New York, by A. C. Veatch.

Unusual minor fluctuations may affect both the water table and pressure surface of confined water. However, most of the unusual fluctuations affect the level of confined water in a well and not the water table. King[3] has described fluctuations in shallow wells due to the wetting of the ground surface over a large area and confinement of air underneath this wetted layer. The increase in pressure over the entire area was due to the weight of precipitated water which compressed ground air, put pressure on the water table, and thus raised the level in shallow surface wells (see Fig. 114, page 333). King also describes fluctuations of a shallow and presumably water-table well due to the passage of heavy freight trains.[4] Such fluctuations are commonly observed in wells tapping confined water but are unusual in water-table wells. An explanation of this effect on the water table is that the freight train actually compressed the water-bearing material, squeezing out water and raising the water table.

Water-table wells are not usually affected by plastic deformation of water-bearing materials due to barometric change, load of an advancing ground-water mound, tidal loading, and such

[1] WENZEL, L. K., Several Methods of Studying Fluctuations of Ground-water Levels, *Trans. Amer. Geophys. Union*, pp. 400–405, 1936.

[2] Symposium on Fluctuations of Ground-water Level, *Amer. Geophys. Union Trans.*, pp. 337–391, 1936.

[3] KING, F. H., Observations and Experiments on the Fluctuations in the Level and Rate of Movement of Ground Water on the Wisconsin Agricultural Experiment Station Farm, and at Whitewater, Wis., *U.S. Weather Bureau Bull.* no. 5, pp. 20, 72–73, 1892.

[4] *Ibid.*, pp. 67–68.

fortuitous occurrences as seismic vibrations and passage of trains, but confined water may be affected by such agencies (pages 332–338).

GEOPHYSICAL METHODS OF LOCATING WATER TABLE AND BEDROCK

Geophysical methods of exploration may furnish direct or indirect information regarding the occurrence and composition of ground water. The most valuable direct information is depth to the saturated zone (location of the water table) and thickness of saturated pervious formations down to bedrock. Some direct information regarding the salinity of ground water, especially that confined in deeper aquifers, is furnished by resistivity methods.

To date the principal purpose of geophysical exploration has been to determine geologic structure, which may furnish indirect information regarding the occurrence of ground water. Geologic structure, whether determined by geologic field studies or by geophysical exploration, can be interpreted by the ground-water geologist if the hydrologic properties of the formations are known, and this text is largely a discussion of the interpretation of hydrologic properties and geologic structure. Hence the interpretation of the various types of geophysical research as to geologic structure is not discussed in this brief summary but is taken up in the appendix to this chapter.

The location of the water table is one of the most important hydrologic measurements. If ground water is contained in pervious sand and gravel aquifers and resistivity measurements are not affected by moist clay strata above the water table, the depth to water table can be determined. Unfortunately, however, most of the curves indicating change in geophysical properties due to saturation of rocks are smooth and therefore saturation is not indicated by sharp peaks; hence depth to water is not generally indicated with the accuracy desired for hydrologic interpretation. Where the water table is deep and water-bearing materials contain boulders, making boreholes expensive, the water table can be located more cheaply by geophysical methods than by direct measurements in boreholes and shafts but not with the accuracy of the latter methods.

Electrical methods, especially resistivity methods, are least expensive and most satisfactory for the location of the water table, and for this reason a description of electrical prospecting methods applicable to the direct measurements of the water table and depth to bedrock prepared at the request of the author by J. J. Jakosky, who has pioneered in and successfully developed the procedure of investigation, is included in the following paragraphs. Because of the advances in geophysical methods in recent years and the great interest of ground-water investigators in the application of geophysical methods to ground-water problems, the author asked C. A. Heiland, Professor of Geophysics at the Colorado School of Mines, to summarize the possible application of all methods of geophysical research to ground-water studies. His technical contribution with full references to the literature is appended to this chapter.

Electrical Methods

By J. J. Jakosky

The electrical methods may be described briefly as follows. The resistivity of the subsurface is determined by passing an electric current between two electrodes placed on the surface of the ground.[1] The current spreads out through the earth included between the two electrodes and the depth of penetration is governed largely by the separation between the electrodes. This may be illustrated by reference to the simple two-layer problem illustrated in Fig. 89. When the distance between the two electrodes is small, the current flow is confined largely to the upper layer x and the resistivity value is that of this layer. As the separation of the electrodes is progressively increased, however, the current spread increases and at relatively large electrode separations the resistivity value is a summation effect, with the electrical characteristics of the lower layer y predominating. When the relationship between resistivity and electrode separation is plotted, a curve similar to that shown on the right-hand side of the figure is obtained, assuming the lower material to have a resistivity greater than the upper material.

---

[1] WENNER, FRANK, A Method of Measuring Resistivity, *U.S. Bur. Standards Bull.*, vol. 12, 1916.

The flow of electricity through subsurface rock included between two electrodes is by means of electrolytic conduction through subsurface water in which various mineral salts are dissolved. Interpretation of the conductivity data takes into account the vertical and lateral subsurface distribution of ground water and its variation in chemical content, and variation in subsurface temperatures.

The distribution of subsurface water and the nature of the dissolved salts vary with stratification. In some areas this

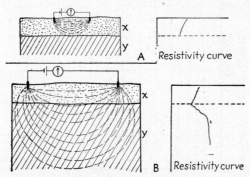

Fig. 89.—Relation of distance between electrodes to depth of penetration of current, and resistivity curves developed. *A*, distance between electrodes small; current confined to upper layer x; *B*, distance between electrodes increased; current penetrates lower layer y.

distribution is uniform for considerable distances in a lateral direction. In other areas the geologic section changes rapidly, and in the case of alluvial materials the water-bearing formations may be lenticular.

Previous work on the conductivities of various rock types[1] shows that these materials are very poor conductors (in fact, almost perfect insulators) when dry, and that their conductivity is a function of (1) the percentage of moisture disseminated through the materials, (2) chemical properties and ionization factors of the soluble salts in the material, and (3) the nature of the rock material itself. The relationship between electrical conductivity and water content may be seen by reference to Fig. 90. This figure contains curves from representative shales, limestones, clay gouges, and alluvial fill materials. In order to

[1] JAKOSKY, J. J., and C. H. WILSON, Electrical Conductivity of American Ores and Minerals, University of Utah, 1928.

obtain information regarding the mechanism of electrolytic conduction, the effects of soluble salts in the gouges were studied. Specimens of the salt-charged gouges of curves 6 and 7 were thoroughly leached with distilled water and a complete series of measurements made again. The results of these tests are shown in curves 6A and 7A.

It is apparent from the curves that the resistivity of these rocks and fault gouges varies inversely with the percentage of moisture

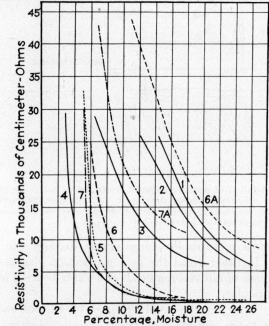

Fig. 90.—Resistivities plotted against moisture percentages for various rocks. 1, Kaibab limestone; 2, Coconino sandstone; 3, Supai sandstone; 4, Moenkopi shale; 5, altered granodiorite; 6 and 7, fault gouge; 6A and 7A leached gouge.

contained in the material. The critical point for the materials containing high percentages of soluble salts occurs in the neighborhood of about 10 to 15 per cent moisture. For greater percentages of moisture content the curves are relatively flat with small changes in value. The materials containing water low in salt content have higher resistivity values and do not exhibit sharp changes in resistivity as the percentage of moisture changes. These relationships between electrical resistivity, moisture content, and ionization factors, illustrated by the curves in Fig. 90 form the basic factors of geophysical studies.

Porous alluvial and detrital fill has larger capacity for water than the solid and compacted types of rocks.   Large differences in resistivity are therefore present between such porous materials and the more impervious rocks.   A typical curve from a recent water-supply investigation is shown in Fig. 91.[1]   The high resistivity value near the surface of the ground is due to the low moisture content.   At greater depths the percentage of water

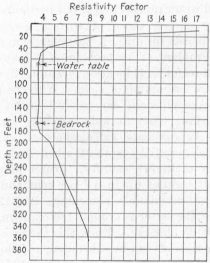

FIG. 91.—Typical curve showing relation of resistivity factor to depth and increase in water content.

increases with a resultant decrease in resistivity.   At a depth of approximately 70 ft. the minimum resistivity is encountered, which is the depth where the water table exists.   The resistivity remains constant for an interval of approximately 100 ft., when at a depth of 170 ft., there is a sudden rise in resistivity which indicates a smaller water content of the rock and is interpreted as indicating bedrock.   In the usual geophysical investigation, studies are made at a number of locations throughout an area. By correlation of the critical points on the curves the water table and depth to bedrock are mapped.

[1] JAKOSKY, J. J., Geophysical Examination of the Gillespie Dam, Arizona, Professional report of International Geophysics.

APPENDIX

PROSPECTING FOR WATER BY GEOPHYSICAL METHODS

By C. A. Heiland

Introduction.—Prospecting for water is one of the most diffi-cult problems of practical geophysics and requires exceptional geologic ability on the part of the geophysicist. Progress in this problem has been slow. From the commercial point of view geophysical water prospecting is not particularly attractive; costs frequently exceed those of surface geological surveys and approach expenses for drilling, particularly in small projects.

Definition of Problem.—The problem of geophysical prospect-ing for water is threefold: (1) location of water; (2) determination of salinity; and (3) estimation of yield. With the present status of technique the geophysicist can rarely hope to predict yields unless he is working close to wells reaching formations with known yields. Approximate calculations of salinity can be made by electrical-resistivity methods when working away from wells with water of known salinity. Water may be used for cattle with a salt content up to 0.7 per cent and for domestic water the highest permissible percentage is 0.12 per cent.[1,2] The resistivity of the latter is around 180 ohm-cm.[3] and that of the former about 65 ohm-cm. From this the resistivity of salt-contaminated formations can be calculated, as follows: Assuming spherical grains in cubic arrangement, the resistivity ρ_x of a sand with the pore volume of v per cent may be obtained from the resistivity ρ of the water filling the pores[4]: $\rho_x = 3\rho/v$, so that for a porosity of 40 per cent a formation with a resistivity of lower than 1350 ohm-cm. must be avoided if water is to be used for human needs, and for purposes of watering stock formations with resistivities down to 500 ohm-cm. are tolerable.

---

[1] This is the extreme limit for human consumption. U.S. Treasury Department requirements set a limit of 250 p.p.m. chloride ion content, or 0.12 per cent, for human consumption.

[2] Bruckshaw, J. M., and F. Dixie, *Mining Mag.*, vol. 50, nos. 2, 3, pp. 73–147, 1934.

[3] Sundberg, K., *Amer. Inst. Min. Met. Eng., Trans.*, Geophysical Pros-pecting, p. 367, 1932.

[4] *Ibid.*

TABLE 12.—GEOLOGIC-GEOPHYSICAL CLASSIFICATION OF GROUND WATER AND OF GEOPHYSICAL LOCATION METHODS

Type of water	Reservoir formed by	Methods of location			
		Structural	Stratigraphic		Direct
			Low salinity	High salinity	
I. Ground water in pervious granular material. Aquifers usually of large size; those in alluvium most important	1. Stratigraphic boundaries	Gravitational, magnetic, seismic, resistivity	Resistivity Seismic, acoustic, electrical coring	Resistivity, inductive, radio	Moisture gradient (rate of motion determined by salting and potential measurement)
	2. Stratigraphic boundaries with lateral confinement by impervious formations (faults)		Resistivity Seismic, acoustic, electrical coring	Resistivity, inductive	
	3. Erosional boundaries (valley fill important)		Same as 1 above		
II. Ground water in cemented or crytalline rocks. Aquifers usually limited in extent	1. Horizontal boundaries of porosity		Resistivity Seismic, acoustic, electrical coring	Resistivity, inductive, radio	Moisture gradient
	2. Horizontal boundaries with lateral confinement (dikes, faults, fracture zones)		Resistivity Seismic, electrical coring	Resistivity, inductive	
	3. Irregular surface of impervious rock.		Resistivity Seismic, electrical coring	Resistivity, inductive	
III. Fissure water	Crevices, faults, fissures		See II-2		Inductive, radio, radioactive, resistivity
IV. Cavern water	Solution openings in limestone or dolomite		Resistivity	Resistivity, inductive, radio	Inductive, radio
	Rock salt				Resistivity, inductive, radio
V. Mineral springs (thermal, saline, radioactive)					Geothermal, inductive, radioactive
VI. Pipe leaks				Resistivity	Acoustic

Geophysical Classification of Underground Water.—For geophysical purposes underground waters may be divided into groups shown in Table 12.

I. Ground water in pervious granular material.

II. Ground water in consolidated (dense) rocks of small permeability and usually of small porosity.

III. Fissure water.

IV. Cavern water.

V. Spring water.

VI. Water issuing from leaks in water pipes.

In groups I and II three subdivisions have been made, classifying the water in these formations with respect to the shape of the reservoir, as this determines largely the type and procedure of geophysical surveying. The simplest case is the one of horizontal boundaries with emphasis on the determination of the upper surface of the saturated zone or water table. The second manner of occurrence is similar to the first except that lateral circulation is interrupted, often by faulting. In the third type the water occurs in erosional troughs bounded by impervious rocks. Here the geophysical problem is not only one of determining the upper surface (water table), but frequently the lower erosional surface or bedrock as well, or the latter alone if the water-table position cannot be determined.

Methods of Location.—The geophysicist has three ways at his disposal for the location of subsurface geologic bodies: (1) direct location, (2) stratigraphic determination, and (3) structural mapping. The first method of location is the exception rather than the rule in geophysical work, although certain substances like rock salt, magnetite, sulphide ores, and radioactive substances may be definitely identified in suitable types of surveys by the experienced interpreter. Liquid and gaseous substances occurring as impregnations like oil, gas, and water are particularly difficult to locate directly. It is obvious, however, that water occurring in the form of thermal, saline, and radioactive springs may be located by temperature, electrical, and radioactive measurements. Equally obvious is the direct location of water by its noise when escaping from pipe leaks, and the determination of brine accumulations in salt mines by electrical resistivity, inductive, and radio transmission observations. Water occurring in caves and fissures is on the border line of direct and stratigraphic location, as it is not always easy to decide whether the water as such gives the indication or by virtue of an impregnated medium. Water filling large cavities in limestone or dolomite may be located directly by resistivity measurements or, if sufficiently conductive, by inductive or radio methods. Water which occupies fissures is often heavily mineralized and may thus be detected by inductive, resistivity, radioactive, and radio measurements. Direct applications of geophysics to the location of the water table are limited to such special problems as the determination of the vertical moisture gradient by hygrometric observations at different depths, and calculation of the rate of motion of a ground-water stream in wells by salting the water and measuring the rate of motion of the surface potential peak due to the lateral motion of the salt-water front.[1]

The chief applications of geophysics to the location of underground water are of a stratigraphic or a structural nature. As stated previously, the resistivity of the impregnating water affects the resistivity of the rock in which it occurs and therefore it is possible to distinguish a dry rock from a water-bearing rock under certain favorable circumstances. Water can thus be located by means of a local physical rock classification based on differences in rock conductivity. In analogy to the procedure employed in geology, this may be termed a "stratigraphic" method of water location. Secondly, water may be located by determining structures favorable for its occurrence. This involves the mapping of certain key beds which may or may not be aquifers. The method is purely an indirect one, as structurally favorable points may not contain water owing to unfavorable hydrologic properties of the formations. This method, therefore, is called the "structural" method of locating water. Details of the latter will be discussed first.

Methods Applicable to Structural Interpretation.—Referring to the tabulation (Table 12), structural methods are applicable to the location of water confined by stratigraphic boundaries only if the geologic structure is favorable to the accumulation of water. In this case the object of the structural investigation is to locate synclines, troughs, and areas of general depression. Geophysically this problem is similar to that of mapping erosional

[1] DeCeccaty, R. P., and M. Jabiol, "L'Eau," Asnières, Seine, 1935.

troughs. All major geophysical methods are applicable to the location of erosional troughs and depend on whether differences in *density, magnetism, elasticity,* or *conductivity* occur on the erosional boundary. Thus water-bearing gravel channels and valley fills may be mapped by the torsion balance, by seismic methods, and by resistivity methods of electrical prospecting. If the bottoms of the troughs consist of igneous or crystalline rocks, the magnetometer may be used for outlining their buried topography. For water reservoirs confined laterally by faults gravitational, seismic, and resistivity methods are applicable; also magnetic methods if the faulting has affected magnetic basement rocks or if dikes of igneous origin cut through the water-bearing strata.

For structural investigation of consolidated water-bearing rocks the same geophysical methods apply, provided sufficient differences exist in density, elasticity, and electric conductivity to map significant key beds. In connection with fissure water the function of structural geophysical work is the location of fissures or faults. Here gravitational, magnetic, seismic, and electrical methods apply, depending on whether strata with differences in density, magnetism, elastic or electric properties have been placed in juxtaposition by the faults.

Summing up, structural location of water is applicable where the structural relation of the occurrence of water to detectable key beds has been established, and such geophysical methods may be used as are employed in structural geophysical work for other purposes.

Methods Applicable to Stratigraphic Interpretation.—In contrast to the structural methods of water location, the aim of the stratigraphic methods is to determine condition of and depth to the aquifer itself. Here the choice of geophysical methods is limited. The increase in the density of a rock due to moisture is too small to be detected with certainty by the present most sensitive gravity instruments. Moreover the torsion balance is a poor indicator of horizontal discontinuities. Moist and dry rocks do not differ in their magnetic properties. However, seismic methods are applicable under favorable conditions, as the elastic wave velocity is greater in moist than in dry unconsolidated formations. Both the seismic refraction method[1] and, under

---

[1] HEILAND, C. A., *Explos. Eng.*, vol. 13, no. 12, p. 359, Dec. 1935.

favorable circumstances, a binaural method of geophone detection[1] is applicable. Although more expensive than electrical methods, seismic and acoustic methods deserve more attention than they receive at present, as their possibilities are as great if not greater, particularly in giving additional safety in the interpretation of results.

The application of electrical methods to the location of aquifers rests on the fact that water in the pores of rocks will change their conductivity appreciably, so much that the conductivity of the mineral substance is virtually without effect. A formula was given on page 264 for an approximate calculation. In practice there are altogether four factors which determine the resistivity of formations.

1. Porosity.
2. Percentage of pores filled.
3. Electrolytic conductivity of the water.
4. Length of contact of the water with the rock.

The first two factors do not require further explanation. The last two are intimately associated with one another and factor (4) depends on factor (1). When pure rain water is stored in the pores of a formation, a certain amount of mineral matter will go into solution and change its electrolytic conductivity. The conductivity is increased the longer the water is in contact with the rock. Thus fine-grained materials, such as clay containing fixed ground water, have much greater conductivities than coarse-grained sands and gravels. Moist clays have resistivities of about 0.5 to 1.5 kilo-ohm-cm., while moist sands have from 5 to 20 kilo-ohms-cm. The rate of motion of water through rocks affects their conductivity. Conductivity of medium-grained sands in which the water moves at a comparatively slow rate will generally increase in the direction of ground-water percolation, while coarse-grained sands or gravels, particularly those containing artesian water, will be poor conductors throughout their entire length.

Conductivity which increases with progressive increase in salinity of ground water may be called "secondary conductivity." "Primary conductivity" is a property of formations containing connate water. Connate water occurs in the deeper sections of

[1] HEILAND, C. A., *Colorado School Mines Quart.*, vol. 24, no. 1, p. 86, March, 1929.

sedimentary formations and has been studied extensively in connection with oil fields.   The conductivity of formations filled with connate water is exceedingly high, of the order of 0.1 to 0.4 kilo-ohm-cm.[1] Connate water is too saline for agricultural or domestic purposes and usually too deep for any commercial exploitation, although its location and depth determination (down to 1500 ft.) is often easier than the location of near-surface ground water.[2]

The electrical location of waters of secondary conductivity presents a twofold problem, depending on whether water of good or poor conductivity is involved.   This is indicated in the tabulation (Table 12).   Ground water of low salinity can generally be detected successfully only by the application of some surface potential or resistivity method, while waters of high salinities may be located not only by these methods, but in addition by inductive or radio methods.   As the tabulation shows, this rule applies to all occurrences of ground water, regardless of whether it occurs in unconsolidated or consolidated rocks and whatever the form of the reservoir.

It is obviously impossible to recognize water by a specific value of rock conductivity; in other words, the change in conductivity brought about by the presence of water is not great enough to produce really outstanding values of rock conductivities.   Here again the analogy with stratigraphic methods of geological investigation applies, for it is not the absolute composition that is of value for correlation purposes, but the type of variation with depth and consistency in a horizontal direction.

It is almost impossible to select any arbitrary location in virgin territory and to determine the presence and depth of water from the geophysical response.   However, where the presence of an aquifer has been established in a well or from exposures, it is possible to correlate conductivities with water-bearing formations, their depth, type, and thickness, and to follow this type of indication into unknown territory until a complete change in character occurs.

[1] SUNDBERG, K., *Amer. Inst. Min. Met. Eng., Trans.*, Geophysical Prospecting, p. 367, 1932.

[2] ZUSCHLAG, THEO., *Amer. Inst. M n. Met. Eng., Trans.*, Geophysical Prospecting, p. 144, 1932.

It is also evident why, as previously stated, yield determinations from electrical results are generally impossible. While the increase in conductivity in a sand can as a rule be taken as an indication of the presence of water, a moist clay which does not yield water may give the same indication.

Summing up, stratigraphic location of water by electrical geophysical methods involves many difficulties. Saline waters are easy to locate, but the better the indication, the less usable they are. Moist beds of low yield are likely to give better indications than water gravels of high yield. Finally, beds with the best type of water give indications which are most readily confused with those from formations which are not water bearing.

Instruments for Water Location.—For the direct location of water the geothermal, radioactive, inductive, and radio methods were mentioned. For details on these the reader is referred to the literature.[1] Inductive methods of electrical prospecting utilize an insulated cable or loop to energize conductive beds the magnetic field of which may be picked up by search coils at the surface and surveyed in reference to phase and amplitude. Details of this method may be found in the literature.[2] Radio methods differ from inductive methods in the use of a much higher frequency; the radiation from the transmitter is propagated in poor conductors and reflected from good conductors. Application of these methods is limited by the high rate of absorption in surface formations in temperate climates but appears to be more promising for water search in arid regions.[3]

With reference to structural water location, it has been stated that virtually any of the major geophysical methods may be used when a definite relation between structure and occurrence of water has been established. However, practical consideration will limit the application of some of them. For instance, the torsion balance is slow, limited by rugged topography, and too expensive compared with the electrical and seismic methods. Applications of the magnetometer are rare and indications at

[1] See references, pp. 288–290, also references given in Ambronn's book.

[2] See especially Edge-Laby, "Principles and Practice of Geophysical Prospecting."

[3] Details on methods and results may be obtained from articles by Petrowsky and Fritsch (see references).

times too indefinite, although it has the merit of speed and inexpensive operation. Instruments for gravimetric and magnetic prospecting will, therefore, not be described here. Discussions of principles and operations may be found in most geophysical textbooks. For structural work, seismic and electrical methods are foremost in speed and definiteness of interpretation. The same is true for stratigraphic water location.

Of the seismic and electrical methods, the seismic refraction and the electrical surface potential (resistivity, potential ratio, and potential gradient) are the ones in chief use at present but a number of other seismic and electrical methods in less frequent use for water location may be mentioned.

Two electrical methods which aim to accomplish similar results as now obtained by the resistivity method are the electromagnetic method of Haalck[1] and the ring induction method of Königsberger.[2] In the former an alternating-current generator is grounded at two points. The spacing between them is varied as in the resistivity method, the depth penetration being approximately one-third of the electrode interval. Between the two electrodes an induction frame is set up, with plane vertical and parallel to the electrode basis. As the current from the electrodes traverses strata of differing conductivities and different depths, the electromagnetic field changes and with it the inclination of the induction frame for zero induction. The tilt angles of the frame are plotted against electrode separation; breaks in the curve so obtained are assumed to correspond to vertical changes in conductivity (formation boundaries). In Königsberger's central induction method, current is supplied to the ground inductively by a ring-shaped loop the diameter of which is increased step by step to obtain increased depth penetration. The secondary field is picked up by a horizontal induction coil and measured in respect to phase and amplitude. The apparent resistivity can be calculated from the secondary field and is plotted against radius of the induction loop. Application of this method for problems involving depths less than 150 ft. is not recommended by the author.

[1] HAALCK, H., and L. EBERT, *Z. Geophys.*, vol. 8, no. 8, p. 409, 1932.

[2] KÖNIGSBERGER, J., *Beitr. angew. Geophysik*, vol. 3, no. 4, p. 392, 1933; vol. 4, no. 2, p. 201, 1934.

An electrical method which is sometimes useful in establishing actual resistivities in a water-bearing section penetrated by wells and in extending resistivity measurements into territory unexplored by wells is the electrical-coring method of Schlumberger.[1] However, it must be applied in water wells before they are cased.

In the seismic field, methods which have been applied occasionally and show promise for the future are the acoustic or geophone method and the reflection method. The geophone is an instrument constructed like a stethoscope and used for the detection of sound by ear. It is applied chiefly for locating water leaks from pipes by the noise of the water impinging on surrounding gravel or other material. For ground-water location two phones may be used connected through a compensator to determine the direction of sound as reflected from the water-bearing strata.[2] Reflection methods based on travel-time observations with seismic detectors have found extensive application in the oil fields but have been barred from civil engineering and ground-water applications because of the difficulty of eliminating interference of shallow reflections with the first refraction impulses. However, a solution of this problem is very probable in the course of the next two years.

The methods used chiefly at this time for the location of ground water are the seismic refraction and the electrical resistivity and/or potential methods. A seismic refraction equipment may be used for the purpose at hand in two ways: with or without amplifiers between detector and recording galvanometer. The insertion of the latter gives far greater sensitivity but calls for more equipment. The function of the detector (pickup, seismograph, geophone) is to convert the mechanical ground vibration into electrical impulses. This can be done in various ways: (1) by adaptation of the carbon microphone principle (not recommended on account of the high noise level); (2) by the use of a condensor microphone; (3) by using an inductive seismograph (adaptation of the dynamic speaker principle); and (4) by a reluctance seismograph (a reversed magnetic speaker, such as

---

[1] SCHLUMBERGER, C. and M., *Amer. Inst. Min. Met. Eng., Trans.,* Geophysical Prospecting, p. 237, 1934.

[2] HEILAND, C. A., *Amer. Inst. Min. Met. Eng., Trans.,* Geophysical Prospecting, p. 237, 1932.

the Baldwin type). The last two types are commonly used. The vibration detectors may be connected to intermediate amplifiers, depending on the sensitivity required. From the amplifiers or from the detectors directly the impulses are transferred to a recording galvanometer of the coil, string, or oscillograph loop type. In refraction work a much higher sensitivity than that of the customary oscillograph is required, of the order of 0.1 mm. deflection per microampere. The galvanometer deflections are photographed on rapidly moving paper in a recording field camera. Time marks at intervals of $\frac{1}{100}$ sec. are provided on the record and likewise the instant of the shot is transferred to the record electrically. Details of this equipment may be found in one of the author's recent articles.[1] Generally six detectors, six amplifiers, and six galvanometers are used, but time can be saved both in the field and in the evaluation of the records by using twelve channels. After the shot has been fired and records have been obtained in six or twelve distances respectively, the times elapsed between the shot instant and the first arrivals are taken from the record and are plotted as travel-time curves from which depths of boundaries of formations and elastic wave speeds within them may be calculated.

In the electrical-resistivity method generally four electrodes are driven into the ground and the external pair is connected to batteries and an ammeter. The current passing through the ground is measured and the potential difference set up between the internal pair is observed on a potentiometer or voltmeter. The ratio of current and voltage, multiplied by a factor depending on the spacing of the four electrodes, gives the apparent resistivity. The method may be used in two ways. In resistivity "sounding," that is, in the determination of the vertical variation of resistivity at one point, the electrode interval is increased in steps. As the depth penetration is approximately equal to the electrode interval, the apparent resistivity is plotted against electrode spacing, the curve thus obtained is rotated 90 deg. and a diagram obtained which gives the apparent resistivity as a function of equivalent depth (Fig. 93, page 281). Theory[2] and practice show that no sharp breaks are obtained at

[1] HEILAND, C. A., *Explos. Eng.*, vol. 13, no. 12, p. 359, December, 1935.
[2] Curves of this type may be calculated theoretically when resistivities and formation depths are given. The theory of apparent resistivity curves

formation boundaries with this method; as a matter of fact, depth calculations are somewhat involved. When the problem is one of determining relative depth of a given horizon (water horizon or bedrock) in an area, another process is applied called "resistivity mapping." In this process the electrode separation is adjusted to a large enough value to penetrate below the horizon to be mapped and is kept constant; locations in the area to be explored are occupied with this arrangement whereby apparent resistivity contours may be drawn which represent approximately the changes in depth of the key beds.

Two variants of the resistivity method are the potential-drop-ratio method[1] and the potential gradient method. The purpose of both is to improve the depth indications obtained with the resistivity method. In the potential-drop-ratio method two electrodes are grounded far apart and connected to a 500-cycle generator. Measurements are made in the vicinity of one power electrode with an alternating-current bridge arrangement which is grounded at three points and makes possible the determination of the ratio of the potentials along the two intervals formed by the three electrodes. This ratio is measured on traverses radiating out from the power electrode or along a traverse at right angles to the electrode basis and plotted as a function of the distance of the center secondary electrode from the power electrode. These horizontal distances are multiplied by a factor and the diagram rotated 90 deg. Formation boundaries then will appear as peaks in the curve. A peak to the right means a change from a good to a poor conductor and a peak on the left a change from a poor to a good conductor.

In the resistance gradient method a higher derivative of the surface potential function is measured in such manner that the depth to formation boundaries is read directly from the instrument which consists of an alternating-current, direct-reading bridge with a highly sensitive galvanometer as zero instrument. Low instead of high frequency is used to increase the depth penetration, which eliminates the necessity for phase determinations. Measurements are again made near one of the power

---

is treated in articles by Hummel, Tagg, Ehrenburg, and Watson, Peters and Bardeen, Roman, Slichter, Knaebel, Pirson, and Poldini.

[1] Zuschlag, Th., *Amer. Inst. Min. Met. Eng., Trans.*, Geophysical Prospecting, p. 47, 1932.

electrodes, readings are plotted, the diagram is rotated 90 deg., and a curve is obtained as shown in Fig. 92. The measurements shown in this figure were made to determine the depth to water table. In this method deflections of the curve to the right indicate good conductors and deflections to the left poor conductors, while formation boundaries show as intersections with the depth ordinate. It is seen from the results obtained that the

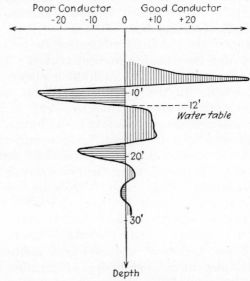

Fig. 92.—Water-table determination near Golden, Colorado, by resistance-gradiometer.

depth determination made with this instrument agreed well with the depth to water as determined in an adjacent well.

Discussion of Results. —Results obtained with geophysical methods in the direct, structural, and stratigraphic water locations are scattered widely throughout the literature in various languages. The following discussion of results is not complete, but an attempt is made to cover the most important and significant data.

As far as the *direct location of water* is concerned, most of the available literature deals with fissure and fault water. Radioactive reactions above them have been described by Ebert[1]

[1] EBERT, A., *Z. deut. Geol. Ges.*, vol. 85, no. 7, p. 496, 1933.

and Ludewig.[1] Such reactions are distinct only when the overburden is thin. Ludewig's objective was the location of radioactive waters of medicinal importance in the vicinity of a spa. Highly conductive water on faults and fissures can generally be located rather well by high-frequency inductive methods. Cloos[2] could detect their presence by "dead spots" in radio reception. However, there is some doubt as to whether some of these observations should not more properly belong in the group of structural methods.

Attempts have been made to locate subterranean cavern water by radio observations.[3] Good results may also be obtained by the use of electromagnetic methods using 500-cycle frequency, as demonstrated by a survey of reception-coil tilt angles over subterranean water courses, published by Reich.[4]

A number of examples have been published on the *structural indirect water location* by torsion balance, magnetic, seismic, and electrical methods. Where the water accumulation is controlled by the topography of buried valleys, the bedrock surface may be contoured with the torsion balance. Holst[5] has published such a survey of the Dreisam valley in Baden, and McClintock and Phemister[6] demonstrate the results of torsion balance measurements above the buried Kelvin River valley near Glasgow. Examples are numerous in the literature of other structural applications of the torsion balance to the location of faults, dikes, and other structures. The possibilities of the magnetic method for indirect water location were investigated by Grohskopf[7] who found that in many regions in Missouri the accumulations of ground water occurred at the flanks of magnetic highs and near magnetic lows but not on magnetic highs. The magnetic relief followed in a general way the topography of the igneous basement rocks.

[1] LUDEWIG, P., and H. WITTE, *Z. Geophys.*, vol. 2, no. 70, 1926.

[2] CLOOS, E., *Amer. Jour. Sci.*, vol. 28, no. 166, p. 255, 1934.

[3] FRITSCH, V., *Beitr. angew. Geophysik.*, vol. 4, no. 4, p. 416, 1934; vol. 5 no. 3, p. 315, 1935; vol. 5, no. 4, p. 375, 1936.

[4] REICH, H., *Angewandte Geophysik*, II, pp. 121–134, 1934.

[5] HOLST, H., *Beitr. naturw. Ges. Freiburg*, no. 3, 1925.

[6] McCLINTOCK, W. F. P., and J. PHEMISTER, *Roy. Soc. Edinburgh*, 56(I), no. 7, p. 141, 1929.

[7] GROHSKOPF, J. G., and C. O. REINOEHL, *Miss. Bur. Mines 57th Bienn. Rept.*, App. IV, p. 18, 1933.

The location of water-bearing valley fills and gravel channels has most frequently been undertaken with seismic and electrical methods. The seismic problem is discussed, for instance, by Edge and Laby,[1] although their surveys were made primarily for a different purpose. The same authors have applied resistivity measurements to the location of such channels. Frequent reference is made in the literature to the location of sand and gravel lenses in clays by resistivity measurements.[2] The problem becomes one of structural water location if the sands, as is often the case, are water bearing. DeCeccaty[3] has published a resistivity survey of a valley filled with water-bearing alluvial beds above impervious Cretaceous marls, in Algiers, and one of the topography of impervious nummulite chalk under water-bearing Quaternary deposits near Biarritz. Again, where faults,[4] dikes, or fracture zones[5] are associated with the occurrence of water, they may likewise be located by resistivity and seismic measurements.

As to *stratigraphic methods* of water location, results obtained with methods other than resistivity or potential drop methods will be discussed first.

As stated before, waters of high salinity may be located with comparative ease by the use of inductive methods. Sundberg[6] and Zuschlag[7] have published in detail the results obtained with their inductive methods in structural studies by using the high salinity of sedimentary beds in oil fields. Königsberger[8] gives an example of the reaction obtained by using his central induction method on a section with water-bearing gravels above conductive

[1] EDGE-LABY, "Principles and Practice of Geophysical Prospecting," Cambridge University Press, 1931.

[2] HEILAND, C. A., *Amer. Inst. Min. Met. Eng., Trans.*, Geophysical Prospecting, p. 546, 1934; HUBBERT, M. K., *Ibid.*, p. 9; KURTENACKER, S. A., *Ibid.*, p. 49.

[3] DeCECCATY, R. P., et M. JABIOL, "L'Eau," Asnières, Seine, 1935.

[4] HUBBERT, M. K., *Amer. Inst. Min. Met. Eng., Trans.*, Geophysical Prospecting, p. 40, 1934.

[5] HEILAND, C. A., *Terr. Mag.*, vol. 37, no. 3, p. 343, September, 1932.

[6] SUNDBERG, K., *Amer. Assn. Pet. Geol. Bull.*, vol. 14, no. 9, p. 1145, September, 1930.

[7] ZUSCHLAG, THEO., *Amer. Inst. Min. Met. Eng., Trans., Geophysical Prospecting*, p. 144, 1932.

[8] KÖNIGSBERGER, J., *Beitr. angew. Geophysik*, vol. 3, no. 4, p. 392, 1933; vol. 4, no. 2, p. 201, 1934.

clays and marls. Loewy and Leimbach[1] have described the determination of the distance of a ground-water level from below by measurements in the interior of a salt mine and have given a brief summary of the applications of their radio-interference method of ground-water location in desert regions of Southwest Africa. Stern[2] discusses the application of reflection of radio waves from a water surface in a quarry, but points out also that their depth penetration is exceedingly limited; for a wave-length of about 50 meters the penetration for fairly dry limestone and sandstone is from 30 to 70 meters, while for clay it would be only about 8 meters. Hence the usefulness of radio methods for ground-water locations in temperate and moist climates is doubtful. With his electromagnetic method Haalck[3] tested lignite deposits in Germany and found distinct changes in the electromagnetic field, depending on the change of water content of the deposits with depth.

A number of examples have been published showing the possibilities of the seismic methods in the location of water-bearing strata. The increase in velocity due to water saturation of unconsolidated sediments is appreciable. Heiland[4] illustrates this with a number of travel-time curves obtained by Rieber in California on shallow water sands. While the longitudinal wave velocities in dry, loose formations seldom exceed 2000 ft. per second, these same formations may show speeds up to 4500 to 6000 ft. per second when saturated with water. DeCeccaty[5] has published travel-time curves obtained in the location of a Cretaceous chalk with artesian water supply in south Tunis and has reproduced reflection seismograms obtained in the study of artesian horizons, likewise in Tunis, with reflecting beds at depths of 350 and 800 meters.

By far the majority of ground-water studies have been made with the *electric-resistivity method*. Results of various types obtained in all parts of the world by different authors are discussed below and an attempt is made to classify results in accord-

[1] LOEWY, H., and G. LEIMBACH, *Phys. Z.*, vol. 13, p. 397, 1912; vol. 20, p. 416, 1919; *Beitr. angew. Geophysik*, vol. 5, no. 2, p. 257, 1935.

[2] STERN, W., *Beitr. angew. Geophysik*, vol. 1, no. 4, p. 454, 1931.

[3] HAALCK, H., and L. EBERT, *Z. Geophys.*, vol. 8, no. 8, p. 409, 1932.

[4] HEILAND, C. A., *Explos. Eng.*, vol. 13, no. 12, p. 359, December, 1935.

[5] DeCECCATY, R. P., et M. JABIOL, "L'Eau," Asnières, Seine, 1935.

ance with the type curves of Fig. 93. Most of the curves were obtained from field data but were simplified for this figure. Apparent resistivity is plotted to the right, electrode separation and thus depth is plotted downward. In no case are there sharp breaks[1] on the formation boundaries. This is substantiated by both theory and results obtained in the field with equipment of good construction.

The case of *two layers* is illustrated by two sets of identical curves on the left-hand side of the figure; that of the *three-layer* case on the right-hand side. Two curves have also been drawn for *intermediate* cases, so named because the apparent resistivity curves are of a type which corresponds either to an extreme of a two-layer setup with thin surface layer, or a three-layer case in which the conductivities either increase or decrease in three steps downward. They are similar in type to the three-layer case except that the peaks in the intermediate layer are no longer noticeable. The two-layer section of the intermediate case is shown on the left (*a*) side of the four curves and the three-layer section on the right (*b*) side. In the three-layer case strata of different conductivities are interbedded between a surface and a bottom layer the conductivities of which are similar. Curves of the same appearance have been arranged below one another to show the difference in interpretation between curves obtained when the aquifer is a good conductor and those obtained when it is a poor conductor.

As indicated before, the practical examples where the aquifer is a poor conductor are less numerous than the ones where it is a good conductor. This assists in the practical application of the diagrams. The two-layer curves are less frequent in practice than the three-layer curves. Of the former $A1$ is most frequent, $A2$ ranks next, then follows $B2$ and last $B1$. The three-layer group is observed more often than the intermediate group. It is difficult to give curves in this latter group different ranks; probably $A3$ is most frequent. As to the three-layer group, curve $A5$ is predominant. Type $A6$ is also common. Curves $A5$ and $A6$ are the most valuable indicators of the position of the zone of saturation. Of the B-type curves, $B5$ probably comes first and $B6$ last.

---

[1] Sharp breaks on boundaries are obtained with the potential-drop-ratio and potential-gradient methods.

The type $A5$ indication is obtained when the water table occurs in sand and gravel and thus makes the lower portion more conductive, while the dry portion above remains a poor conductor. A moist surface formation is the top conductive layer in this combination. The ground-water level in virtually all of these curves occurs slightly below the peak. This was probably first observed by W. J. Rooney[1] in the copper country

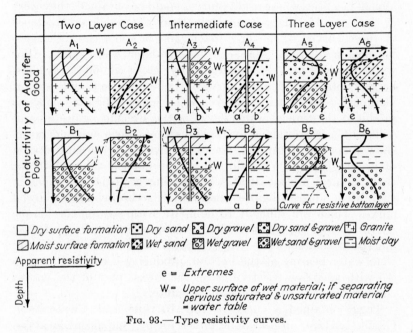

Fig. 93.—Type resistivity curves.

of Michigan for a water level 25 ft. below ground surface in glacial drift, above Keweenawan rocks at about 70 ft. in depth. Some of his curves show a rise instead of the drop below water table in type $A5$. At Huancago[2] he obtained typical water curves in alluvial deposits and states that wells dug in the general area in search for water did not find it (possibly the wells were not deep enough; the curves indicated low resistivity level at about 80 ft. in depth). In 1930, Jakosky[3] conducted surveys in the San

[1] ROONEY, W. J., *Terr. Mag.*, vol. 35, no. 2, p. 61, June, 1930.
[2] *Ibid.*
[3] JAKOSKY, J. J., *Arizona Min. Jour.*, Jan. 15, 1931.

Fernando Valley in California and obtained a series of good
ground-water indications of the same type. In the following
years extensive ground-water studies were made at the Colorado
School of Mines. A number of typical ground-water curves were
published by Tattam[1] and Heiland[2] from Colorado, New Mexico,
and Texas and similar curves were contributed by Henderson from
California. Tattam[3] continued his studies in Nigeria and in virtually all localities where usable curves could be obtained, they were
of the type $A5$. Depth determinations were made on the basis
of these curves whenever possible and in some cases the geophysical predictions were checked by later water wells. For
water-bearing gravels underlain by clays at 60-ft. Königsberger[4] obtained a distinct curve of the same type near Freiburg,
Germany. Dry sands above water-logged lignite deposits
produced the typical water curve in the Rhenan lignite area of
Ville.[5] Curves obtained by Hawkins[6] on Ontario lignite deposits
show almost an identical character, probably for the same reason
of water logging. Virtually all curves published by Stern for
the Ville area are identical, while similar geologic conditions in
the Niederlausitz lignite districts (Czechoslovakia) showed
curves which are difficult to compare with any of the simple
curves of Fig. 93, because of more frequent alternation of good
and poor conductors. Near Cologne sands above the lignite
were water bearing at the bottom, producing a curve similar to
$A5$ with very low resistivities on the lowest part of the curves
corresponding to the water-logged lignite.

Tagg[7] obtained a curve of the $A5$ type near Cheltenham,
Gloucestershire, on limestone underlain by sand at one location,
while at another the curve completely reversed itself and, for
the same surface formation, became the $A6$ type. The interpre-

[1] TATTAM, C. M., Dissertation, Colorado School of Mines, Golden, 1932.

[2] HEILAND, C. A., Terr. Mag., vol. 37, no. 3, p. 343, September, 1932.

[3] TATTAM, C. M., Colorado School Mines Quart., vol. 31, no. 3, July 1936.

[4] KÖNIGSBERGER, J., Beitr. angew. Geophysik, vol. 3, no. 4, p. 392, 1933;
vol. 4, no. 2, p. 201, 1934.

[5] STERN, W., Beitr. angew. Geophysik, vol. 3, no. 4, p. 408, 1933; Braunkohle, ibid., pp. 893, 909, 1932.

[6] HAWKINS, R. H., Amer. Inst. Min. Met. Eng., Trans., Geophysical Prospecting, p. 76, 1934.

[7] TAGG, G. F., Amer. Inst. Min. Met. Eng., Trans., Geophysical Prospecting, p. 135, 1934.

tation was that in the first case a calcareous deposit was underlain by sand, taking up the moisture filtered through the overlying deposit, while in the second case clay was assumed to exist which kept the moisture in the lower portion of the calcareous deposit. In a technical memo published by the manufacturers of the "Megger" resistivity instrument, Tagg[1] presents a typical ground-water curve obtained in England and demonstrates how the depth to the water level is calculated.

The second type of typical water indication, $A6$, is obtained when water-bearing sand, gravel, valley fill or wash rest on impervious formations of high resistivity, such as limestone and granite. Then the upper layer is generally not altogether filled with water. This results in its being split up into a dry and poorly conductive surface layer and a moist and conductive intermediate layer. In this case the water-bearing rock registers low resistivity, minimum resistivity occurring below the water level. The curve is the reflected form of $A5$. Frequently the extreme form e (see Fig. 93) is observed. Contrary to statements by some authors, this does not imply that the bottom layer is of low resistivity; in fact, Poldini[2] calculated that this curve may be obtained for *infinite* bottom-layer resistivity if the conductivity of the intermediate layer is great enough (saline waters). This regular $A6$ type of water indication was obtained as early as 1925 by Gish and Rooney[3] in the Bradley Hills, Maryland, for Pleistocene strata about 100 ft. thick on crystalline bedrock. The extreme e curve was obtained by Gish at College Park, Maryland (water-bearing Pleistocene on granite), in Washington (filled ravine), and near Watheroo, Australia. Rooney[4] found the same for water in the low portion of overburden above Keweenawan formation in Michigan. Distance of this overburden from a mine stope below was then also determined. In this problem the sequence of formations and hence the curve was reversed (as in $A5$). In the many investigations carried out by Schlumberger and his collaborators for the determination of depth to bedrock, conductive water-bearing portions in glacial drift above crystalline rocks have been frequently encountered

[1] TAGG, G. F., *Evershed Vignoles Tech. Memo.* 55.
[2] POLDINI, E. M., *Bull. Tech. Suisse. Rom.*, Lausanne, 1932.
[3] GISH, O. H., and W. J. ROONEY, *Terr. Mag.*, vol. 30, no. 4, p. 161, 1925.
[4] ROONEY, W. J., *Terr. Mag.*, vol. 32, nos. 3–4, p. 97, 1927.

and gave rise to the typical $A6$ curve, as, for instance, in the survey published by Crosby and Leonardon[1] for a New England damsite.   Likewise Jakosky and Wilson[2] in a water survey in the Santa Rita Mountains, Arizona, obtained the same curve for fill saturated at the bottom, above bedrock, and under similar conditions in Trinity County, California.   The Cypress sandstone above the Mammoth Cave limestone produced, where water-bearing, a distinct drop in resistivity as determined by Eve and others.[3]   A distinct drop in resistivity was found due to water collecting above asphalt sands near Bowling Green, Kentucky, giving rise to a curve similar to $A6$ in its near-surface portion.[4]   Possibly in the same class belong the results obtained by Schlumberger on salt domes in Alsace where highly conductive clays and marls, possibly impregnated with saline waters, overlie poorly conductive sands and resistant salt.[5]   Extensive studies were made of the relation of ground water and apparent resistivities by Loehnberg and Stern.[6]   The section consisted of gravels on top, sand and marls below, and limestone at the bottom. Water is contained in the marl immediately below the sand and in crevices and caverns near the top of the limestone.   Here in many cases the extreme $A6\,e$ curves were obtained, with drops for the near-surface water and gradual rise in the limestones below, interrupted by low resistivity drops for the cavern water. In the absence of the high resistivity surface peak, these curves sometimes degenerated into the $A3$ type.

Next in the order of this discussion are water indications corresponding to the other A types.   To begin with $A1$, this type has been encountered by Schlumberger and others in his foundation investigations,[7] although they do not state specifically that the top layers are water bearing. $A2$ is rare, as this type is

[1] LEONARDON, E. G., and I. B. CROSBY, *Amer. Inst. Min. Met. Eng., Trans.*, Geophysical Prospecting, p. 199, 1929.

[2] JAKOSKY, J. J., and C. H. WILSON, *Amer. Inst. Min. Met. Eng., Trans., Tech. Publ.* 515, December, 1923.

[3] EVE, A. S., *et al.*, *Canad. Geol. Surv. Mem.* 165, II, 1929.

[4] *Ibid.*

[5] POLDINI, E. M., *Bull. Tech. Suisse. Rom.*, Lausanne, 1932.

[6] LOEHNBERG, A., and W. STERN, *Z. Geophys.*, vol. 8, nos. 6–7, p. 283, 1932.

[7] LEONARDON, E. G., and I. B. CROSBY, *Amer. Inst. Min. Met. Eng., Trans.*, Geophysical Prospecting, p. 199, 1929.

likely to occur more often in the three-layer form of $A5$. More examples are available for the $A3$ type which is obtained where water occurs near the surface and highly resistant media below. It is similar to $A1$ and $A6$. Numerous curves of this type were obtained by Stern and Loehnberg.[1] The same curves were observed by Edge and Laby[2] for sands and clays above coral filled with water of low salinity (therefore possibly belonging in the $B3$ type). For the identical section, however, the curves changed to the opposite $A4$ and $A5$ types where the waters were saline. Some of the curves published by Stern[3] for the Niederlausitz lignite deposits possibly belong in the $A3$ class, as they start out with low resistivities for the moist surface sands, then gradually increase for the moist lignite, and reach their highest value for the footwall sands which are probably dry.

As far as the indications of poorly conductive waters are concerned, results published are exceedingly scarce. This is probably due to the fact that this type of indication is difficult to obtain and is readily confused with the A type. Furthermore, dry gravel and gravel saturated with pure water of low conductivity are not readily distinguished. However, what little has been published is definite enough. Hubbert,[4] by resistivity mapping, definitely established that indications from water-bearing gravels may be determined by resistivity values. Kelly reports having mistaken a deeply buried gravel deposit in a damsite investigation for bedrock, no doubt on account of the purity of the water contained therein. That this is readily possible may be verified by comparison of types $A1$ and $B1$. Water indications of the $B5$ type have been obtained by Rothrock[5] in a South Dakota water survey, where conductive glacial clay occurred at the top, water gravel below, and resistive shale at the bottom. In the $B5$ type of Fig. 93 the clay was assumed to be conductive;

[1] LOEHNBERG, A., and W. STERN, *Z. Geophys.*, vol. 8, nos. 6–7, p. 283, 1932.

[2] EDGE-LABY, "Principles and Practice of Geophysical Prospecting," Cambridge University Press, 1931.

[3] STERN, W., *Beitr. angew. Geophysik*, vol. 3, no. 4, p. 408, 1933; *Braunkohle, ibid.*, pp. 893, 909, 1932.

[4] HUBBERT, M. K., *Amer. Inst. Min. Met. Eng., Trans.*, Geophysical Prospecting, p. 9, 1934.

[5] ROTHROCK, E. P., and B. C. PETSCH, *South Dakota Geol. Surv., Rept. Invest.* no. 24, January, 1935.

Rothrock's indications, therefore, approach the $A3$ and $A6$ types.

In surveys made by Lee[1] in Nevada deserts, water-bearing gravel appeared as high-resistivity indications, the type indication approaching $B3$, a. In a tidal basin of the Potomac Gish[2] carried out some "model" experiments with (river) water on top, mud below, and hard rock at the bottom and obtained a curve of the type $B6$ (with bedrock in place of water table) which originates from $B2$ by addition of a third resistive bottom layer.

Stern's[3] measurements near the bight of Cologne give definite information regarding the highly resistant nature of water-bearing gravel. The curves obtained there are typical water curves, but they are not interpreted as type $A5$ but as $B5$, as the water does not occur below the peak, but above. This was verified by a comparison of the resistivity results with wells.

Owing to the fact that the *potential-drop-ratio methods* are of comparatively recent date, very little has been published on results obtained by these methods, although they merit much greater attention for water location than they have received thus far. Cox[4] attempted to locate water-flooded portions of mine workings by ratio mapping at the surface, but found that the indications were overshadowed by surface resistivity variations caused by outcrops of different beds to such an extent that it was not possible to determine definitely the boundaries of the flooded areas. Probably in most cases the flooded areas were too small in comparison with their depths, being 200 to 300 ft. deep in one case and 700 ft. in another. Only in a third location where the depth was around 60 ft. could fairly promising indications be obtained.

A survey indicative of the possibilities of the potential-ratio methods has been published by Lundberg and Zuschlag.[5] In an area where arkose bedrock was overlain by glacial drift, the lower portion of which was water-bearing, the water level was

---

[1] LEE, F. W., Geophysical Prospecting for Underground Waters in Desert Areas: *U.S. Bur. Mines. Inf. Circ.* 6899, August, 1936.

[2] GISH, O. H., and W. J. ROONEY, *Terr. Mag.*, vol. 30, no. 4, p. 161, 1925.

[3] STERN, W., *Beitr. angew. Geophysik*, vol. 3, no. 4, p. 408, 1933; and *Braunkohle, ibid.*, pp. 893, 909, 1932.

[4] Cox, A. H., *Mining Mag.*, vol. 53, no. 2, p. 73, August, 1935.

[5] ZUSCHLAG, TH., *Amer. Inst. Min. Met. Eng., Trans.*, Geophysical Prospecting, p. 47, 1932.

clearly indicated by peaks to the left in the potential ratio-depth curve. Thus the water-table depth was indicated much more distinctly than by resistivity measurements; in that case curve *A*6 would have been obtained.

Economic Aspects of Geophysical Water Location.—The foregoing discussion of results obtained with various types of geophysical methods in the direct, structural, and stratigraphic location of water brings out the fact that a geophysical water survey is doomed to failure unless undertaken by someone well versed in the occurrence of ground water. As it is, a geophysical survey is expensive and its cost is comparable with that of drilling shallow wells or having an expert geologist examine the prospect. Therefore it is doubtful whether geophysical methods are economical for the location of a single or even a few wells. If the project is large enough, a geophysical survey of such proportions as to acquaint the operator with all geological and geophysical possibilities appears to be warranted. When undertaken, the closest cooperation between the geophysicist and geologist acquainted with the area is necessary. Unless surveys of this type can be undertaken on a cooperative basis with scientific institutions, the application of the more expensive methods such as torsion balance is generally not economical. Next in expense are seismic methods, which when properly handled are likely to give results equivalent or superior to those obtained with resistivity methods. In most cases the choice will be the resistivity method, but owing to the superiority in depth determinations from field data without elaborate calculations, the potential-drop or gradient methods are also likely to attain a definite place in electrical water search.

References

General

BAILEY, PAUL, Engineering Investigation of Percolation from Alameda Creek and Ground-water Studies in the Niles Cone, *Calif. State Water Comm., 3d Bienn. Rept.* 1921, pp. 95 *et seq.*

BAKER and CONKLING, "Water Supply and Utilization," pp. 346–369, John Wiley & Sons, Inc., 1930.

BARKSDALE, H. C., A Ten-year Record of Water-table Fluctuations near Runyon, N. J., *Trans. Amer. Geophys. Union*, pp. 446–471, 1933.

CLARK, W. O., Ground Water in the Santa Clara Valley, Calif., *U.S. Geol. Surv. Water-Supply Paper* 519, pp. 16–18, 58–75, 93–94, 1924.

LEE, C. H., An Interpretation of Water-levels in Wells and Test-holes, *Trans. Amer. Geophys. Union*, pp. 540–554, 1934.

——— Water Resources of a Part of Owens Valley, Calif., *U.S. Geol. Surv. Water-Supply Paper* 294, pp. 72 *et seq.*, 1912.

MEINZER, O. E., and N. D. STEARNS, A Study of Ground Water in the Pomperaug Basin, Conn., *U.S. Geol. Surv. Water-Supply Paper* 597-B. pp. 116–131, 1929.

——— Outline of Ground-water Hydrology, *U.S. Geol. Surv. Water-Supply Paper* 494, pp. 32–37, 1923.

——— The Occurrence of Ground Water in the United States, *U.S. Geol. Surv. Water-Supply Paper* 489, pp. 30–31, 95–96, 1923.

SLICHTER, C. S., Motions of Underground Water, *U.S. Geol. Surv. Water-Supply Paper* 67, pp. 24–43, 1902.

SMITH, G. E. P., Ground-Water Supply and Irrigation in the Rillito Valley, *Univ. Ariz. Agr. Exp. Sta. Bull.* 64, pp. 176–187, 1910.

STEARNS, H. T., and L. L. BRYAN, Preliminary Report on the Geology and Water Resources of the Mud Lake Basin, Idaho, *U.S. Geol. Surv. Water-Supply Paper* 560-D, pp. 107–110, 1926.

THOMPSON, D. G., The Mojave Desert Region, Calif., *U.S. Geol. Surv. Water-Supply Paper* 578, pp. 326–342, 1929.

VEATCH, A. C., Fluctuations of the Water Level in Wells, with Special Reference to Long Island, N.Y., *U.S. Geol. Surv. Water-Supply Paper* 155, 1906.

VEATCH, A. C., and others, Underground Water Resources of Long Island, N.Y., *U.S. Geol. Surv. Prof. Paper* 44, pp. 50–60, 1906.

WENZEL, L. K., Several Methods of Studying Fluctuations of Ground-water Level, *Trans. Amer. Geophys. Union*, pp. 400–406, 1936.

Symposium on Fluctuations of Ground-water Level, *Trans. Amer. Geophys. Union*, pp. 337–391, 1936.

The following *Water-Supply Papers* discuss the fluctuations of the water table: Nos. 10, 12, 18, 29, 30, 58, 67, 136, 137, 138, 139, 142, 153, 164, 213, 219, 232, 251, 256, 258, 294, 319, 320, 331, 343, 345-*G*, 345-*H*, 375-*A*, 400-*E*, 423, 446, 467, 560-*D*, 578, 597-*B*, 616, 619, 777.

Fresh Ground Water Floating on Salt Ground Water

BADON GHYBEN W., Nota in verband met de voorgenomen put boring nabij Amsterdam, *K. Inst. Ing. Tijdschr.*, p. 21, The Hague, 1888–1889.

BROWN, J. S., A Study of Coastal Ground Water, *U.S. Geol. Surv. Water-Supply Paper*, 537, pp. 14–39, 1925.

——— Relation of Sea Water to Ground Water along Coasts, *Amer. Jour. Sci.*, 5th ser. vol. 4, pp. 274–294.

HERZBERG, D., Die Wasserversorgung einiger Nordseebäder, *Jour. Gasbeleuchtung und Wasserversorgung*, Jahrg. 44, Munich, 1901.

WHITTAKER, W., The Water Supply of Essex from Underground Sources, *Great Britain Geol. Surv.*, pp. 24–34, 1916.

Geophysical Prospecting

AMBRONN, R., "Elements of Geophysics," McGraw-Hill Book Company, Inc., New York, 1928.

BRUCKSHAW, J. M., and F. DIXIE, Ground-water Investigations by Geophysical Methods, *Mining Mag.*, vol. 50, no. 2–3, pp. 73–147, February-March, 1934.

CLOOS, E., Auto Radio—An Aid in Geologic Mapping, *Am. Jour. Sci.*, 5th ser., vol. 28, no. 166, pp. 255–268, October, 1934.

COX, A. H., Geophysical Surveying in South Wales, *Min. Mag.*, vol. 53, no. 2, pp. 73–82, August, 1935.

DeCECCATY, R. P., and M. JABIOL, "L'Eau," Asnières (Seine), 1935.

EBERT, A., *Zeitsch. deut. Geol. Ges.*, vol. 85, no. 7, p. 496, 1933.

EDGE-LABY, "Principles and Practice of Geophysical Prospecting," Cambridge University Press, 1931.

EVE, A. S., *et al.*, *Canadian Geol. Surv. Mem.* 165, II, 1929.

FRITSCH, V., *Beitr. Angew. Geophysik*, vol. 4, no. 4, pp. 416–425; vol. 5, no. 2, pp. 251–256, 1935; vol. 5, no. 4, pp. 375, 1936.

GISH, O. H., and W. J. ROONEY, *Terrestrial Magnetism*, vol. 30, no. 4, 1925.

GROHSKOPF, J. G., and C. O. REINOEHL, Magnetic Surveys, *Miss. Bur. Geol. Mines, 57th Bienn. Rept.*, App. 4, 1933.

HAALCK, H., and L. EBERT, *Zeitsch. Geophysik*, vol. 8, no. 8, pp. 409–419, 1932.

HAWKINS, R. H., Application of Resistivity Methods to Northern Ontario Lignite Deposits, *Amer. Inst. Min. Met. Eng.*, *Contr.* no. 40, 1933; *Trans.* vol. 110, Geophysical Prospecting, pp. 76–120, 1934.

HEILAND, C. A., A New Geophone, *Amer. Inst. Min. Met. Eng.*, *Trans.*, Geophysical Prospecting, pp. 237–244, 1932.

——— Geophysics in the Nonmetallic Field (with discussion), *Am. Inst. Min. Met. Eng.*, *Trans.*, vol. 110, Geophysical Prospecting, pp. 546–577, June, 1934.

——— A Demonstration of the Geologic Possibilities of the Resistivity and Magnetic Prospecting Methods, *Terrestrial Magnetism*, vol. 37, no. 3, pp. 343–350, September, 1932.

——— Exploring with Explosives, *Explos. Eng.*, vol. 13, no. 12, December, 1935.

——— Geophysical Methods of Prospecting—Principles and Recent Successes, *Colorado School Min. Quart.*, vol. 24, no. 1, March, 1929.

HOLST, H., *Beitr. naturw. Ges.*, Freiburg, Heft. 3, 1935.

HUBBERT, M. K., Results of Earth-resistivity Survey on Various Geologic Structures in Illinois (with discussion), *Am. Inst. Min. Met. Eng.*, *Trans.*, vol. 110, Geophysical Prospecting, pp. 9–39, 40–48, 1934.

JAKOSKY, J. J., Practical Aspects of Geophysical Surveys, *Min. Jour.*, Phoenix, Ariz., vol. 14, no. 16, pp. 7–9, 29, Jan. 15, 1931.

JAKOSKY, J. J., and C. H. WILSON, Geophysical Studies in Placer and Water Supply Problems, *Amer. Inst. Min. Met. Eng.*, *Tech. Publ.* 515, 1934.

——— Electrical Conductivity of American Ores and Minerals, Univ. of Utah, 1928.

——— Electrical Mapping of Oil Structures, *Min. & Metal.*, pp. 231–237, May, 1936.

KOENIGSBERGER, J., *Beitr. Angew. Geophysik*, vol. 3, no. 4, 1933; vol. 4, no. 2, 1934.

KURTENACKER, K. S., Some Practical Applications of Resistivity Measurements to Highway Problems, *Amer. Inst. Min. Met. Eng., Trans.*, vol. 110, Geophysical Prospecting, pp. 49–59, 1934.

LEE, F. W., Geophysical Prospecting for Underground Water in Desert Areas: *U.S. Bur. Mines Inf. Circ.* 6899, August, 1936.

LEONARDON, E. G., and I. B. CROSBY, Electrical Prospecting Applied to Foundation Problems, *Amer. Inst. Min. Met. Eng., Trans.*, Geophysical Prospecting, pp. 199–210, 1929.

LOEHNBERG, A., and W. STERN, *Zeitsch. Geophysik*, vol. 8, nos. 6–7, p. 283, 1932.

LOEHNBERG, A., and A. LOEWENSTEIN, *Beitr. Angew. Geophysik*, vol. 6, No. 1, p. 52, 1936.

LOEWY, H., and G. LEIMBACH, *Phys. Zeitsch.*, vol. 13, p. 397, 1912; vol. 20, pp. 416, 919; *Beitr. Angew. Geophysik*, vol. 5, no. 2, p. 257, 1935.

McCLINTOCK, W. F. P., and J. PHEMISTER, *Roy. Soc. Edinburgh*, vol. 56, (I-7), p. 141, 1929.

PETROWSKY, A., *Beitr. Angew. Geophysik*, vol. 3, no. 2, p. 149, 1933.

POLDINI, E. M., *Bull. Techn. Suisse. Rom.*, Lausanne, 1932.

REICH, H., *Angewandte Geophysik*, pp. 121–134, 1934.

ROONEY, W. J., *Terrestrial Magnetism*, vol. 32, nos. 3–4, p. 97, 1927; vol. 35, no. 2, p. 61, June, 1930.

ROTHROCK, E. P., and B. C. PETSCH, A Shallow Water Supply for Huron, S.D., *South Dakota State Geol. Surv., Rept. Invest.* 24, January, 1935.

SCHLUMBERGER, C. and M., and E. G. LEONARDON, A New Contribution to Subsurface Studies by Means of Electrical Measurements in Drill Holes, *Am. Inst. Min. Met. Eng., Trans.*, vol. 110, Geophysical Prospecting, pp. 273–389, 1934.

—— Electrical Exploration of Water-covered Surfaces, *Amer. Inst. Min. Met. Eng., Contr.* no. 71, March, 1934.

STERN, W., *Beitr. Angew. Geophysik*, vol. 1, no. 4, p. 454, 1931; vol. 3, no. 4, p. 408, 1933.

STERN, W., *Braunkohle*, pp. 893, 909, 1932.

SUNDBERG, KARL, Electrical Prospecting for Oil Structure, *Amer. Assn. Pet. Geol. Bull.*, vol. 14, no. 9, pp. 1145–1163, September, 1930.

—— Effect of Impregnating Waters on Electrical Conductivity of Soils and Rocks, *Amer. Inst. Min. Met. Eng., Trans.*, Geophysical Prospecting, pp. 367–391, 1932.

TAGG, G. F., *Amer. Inst. Min. Met. Eng., Trans.*, Geophysical Prospecting, p. 135, 1934.

—— Evershed and Vignoles, *Tech. Memo* no. 55.

TATTAM, C. M., *Colorado School Mines Quart.*, vol. 31, no. 3, July, 1936.

WENNER, FRANK, A Method of Measuring Resistivity, *U.S. Bur. Standards Bull.*, vol. 12, 1916.

ZUSCHLAG, THEO., *Amer. Inst. Min. Met. Eng., Trans.*, Geophysical Prospecting, pp. 47, 144, 1932.

CHAPTER X

GROUND WATER IN FRACTURES AND SOLUTION OPENINGS

GROUND WATER IN FRACTURES

The water table in fractured impervious rock is the surface at the contact between the water body in the fractures and the overlying ground air. The water table is interrupted by the impervious rock between fractures and constitutes only a small portion of the surface projected through the water-air contact in the network of fractures.

The water body filling fractures is curiously skeletonized in shape,[1] consisting of intersecting tabular members with tubular enlargements at the intersections (Fig. 94). This hollow network of open fractures may be irregular, but more commonly is regular, especially if the fissures are opened up on a regularly spaced and oriented joint system. The tabular water bodies vary in thickness and may be mere filaments of water. The tubular water bodies are usually of supercapillary size and subject to rapid flow. Interconnection of fissures may extend over large areas, or the water body in a single fracture or group of fractures may be disconnected with the water body in adjacent openings.

Inasmuch as the water bodies in sedimentary and alluvial material are usually larger and more important than water bodies in fractured rock, study of the latter has been neglected. Unfortunately it has been assumed not only that the properties of this type of water body are similar to those of the better known type in pervious granular material, but also that the water table in fractured rock bears the same relation to the motions of the underlying water body as that which exists between the water table and ground water in pervious granular material. In the following discussion emphasis is laid on the dissimilar features

[1] DAVIS, W. M., Origin of Limestone Caverns; *Bull. Geol. Soc. Amer.*, vol. 41, pp. 486, 499, 1930.

of the two types of water tables and the underlying water bodies in order to combat the tendency to assume similarities that do not exist.   It should be noted that the analysis of water-table slopes in the preceding chapter does not hold for the water

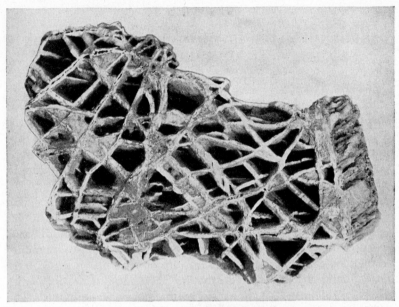

Fig. 94.—Photograph of quartz veinlets which fill the openings of an intersecting fracture system.   After deposition of the quartz the rock was removed by solution.   The specimen illustrates the skeletonized form of a fracture system.

table in fractured rock, or holds only in part where the fractures are minutely interconnected below the water table.

Classification of Fractures

The occurrence and motions of vadose and ground water are controlled chiefly by the extent, pattern, size and openness, continuity and interconnection of fractures; by the hydrologic characteristics (chiefly size and openness) of the master or discharge aquifers at or near the ground surface; and by topography which usually locates the escape of effluent percolation or flow.   The character of fracturing is determined by the physical properties of the fractured rock and the geological processes that have acted upon it, and therefore must be investigated by geological methods of research.

For the purpose of this discussion fractures may be classified as (1) deep-seated, (2) superficial, and (3) those characteristic of lavas.

Deep-seated Fractures.—Deep-seated fractures are produced by earth stresses originating at depth below the surface. These include faults, shear zones, breccia zones, as well as regular and irregular systems of deep-seated fractures such as conjugate fissure systems, rectangular and rhombohedral systems, and curvilinear, horsetail, and braided systems. The depth to which open fractures may extend is limited by the competence of the rock to hold fractures open under the weight of overlying material. They are believed to extend to depths of several miles and may persist as closed fractures to greater depths.

The major fractures and fracture zones of the deep-seated type are usually widely spaced. Crushing, shearing, and brecciation are usually limited to definite zones separated by unfractured or only moderately fractured material. Faults may be many miles apart. In regions of great dynamic disturbance, however, large areas may be affected by deep-seated crushing and brecciation. A description of unusually intense fracturing is taken from a report of the Consulting Board for the San Gabriel project Los Angeles County, California.[1]

The San Gabriel Mountains as a whole, including those portions traversed by the main trunk and the East and West Forks of the San Gabriel River, are greatly broken by major and minor faults.

There are also shear zones (parallel fractures with small movements distributed on many parallel planes) and joint planes (with little or no displacement along the joint surfaces) roughly parallel to the three major directions of faulting.

The tremendous dynamic activity that elsewhere in Southern California has deformed the Cretaceous and Tertiary sedimentary rocks by folding and faulting and has been capable of overturning major folds so that the younger rocks lie under the older strata, as in the Santa Barbara mountain ranges, has found relief solely in fracture, faulting and crushing of the granitic rocks of the San Gabriel region.

The result is as if the rocky formations of the San Gabriels were pinched in the jaws of a gigantic laboratory testing machine. The joint planes, shear planes and faults have cut the bedrock into innumer-

[1] Los Angeles County Flood Control District, San Gabriel Project Progress Report of Consulting Board, Oct. 27, 1931, Supplementary Geological Data, p. *A*2-3.

able blocks, slabs and wedges of rhombohedral, polygonal and prismatic shapes.

Superficial Fractures.—In addition to and quite distinct from the occasional widely spaced fracture systems formed and opened up by deep-seated stresses, innumerable planes of strain, of incipient fracture, rock weakness, and easy parting have been formed in rigid crystalline rocks by deep-seated stresses. In schistose rocks schistosity affords planes of easy parting and in cemented and recrystallized sedimentary rocks planes of sedimentation are usually planes of weakness.

These planes of weakness and incipient fracture, as well as the planes of actual rupture, are opened up by weathering. The processes of weathering are most active at or near the surface and are usually limited to the zone of alternate wetting and drying above the water table. Most of the fractures close and disappear at the water table and only the open fractures produced by other processes than those of weathering extend into the saturated zone. Only in soluble rock such as limestone and gypsum are openings which may function as conduits dissolved out within the saturated zone, and solution of this type is not usually classified as weathering (pages 301–307).

Structure and Hydrologic Properties of the Fractured Zone

The superficial zone of porosity discussed above has a characteristic structure and resulting hydrologic properties regardless of the type of impervious rock, thickness of the fractured zone, or pattern of the fractures.

At the surface the completely fractured and disintegrated rock, often overlain by residual soil and locally by talus material, constitutes a sponge and temporary reservoir which absorbs rainfall and delivers it to the underlying fracture system, thus reducing runoff which is rapid on rock devoid of such covering. Such localized reservoirs are an important source of water supply for the fracture systems draining them.

Below the Surface to the Water Table.—The small fractures usually disappear with depth, the system becomes more widely spaced, and the intervening blocks of rock become larger and less weathered. The change from weathered fractured material to fresh unaltered rock is usually sharply localized at the water table unless the latter has recently been elevated or depressed.

Below the water table the structure is dependent upon the open fractures produced by deep-seated stresses. Usually the number of open fractures is far less than in the zone of aeration. The major fractures are often unconnected with each other and each carries an individual and isolated water body. Occasionally they contain hot, mineralized or unmineralized water ascending from depth.

Size of Water Body.—Open fractures are not abundant below the water table, and hence the quantity of water stored therein is usually small. Even where the water body has risen into the fractured zone, the supply is meager compared with that stored in alluvial and sedimentary materials. Occasionally, however, water flows in fractures encountered by mining operations are spectacular (pages 312–313).

Owing to physical differences of layered formations, fractured rock may be underlain by a body of unfractured rock. The unfractured formation then constitutes the lower limit of the water body and the contact may control important water flows, especially if the unfractured formation is nearly flat and has been truncated by stream valleys. The spectacular springs that issue from pervious and fractured lava above its contact with an impervious stratum are fed by ground-water flows of the above-described type (pages 457–460).

Effect of Erosion and Earth Movements on Water Table.— Changes in elevation of the ground surface due to earth movements affect the absolute elevation of the water table (measured from a fixed point and not from the ground surface). Movement of the land surface carries the water table with it. As far as the effect on the water table and on the quantity and movements of ground water are concerned, the absolute changes in elevation are not so important as changes measured from ground surface. Erosion in the youthful stage when canyons and deep valleys are being excavated lowers the water table rapidly below ground surface, and the water table rises toward ground surface in mature and old-age stages of erosion. A rise of the water table toward the surface makes the lower portion of the porous weathered zone available as storage space. Lowering of the water table limits storage to the occasional fractures opened up below the water table. Changes of this type take place slowly during the topographic cycle of erosion but interruption of the cycle may result in sudden changes.

Fluctuation of Water Table during Cycle of Erosion.—Starting with an elevation of the ground surface, which initiates a new topographic cycle, the water table in the superficial fractured zone remains near the surface until youthful canyons furnish lower points of escape for ground water. The water first drains out of the deeper fractures truncated by the youthful valleys and out of fractures connected with them. On account of irregularity of interconnections between the fissures, the water table may not be lowered uniformly but may be split up into different units, each of which may have a different escape point and hence a different elevation. Some of the water tables may be adjusted to the elevation of the valley floors, some may be adjusted to discharge of water on the sides of valleys, and some water tables in fissures unconnected with canyons may stand far above the stream levels.

Later on, in the mature stage of erosion, after the main streams and many tributaries have reached grade and weathering has had sufficient time to open up minor interconnecting fissures, a general water table may be adjusted to the elevation of the stream courses over a large area. In the stage of old age, when the region is approaching a peneplain and small difference in elevation exists between the stream courses and the adjacent flat country, ground water filling fissures, fractures, and decomposed material may develop slow percolation in the direction of the water-table slope and stand close to the surface.

If the topographic cycle is interrupted by sinking or tilting of the land so that the stream channels are invaded by lake or ocean water (drowned valleys) and lacustrine or marine sediments are deposited in them, or if they are filled with alluvial sediment or with detrital and volcanic materials, the discharge level of the fissure systems will be elevated, and the water level will be raised and fill the more capacious reservoir developed by weathering above the former water table. If decomposition and disintegration of the rock are complete, the weathered material may be pervious and granular. Water movement is not limited to fissures and the behavior of ground water may be similar to that of the diffuse water body in pervious alluvial or sedimentary material.

Water Table and Movements in the Fractured Zone

Water Movements above the Water Table.—Vadose water movement (influent seepage) takes a circuitous course down interlaced fractures to the water table. Water moves from innumerable small feeding fractures into the main trunk channels furnished by the larger fractures. In large open fractures the potential movement is rapid, but the feeding fractures control the quantity of water supplied, and above the water table the fractures are lined by a temporary film of water and filled with ground air. The rate of movement may vary greatly with the quantity of water supplied and the size of the opening. This movement is very different from seepage in pervious granular material, in which movement is straight down and is impeded on the even pellicular front wherever the films of pellicular water have been depleted by evaporation, transpiration, or chemical reaction. A somewhat similar retardation of downward movement may take place in small fractures if their surfaces have been robbed of water, especially by the chemical processes of weathering known as hydration, because the fracture surfaces must be rewetted before seepage can take place. This retardation is less effective in larger fractures and is far more irregular in fractured rock than in granular pervious material. The downward movement in fractured impervious rock is truly a wandering down the most suitable pathway in a system of intersecting fissures, and the term "vadose water" is aptly applied to water trickling down fractures to the water table.

Movement of Water at and below the Water Table.—The movement of ground water in fractured rocks is (1) turbulent ground-water flow or percolation of free water along the intersection of the fracture or fracture system with the water table, and (2) a confined downward movement in fractures which extend to considerable depths below the water table, to rise again to the point of exit of the fissure.

Water-table flow is in the direction of water-table slope and is limited strictly to the superficial portion of the water body in a single fracture or interconnected group of fractures. It may be pictured as an *overflow* as distinguished from the *underflow* of confined water. The direction of overflow would be shown in a map of the water table in an interconnected group of fractures (Fig. 95).

The water-table slope in fractured rock is usually flatter than in pervious alluvial and sedimentary material because most of the fractures are of supercapillary size and frictional resistance

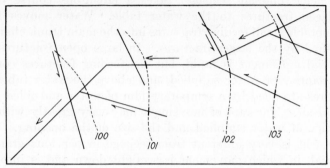

Fig. 95.—Contour map of the water table in fractured rock, illustrating overflow in the direction of water-table slope.

to movement is less than in interconnected capillary openings. Water-table flow may be important in flat regions where stream valleys do not intersect deeper fissures and thus afford an escape

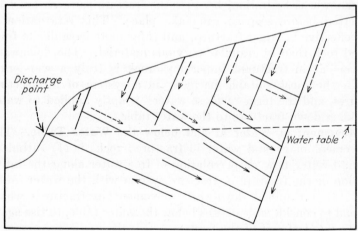

Fig. 96.—Cross section in fractured rock, illustrating underflow in fractures below the water table. Seepage indicated by dashed arrows, flow by solid arrows.

at a lower level than the collecting area. Usually, however, confined flow is more important than water-table flow.

Confined flow in fractures commonly extends to considerable depths and rises along master fractures to the discharge point of the major fractures (Fig. 96). The outlet of the major aquifer controls the water level in the system of fractures tributary to it. If all the outlets are at the bottom of a large valley, the water levels in all the fractures tributary to the aquifers discharging into the valley are adjusted to the depth of the valley floor. The elevation of the discharge point of the main aquifer, however, is only one element in determining the standing level of the water in the tributary fractures. The other factor is the friction of flow, especially in the master aquifer. This friction is developed at points of restriction, especially at or near the outlet. If the outlet is choked, the water level in all the tributary

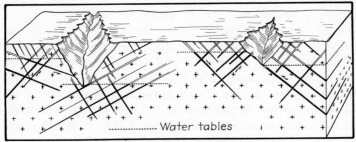

Fig. 97.—Ground water in fracture systems.

fractures may be considerably above the level of discharge (Fig. 97). If the conduit exit is enlarged artificially by cleaning off the soil or debris lying over it, the water level in all tributary fractures may drop rapidly and approach the level of the exit. A tunnel may drain the entire fracture system tributary to the fractures intercepted by it. The volume of rock thus drained may be irregular and may not have the shape of the ground-water trench developed by drainage ditches and tunnels in pervious alluvial or sedimentary material. The lowering of the water table in fractured rock by artificial excavations has been the subject of many actions at law.

Comparison of Water Table in Fractured Rock with That in Pervious Granular Material

The water table in fractured rock may be the upper surface of overflow or more commonly the fountain head of confined water in the deeper fractures or both. If underflow is important, the water table will vary in each group of interconnected fissures, and therefore a group of such water tables may be terraced or constitute a series of elevated and depressed surfaces. These terraces may have no relation to "ground-water dams" and develop no "ground-water cascades" as have been described for the water table in pervious granular material (pages 234–235).

The water table of an interconnected fissure system slopes from the intake to the discharge point usually at a much flatter grade than the water table in alluvial or sedimentary material. The water table in a superficial fissured zone can rarely be properly designated as "a subdued replica of the surface topography."

A general diffuse movement of water in the direction of the water-table slope as has been described for ground water in pervious granular material is probably uncommon, and the principal movement takes place in enlarged portions of fractures. This flow may be rapid and often descends to considerable distance below the water table and ascends finally to the point of discharge of the aquifer at the surface. It appears therefore that diffuse percolation of free ground water near the water table is important in pervious granular material, and confined flow below the water table and concentrated in the larger fractures is the important type of movement in fractured rock.

Source of Information Regarding Ground Water in Fractured Rock

The above generalizations regarding the water table and movements of a water body in fractured rock are not drawn from comprehensive investigations of natural conditions, because such studies have not been made by the writer and are not described in the literature. They are deduced from the well-known behavior of water supplied by fractured material in wells, springs, superficial excavations, and mines.

Great variations in the quantity of water and the head under which it issues are shown in excavations in fractured rock. A single fracture may furnish a large flow and the remainder of the fractures mere exudations of moisture. The water level in wells may be fairly uniform and, again, striking differences in water level may occur in short distances.

The limited amount of water held even in a deep fracture system is indicated by the water encountered in mines. Ore bodies often occur in faulted and fractured regions, yet large flows of water are encountered chiefly in occasional large open fractures or solution channels, and these are usually short-lived unless the aquifers are directly connected with surface water or with structures functioning as subsurface reservoirs. Gouge and ground-up fault filling often seal large faults and fractures so that they are completely dry. The bulk of the water in a mine is usually encountered in the upper workings and hence pumps are often installed in upper levels to take care of the water draining from the surface. When this is done the deeper levels may be relatively dry and in some cases even dusty.

GROUND WATER IN SOLUTION OPENINGS

Solution openings are formed chiefly in rocks appreciably soluble in water, such as limestone, dolomite, gypsum, and salt. However, difficultly soluble rocks may be dissolved, especially if crushed, for crushing increases enormously the rock surface exposed to solution. If a crushed zone is bounded by impervious formations, especially by gouge, and concentrated ground-water movement continuously supplies undersaturated water to the rock surfaces, solution cavities may be formed occasionally in such relatively insoluble materials as granite, quartzite, schist, and slate.[1]

The most important and spectacular work of solution is performed in limestone. Limestone openings discharge the largest known springs (pages 453–457) and may deflect all surface flow underground to be stored in solution channels and discharged by perched underground streams or water-table rivers, or by flows from subwater-table conduits. Vadose and ground-water solutions are guided by fractures in the rock which may be gradually enlarged by solution, and a characteristic type of vadose and ground-water flow established in the openings thus formed.

Limestone formations which act as hosts for solution openings may be either porous and pervious or nonporous and impervious. The pattern of openings in impervious (dense and crystalline) limestone is different in strata with flat-lying attitude from those with markedly inclined dip. Hence the development of openings and water movements therein are discussed under the

[1] Solution channels have been observed by the writer in the above-mentioned rock types in mines, tunnels, and excavations for dams.

following headings: (1) impervious limestone in flat-lying beds, (2) impervious limestone in inclined beds, and (3) porous limestone.

Ground Water in Impervious, Flat-lying Limestone

Dense impervious limestone and dolomite occur generally north and west of the Atlantic Coastal belt and the Tertiary embayment of the Gulf of Mexico, and are of pre-Tertiary age. As far as appreciable subsurface water movement is concerned, these limestones are practically impervious, although water may circulate freely through them in fractures and solution openings.

Structural Attitude.—A nearly horizontal attitude is characteristic of the massive, impervious limestone formations in the region west and northwest of the Appalachian-Ouachita mountain arc of close folding, and east of the Rocky Mountain belt of uplift, folding, and faulting. Also areas underlain by relatively flat beds are found in the crests of large anticlines and in the centers of synclines within regions that have been subjected to pronounced structural disturbance. In formations lying in approximately horizontal position, shale layers or laminae, or even a stratum of less soluble limestone, may act as barriers to downward solution and therefore to downward movement of water. Horizons of solution galleries may be located above such barriers (Fig. 100A, page 306). In inclined limestone strata the water table is usually the most important barrier to downward solution and to the circulation of water.

Development of Openings.—Horizontal beds of limestone are usually transected by a regular and nearly vertical system of joints (Fig. 98) of rectangular or rhombic pattern or occasionally by a polygonal system consisting of vertical planes oriented parallel to three major directions. Horizontal parting planes parallel to the bedding planes combined with the nearly vertical joints divide the limestone into regular blocks (Fig. 99). At depth the joint and bedding planes are merely planes of easy separation which are opened up near the surface by weathering. However, large joints may be opened up below the water table by stresses engendered by earth movements. The joints opened by weathering in limestone are usually widely spaced. Were it not for solution, most of them would remain closed and all but the largest would hold and deliver only meager quantities of water.

The Process of Solution.—The solubility of calcite or limestone rock is stated by Davis[1] to be one in about 30,000 parts by weight of pure water, but calcium carbonate is seven times more soluble in water charged with carbon dioxide under ordinary atmospheric pressure than in pure water. Aragonite is more soluble than calcite and therefore occurs only in limestone of recent age.

Acid soil solutions, especially those derived from decaying swamp and forest vegetation, are active solvents of calcium carbonate, as evidenced by the prevalence of pedalfer soils wherever acid soil solutions occur (pages 130–132). Even in the

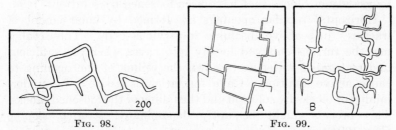

FIG. 98.   FIG. 99.

FIG. 98.—Plan of part of Donnehues Cave, Indiana, an excellent example of conduits opened up on a rectangular fracture system. (*After Blatchley.*)

FIG. 99.—Plan of solution galleries formed on a joint system, showing transformation of angular into curved passages. (*After Davis.*)

pedocal soils of arid regions the soil solutions leach calcium carbonate out of horizon *A* of the soil and concentrate it in horizon *B*. Acid waters of mines also produce large solution openings below the water table.

The vadose water of humid grass- and forest-covered regions, and to a less degree of arid regions, dissolves passageways in vertical joints of dense limestone, especially at their intersections, and also opens up nearly horizontal conduits (1) just above less soluble and unfractured barriers, such as shale strata (Fig. 100*A*); (2) at the water table; and (3) below the ground-water level (Fig. 100, *D* and *E*). The processes by which these openings have been produced and their size, shape, and arrangement have been described repeatedly in geological literature dealing with the origin of limestone caves.[2]

[1] DAVIS, *op. cit.*, p. 486.

[2] The reader is referred to citation of important geological descriptions of caves and their formation in limestone in "Origin of Limestone Caverns," by Davis, *op. cit.*, pp. 477–483.

As may be inferred from the literature on the subject of caves, vadose water carrying carbon dioxide and reagents derived from the soil descends in the fairly widely spaced vertical openings occurring at the intersections of fissures. Solution of limestone is more active at the intersections than elsewhere on the fractures because of the larger volume of undersaturated water moving in the intersections. The descending water excavates vertical shafts at the intersections, which may develop into funnel-shaped sinkholes due to enlargement at the ground surface by solution, mechanical abrasion, surface wash, and dislodgment by gravity of blocks that have been loosened by solution.

Horizontal tubular openings are formed by enlargement of fractures just above insoluble impervious beds. These tubes may be further enlarged locally into caves wherever sufficient undersaturated water flows down the ceiling of the opening to cause active solution. Cave formation is assisted by undermining of blocks by solution and the falling of the loosened blocks. This process might be aptly denominated *solution stoping* (Fig. 100*E*).

Sinkholes are also formed by the collapse of caverns the roofs of which have been thinned either by subsurface solution or erosion of the ground surface. Diversion of surface water increases with increase in number and size of openings connected with the surface until all the surface water of the area underlain by limestone may be diverted underground.

Filling of Cavities by Precipitation.—Vadose water precipitates as well as dissolves. After caverns have been enlarged and the subsurface streams are diverted into lower levels, films or thin sheets of water moistening the roofs of the caverns may become supersaturated with $CaCO_3$, owing probably to slow movement which gives time for saturation, to the escape of CO_2 into the ground air of the caves, and to evaporation. At the dripping points on the roof "rock icicles" or stalactites are formed, and underneath them on the floor the spattering drops build up stalagmites. If the process continues long enough, the cave may be nearly filled with "dripstone."

Subsurface Perched Streams.—The flat tubular conduits carry intermittent subsurface streams. These may cascade or form rapids as they descend from an upper to a lower horizon of horizontal openings and may enlarge the openings by corrasion as well as by solution. Vadose water in solution horizons above the water table is concentrated largely into *subsurface perched streams*.

Water-table Streams.—The water table is the final barrier to downward vadose movements and on it are located subsurface streams which occupy the larger tunnels opened up by concentrated and therefore unsaturated ground-water turbulent flow. In *impervious soluble* rock most of the ground water is concentrated in large openings and flows with the freedom of surface streams. These larger streams are usually perennial, although their flow increases greatly after heavy rains, when the subsurface floods may be loaded with sediment washed down from the surface. This type of subsurface stream may be called a *water-table stream*.

Topographic Control of Water Table.—The ground-water level is controlled by the escape of water to the surface and therefore is controlled by topographic relief. The relation of ground-water level, water-table streams and their development, and the resultant subsurface stream pattern to the erosion cycle has been treated in detail by Davis[1] and is not considered here.

Solution Conduits Formed below the Water Table.—As emphasized by Davis, the majority of geologists have assumed that solution does not take place below the water table, and therefore conduits now filled with ground water have been drowned by a rising water table. Davis, however, gives convincing evidence that conduits are formed *below* the water table. He presents cross sections showing that conduits are curved in a vertical plane (Fig. 100, *D* and *E*) and hence could not be dissolved by perched or by water-table streams. The occurrence in mines of spectacular flows of water in solution openings far below the surface and below the present or any pre-existing water table is further evidence of the formation of solution conduits below the water table. In a limestone terrain strong artesian flows tapped by wells and also discharged by large sub-oceanic springs prove the existence of conduits below the water table, but not their excavation below it. Rapid confined flow in the larger openings below the water table would bring large quantities of *undersaturated water* in contact with limestone, and solution would enlarge the fractures into tubular passages below the water table.

[1] DAVIS, *op. cit.*, p. 486.

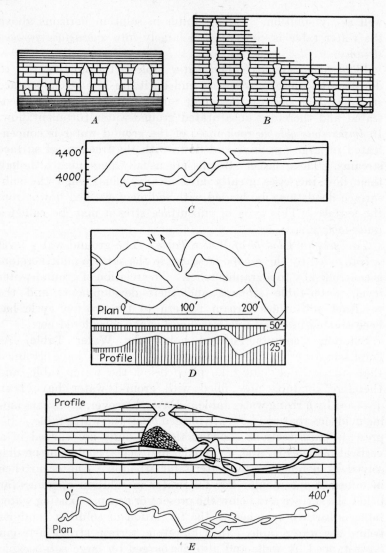

Fig. 100.—*A, B,* growth of solution openings.   *A,* above impervious stratum; *B,* on vertical fracture. (*After Davis.*)   *C,* profile of Carlsbad Cavern, New Mexico, showing development of conduit at different elevations. (*After Lee.*) *D,* plan and profile of Saltpeter Cave, Missouri, showing conduit curved in vertical plane. (*After Detweiler and Townsend.*)   *E,* plan and profile of Marble Cave, Missouri, illustrating solution stoping and curved conduits formed below the water table. (*After Hovey and Winslow.*)

Rapid flow below the water table occurs only in a conduit system with free discharge of confined water. Such freedom of flow is less common below the water table than in conduits above it. Therefore, probably, more solution conduits are formed above or at the water table than below it.

Ground Water in Impervious, Inclined Limestone Beds

W. M. Davis's discussion of the caverns of the Shenandoah Valley, where steeply dipping limbs of a syncline bring massive inclined beds of limestone to the surface, presents the salient features of this type of solution openings. Davis states:

The larger chambers are developed at consistent levels, which cross the inclined layers at strong angles and suggest a control of solution by the former water table, which was itself controlled by the local base-level. . . . [1]

Hovey, quoted by Davis, states, "The outlet of the subterranean stream (by which he assumed the cavern was excavated) became obstructed, and the pentup waters were accumulated till the entire cavern was filled from the lowest pit to the loftiest gallery—a fact proved by the earthy deposits amid the highest cluster of stalactites, as well as by the uniform erosion of dripstone. . . . There is every indication that when the flood left the cave it did so with violence, tearing down loosened rocks, hurling stalactites to the ground, and felling huge columns like trees in a tornado's path."[2]

The important differences in the excavation of passages in inclined limestone and in flat-lying limestone may be summarized as follows: Vadose water is not held up above flat impervious barriers, but sinks straight down to the water table or moves down on the inclined beds to the saturated zone. The first important barrier is the water table, on which important galleries are constructed regardless of dip of beds. The stoppage and sudden drainage of such openings may produce flows of stored water of destructive character.

Ground Water in Porous Limestone

Original Openings in Porous Limestone.—Porous limestone is usually of fairly recent geological age (chiefly Tertiary and

---

[1] Davis, *op. cit.*, p. 606.

[2] Hovey. H. C.. Celebrated American Caverns, 1882, 1896, pp. 176–178; Davis, *op. cit.*, p. 607.

Quaternary).[1] It retains the openings of the original aggrega-
tion of shells and skeletons of lime-secreting organisms. Such
original porosity is well developed in calcareous reef formations
and in many of the Tertiary detrital marls. This initial porosity
may be increased by differential solution of the more soluble
constituents of the calcareous deposit by sea water or by reaction
with magnesium-bearing ocean water to produce dolomite.[2]
However, alteration of calcite or of consolidated, crystalline
limestone to dolomite by subsurface mineralizing solutions
probably produces a larger porosity than reactions on unconsolidated calcareous sediments by ocean water.

Original openings are gradually eliminated by compaction of
the calcareous sediment and slow recrystallization of the con-

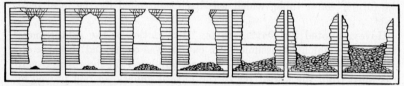

Fig. 101.—Development of sinkholes in porous limestone. (*After Cole.*)

stituent carbonates. Calcite and dolomite readily recrystallize
under moderate pressure and temperature, which accompany the
accumulation of thick deposits of overlying sediments and act
through long periods of geologic time. Even moderate earth
stresses accompanying elevation and depression of the rocks
assist recrystallization.

The Tertiary limestone formations of the United States are
generally porous throughout, as are possibly some calcareous
reef limestone formations of greater age in Texas and New
Mexico. The Tertiary limestones of Florida are good examples
of this type of porous formation and from them issue the largest
springs of the United States (pages 455–456). This type of
formation encloses important aquifers.

In pervious limestone horizontal barriers are less important
and vadose movement is less impeded and less localized in large
conduits than in impervious limestone. The joint systems may,

[1] Cooke, C. W., and Stuart Mossom, Geology of Florida, 20*th Ann.
Rept. Florida State Geol. Surv.*, pp. 29–228, 1929.

[2] Steidtmann, E., The Evolution of Limestone and Dolomite. *Jour. Geol.*,
vol. 19, pp. 323–345, 392–428, 1911.

however, still guide descending solutions which dissolve out vertical shafts which are further enlarged at the surface into funnel-shaped sinkholes by subaerial weathering and side washing by descending storm water (Fig. 101).

A pervious limestone formation functions largely as a reservoir, the water table of which is flat, and is exposed to the air in partly filled sinkholes. Discharge from the reservoir may take place by overflow in water-table streams or by underflow through subwater-table conduits. The discharge of the great springs of Florida and adjacent regions forms large surface rivers. They may be fed by water-table streams or subwater-table conduits. Davis describes the water table in pervious limestone as follows:

Enlargement will continue until the passage roofs, reduced in thickness by wasting of both their upper and under surfaces, cannot support themselves; they then collapse and form pond-holding sinks or lake-holding basins; and as a rule the pond and lake surfaces stand at the level of the water table (Fig. 101). As the general surface of the land is more and more degraded and subterranean passages are more and more enlarged, the lakes increase in number and area. At a late stage in the cycle of erosion the land surface between the lakes will be worn down lower and lower, closer and closer to baselevel; but the lake bottoms may lie decidedly below baselevel, unless their excavation is overcome by deposition or by abundant plant growth.[1]

GROUND WATER IN LAVA

Lava is made porous and pervious by openings formed during or after solidification. The various types of openings in lava have been mentioned in previous chapters and in this section attention is directed to the pattern of openings and its control over ground-water movements and storage. Inasmuch as the openings consist of both fractures and flow tunnels, the occurrence and movements of water are similar in some respects to those described in fractures and in solution openings and hence detailed discussion of principles may be omitted.

The characteristic features governing ground-water movements and accumulation in lava are (1) vertical permeability due to fractures, (2) horizontal porosity and permeability in horizons containing openings due to flow and gas expansion during solidification, and (3) occurrence of impervious horizons and dikes.

[1] DAVIS, *op. cit.*, pp. 489–490.

Fig. 102.—Owens River gorge excavated in lava plateau. The lava formation is permeable due to innumerable fractures which lead water down to the underlying pervious glass sand (not shown in photograph). Canyon is about 1,000 feet deep.

Massive unfractured lava is impervious. Flow porosity is developed chiefly in basaltic lava which when melted flows readily. This develops both flow tunnels and irregularities on the surface of the flows which constitute aquifers after burial. Openings due to gas expansion, producing amygdaloidal and scoriaceous textures, are best developed in rhyolite which is viscous in the molten state, but, if openings are not interconnected, the material is impermeable. Such zones are apt to be permeable in basalt, as the cavities are often fractured by flow of the molten portion and by stress developed during the cooling of the lava.

Fractures in lava reach the highest development in thin basaltic flows. These are due to stress developed by flow of the molten portion acting on the solidified portion, and by contraction due to differential cooling of the upper and lower surfaces of the flow which develops the well known columnar structure[1] (Fig. 102). These fractures are at right angles to the flows and are an important factor in the development of the vertical permeability characteristic of thin basaltic flows. Later movements affecting a series of bedded flows tend to crack the thin, brittle lava at right angles to layering. Pervious formations consisting of volcanic ejecta and zones of intense fracturing often occur in volcanic cones and around volcanic centers. Interbedded volcanic ash, agglomerate, and gravel often constitute pervious members. The impervious members in lava are dense unfractured flows, interstratified layers of tuff, shale, or soil, and dikes or sills.

The above-described structural characteristics are best developed in the Columbia Plateau lava fields and their extensions in northern California, and in the Hawaiian Islands. In the Columbia Plateau lava region the general vertical permeability conducts influent seepage generated by rainfall and irrigation over vast areas to the first impervious stratum, and the water is discharged as a series of great springs at the intersection of the aquifer with the canyon walls.[2] In the Hawaiian Islands the complex lava mass is extremely permeable and influent seepage generally descends many thousand feet to the "basal groundwater body" which occurs floating on salty ground water derived

---

[1] CHAMBERLIN and SALISBURY, "Geology," *op. cit.*, vol. 1, pp. 498–500.

[2] MEINZER, O. E., *Water-Supply Paper 489*, *op. cit.*, pp. 138–141; *Water-Supply Paper 557*, *op. cit.*, pp. 42–55. See also pp. 457–460 of this text.

from the ocean.   Water perched on tuff beds and water confined between dikes is important at elevations too high to reach the basal ground water with wells (pages 547–548).

GROUND WATER IN FRACTURES IN LIMESTONE

The following is a description of an unusual water body which has characteristics of ground water in fissures and in conduits in limestone and is also directly connected with a great water body in an undrained alluvial desert basin.

The water body tapped by the workings of the Ojuela mine, Durango, Mexico,[1] fills the alluvium of the Bolsón de Mapimi and extends into the severely fractured and mineralized limestone bounding the basin.   The water level in the mine is but slightly higher than that underlying the bolson.   The ore deposits occur in large fissures and also replace beds of limestone where intersected by fissures.   The latter are open and contain water courses which discharge enormous flows where intersected by the mine workings.   The fissures are of deep-seated origin and the solution openings along them may have been dissolved in part by hot mineralizing solutions.

The water level in the mine normally stands 50 to 80 ft. below the twelfth level, but in an abnormally wet season it rose above this level and the flow into the twelfth level then amounted to 20,000 g.p.m.   To handle the water below this level a drain tunnel over 6000 ft. in length was driven above the level and pumps capable of handling 9000 to 10,000 g.p.m. were installed, discharging into the drain tunnel.   These pumps were operated 20 months, raising an average of 7500 g.p.m. during that period, and lowered the water level only three inches.

After the failure to handle the water in the group of fissures penetrated by the mine workings it was decided to drain and mine each ore fissure separately.   The stopes on individual fissures tapped flows from 3500 to 10,000 g.p.m.   Below the twelfth level each ore body was equipped with two shafts, one for pumping and one serving mining operations.   Each pumping plant at first discharged into the drain tunnel but later the water from the individual stopes was pumped into adjacent fissures instead

---

[1] TRIPLETT, W. H., General Manager, Compania Minera de Penoles, S.A., and H. F. LYNN, formerly geologist with the company, personal communications.

of into the drain tunnel. As the limestone is impervious and the fissures are not cross-connected but join the main water body in the Mapimi alluvial basin, pumping from one fissure had slight effect on the level of the general water body. Careful measurements showed that only 10 per cent of the water pumped at the rate of 3500 g.p.m. into a stope on an adjacent fissure returned to the working being pumped. Mining by these methods has reached a depth of 1100 ft. below the general water level.

Many ingenious methods[1] were developed for handling these great flows of water. Water drifts were often driven below the working levels and 5-in. diamond drillholes were drilled to the ore fissures above to tap the water, which was then pumped from the water drift. In sinking shafts a long hole was driven ahead of shaft operations and water pressure in the hole was gaged. If excessive, the working was abandoned. Diamond drillholes were also driven ahead of drifts and flows of water were sealed off by pumping sawdust and finally cement into the water fissures. The seal was successful even under water pressure from 250 to 400 lb. per square inch.

During the period the drain tunnel was used, the Mexicans established small farms at and below the portal of the mine. After pumping into the drain tunnel ceased, the farmers immediately filed suit demanding that the mining company continue pumping. It was with considerable difficulty and after a large expenditure of money that the company defeated the farmers' injunction suit.

References

ADDINGTON, A. R., Subterranean Drainage Phenomena: *8th Ann. Rept.*, *Dept. Conserv. Indiana*, pp. 18–23, 1928.

BEEDE, J. W., The Cycle of Subterranean Drainage as Illustrated in the Bloomington Quadrangle, *Proc. Indiana Acad. Sci.*, pp. 81–103, 1910.

CUMMINGS, C. R., The Weathering of the Sub-Carboniferous Limestone of Southern Indiana, *Proc. Indiana Acad. Sci.*, pp. 85–89, 1905.

DAVIS, W. M., Origin of Limestone Caverns, *Bull. Geol. Soc. Amer.*, vol. 41, pp. 475–628, 1930.

ELLIS, E. E., Occurrence of Water in Crystalline Rocks, *U.S. Geol. Surv. Water-Supply Paper* 160, 1906.

[1] The late A. B. Carstens devised the various methods of handling the water flows. Unfortunately he lost his life in his line of duty in the warfare to control ground water.

FULLER, M. L., Underground Waters of Eastern United States, *U.S. Geol. Surv. Water-Supply Paper* 114, pp. 27–28, 1905.

——— Underground Waters for Farm Use, *U.S. Geol. Surv. Water-Supply Paper* 255, pp. 14–18, 1910.

GREENE, T. C., Caves and Cave Formation of the Mitchell Limestone (Ind.), *Proc. Indiana Acad. Sci.*, pp. 175–184, 1908.

HALL, G. M., Ground Water in the Ordovician Rocks near Woodstock, Va., *U.S. Geol. Surv. Water-Supply Paper* 596-C, pp. 57–59, 1907.

JOHNSTON, W. D., JR., Ground Water in the Paleozoic Rocks of Northern Alabama, *Ala. Geol. Surv. Spec. Rept.*, 16, 1933.

LIVINGSTON, P. and others, Water Resources of the Edwards Limestone in the San Antonio Area, Texas, *U.S. Geol. Surv. Water-Supply Paper* 773-B, pp. 72–74, 1936.

MATSON, G. C., Water Resources of the Blue Grass Region, Ky., *U.S. Geol. Surv. Water-Supply Paper* 233, pp. 42–49, 1909.

MEINZER, O. E., Occurrence of Ground Water in the United States, *U.S. Geol. Surv. Water-Supply Paper* 489, pp. 111–116, 131–132, 1923.

PIPER, A. M., Ground Water in North-Central Tennessee, *U.S. Geol. Surv. Water-Supply Paper* 640, pp. 69–89, 1932.

THEIS, C. V., Ground Water in South-Central Tennessee, *U.S. Geol. Surv. Water-Supply Paper* 677, pp. 33–46, 1936.

VANHISE, C. R., A Treatise on Metamorphism, *U.S. Geol. Surv. Monog.* 47, pp. 1022–1028, 1904.

CHAPTER XI

CONFINED WATER

Confined water commonly occurs beneath material sufficiently impervious to sever hydraulic connection with overlying free ground water except at the upper edge of the confined aquifer. The hydraulic gradient starts at the upper edge of the confining stratum and extends downslope as far as confinement exists. The impervious material must be of sufficient extent to develop a hydraulic gradient quite distinct from and unrelated to the water-table slope of free water.

A less common occurrence of confined water is in lenticular bodies of sand surrounded by impervious nonindurated material. In such a body of confined water there is poor hydraulic connection or even no connection with an intake area drawing on free water.

The term *artesian water* was first applied to water under sufficient head to carry it above the ground surface in a well piercing the confined aquifer. Such a well was called an *artesian well*. Artesian flow and artesian head are exhausted only if the well produces more water than the natural supply tributary to the well. In most artesian fields and universally in the United States the natural artesian supply is overdrawn and hence the wells slowly lose head and in many cases the water level in the well is reduced below the level of the water table. The water body remains confined regardless of whether the variable water level in the well happens to be above or below the ground surface or above or below the water table. Some writers have expanded the term artesian to include all confined water and designate head above the water table as *positive artesian head* or *positive pressure* and below the water table as *negative artesian head* or *negative pressure*. The term has even been expanded to include all deep wells, but it is evidently inappropriate to apply the term artesian to a well that taps unconfined water only.[1] Meinzer

[1] See summary of current usage of term artesian by M. L. Fuller, *U.S. Geol. Surv. Water-Supply Paper* 160, pp. 9–15, 1906.

has suggested that the term *artesian well* be limited to a well
with water level above that of the adjacent water table[1] and
that nomenclature is adopted in this book.

The term *confined water* is herein applied to water in aquifers
not in hydraulic connection with overlying water bodies except
at the fountain head, regardless of the position of the water
level in wells. Pressure is transmitted from a distant source by
water completely filling the conduit. The German usage is
"confined" or "pressure" water for water in confined aquifers,
and "free" water for that portion of ground water the movement
of which is not restrained by confining formations. This nomenclature is also adopted in this book.[2]

History of Development of Artesian Wells.—Keilhack's[3]
review of the history of drilling wells or sinking shafts for artesian
water obtained from the detailed historical review of artesian
well drilling by Corraza[4] is summarized below with minor
additions.

The art of winning artesian water from wells or shafts is very old.
Long before the time of Christ the Egyptians were in possession of the
art, and from them Moses learned how to smite water from the rocks.
Two thousand years before Christ the oases of Theben, Sharb, and
Dachel were watered by numberless artesian shafts up to 300 ft.
in depth. Five centuries before Christ, wells up to 500 ft. deep had
been dug.

In Europe the art of boring artesian wells was developed in the twelfth
century. The first artesian well was brought in at Lilliers, in the
Province of Artois, southern France, in 1126 and has been flowing ever
since. The slight development of technique of drilling and the great
cost of wells retarded the search for artesian water, but in the seventeenth century artesian wells were successfully completed in Italy and
lower Austria. In the last 75 years the technique has advanced astonish-
ingly and as a result mighty streams of artesian water have been brought
to the surface in all parts of the world.

[1] MEINZER, O. E., *Water-Supply Paper* 494, *op. cit.*, p. 39.

[2] The water surface in a conduit partly dewatered by pumping has been
called a "local water table in a conduit." Pressure is not transmitted in
the partly filled portion of the conduit.

[3] KEILHACK, K., "Grundwasser und Quellenkunde," 3d ed., Gebrüder
Borntraeger, Berlin, 1935.

[4] CORRAZA, O., "Geschichte der artesischen Brunnen," Leipzig u. Wien,
p. 119, 1902.

In 1841 the first great well drilled by cable tools was brought in at Grenelle near Paris, France. The history of the seven years incessant labor expended in its construction has been equaled in interest by that of few other engineering enterprises. It was in drilling this well that workmen first learned the requirements of deep drilling and first exercised their ingenuity in recovering broken parts of the drill. A depth of 1798 ft. was reached. The hole was stopped in a large cavity from which water having a temperature of 82°F. rose with great force to the surface, forming a large flowing artesian well—"a parabolic fountain" many feet in height.[1]

A *high-pressure artesian well* is both a powerful mechanical engine capable of doing much work and an artificial fountain of great beauty. Moderate flows under high pressure rise as slender wind-tossed columns, and a large high-pressure flow may be spread out as a symmetrical dome of living water. The artesian wells of the Dakota artesian system shot columns of water over 200 ft. in the air, rivaling the great geysers of the Yellowstone in height. The Passy well at Paris, France, was drilled to a depth of 1923 ft., diameter 28 in., artesian head 54 ft., and flowed nearly 3900 g.p.m. (approximately 9 sec.-ft.).[2] A well drilled at Springfield, North Dakota, with a static pressure of 86 lb. per square inch, yielded 4,750,000 g.p.d. (7 sec.-ft.) and furnished power for a 100-barrel flour mill. Another well at Woonsocket, South Dakota, came in with a static pressure of 130 lb. and was discharged into a Pelton water wheel which furnished power for a 125-barrel flour mill.[3]

High-pressure flows are obtained chiefly from the sheetlike aquifers of great extent, such as the Potsdam and Dakota sandstones, in a sedimentary sequence of sandstone and shale; and, of course, topographically the discharge area of the aquifer must be considerably below the intake area.

Low-pressure artesian flows, occurring in the lower portions of the great alluvial cones of southwestern United States, are usually larger than high-pressure flows from sandstone, and the gross amount of water produced from them is probably greater than

---

[1] BOWMAN, I., Well Drilling Methods: *U.S. Geol. Surv. Water-Supply Paper 257*, pp. 24–25, 1911.

[2] *Ibid.*, p. 24.

[3] NETTLETON, E. S., Artesian and Underflow Investigation, *52d Cong., 1st Session, Sen. Ex. Doc. 41*, pt. 2, p. 42, 1892.

from all other types of artesian wells combined.   Low-pressure
flows are also encountered in wells tapping conduit water in
solution openings.   An artesian well of the Oasis Cotton Company in the Roswell basin, New Mexico, had a measured flow of
5710 g.p.m. in April, 1926, with an artesian head of 5 ft.   The
flow at the time of completion of the well, in the previous month,
was estimated to have been about 6000 g.p.m. with artesian
head several feet higher.   This well has yielded more water by
artesian pressure than any other in the United States and
probably in the world.[1]

Origin of Artesian Pressure.—The chief moving force of
artesian flow[2] is usually hydrostatic pressure.   The hydrostatic
pressure of the column of water extending up to the water table
at the fountain head above the upper edge of the confining formation rests upon the confined water and causes movement if there
is escape at any point below.   Confined aquifers are usually
inclined and the pressure is greater in the lower portion.   Slow
escape of water may take place at the lower end, although the
confining formation may not increase in permeability.   A well
passing through the confining stratum and piercing the artesian
aquifer releases the water, and if artesian pressure is sufficient,
may discharge it as a fountain reaching far above the ground
surface.

Chamberlin said, "The basal principles of artesian wells are
simple.   The schoolboy reckons himself their master."[3]   The
simplicity of the concepts and principles of water movement in
subsurface conduits by hydraulic pressure, the discovery of
competent conduits for the important artesian systems, and the
determination of their size, shape, inclination, and outcrop by
geological study led to the general acceptance of the theory that
hydraulic pressure in artesian aquifers is the source of artesian
pressure.

[1] FIEDLER, A. G., and S. S. NYE, Geology and Ground-water Resources
of the Roswell Artesian Basin, New Mexico, *U.S. Geol. Surv. Water-Supply
Paper* 639, pp. 193–194, 1933.

[2] The *flow* of a well is its discharge, or the quantity of water produced in a
given time.   It has no significance as to the type of subsurface movement of
water feeding the well, which is usually percolation (laminar flow) but
occasionally turbulent flow.

[3] CHAMBERLIN, T. C., The Requisite and Qualifying Conditions of Artesian Wells, *U.S. Geol. Surv. 5th Ann. Rept.*, p. 131, 1885.

However, there are certain modifications in the functioning of an artesian system due to the fact that aquifers are not rigid but are compressible and may be elastic or relatively inelastic. Relief of pressure in the aquifer due to well production may permit the pressing out of water from the confining strata by the weight of the overlying material and thus accelerate the process of compaction which affects all clayey or silty deposits. These modifying factors caused by reduction of pressure, due chiefly to overpumping, may produce water in excess of that percolating toward the well from the fountain head. This source of water may be large and is discussed in detail in following pages.

HYDRAULIC PRINCIPLES OF CONFINED PERCOLATION

The apparatus used to illustrate hydraulic pressure gradients developed in a sand-filled conduit with variation in velocity of

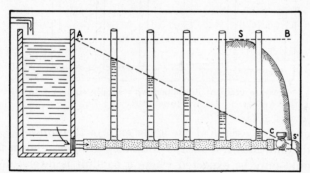

FIG. 103.—Pressure gradient developed with constant supply and free exit. *AB*, static level; *AC*, pressure gradient.

percolation and in permeability of water-conducting material consists of a large rubber tube cut in sections and fitted over short glass tubes into which vertical tubes of small diameter are welded to show pressure conditions in the conduit (Figs. 103–107). Screens are placed at the bottom of the vertical tubes to keep sand out. Reservoir level is kept at *A* by an overflow pipe (Fig. 106). A pinchcock is fitted on the reservoir discharge pipe (Fig. 107) to adjust the supply to the sand-filled tube, and a stopcock is attached at the discharge end of the sand tube.

A. Stopcock at Discharge Point Closed.—The gradient *AB* is horizontal (Fig. 103). Static pressure affects the entire rubber tube. The tube expands slightly under pressure, but after expansion the water will rise to the static level.[1] This shows that complete closing of the exit of an aquifer would bring up the hydrostatic head and hence the water level in wells to static level. However natural aquifers probably always suffer leakage through the sides and at the end. This causes water movement in the aquifer above the zone of leakage and the friction engendered thereby develops a hydraulic gradient sloping in the direction of percolation in the aquifer (*AC*, Fig. 103).

B. Stopcock Open.—1. The steep gradient *AC* (Fig. 103) is developed by opening the stopcock until it passes a large flow. By slowly closing the tube the gradient is decreased and rotated with *A* as axis, until with complete closure it again assumes the position *AB*. This illustrates that high artesian pressures are

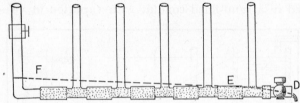

Fig. 104.—Pressure gradient developed with supply sufficient to fill tube only to point *E*.

due to retarded escape at the lower ends of the aquifers. Under natural conditions free escape and steep gradient shown for Fig. 103 would only be expected where a conduit is intersected by a cliff and discharged by a spring.

2. The stopcock is opened farther to represent spring discharge of a conduit with large orifice at cliff surface, or a well passing through a conduit with the water level in well drawn down below the upper surface of the aquifer (Fig. 104). Under these conditions a water table is developed in the conduit above the spring or well. If an obstruction decreases permeability of the conduit, it may be partly dewatered below the obstruction and the pressure gradient starts above the point of obstruction. However, overdraft usually exceeds supply for a long period before water level in wells is reduced below the conduit surface; overdraft causes

---

[1] In natural conduits this level would be at the elevation of the fountain head and, as the water level in wells never rises to this level, it may be designated as the *theoretical static level*.

lowering of water level *at the intake* and produces a local water table in the upper end of the conduit.

C. Stopcock Partly Closed.—Small discharge is developed at the outlet on account of the small cross-sectional area of escape. In the hose the velocity is low and hydraulic gradient is flat

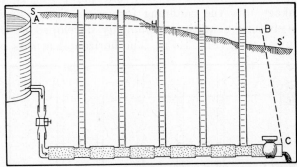

FIG. 105.—Pressure gradient developed with small discharge. *ABC*, pressure gradient.

except at the outlet, where velocity and friction will be large on account of the small opening and the hydraulic gradient will be steep (Fig. 105).

Assume that the tube represents a subsurface aquifer, ground surface at *SS'*. The pressure surface will be above the ground

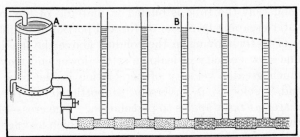

FIG. 106.—Pressure gradient developed with decrease of permeability toward discharge.

surface between *H* and *B*, and the area thus represented has been denominated the "artesian basin." It is the area in which flowing wells are obtained. The pressure profile *BC* could not exist under natural conditions because free discharge of water in the aquifer cannot take place at depth below the ground surface.

D. If the end of the tube is filled with material of small permeability, the hydraulic gradient will be flat in the coarse material and steep in the material of low permeability (Fig. 106).

E. If the tube, with discharge stopcock closed, is packed with materials of decreasing permeability toward the discharge end and perforated by numerous very fine pin pricks to develop slight leakage into the confining formation, the apparatus will illustrate pressure conditions commonly developed at the foot of an alluvial cone (Fig. 107). The horizontal arrows indicate

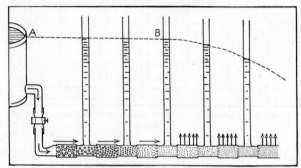

Fig. 107.—Pressure gradient developed in material of decreasing permeability with discharge by leakage toward end of conduit.

movement of water in the tube, developed by the slow leakage at the discharge end.

Assuming that the tube is buried in material of low permeability, water escaping from the perforated portion is equal to the quantity of water moving in the conduit above the leaking section. The slow velocity of leakage at the lower end may represent a much greater velocity of percolation in the tube at the upper end. Velocity is inversely proportional to the cross-sectional area at right angles to percolation. The cross-sectional area of the tube is πr^2, and the area through which leakage occurs is $2\pi r l$, where r = radius of tube and l = length of leaking section. The ratio of velocity of percolating water in the conduit upslope from the leakage area to water escaping by leakage is $2l/r$. If an aquifer is 10 ft. in diameter and the leaking area is 1 mile long, the ratio of velocity of percolation in the conduit to that of ascending leakage in the area of discharge is 10,560/5.

F. Pressure conditions in the zone of leakage can be represented by bending up the end of the hose filled with materials of varying permeability, corresponding to those at the same depth below the surface in the region of artesian discharge, and observing the pressure conditions in the tube at various distances below the surface (Fig. 108).

EF represents the natural position of a leaking conduit, and *EG* the hose filled with material of low permeability, equal to the permeability of materials in the discharge zone at corresponding depths below the surface. In the position *EG* the tube represents pressure conditions in the zone of leakage from *EF* to the surface. As water leaks upward, pressure head is consumed and

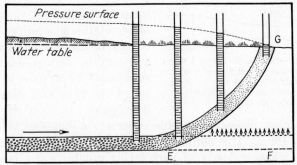

Fig. 108.—Pressure conditions in the zone of leakage above a confined aquifer illustrated by a bent tube. *EF*, natural position of aquifer.

at the water table, which is normally at the surface in the zone of leakage, it is zero. With depth the pressure head increases until the horizon of the aquifer is reached.

With increase in depth of a well, a slight rise of the water level in the well above the water table occurs in the zone of artesian discharge. A still smaller pressure head is registered by the static level in the well where ground water is forced to rise from depth by contraction of the cross-sectional area of an aquifer filling a stream channel cut in bedrock. In both cases the water level in the deep well is slightly above the water table because resistance to rising ground water is less in the well casing than in the material surrounding the well.[1] Decrease in permeability of water-bearing material at or near the surface increases this pressure effect.[2]

[1] FULLER, M. L., Summary of the Controlling Factors of Artesian Flows, *U.S. Geol. Surv. Bull.* 319, p. 22, 1907.

[2] KEILHACK, *op. cit.*, p. 225.

The writer listened to an announcement in court of a "general law" based on the phenomena discussed in the preceding paragraphs that *"artesian head always increases in direct proportion to the depth of the well"!*

Comparison of Flow in Pipes with Percolation in Confined Aquifers.—Hydraulic principles of flow in pipes differ in a number of respects from those of percolating confined water. Flow in pipes is chiefly turbulent, whereas percolation follows

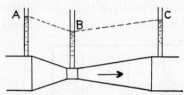

the laws of streamline or laminar flow (pages 191–200). The velocity of flow in pipes is commonly far greater than velocity of percolation in aquifers and the energy of flow in pipes is large and may be converted into pressure head[1] by increase in diameter of the pipe and consequent decrease in velocity. The

Fig. 109.—Sectional view of Venturi meter showing conversion of pressure head to velocity head (*A* to *B*) and reversion to pressure head (*B* to *C*). (*Modified after Russell.*)

reverse takes place where pipe contraction increases velocity[2,3] (see Fig. 109). This conversion is not appreciable in sand filled conduits where velocity of percolating ground water is small.

An apparatus showing how pressure gradient in the *reverse* direction of flow can be developed by change in velocity is illustrated in Fig. 110. A pipe perforated at regular intervals is closed at one end. Escape of water is through the perforations. Maximum velocity occurs at the first hole, decreases toward the closed end, converting energy of flow into pressure head, and the height of spurting water increases toward the closed end. In the case of percolation, gradients in the reverse direction due to conversion of velocity head to pressure head are probably not measurable, and the categorical statement that water always moves in the direction of hydraulic gradient is probably commonly correct for ground water.

[1] Pressure head is pressure on the walls of the conduit and is registered by the height of water in a pressure tube or in a well tapping confined water. Velocity head is the energy of flow available for conversion into pressure head.

[2] RUSSELL, G. E., "Textbook on Hydraulics," 4th ed., p. 213, Henry Holt and Company, 1934.

[3] SCHODER, E. W., and F. M. DAWSON, "Hydraulics," 2d ed., pp. 127–128, McGraw-Hill Book Company, Inc., 1934.

Effect of Change in Cross-sectional Area of Conduit.—As discussed above, the velocity of percolation is slow and changes in pressure gradient due to conversion of velocity head into pressure head may be neglected. But change in cross-sectional area of conduits controls velocity and is probably very important, and head consumed by friction at contractions of natural aquifers is large. Therefore contraction of confined aquifers should cause

FIG. 110.—Reverse gradient caused by conversion of velocity head into pressure head in closed pipe.

steepening of the pressure gradient in the contracted portion, and flattening above the contraction owing to retardation of percolation. Detailed studies of gradients of confined water in relation to cross-sectional area of conduits have not as yet been undertaken but are mentioned by Thiem.[1]

Some Hydraulic Phenomena Due to Pumping

Pressure Changes Due to Well Flow.—When a confined-water well is not pumping or when the discharge valve of an artesian

[1] THIEM, G., "Hydrologische Methoden," pp. 16–19, Alfred Kröner Leipzig, 1926.

well is closed, hydrostatic pressure of the column of water in the well balances the pressure of the column of water in the conduit. When the pump is started or the valve is opened, the back pressure of the water in the pump column is lifted, the water level in the well casing is reduced, and head (measured by the difference between static and pumping level) is first consumed in starting the water moving from the aquifer to and into the well. With the movement of water toward the well, friction of percolation reduces hydraulic pressure within the conduit and the outward pressure on the conduit walls underneath the entire area of influence, and, if the conduit is elastic, produces a contraction of the conduit which temporarily furnishes water additional to that moving in the conduit toward the well. This withdrawal of water from storage in the aquifer ceases when the volume of the conduit is adjusted to change in pressure produced by pumping, and when well flow stops, the withdrawal is returned to the aquifer by water moving toward the well during expansion of the conduit. All conduits probably have some volume elasticity, and hence this temporary deformation of the conduit always accompanies pressure relief.

If the conduit is compressible and relatively inelastic, its contraction by pressure relief may be permanent and the aquifer is permanently compacted. Reduction of pressure in the conduit may also cause partial draining and compacting of the adjacent confining formation. These phenomena are discussed in following pages.

Cone of Pressure Relief.—The wave of pressure relief generated by the lifting of the water column in the well moves outward from the producing well with great velocity if the conduit is rigid, because the unbalanced pressure in the conduit is not consumed in deforming the conduit. The rate of propagation of the wave is reduced if the conduit is compressible and suffers compaction. Movement of water toward the well develops a pressure gradient in the aquifer directly proportional to the velocity of percolation and inversely to the permeability of the water-bearing material. This effect extends radially from the well and is limited to the areal extent of the conduit furnishing water to the well. The depression in the pressure surface caused by pumping is called the *cone of pressure relief* and the areal extent of this depression is the *area of influence* (pages

388–391).   The standing level in all wells reaching the conduit tapped by the pumping well is lowered within the area of influence and the latter expands until the reduction in pressure is sufficient to move in from all directions the quantity of water discharged by the pump.

Depleted Pressure Surface.—If natural percolation in the aquifer underneath the area affected by reduced pressure is sufficient to supply well draft, there will be no further lowering of the pressure surface or enlargement of the area of influence and after pumping ceases complete recovery will take place.

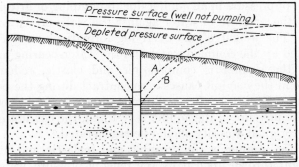

Fig. 111.—Depleted pressure surface produced by overpumping.   *A*, cone of pressure relief at start of pumping; *B*, cone produced by pumping in excess of replenishment.

If well flow exceeds natural supply tributary to the cone of pressure relief, there will be a gradual progressive lowering of the water level in the well and of the pressure surface, and this lowering will continue until pumping is decreased to the natural supply.   The pressure depression may work up to the intake and in that case the water level in the conduit at the intake will be lowered.

If pumping is stopped at the close of the pumping or dry season, the supply of water during the wet season may build up the depleted water level in the well and the general pressure surface. Such depletion and recovery are spoken of as *seasonal depletion and recovery*.   A pressure surface lowered by overpumping is called a *depleted pressure surface* (Fig. 111).   If a cycle of dry years decreases the supply of water available to the confined aquifer from the upslope direction, the principal supply may be drawn out of storage downslope from the well.   Such a condition is described for the San Francisquito alluvial cone at Stanford University, California (page 377).

Summarizing, the cone of pressure relief is temporary, it disappears with well-level recovery after pumping ceases. A depleted pressure surface is long lived and may be permanent. It may spread over the entire area of the artesian basin, being registered by a lowered water level in every well tapping confined water.

EFFECT OF PRESSURE RELIEF ON THE AQUIFER AND CONFINING FORMATIONS

Relief of pressure in an aquifer due to pumping or artesian flow reduces the pressure of water against the walls of the confining strata. The weight of the overlying formations was originally supported by the confined water and the water-bearing material.

1. If the aquifer is compressible and elastic, reduction of pressure in the conduit causes it to contract during the period of pumping. However, after well production stops and the original hydraulic pressure in the aquifer is restored, the conduit expands and the original porosity should be regenerated.[1]

2. If the aquifer is compressible and inelastic and yields to the weight thrown upon it by the relief of pressure, water originally stored in the pore space destroyed by the yielding of the aquifer is supplied to the well and reduction of pore space may be permanent (Fig. 112).

3. If the aquifer is overlain by impermeable clay or by a difficultly permeable formation, such as fine silt, water may be supplied to the aquifer by the reduction of pressure in the aquifer against the adjacent aquicludes under the following conditions:

[1] Meinzer states, "There is a very general misunderstanding of the effects of rock pressure and other conditions that give volume elasticity to the artesian system. My concept is that rock pressure and hydrostatic pressure are not two separate things but that they are different parts of the same process. In the case of a bow and arrow, the bent bow has energy but this energy is provided by the archer; likewise, in an ordinary artesian basin the energy is provided by the water which percolates into the aquifer at the high-level outcrop and by adding its weight produces hydrostatic pressure upon the water where it is confined. This hydrostatic pressure is a force that tends to lift the overlying confining bed and to produce other elastic strains. . . . The effect of the elastic properties of the formations and of the water itself appears to be present whenever water is withdrawn from an artesian well either by flow or by pumping." (Personal communication.)

a. If the clay is not completely compacted by the weight of overlying formations, reduction of the pressure of the confined water in the aquifer on the confining strata will permit some of the water held in the clay to be squeezed out into the aquifer by the pressure of the overlying material and results in further compaction of the clay. Such compaction may be permanent.

b. If the confining formation is slightly permeable, reduction of pressure in the aquifer will produce a hydraulic gradient from the confining stratum to the aquifer throughout the entire area

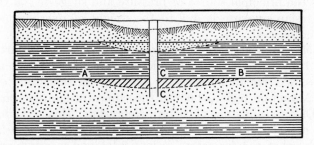

Fig. 112.—Surface subsidence due to permanent compaction of inelastic aquifer Pumping reduces pressure in aquifer which yields to *AC'B*.

of contact of aquifer and aquiclude within the area of influence. Slow movement of water out of the confining formation into the aquifer throughout the large area of contact may supply considerable water to the aquifer.

4. If a lenticular mass of coarse sand is surrounded by relatively impervious, incompetent material, the sand and interstitial water will be under the pressure of overlying material. If a well pierces the sand, the water will be under a high initial pressure owing to the weight of overlying material, but a small production of water from the well will throw the pressure on the sand and the high pressure shown in the well will be reduced. Subsequent pumped water may be derived (*a*) from compaction of the sand, (*b*) from water squeezed out by yielding and compacting of confining beds, or (*c*) from slow percolation from the less pervious confining material into the pervious sand body.[1]

[1] Meinzer criticizes this possibility of the origin of artesian pressure. He states, "The idea that artesian pressure is produced by rock pressure instead of hydrostatic pressure from the water at the high-level outcrop is not my concept, but is a particular application of the theory of elasticity which may

The cases summarized include all the occurrences known to the writer or described in the literature in which it appears to him that the relief of pressure on confined water by a pumping well may furnish an appreciable water supply additional to that percolating from the fountain head. The effect of pressure changes in elastic or compressible aquifers is treated in following pages.

Literature on Effect of Pressure Relief.—Von Jentzsch criticized the theory that hydraulic pressure generated at the fountain head is the principal source of pressure and suggested[1] a theory that artesian pressure is due to the weight of overlying strata and microseisms.

Russell,[2] from a study of the geology of the Dakota artesian region, believes that the hydraulic pressure theory is not applicable to that region because (1) the Dakota sandstone of the Rocky Mountain region is not in the same stratigraphic position as the Dakota sandstone of eastern Nebraska. Hence the formation is not continuous from intake to discharge area. (2) He concludes that the formation is lenticular and water migration from lens to lens is not likely. Other data advanced against the hydraulic pressure theory are (3) the irregular distribution of fresh and salt water in the Dakota sandstone; (4) the isopiestic lines (pressure contours) do not circle the Black Hills in a regular manner; (5) the head is lower under the valleys than under the ridges, suggesting greater load on aquifers under ridges, and (6) the modification of the upslope pressure surface does not indicate that pumped water has been derived solely from that direction.

---

or may not be the correct explanation of some conditions that have been described.". (Personal communication.)

[1] The thought has been expressed by von Jentzsch and Tornquist that the head of artesian water depends upon the pressure of the impervious strata overlying the aquifer. Stapf has shown, however, that such a pressing out of water from a bed is only possible when the individual grains of the aquifer are crushed so that they occupy a lesser volume. This never happens and therefore the assumption of hydrostatic pressure is the only reliable one.

Von Jentzsch has further expressed the opinion that the head of artesian water may be due to small microseismic pulsations of the earth. In other words, that it is not hydrostatic but hydrodynamic. In my opinion not the slightest proof has been adduced in favor of the correctness of this view. (KEILHACK, *op. cit.*, pp. 228–230.)

[2] RUSSELL, W. L., The Origin of Artesian Pressure, *Econ. Geol.*, vol. 23, pp. 132–157, 1928; vol. 24, no. 5, pp. 542–554, 1929.

Meinzer[1] emphasizes the elastic character of conduits and believes that relief of pressure produces an elastic contraction of the aquifer and occasionally permanent deformation resulting in drawing of water from storage in the aquifer in addition to the water drawn from the intake.[2]

Terzaghi[3] suggests in regard to the theory that water is derived from the compression of the confining beds, "water is not squeezed out of clay encasing an aquifer unless the enclosing clay is still in the state of progressive consolidation and compaction." It would appear that such an origin of confined water might be of some importance in soft, recently deposited alluvial cones and river flood plain and delta deposits, but not in indurated sedimentary rocks.

Relief of pressure due to pumping or flow of artesian wells is important in producing water in excess of that moving toward the well from the intake if the aquifers are elastic or compressible, and therefore phenomena indicating elasticity of artesian aquifers are discussed in detail in the following section.

PHENOMENA INDICATING COMPRESSIBILITY AND ELASTICITY OF ARTESIAN AQUIFERS AND AQUICLUDES

This discussion is based largely on data and arguments presented by Meinzer in his paper on compressibility of artesian aquifers.[4] The interpretations of minor fluctuations of water levels in wells tapping confined water due to barometric and tidal effects and earthquakes on compressible and elastic aquifers and aquicludes are among the most interesting presented in the

[1] MEINZER, O. E., Compressibility of Artesian Aquifers, *Econ. Geol.*, vol. 23, pp. 263–291, 1928.

[2] Meinzer states, "The evidence indicates that there are only very moderate amounts of contraction and expansion as a result of the changes of pressure produced by operation of wells. Nevertheless, the amounts are more than can be attributed to the elasticity or other volume changes in the water itself and they are large enough to affect radically conclusions in regard to the recharge, movement, and discharge of the water in artesian aquifers." (Compressibility of Artesian Aquifers, *op. cit.* p. 265.

[3] TERZAGHI, C., Origin of Artesian Press, *Econ. Geol.*, vol. 24, no. 1, pp. 96–97, 1929.

[4] MEINZER, O. E., Compressibility of Artesian Aquifers, *op. cit.*

paper; hence these fluctuations are accorded special discussion in the text.

Minor Fluctuations of Wells Due to Barometric and Tidal Effects

Water-table Wells.—Barometric pressure is usually transmitted through the air-filled formations above the water table and affects the water table in the same degree that it affects the water level in the well. Under these conditions barometric changes should not be registered in the water level of a water-table well (Fig. 113). However, water-table wells are reported to fluctuate with changes in barometric pressure when the ground surface is frozen or saturated by rain.[1] After excess water has

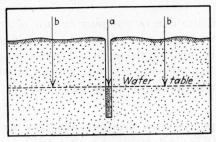

Fig. 113.—Barometric pressure on water level in well *a* and on water table *b* transmitted through air-filled formation.

drained away, pressure transmission through air-filled interstices should prevent fluctuations of water level due to changes in barometric pressure[2] (Fig. 114).

Wells Tapping Confined Water.—Hydrostatic pressure acting on the walls of a conduit is proportional to the height of the water column in the conduit and, if the conduit walls are flexible, will expand the conduit. Such expansion, of course, is resisted by the weight of the overlying material.

Effects of Atmospheric Pressure on Rigid and Elastic Conduits.—The principles governing the reaction of the water level in wells tapping confined water to varying atmospheric pressures may be illustrated by experiments with a rigid metal pipe and rubber tube both of the same diameter and closed at one end. If

[1] KING, F. H., *U.S. Weather Bur. Bull.* 5, *op. cit.*, pp. 20, 72–73.

[2] Replenishment of Ground Water Recorded by Observation Well near Washington, D.C., *Department of Interior Memo for the Press*, Feb. 25 1932.

filled with water to the same height, the rubber tube will hold more water because of dilation. If atmospheric pressure is

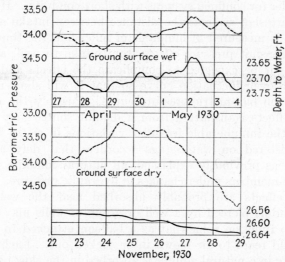

FIG. 114.—Effect of atmospheric pressure in feet of water (dashed line) on the water level (solid line) in a water-table well during rainy season when soil moisture reservoir is filled and after the soil has dried out. (*Courtesy of U.S. Geological Survey.*)

increased by the same amount in both tubes by attaching a hose from an air pump, the water level in the metal tube will not be lowered appreciably but that in the rubber tube will be lowered (Fig. 115).

Probably no natural aquifer has rigid walls and moreover, in addition to expanding the conduit, increased atmospheric pressure is expended in forcing water back into cracks and more pervious portions of the confining formation, in compressing air in pockets below the confining stratum if such pockets exist, and in compressing the water in the conduit.

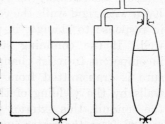

FIG. 115.—Rigid pipe and flexible rubber tube. The latter expands and the water level is lowered by increase in air pressure.

These combined effects probably cause all natural conduits to function like the rubber hose in the foregoing experiments, *although retaining walls may be relatively rigid.*

Pressure Effects on Intake and Well.—Atmospheric pressure effects on intake and well may be considered simultaneous and of like order for confined systems with short conduits. However, in some artesian systems the distance between intake and well discharge is measured in hundreds of miles and the time necessary to transmit pressure effects from intake to well, and vice versa, might be expected to complicate the effects and distort the water-level fluctuation curve so that it will show no similarity to the barometric-pressure curve. Possibly the reaction of such effects transmitted from a distant source may be one cause of the innumerable irregular variations in water levels in wells registered on water-stage recorders that defy analysis. However, as previously explained, all natural conduits perform as flexible members under changes in hydraulic pressure. Minor pressure effects are probably absorbed near the well-intake and a conduit pierced by a well or group of wells may be considered to function somewhat as a balloon attached to a small tube would react to air blown in or sucked out. Each change in pressure in a natural aquifer is absorbed in the close neighborhood of the well or well field.

Characteristics of Aquiclude and Overlying Strata.—The most interesting conclusions drawn from a study of barometric-pressure effects on water levels deal with the physical characteristics of the confining strata and the formations through which pressure effects may be transmitted from the ground surface. Even with rigid walls the conduit functions as an elastic member in response to changes in pressure on the water surface in the well. If the confining stratum and overlying materials are incompetent to resist changes in atmospheric pressure and pressure is transmitted from the ground surface to the conduit walls by the yielding of the incompetent formations overlying the conduit, this exterior pressure will balance pressure transmitted from the water surface in the well to the conduit walls (Fig. 116*B*). Hence the water level in the well will not register change in barometric pressure but, on the other hand, will respond to tidal loading and other exterior loads, such as the passage of trains or the piling up of flood water on an alluvial cone.[1]

If barometric pressure is not transmitted through the ground and the conduit is not distorted, the effect of pressure changes in

[1] KING, F. H., *U.S. Weather Bur. Bull. 5, op. cit.*, pp. 52–53, 67–68.

the conduit is not compensated and the well will function as a water barometer (Fig. 116*A*). This condition may be interpreted as indicating that the confining medium is competent to resist slight pressure deformation and that tidal and other surface loading will not affect the water level.[1]

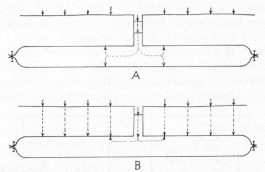

FIG. 116.—*A*, a rubber tube filled with water; pressure transmitted only through the vertical open tube. The water level varies with change in atmospheric pressure. This illustrates the functioning of a confined aquifer with overlying material competent to resist deformation by atmospheric pressure. *B*, rubber tube filled with water; equal pressure affects both the water surface in open tube and walls of the conduit, and no change in water level occurs with variation in atmospheric pressure. This represents the action of atmospheric pressure on a confined aquifer with overlying aquiclude incompetent to resist atmospheric pressure.

As Meinzer[2] shows, if the formation yields partially to barometric and tidal loading, the water level of a well will show both small barometric and tidal fluctuations.

. . . The ratio of the movements in the well to the corresponding movement in the barometer should give a measure to the resistance of the water-bearing and confining beds. If such a well is near the seashore its water level will fluctuate more or less with the tide. In the Atlantic City investigation, by Thompson, it was found that artesian wells near the seashore ending in coastal-plain deposits of sand over-

[1] Thompson (*Trans. Amer. Geophys. Union*, p. 339, 1936) reports a peculiar phenomenon, first observed in the Atlantic City well field, "of the water level in a well penetrating one formation moving in the opposite direction to that in a well in another formation separated by thick clay beds, when pumping of the latter begins or ceases." This type of fluctuation has since been observed by Thompson in two widely separated localities on Long Island.

[2] MEINZER, O. E., Outline of Methods for Estimating Ground-water Supplies, *U.S. Geol. Surv. Water-Supply Paper* 638-C, p. 142, 1932.

lain by clay fluctuated notably with the tide but showed no marked
barometric fluctuations. These results seem to indicate artesian conditions in incompetent strata. In such wells the water level might be
expected to rise as a result of the compression produced by a passing
railroad train. In the Mokelumne area it was found that the water
level in a well drilled through valley fill to a stratum at some depth
below the water table rose whenever a train passed over the railroad
117 feet away, but in a well drilled only to the water table at the same
place the water level was not affected by passing trains.

If a well ends in a formation that is effectively covered by an impermeable bed but is unsaturated in its upper part, thus having an air
chamber between the water table and the overlying impermeable bed,
and if the well is tightly cased to a level below the water table, the water

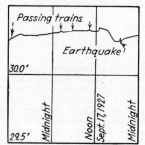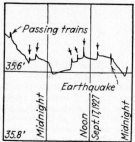

Fig. 117.—Fluctuation of water levels in two deep wells due to passing trains
and earthquake shock. (*After Stearns, H. T., Bull. Seis. Soc. Amer.*, vol. 18,
no. 1, *p.* 13.)

level in the well will behave like that in an artesian well in competent
beds. It will fluctuate through about the same range as the water
level in a water barometer, because, as in the other case, the counter
pressure will remain nearly constant. These conditions were noted by
Thompson[1] in the Grand Prairie region of Arkansas, where some of the
wells were found to perform as perfect barometers, apparently with
100 per cent of barometric fluctuation.

The conclusion may be drawn that in wells tapping confined
systems fluctuations of water levels caused by tides, earthquake,
passing trains, or by flood flow in streams, and fluctuations
equal to part of barometric change indicate compressibility
and yielding of the overlying formations to load (Fig. 117).
And fluctuations of the same order of magnitude as barometric

[1] THOMPSON, D. G., Ground-water Supplies for Rice Irrigation in the
Prairie Region, Ark., *U.S. Dept. Int. Press Mem.* 49844, pp. 8–9, Jan. 26,
1931.

changes and coincident with them indicate sufficient rigidity of formations to prevent yielding to changes in barometric pressure transmitted through the ground.

Effect of Earthquakes on Water Levels in Wells

Sudden displacements of water levels in wells by earthquakes in California, Nevada, and Mexico have been recorded and discussed in recent years. Pronounced effects have been recorded only in deep wells probably tapping confined water. Artesian wells, the pressure levels of which are measured by pressure

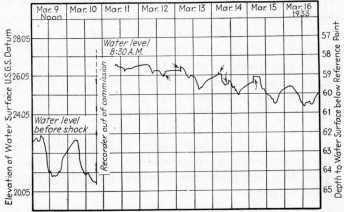

Fig. 118.—Displacement of water level in well by Long Beach earthquake of March 10, 1933. Arrows indicate shocks and displacement of water surface. (*After M. N. Thompson.*)

gages, show maximum effects. Shallow wells penetrating a short distance below the water table showed no displacement at Lodi, California, but neighboring deep wells were affected by the Bishop earthquake (epicenter White Mountains) of Sept. 17, 1927.

The effects of the Nevada earthquake of Dec. 20, 1932; the Japanese earthquake of March 3, 1933; the Long Beach earthquake of Mar. 10, 1933; and the Mexican earthquake of June 3, 1932, were investigated by S. B. Morris.[1] The maximum distances noted from epicenters of these shocks to well disturb-

[1] MORRIS, S. B., Fluctuation of Water Levels in Wells during the Nevada Earthquake of December 20, 1932, with some Observations during Recent Earthquakes, Paper prepared for presentation at meeting of Seismological Society of America, Apr. 8, 1933 (unpublished).

ances are as follows: Nevada earthquake, 826 miles; Japanese earthquake, 5283 miles; Long Beach earthquake, 363 miles; and Mexican earthquake, 1454 miles.

The surge of water surfaces in wells depends upon the distance from the epicenter of the earthquake and the depth of the well, modified by varying conditions of geologic structure, character of well, and recording devices. The surge in a well 581 ft. deep was 4.61 ft., and in a 1400-ft. well 8.08 ft. in the San Bernardino basin.[1] Displacement is registered on the well hydrograph as a vertical line extending above and below normal water level (Figs. 117–118), and usually it is impossible to deduce from the record whether elevation or depression of the water surface occurred first. However, Leggette and Taylor[2] state that an observer standing near a group of flowing wells in Ogden Valley, Utah, during the earthquake of Mar. 12, 1934, reports that "All the flowing wells ceased to flow at the first shock and in a few seconds they spurted up much higher than during normal flow." They conclude that "the first effect of the shock was to expand the water-bearing formation, following which the formation was compressed, causing the water to spurt higher than normal." In some cases there is a semipermanent elevation of water level for several days, and in one case (Owens Valley) a semipermanent depression occurred.

It appears probable that the phenomenon is largely due to the reaction of an elastic conduit to the earth tremor. The semipermanent rise may be due to compression of relatively inelastic conduits and semipermanent depression to dilation and shaking up of the water-bearing materials. Pressure records of capped artesian wells register rapid oscillations in hydraulic pressure better than float records and offer a quantitative method of recording earthquake shock that may yield data not obtained by present methods.[3]

Other Evidence Indicating Compressibility of Aquifers

1. Evidence from Water Production in Excess of Replenishment without Drawdown at Intake.—Meinzer and Hard's

---

[1] MORRIS, *op. cit.*, p. 7.

[2] LEGGETTE, R. M., and G. H. TAYLOR, Earthquakes Instrumentally Recorded in Artesian Wells, *Bull. Seis. Soc. Amer.*, vol. 25, no. 2, p. 172, April, 1935.

[3] LEGGETTE and TAYLOR, *op. cit.*, pp. 173–175.

studies in the Edgeley Quadrangle, North Dakota,[1] show that the artesian peak discharge (between 1905 and 1910) was 10,000 g.p.m.; in 1915 about 5000 g.p.m.; 1920, 2000 g.p.m.; and 1000 g.p.m. in 1923 and pressure head was still declining but the area of influence has not extended to the intake. Therefore recharge was less than 1000 g.p.m.

Since rate of discharge in the area of artesian flow has been more rapid than rate of replenishment from intake, and as the fountain head has not been lowered, some of the water must have been withdrawn from storage near the well. Inasmuch as artesian conduits are full of water at all times, this called for a reduction of pore space by compression of the aquifer.[2]

2. Evidence from Continued Change in Pressure Gradient Extending over a Limited Area.—When pressure is relieved by opening the discharge valve of a flowing well or starting the pump over a well drawing on confined water, a wave of pressure relief traverses the confined water body. The rate of transmission of this effect is reduced by deformation of the conduit caused by elastic strain set up by pressure relief. The adjusted gradient should be reached promptly, if the conduit is fairly rigid, and maintained as long as flow in the well does not exceed recharge. The head should decline gradually if the conduit is deformed and water supply is derived from compaction of the aquifer.

In regard to studies in the Edgeley Quadrangle, Meinzer[3] states:

The head did not drop suddenly, but has been declining gradually for about 40 years. The survey made in 1923 showed that there has been much less decline in the water levels in the wells near the western margin of the area of artesian flow than a few miles farther east, suggesting that in all these years there has not been much readjustment of the hydraulic gradient beyond the area in which artesian water was withdrawn (Fig. 119). Moreover, near the west margin of the area of

[1] MEINZER, O. E., and H. A. HARD, The Artesian-water Supply of the Dakota Sandstone in North Dakota, with special reference to the Edgeley Quadrangle, *U.S. Geol. Surv. Water-Supply Paper 520-E*, pp. 90–93, 1925.

[2] Meinzer shows that pore space occupied by the water withdrawn near the well has not been filled by the expansion of water under decreased head, by chemical precipitation under decreased pressure, or by expansion of gases dissolved in water as pressure is released. (*Econ. Geol.*, vol. 23, *op. cit.*, p. 270.)

[3] MEINZER, Compressibility of Artesian Aquifers, *op. cit.*, pp. 261–272.

artesian flow, for which data are available, the hydraulic gradient has not flattened out but instead has become steeper.

In order to reach conclusive results more data are needed as to the head in the large region between the area of flow and the outcrop, but the data at hand certainly point to the conclusion that the Dakota sandstone has not behaved like an incompressible reservoir; that the water discharged by the flowing wells has largely been derived locally from storage and not by transfer of water all the way from the outcrop.

3. Evidence from Phenomena of Recovery.—Assuming that flow of the well is less than replenishment, when the well is shut down the cone of pressure relief is effaced and the original water pressure is thrown back on the conduit walls. If the conduit is rigid, the prepumping pressure head will then be re-established almost immediately. If the conduit is compressible and elastic, the pressure will recover more slowly but completely.[1] If the conduit is compressible and the elasticity insufficient to bring the conduit to its original volume, recovery will be slow and incomplete. Recovery of most artesian wells is slow and incomplete.

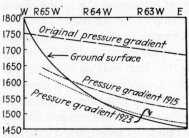

Fig. 119.—General east-west section of area of artesian flow from Dakota sandstone in Edgeley Quadrangle, showing original hydraulic gradient and gradients of 1915 and 1923. (*After Meinzer and Hard.*)

If well production is larger than supply, it is difficult if not impossible to differentiate the slow recovery after overpumping the supply from that due to elasticity and compressibility of the conduit. Hence in testing the elastic reaction of the conduit, rate of pumping should be less than natural supply.

4. Evidence from Laboratory Tests.—Meinzer[2] summarizes laboratory tests on the compressibility of aquifers as follows:

Tests made by different investigators have shown that in general sand is much less compressible than clay. This difference is due in part to the greater size of the grains but largely to their better rounding.

[1] In an Atlantic City artesian well observed by Thompson the water level rose for at least three months after pumping ceased. (*Trans. Amer. Geophys. Union*, p. 338, 1936.)

[2] MEINZER, *Econ. Geol.*, vol. 23, *op. cit.*, pp. 267–268.

The compressibility is least in materials consisting of uniformly well-rounded grains and greatest in materials of irregular, angular, and elongated particles. It has been shown by Terzaghi[1] that sand with admixture of mica has compressibility comparable to that of clay, and he has, moreover, produced evidence from various sources to show that many clays do contain a considerable percentage of mica or other scale-like particles.

The compressibility of sand has been demonstrated by laboratory tests. An experiment was described by King[2] in which an upright cylinder was filled with saturated sand. In this experiment some of the water was squeezed out of the interstices by the pressure produced by the settling of the sand and was forced through a pipe at the bottom of the cylinder and through an attached hose to a level 6 inches above the water level in the cylinder from which it came.

In a test recently made by Terzaghi[3] "pressure was applied to a sample of compacted sand up to about 1250 lb. per square inch and the porosity of the sand was decreased by this pressure from about 40 to 34 per cent."

5. Evidence from Surface Subsidence around Wells.—Compression of the aquifer or compaction of confining strata must be registered in sinking of the surface of the ground. Great subsidences have been noted around wells at Schneidelmühl, Germany,[4] and Goose Creek oil field, Texas.[5] Investigation of these occurrences has not been sufficiently detailed, however, to prove how much (if any) of the subsidence was due to compression of the aquifer and what portion was due to ejection of sand.

The extraordinary sinking of the ground surface in the Santa Clara Valley, Santa Clara County, California, was brought out by six successive precise levelings carried out by the Coast and Geodetic Survey. The original line, run during 1911–1912,

[1] TERZAGHI, CHARLES, Principles of Final Soil Classification, *Mass. Inst. Tech. Publ.*, vol. 63, pp. 41–43, 1927.

[2] KING, F. H., Principles and Conditions of the Movements of Ground Water, *U.S. Geol. Surv.*, 19th *Ann. Rept.*, pt. II, pp. 78–80, 1899.

[3] TERZAGHI, C., *Eng. News-Record*, vol. 95, pp. 987–990, 1925.

[4] HÖFER-HEIMHALT, *op. cit.*, p. 115.

[5] PRATT, W. E. and D. W. JOHNSON, Local Subsidence of the Goose Creek Oil Field, *Jour. Geol.*, vol. 34, pp. 577–590, 1926; L. C. SNIDER, A Suggested Explanation for the Surface Subsidence in the Goose Creek Oil and Gas Field, *Amer. Assn. Pet. Geol. Bull.* vol. 11, no. 7, pp. 729–745, July, 1927.

followed the Southern Pacific railroad from Brigham, Utah, through Niles and San Jose to San Francisco. In 1920 the line was extended from San Jose to Santa Ana. The first releveling, 1931–1932, revealed divergence from the original line beginning at Redwood City and extending to Coyote, a distance of about 35 miles, with a maximum of 3.6 ft. at San Jose. The 1932–1933 leveling showed increasing subsidence over this distance with a total depression at San Jose of 4.1 ft., or 0.5 ft. since the previous winter. In order to investigate this unusual phenomenon a

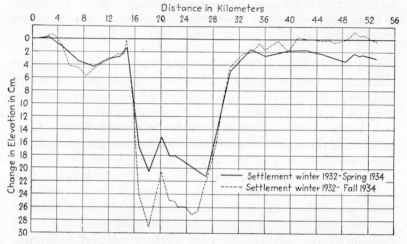

Fig. 120.—Graph showing settlement from Morgan Hills to Niles, Santa Clara Valley, for periods winter 1932 to spring 1934 (solid line) and winter 1932 to fall 1934 (dashed line).

net of level lines was laid out across the valley from the San Andreas fault on the west to the Hayward fault on the east, and after releveling of these lines the area affected by subsidence was found to be trough-shaped. Figure 120 is a cross section of the area from Morgan Hill to Niles, showing changes in elevation in the spring and fall of 1934 since the winter of 1932. The amount of subsidence which occurred during the past year (1935–1936) is shown by contours in Fig. 121 which shows the sinking area as a trough parallel to San Francisco Bay.

The average lowering of water level in wells in the Santa Clara Valley was estimated as follows: Average depth to ground water

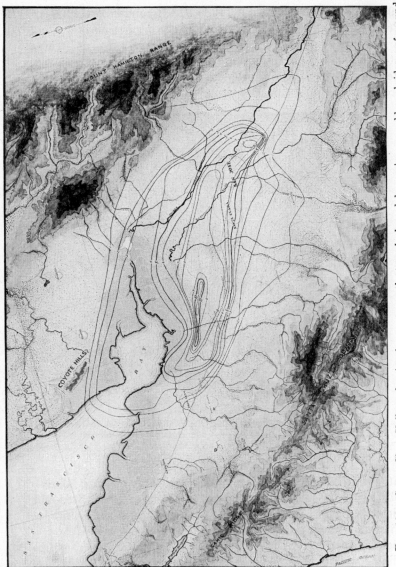

Fig. 121.—Santa Clara Valley, showing by contours the trough-shaped depression caused by subsidence of ground surface (contour interval = 1cm.). Contours represent subsidence during a period of one year from the spring of 1935 to spring 1936, maximum 11 cm. (4.33 inches). The mountain areas are shaded; the alluvial cone structure is indicated by curved and radiating lines. Closely lined areas are tidelands. (Subsidence data from precise leveling by U.S. Coast and Geodetic Survey.)

in 1915, 33.4 ft.; in 1921, 63.4 ft.; 1930, 97.9 ft.; and in 1931, 109 ft.[1]

Possible Causes of Subsidence.—When the occurrence of sinking was first made public, F. H. Tibbetts[2] suggested that it was related to extreme overpumping and drying out of water-bearing materials. Analyzing the problem in detail it appears that the depression of ground surface may be due to tectonic earth move-

Fig. 122.—Protruding well casing lifted the pump off its foundation. The pump foundation dropped 8½ in. between 1931 and 1937, as indicated by scale. The well is 7 miles northwest of San Jose and is about 450 ft. deep. (*Photograph by E. E. Stohsner.*)

ments; or if due to overpumping ground water which is almost wholly confined, may be caused by compaction of aquifers and aquicludes, or may be the result of drying out of surface clays by cutting off effluent seepage from the fingers of aquifers.

Light is thrown on the problem by the phenomenon of "protruding" well casings.[3] Over the sunken area old well casings

[1] TIBBETTS, F. H., Report on Waste Water Salvage Project to Board of Directors, Santa Clara Valley Water Conservation District, San Jose, Calif., p. 12, Oct. 2, 1931.

[2] TIBBETTS, F. H., Areal Subsidence, *Eng. News-Record*, p. 204, Aug. 17, 1933.

[3] STOHSNER, E. E., Santa Clara Valley Subsidence Has Now Reached Five Feet, *Eng. News-Record*, vol. 118, no. 13, Apr. 1, 1937.

have gradually risen above the ground surface, in many cases as much as 2 or 3 ft. This suggests that sinking is caused by compaction distributed throughout the zone penetrated by wells. It does not seem probable that the slight drying of ground surface accompanying overpumping can be the cause of the extensive subsidence over an area covered by various types of surface materials; but that compaction, possibly of aquifers, and principally of aquicludes, is the probable cause.

Logs of wells in the sinking area show a predominance of sticky blue and yellow clay interstratified with numerous layers of sand and some gravel which represent the finger ends of the aquifers. Reduction of pressure by pumping would affect all the fingers of the aquifers throughout the zone of discharge (page 369) at the foot of the alluvial cone. The area of contact between the clay and the innumerable sand filaments is large and would assist draining of the large bodies of clay.

Analysis of data available to date has shown no proved recovery in ground-surface elevation during the rise of the water table in the rainy season. As far as can be determined, subsidence has been continuous. It is hoped that precise leveling will be continued, and levels taken at high- and low-water stages can be compared. The Santa Clara Valley Water Conservation District has been spreading water underground and future surface elevations compared with rise in the water table should determine whether compaction is permanent or temporary.

QUANTITATIVE ESTIMATE OF YIELD DUE TO DEPLETION OF PRESSURE

The quantities of water produced (1) by compaction of the aquifer, (2) by compaction of adjacent aquicludes, (3) by very slow percolation out of confining formations, all due to lowering of water levels in wells by overpumping, cannot as yet be measured separately. But if all other gains and losses of conduit water are known, the total quantity of water yielded as a result of depletion of hydraulic pressure in the aquifer can be estimated. Very seldom are the data available over the necessary period of years to compute this amount, which should appear in the ground-water inventory as X until the necessary information is available to determine this factor.

A satisfactory solution of the quantity X was made by M. B. Smith[1] who assembled the exhaustive data available on pumping and recharge in the Livermore Valley, California. He found that the water level has undergone cyclic variation owing to climatic conditions and resultant heavy pumping in dry years. Water in wells has returned to the same level twice, first after a period of very moderate pumping and small reduction in the general water level, and again after years of heavy pumping and severe depletion of water level. During the first period he assumed that no appreciable withdrawals of water were furnished by the process of compaction and completed his inventory for the first cycle under this assumption. In the following cycle he found that withdrawals far exceeded additions to ground water. This excess yield represents the quantity of water produced by compaction of aquifers and aquicludes and by slow percolation from confining strata, all of which are due to depletion of pressure in confined conduits as shown by depressed water levels in wells. These studies are summarized in Chap. XVI (pages 495–498).

COMPARISON OF PUMPING CONFINED AND FREE WATER

The hydraulic phenomena accompanying pumping of confined and free water and the effects of pumping on the level of ground water close to the well and in the regions of ground-water intake and of ground-water discharge, both of which are distant from the well, are dissimilar. For this reason detailed comparative study of the effects of pumping these two types of wells has been made in connection with litigation over effects of pumping.

These differences may be summarized as follows:

1. A cone of water-table depression bounds the volume of water-bearing material that has been dewatered by pumping a water-table well (Fig. 123). The cone of pressure relief developed by pumping a confined well is an imaginary surface indicating the pressure conditions in a conduit which remains filled with water (Fig. 124). There is no withdrawal of free water or fluctuation of water table due to pumping a well tapping confined water, except perhaps at the fountain head, unless the well casing is perforated above the confining stratum in the free-water zone or

---

[1] SMITH, MERRITT B., Ground Water in the Livermore Valley, California, Master's Thesis, Stanford University, May, 1934.

has developed leaks, or if the confining formation overlying the aquifer is appreciably permeable (Fig. 127, page 350).

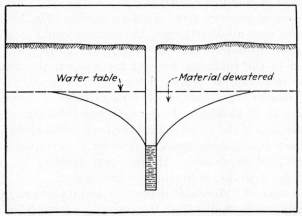

FIG. 123.—Cone of water-table depression produced by pumping water-table well

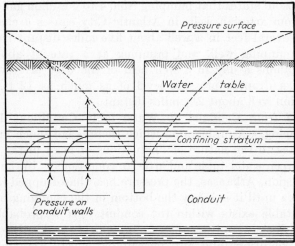

FIG. 124.—Cone of pressure relief produced by pumping from a confined aquifer. The vertical arrows indicate the amount of pressure exerted upon the walls of the conduit, as shown by the curved arrows.

2. The cone of water-table depression grows *slowly* as the materials are gradually dewatered (Fig. 129, page 352). It increases until the ground water percolating into the cone of depression equals the quantity of water pumped. If pumping

exceeds replenishment, the water level is lowered as long as this condition continues. This overdraft is termed *water-table depletion* or *ground-water depletion.*

The cone of pressure relief develops rapidly (Fig. 129) and if the aquifer were absolutely rigid, the transfer would theoretically be almost instantaneous. However, owing to the flexible character of the confining walls of the aquifer, the transfer of pressure reduction is slowed down. For instance, in Owens Valley, transfer of pressure effects for a distance of about 3 miles took place in 24 to 36 hr. If the wells had been pumping from free water, and if the effect could have been felt that distance, it would have taken many years to dewater a corresponding cone of water-table depression. Hence rapid transfer of pressure effects is one criterion indicating confined water.

3. The cone of water-table depression and its area of influence are usually much smaller than the cone of pressure relief and its area of influence.

Thompson[1] states that pumping from 4 to 5 million gallons per season from artesian wells in Atlantic City causes a change in head of several feet in a well about five miles distant from the nearest pumping well, and pumping at a rate of about $3\frac{1}{2}$ million gallons a day in a well field of the City of New York produces a drop in pressure level of as much as 12 ft. in an observation well about $2\frac{1}{2}$ miles distant.

Change from Confined to Water-table Conditions Due to Overpumping.—A problem on which there is not much information relates to the nature of fluctuations of head in the border zone between water-table and artesian conditions. In the Grand Prairie region, Arkansas, the pressure head has dropped in parts of the area until it is below the bottom of the confining bed and a water table exists within the conduit.[2] It is probable that pressure effects were transmitted more quickly under the original artesian conditions and also measurable effects were felt to a greater distance than under present conditions of depleted pressure. Where drainage has occurred and a water table exists within the conduit, it is probable that the yield of wells has decreased. The question has been raised as to whether a

[1] THOMPSON, D. G., Some Problems Relating to Fluctuations of Ground-water Level, *Trans. Amer. Geophys. Union*, p. 338, 1936.

[2] THOMPSON, *op. cit.*, p. 339.

sharp change in effects of pumping may indicate the change from
confined to free water due to overpumping.

Comparison of Water-level Fluctuations.—The general conclusions outlined are illustrated by comparison of the measured

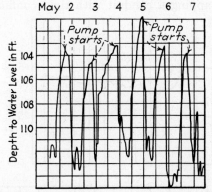

Fig. 125.—Typical daily pressure-surface fluctuations in observation well 800 ft.
from well pumping from confined water. (*After Lee.*)

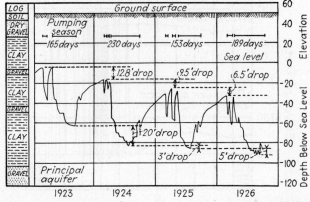

Fig. 126.—Annual fluctuation of pressure surface showing depletion in confined aquifer, expressed by drop in seasonal high and seasonal low levels. (*After
Lee.*)

fluctuations of water levels due to pumping of free- and confined-
water wells. On account of the importance of this subject the
accompanying graphs are reproduced from the excellent report by
Lee on "The Interpretation of Water-levels in Wells and Test
Holes,"[1] and his discussions are summarized.

[1] Lee, C. H., The Interpretation of Water-levels in Wells and Test-
Holes, *Trans. Amer. Geophys. Union*, pp. 540–554, 1934.

Figure 125 shows daily fluctuations of pressure surface and typical rapid changes in water level in an observation well due to pumping confined water from an artesian well tapping the same aquifer. Figure 126 shows annual fluctuations of water level in a well tapping a conduit with rigid confining beds and

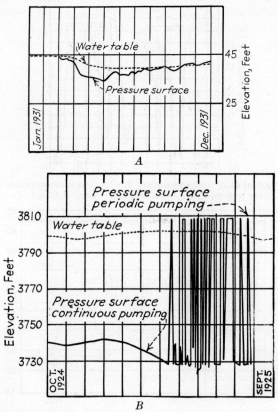

FIG. 127.—Effect on water table of pumping from confined aquifer: *A*, when confining formations are permeable or semi-permeable; *B*, when confining beds are impermeable. (*After Lee.*)

with depletion of supply by overpumping and lowering of the water level in the upper portion of the aquifer.

If the confining formations overlying an aquifer are permeable or semipermeable, the water table will drop more or less uniformly throughout the area of influence of the cone of pressure relief, progressively reaching a stage of equilibrium from the margin inward as it attains the new level of the pressure surface, as shown in Fig. 127*A*. If the confining strata are impermeable, however, there will be no water derived from the free ground-water body and no appreciable fluctuation in water table (Fig. 127*B*).

Two 72-hr. pump tests made by Lee, illustrate the difference in size and rapidity of development between the cones of water-table depression and pressure relief. City of San Diego well No. 9 penetrated a permeable valley fill, logged as 45 ft. sand, 15 ft. sand and gravel, 5 ft. gravel, and 22 ft. cemented sand (impermeable). Water table was 7 ft. below the surface

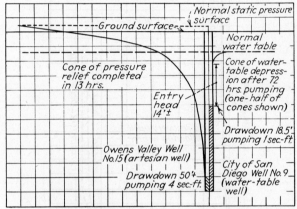

Fig. 128.—Comparison of cones of water-table depression and pressure-relief after 72 hr. of pumping. (*After Lee.*)

and the well had a pumping capacity of 1 sec.-ft. Drawdown in the well at the end of 2 hr. of pumping was 18.5 ft. and remained constant throughout the 72-hr. test. The radius of the cone of water-table depression was 310 ft. at the end of 24 hr. and 340 ft. at the end of 72 hr.

The second test was made on a 12-in. flowing artesian well 265 ft. deep situated in Owens Valley. It penetrates an alluvial cone and ancient lake beds composed of interbedded sand, gravel, and impermeable clay. Approximately 35 per cent of the formation is permeable and 65 per cent semipermeable and impermeable. The well taps only confined aquifers. When pumping started, a cone of pressure relief was formed which was registered by an almost instantaneous drop in water level in adjacent wells. Initial drawdown in the well exceeded 50 ft. and remained constant during the test. The radius of the cone of pressure relief was 5700 ft. at the end of 13 hr. with no increase thereafter.

A comparison of the cones of water-table depression and pressure relief developed by pumping these two wells is shown in Fig. 128. The time required for the radius of the cones of water-table depression and pressure relief to attain various distances from the wells is shown in Fig. 129. The maximum distance

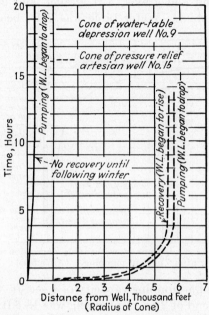

Fig. 129.—Comparison of radii of cones of water-table depression and pressure relief for various durations of pumping. (*After Lee.*)

at the end of 72 hr. for the water-table well was 340 ft., while for the deep artesian well a distance of 3000 ft. was attained within a few minutes and the maximum of 5700 ft. in 13 hr.

The total drop in water levels, as shown in wells or boreholes, at various distances from each pumping well is shown in Fig. 130. The water table surrounding the water-table well dropped progressively during the test and proceeded at a much reduced rate at the end of the 72-hr. period when drainage of voids was almost complete. The drop of pressure surface in nearby surrounding wells was nearly instantaneous; water levels did not change during the test. The smaller rise than drop in water levels is probably due to compaction of aquifers during pumping; and the lag in recovery after pumping stopped, compared with drawdown when pumping started, may be due in part to reduced rigidity of aquifer caused by disturbance during pumping but is largely due to energy consumed by re-inflation of aquifer.

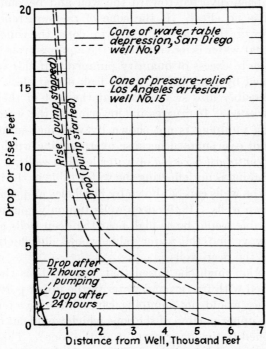

Fig. 130.—Comparison of rise or drop of water levels in water-table and confined-water wells at various distances from the wells, resulting from starting and stopping pumps. (*After Lee.*)

Note: No appreciable rise occurred in the water-table well until the following winter.

Effect of Pumping from Confined System on Water-table Wells and Streams.—The fact that pumping from an artesian or confined system generally has no effect on shallow water-table wells or streams in the vicinity of the deep well has been important in litigation between municipalities or water companies pumping from deep aquifers and property owners in the vicinity of the pumps. For example, land owners usually claim that pumping causes the water table to drop and removes the support from under flowing streams of the region and also diminishes natural subirrigation regardless of whether the well is supplied by free or confined water.

If confined water only is pumped (wells not perforated in free-water zone), the usual answer to such allegations is that the cone of pressure relief registers the area under which the conduit water has been diverted toward the well and beyond this area pumping has no effect. If the cone of pressure relief has not extended far up the slope of the alluvial cone, the conclusion can be drawn that water is moving down the aquifers from the intake region above in excess of quantity pumped. If this water were not reclaimed by pumping, it would leak out at the ends of the aquifers, possibly into swamp land at the foot of the cone and would be wasted. If progressive lowering of the water level in wells during pumping is not shown by well measurements, the supply is not overpumped because overpumping would be registered by a *continued lowering* of water level in wells.

That pumping is not affecting the water table in the immediate vicinity of the wells can be shown by boreholes and shallow wells near the deep wells. If the deep wells tap only confined water, the water table would be as high near the deep wells as at some distance away, and the water table would not fluctuate with pumping of the deep wells.

The question might be raised that, inasmuch as the aquifers are connected with free ground water in the upper portion of the alluvial cone, would not pumping cause lowering of the water table in the upper portion of the cone which would cut off ground water supplied to the lower portions of the cone? This question might be answered in part by finding out if the cone of pressure relief does or does not extend up to the intake area. If not, the water moving in the conduit has not been overpumped and ground-water conditions at the intake have not been affected.

If the supply has been overpumped and if pressure wells are drawing free ground water from the upper part of the alluvial cone into confined conduits, thus lowering the water table, the validity of the claim that this lowering of water table has removed the support from under streams, thereby reducing stream flow, would depend on whether the stream is effluent and is receiving water from the water table and is supported thereby, or whether the stream is influent and stream flow is not in contact with the water table. In the latter case water-table lowering would have no effect on stream-seepage loss. In the intake area of an alluvial cone streams are influent and hence stream flow is not affected by water-table fluctuations.

References

Principles and Occurrence of Confined Water

BAILEY, P. and E. HYATT, The Precise Determination of Replenishment and Draught from Niles Cone Aquifer, Engineer's Thesis, Stanford University, 1920.

CHAMBERLIN, T. C., Requisite and Qualifying Conditions of Artesian Wells, *U.S. Geol. Surv. 5th Ann. Rept.*, pp. 131–173, 1884.

FIEDLER, A. G., and S. S. NYE, Geology and Ground-water Resources of the Roswell Artesian Basin, New Mexico, *U.S. Geol. Surv. Water-Supply Paper* 639, 1933.

FULLER, M. L., Summary of Controlling Factors of Artesian Flows, *U.S. Geol. Surv. Bull.* 319, 1908.

FULLER, M. L., Significance of the Term "Artesian," *U.S. Geol. Surv. Water-Supply Paper* 160, pp. 9–15, 1906.

HÖFER-HEIMHALT, H., "Grundwasser und Quellen," Friedr. Vieweg & Sohn, Braunschweig, Germany, 1920.

KEILHACK, K., "Grundwasser und Quellenkunde;" pp. 218–257, 3d ed., Gebrüder Borntraeger, Berlin, 1935.

LEE, C. H., The Interpretation of Water-levels in Wells and Test-holes, *Trans. Amer. Geophys. Union*, pp. 540–554, 1934.

LEGGETTE, R. M., and G. H. TAYLOR, The Transmission of Pressures in Artesian Aquifers, *Trans. Amer. Geophys. Union*, pp. 409–413, 1934.

LIVINGSTON, P., and T. W. BRIDGES, Ground-water Resources of Kleberg Co., Texas, *U.S. Geol. Surv. Water-Supply Paper* 773-D, 1936.

MEINZER, O. E., Compressibility and Elasticity of Artesian Aquifers, *Econ. Geol.*, vol. 23, pp. 263–291, 1928.

MEINZER, O. E., and H. H. HARD, The Artesian Water Supply of the Dakota Sandstone in North Dakota, with Special Reference to the Edgeley Quadrangle, *U.S. Geol. Surv. Water-Supply Paper* 520-E, 1925.

MEINZER, O. E., and L. K. WENZEL, Water Levels and Artesian Pressure in the United States in 1935, with Statements Concerning Previous Work and Results, *U.S. Geol. Surv. Water-Supply Paper* 777, 1935.

NETTLETON, E. S., Artesian and Underflow Investigations, *52d Cong. 1st Sess. Ex. Doc.* 41, pt. 2.

PIPER, A. M., The Origin of Artesian Pressure, *Econ. Geol.*, vol. 23, no. 6, pp. 683–696, 1928.

ROBINSON, T. W., Decline of Artesian Head in West-Central South Dakota, *Trans. Amer. Geophys. Union*, pp. 363–366, 1936.

RUSSELL, W. L., The Origin of Artesian Pressure, *Econ. Geol.*, vol. 23, pp. 132–157, 1928.

SIMPSON, H. E., Methods of Reducing the Flow of Artesian Wells, Grand Forks Univ. Sta., *Geol. Surv. North Dakota Bull.* 3, 1924.

SLICHTER, C. S., Motions of Underground Waters, *U.S. Geol. Surv. Water-Supply and Irrigation Paper* 67, pp. 79–101, 1902.

STRINGFIELD, V. T., Artesian Water in Florida, *U.S. Geol. Surv. Water-Supply Paper 773-C*, 1936.

—— The Piezometric Surface of Artesian Water in the Florida Peninsula, *Trans. Amer. Geophys. Union*, pp. 524–529, 1935.

THEIS, C. V., The Relation between the Lowering of the Piezometric Surface and the Rate and Duration of Discharge of a Well Using Ground-water Storage, *Trans. Amer. Geophys. Union*, pp. 519–524, 1935.

THOMPSON, D. G., The Origin of Artesian Pressure, *Econ. Geol.*, vol. 24, pp. 758–771, 1929.

Compaction

ATHY, L. F., Density, Porosity, and Compaction of Sedimentary Rocks, *Bull. Amer. Assn. Pet. Geol.*, vol. 14, pp. 1–24, 1930.

—— Compaction and Its Effect on Local Structure, "Problems of Petroleum Geology" (Sidney Powers Memorial Volume), pp. 811–823, Amer. Assn. Pet. Geol., Tulsa, Okla., 1934.

GILBOY, G., The Compressibility of Sand-mica Mixtures, *Proc. Amer. Assn. Civ. Eng.*, vol. 54, pp. 555–568, February 1928; vol. 55, pp. 979–981, 1929.

HEDBERG, H. D., The Effect of Gravitational Compaction on the Structure of Sedimentary Rocks, *Bull. Amer. Assn. Pet. Geol.*, vol. 10, pp. 1035–1072, 1926; vol. 11, pp. 875–886, 1927.

—— Gravitational Compaction of Clays and Shales, *Amer. Jour. Sci.*, vol. 31, pp. 241–287, 1936.

JENKINS, C. F., The Pressure Exerted by Granular Material; An Application of the Principles of Dilatancy, *Proc. Roy. Soc., Ser. A.*, vol. 131, pp. 53–89, 1931.

MEAD, W. J., The Geologic Role of Dilatancy, *Jour. Geol.*, vol. 33, pp. 685–698, 1925.

NEVIN, C. M., and R. E. SHERRILL, Studies in Differential Compaction, *Bull. Amer. Assn. Pet. Geol.*, vol. 13, pp. 1–22, 1929.

ORTENBLAD, A., Mathematical Theory of the Process of Consolidation of Mud Deposits, *Jour. Math. Phys.*, vol. 9, pp. 73–149, 1930.

PRATT, W. E., and D. W. JOHNSON, Local Subsidence of the Goose Creek Oil Field, *Jour. Geol.*, vol. 34, pp. 577–590, 1926.

RUBEY, W. W., The Effect of Gravitational Compaction on the Structure of Sedimentary Rocks, *Bull. Amer. Assn. Pet. Geol.*, vol. 11, pp. 621–633; 1333–1336, 1927.

SNIDER, L. C., A Suggested Explanation for the Surface Subsidence in the Goose Creek Oil and Gas Field, *Amer. Assn. Pet. Geol. Bull.*, vol. 11, pp. 729–745, 1927.

TERZAGHI, CHARLES, *Eng. News-Record*, vol. 95, July-December, 1925:
I. Phenomena of Cohesion of Clay, pp. 742–746
II. Compressive Strength of Clays, pp. 796–800
III. Determination of Permeability of Clay, pp. 833–836

TRASK, P. D., Compaction of Sediments, *Bull. Amer. Assn. Pet. Geol.*, vol. 15, pp. 271–276, 1931.

VERSLUYS, J., The Compacting Pressure of Sediments, *Proc. Konink. Akad. van Wetenschappen te Amsterdam*, vol. 30, pp. 1004–1009, 1927.

CHAPTER XII

GEOLOGICAL CLASSIFICATION OF ARTESIAN AQUIFERS

Confinement of water in aquifers is due solely to geologic structure and hydrologic properties of water-conducting and water-confining formations. There is almost infinite variety in size, shape, extent, and arrangement of pervious and less pervious materials. Therefore a detailed classification of all possible types due to all known or possible arrangements of aquifers and aquicludes (or occasionally aquifuges) is too cumbersome for practical use.[1] If the geological structure is worked out, the resulting artesian system becomes self-evident.

In this book only a few principal types of artesian conditions are described. These types are selected on account of their importance, and on account of definite characteristics related to geologic structure. For further information the reader is referred to the detailed geological descriptions of the principal artesian fields. In the great variety of geologic structure developing confined-water systems certain essential features are common to all those under the control of hydraulic pressure.[2] These are: Water is confined by an overlying body of any type of relatively impervious material that retards escape of water from the aquifer to the surface. Pressure is developed by the weight of a continuous water body to the collecting area, and the static level in a well is reduced below the theoretical static level (height at fountain head) by friction of percolation in the conduit above the discharge area. If escape of water from the

---

[1] Myron L. Fuller describes in detail geologic structures and textures that constitute underground "reservoirs" (aquifers) and all agencies that function as confining formations. The reader is referred to his paper, Summary of the Controlling Factors of Artesian Flows, *U.S. Geol. Surv. Bull.* 319, pp. 20–21.

[2] Keilhack states: "Artesian or pressure water is bounded by an impervious cover and not by a pervious rock the interstices of which are filled with air. The pressure water system is composed of three parts; namely, the collecting area, the pressure area, and the discharge area, in which the water comes to the surface as springs or mixes with the air-capped free ground water." "Grundwasser und Quellen," *op. cit.*, p. 218.

lower end of the conduit is retarded, the velocity of natural percolation in the conduit is slow, the lowering of head by friction is small, and the static level in wells piercing the conduit may be above ground surface.

The above description applies to artesian systems with free connection with the collecting area and the hydraulic pressure of which is due to the weight of the confined water body. Pressure due to the weight of formations overlying the aquifer may also affect confined water, especially where excessive pumping and lowering of water levels in wells have occurred. The known occurrences may be summarized as follows:

1. *Systems with a High Initial Artesian Pressure in Fairly Compact Sedimentary Rocks.*—The artesian aquifer is somewhat lenticular but connection of aquifer with the fountain head is sufficient to develop initially a high head owing to hydrostatic pressure, but not sufficient to furnish all the water produced by well flow. The relief of high head by discharge of wells causes additional pressure to be thrown on the aquifer which is compressed thereby and furnishes water originally stored in the aquifer in the vicinity of the well as an additional supply to the water moving in the conduit toward the well. The Dakota artesian system is taken as a type and Meinzer's description as authority.

2. *Artesian systems with moderate initial head* occur in alluvial cone deposits where confining formations are uncompacted clays and silts. Extreme overpumping and lowering of static levels reduce hydraulic pressure which prior to depletion resisted squeezing out of water from the confining formations by the pressure of overlying material. Escape of water from the confining formations into the aquifer greatly accelerates the process of compaction. Proof of such systems is furnished by a detailed ground-water inventory showing quantity of water furnished by compression and compaction of formations, (pages 495–498)[1] and by sinking of ground surface where water levels have been greatly lowered.[2]

3. *Artesian Systems in Lenticular Sand Bodies Completely Surrounded by Soft Clay and Silt.*—Pressure is due solely to weight

[1] SMITH, M. B., Ground Water in the Livermore Valley, California; Master's Thesis, Stanford University, May, 1934.

[2] See description of subsidence in Santa Clara Valley, pp. 341–345.

of overlying material. When pressure in the sand lens is
reduced by well flow, water is derived from the surrounding
relatively impervious clays and silts, either by very slow percolation or by compaction of both sand lens and surrounding
aquicludes. This type is not fully established but is strongly
suggested by phenomena shown by boreholes encountering sand
lenses in clay and to some extent by conditions observed at
Pittsburg, California (pages 378–379).

IMPORTANT TYPES OF ARTESIAN SYSTEMS
Stratiform Aquifers

The classic paper of Chamberlin[1] is the first comprehensive
and detailed geological description of artesian flow in stratiform

FIG. 131.—Transition of pervious water-bearing bed into close-textured impervious one. *A*, pervious stratum; *B* and *C*, impervious confining strata. (*After
Chamberlin.*)

aquifers with gentle dip from their outcrop in the gathering area
toward the artesian basin. His cross sections have been reproduced in every treatise on ground water and in most technical
discussions of artesian flow (Figs. 131 and 132). It will be noted
that the pressure gradient is flat. Chamberlin did not discuss
the hydraulic gradient as a function of friction of percolation.

FIG. 132.—Ideal section illustrating the chief requisite conditions of artesian
wells. *A*, pervious stratum; *B* and *C*, impervious strata. (*After Chamberlin.*)

The geologic conditions of the Illinois-Wisconsin system are
described briefly as follows: The pressure water is contained in
two extensive sandstone aquifers, the Potsdam sandstone of
Cambrian age, and the St. Peter sandstone of Ordovician age.
The two aquifers are separated by impervious shale of considerable thickness, and the St. Peter sandstone is also overlain by
shale. The gentle dip from the outcrop area in Wisconsin is

[1] CHAMBERLIN, T. C., Requisite and Qualifying Conditions of Artesian
Wells, *U.S. Geol. Surv. 5th Ann. Rept.*, pp. 131–173, 1884.

a little steeper than the surface. Wells reach the sandstone
at depths of 2000± ft. at a distance of 150 to 200 miles from the
outcrop. The sandstone strata are supposed to be continuous,
not lenticular. The Potsdam sandstone is a basal transgressive
formation of great extent. The St. Peter sandstone is continuous
from the outcrop in Wisconsin to south of Chicago. The
decrease in permeability of both aquifers below the artesian
area, which reduces the rate of natural percolation and develops
high artesian head, is due to a gradual change from medium- to
fine-grained sandstone and finally into shale south of the artesian
field.

The hydraulic slope of the artesian system is 1 ft. per mile,
and the velocity of percolation under natural conditions has been

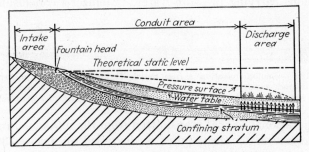

Fig. 133.—Artesian conditions in stratiform aquifer.

calculated as 1760 ft. per year.[1] The small friction developed by
this slow velocity accounts for the nearly flat hydraulic gradient.
The area of escape is not definitely known but may be represented
in part by springs in north central Illinois which are supposed to
rise from considerable depths along faults. The features of this
typical system are illustrated in Fig. 133 with vertical scale
much larger than horizontal scale. For simplicity only one
aquifer is shown.

The simple monoclinal structure of the Illinois-Wisconsin
artesian system has been taken as the type for stratiform conduits. However, there may be great variety in degree of inclination and structure, varying from the regular monocline to the
irregular syncline. Keilhack gives several types of artesian

[1] Schultz, A. R., Some Observations on the Movement of Underground
Water in Confined Basins, *Jour. Geol.*, vol. 15, p. 170, 1907.

systems in sedimentary rock,[1] but the principal features are modifications of those described for the Illinois-Wisconsin system.

Both Chamberlin and Keilhack mention the artesian system in a syncline with fountain head in the conduit at the overflow level of the synclinal basin and upward escape of water retarded by overlying impervious material in the center of the syncline (Fig. 132). The great Dakota system has a shallow syncline superimposed on the monoclinal structure, and the Michigan symmetrical basin yields artesian water from the upper formations.[2]

High-pressure Systems—Water Furnished in Part by Compression of Aquifer.—The only well-described example of this type of artesian flow is the Dakota system. A geological cross section is shown in Fig. 134 which illustrates the structure of the formations carrying pressure water. Meinzer's conclusion that

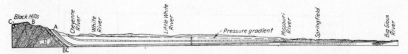

FIG. 134.—Geologic section across South Dakota. *A*, Dakota sandstone; *B*, Deadwood sandstone; *C*, Carboniferous limestone; *D*, schist. Pressure gradient shown by dashed line through section. (*Modified after Darton.*)

water additional to that transmitted from the intake is furnished by compaction of the aquifer is discussed on pages 339–340. Darton[3] describes the geology of the region as follows:

The Black Hills uplift is an irregular dome-shaped anticline, embracing an oval area 125 miles long and 60 miles wide, with its longer dimension lying nearly northwest and southeast. It is situated in a wide area of nearly horizontal beds and has brought above the general level of the plains an area of pre-Cambrian crystalline rocks about which there is upturned a nearly complete sequence of sedimentary formations, ranging in age from middle Cambrian to late Cretaceous, all dipping away from the central nucleus. There are also extensive overlaps of the Tertiary deposits which underlie much of the adjoining plains area. . . . The structure along the sides of the uplift is that of a monocline dipping toward the plains.

The formation here designated the Dakota sandstone is the uppermost member of the series formerly designated "Dakota sandstone"

[1] KEILHACK, *op. cit.*, pp. 220–226.

[2] MEINZER, *Water-Supply Paper* 489, *op. cit.*, p. 172.

[3] DARTON, N. H., Geology and Underground Waters of South Dakota, *U.S. Geol. Surv. Water-Supply Paper* 227, pp. 8–9, 1909.

in the Black Hills region. It extends continuously around the uplift, but being rarely more than 100 feet thick it constitutes only a small part of the hogback range. Nevertheless it is conspicuous, because the

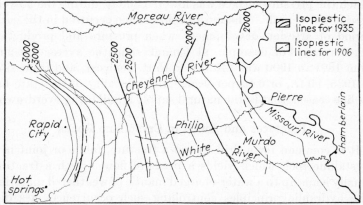

FIG. 135.—Map of part of western South Dakota showing isopiestic lines for 1906 and 1935. (*After Robinson.*)

foothills to which it usually gives rise ascend steeply out of the adjoining valley or level plain underlain by the Graneros shale. It generally consists of gray sandstone, weathering brown. It is hard and massive below, but thinner bedded above. The fossil plants which have been

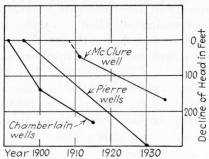

FIG. 136.—Amount of decline of artesian head in west central South Dakota. (*After Robinson.*)

obtained from it are impressions of dicotyledonous leaves, regarded as Upper Cretaceous in age.[1]

The pressure contours for 1906 and 1935 are shown in Fig. 135. Overpumping first produced local depletion of the pressure

[1] DARTON, *op. cit.*, p. 20.

surface, but depletion has now become general and affects all the west central portion of South Dakota (Fig. 136). The largest decline in pressure level occurred in a well near Pierre in which the pressure surface was lowered 300 ft. during the 35-year production period. The most rapid decline occurred in the early period of artesian development when pressure and production were large. For example, at Chamberlain the average decline from 1891 to 1900 was 140 ft., or 15 ft. per year, and from 1920 to 1935, 90 ft., or 6 ft. per year. In no locality of the state has decline ceased; that is, the natural supply is still being overdrawn.[1]

Fractures and Joints in Crystalline Rocks

It is common for a drill to tap a fracture, fault, or joint in a crystalline rock which yields a pressure flow. Such a fracture usually leads up to a water-charged mantle of weathered material. The hydraulic principles controlling such occurrences are discussed in Chap. X. The infinite variety of type and size of fractures that may produce artesian conditions make it inadvisable to go into detail.

Solution Cavities and Lava Tunnels

These geologic structures contain most of the underground rivers. The capacity of these conduits is usually so large that often they are not completely filled and under these conditions will not produce artesian flow. However, enormous artesian flows have been struck in solution openings in limestone (in Paris basin, France, and Roswell basin, New Mexico) and in such cases the solution channel is filled to a short distance above the height indicated by the gage pressure reading on the well. Large flows in limestone have been encountered in mining, but these usually are exhausted after a time.

Pressure Water in Alluvial Cones and Fans[2]

Alluvial cones and fans are the great water producers in western United States and probably produce more water than

---

[1] ROBINSON, T. W., Decline of Artesian Head in West-Central South Dakota, *Trans. Amer. Geophys. Union*, pp. 363–366, 1936.

[2] The distinction between an alluvial cone and fan is based chiefly on slope, but is somewhat indefinite, and the terms have been used interchangeably. The fan has gentler slope than the cone, is made up in general

all other types of confined-water systems combined. They are also of far more economic value, for they furnish the water necessary to bring into production the desert soils of unrivaled fertility. Pressure water in alluvial cones and fans has been studied in more detail than any other occurrence of confined water.

Geologic Structure of Alluvial Cone.—An alluvial cone is a body of alluvial material deposited at the foot of a range of hills or mountains by a stream that debouches from the area undergoing erosion above the apex of the cone. The form of an alluvial cone is roughly a segment of a cone (considerably less than one half) with apex where the parent stream emerges from the mountains. The slope decreases, on radial lines diverging from the apex, toward the foot or lower edge of the cone.

A group of alluvial cones built up by streams debouching from a mountain range usually impinge each on the other and form a *piedmont alluvial deposit.* Each member of this compound deposit has its individual apex at the exit of the parent stream from the mountains and its own set of built-in aquifers (see Fig. 1, frontispiece).

The material furnished to the stream and built into the cone is derived from erosion of the drainage area of the stream. Hence (1) the slope of the drainage area; (2) bedrock formations of the same; (3) the processes of weathering, which in turn are controlled by climate and topography; and (4) the character of rainfall and runoff are the principal factors governing the character of the material supplied to the cone.

Effect of Slope.—If the slope of the drainage area is steep, fine and coarse material alike are carried down the stream channel and the large-size material is deposited at the apex of the cone. If the slope is gentle, more time is allowed to the processes of weathering for breaking up the coarse material and manufacturing fine silt and clay, and on account of gentle slope the stream may not be capable of moving large material. Hence the slope of the cone and the size of the constituent materials vary with the gradient of the source stream.

---

of finer material, especially at the apex where less talus material is incorporated in the deposit. It is usually deposited by a larger stream than the cone, and is therefore of larger size and made up of more uniformly sorted materials.

FIG. 137.—Section of alluvial fan consisting largely of granitic sand. The hydrologic properties of this material approach those of coarse, sorted, lake-bed sediments and there is no confinement of water, as the deposit is pervious throughout. Pervious cones of this type occur chiefly where the parent material is mechanically decomposed granite which disintegrates into its constituent grains of quartz and feldspar.

Effect of Source Rock.—The weathering of certain types of rock such as shale, limestone, numerous kinds of schists, and most lavas furnishes no sand but abundant supply of silt and clay. Therefore the rock formations of the mountains undergoing erosion are important in controlling the composition of the alluvial cone. If only fine material (silt and clay) is supplied, no pervious conduits will be developed in the body of the deposit and the cone will not hold a water supply available for pumping.

The processes of weathering are nearly equal in importance to the type of bedrock in controlling the character of material supplied to the cone. Mechanical disintegration furnishes coarse material and unweathered individual mineral grains. Disintegration of granite and sandstone furnishes abundant sand. Complete weathering of granite transforms all minerals except quartz grains into clay and silt. If disintegration of the country rock produces sand in predominant quantities, sufficient fine material may not be available for the formation of effective confining formations and the entire ground-water body may function as free water (Fig. 137).

Rainfall and runoff are minor agencies in controlling the character of the materials which constitute the alluvial cone, but are the principal agencies controlling the structure of the cone. Perennial stream flow will deposit pervious sand in channels extending from apex to the foot of the cone. Torrential downpour may furnish large amounts of material of intermixed sizes which may be deposited by floods beyond the stream channels, the coarse material at the apex and the fine material toward the foot of the cone.

Depositional Agencies That Build up the Alluvial Cone.—The principal depositional agencies, the interaction of which determines the structure of the cone, are (1) the flow of the source stream confined between stream banks; (2) the flood overflow of the stream; (3) gravity creep and movement of material by avalanche which supply talus to the deposit at the contact of the cone with the mountains; (4) rainwash and cloudburst action which redistribute the surface material on both sides of the stream channel; and (5) eolian deposition, especially in moist areas or localities covered with grass which catch and hold wind-transported dust.

Stream Flow within Banks.—Perennial flow, or flow continuing after the flood period, is usually confined between the banks of the stream. This flow commonly carries sorted materials (sand and gravel) as contrasted with the mass of heterogeneous material carried by flood flow. The sorted materials are deposited between the banks of the stream as a pervious body of great length compared with width and thickness.

Fig. 138.—Largest single boulder moved down the alluvial cones of the Sierra Nevada by cloudburst action, Lone Pine Creek, Owens Valley, California.

Flood Action.—Deposition of sand and gravel in the stream channel decreases the capacity of the channel to carry water, and a succeeding flood may overtop the banks and deposit a heterogeneous layer of material on each side of the channel. A heavy flood may spread coarse material, including great boulders, over the upper portion of the cone, but lower down the deposition of coarse material is limited to the stream channel, and the subsiding flood waters may lay down a layer of silt and clay over the lower portion of the cone.

Combined Stream and Flood Action.—Flood water may break out in large volume at a low point in the banks, especially near the apex of the alluvial cone, and cut a new channel. In all portions of the cone except possibly the nearly flat area at the foot of the cone, the flow will be in a radial direction down the cone. Therefore the course of the new channel will diverge from the older channel. These courses will not cross and recross as do the channels in the flood plain of a river valley. Near the foot of the slope the tendency of the channel to subdivide becomes noticeable because the decreasing gradient accelerates the deposition of material in the channel, the capacity of which is

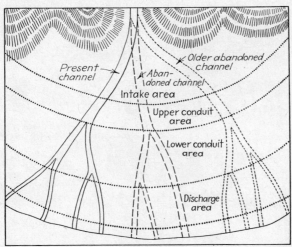

Fig. 139.—Plan of abandoned stream channels and present channel of stream in an alluvial cone.

thereby reduced, and the stream separates into diverging forks. A typical stream pattern is illustrated in Fig. 139. The abandoned stream channels are shown in dashed and dotted lines and present channel in solid lines.

The combined action of flood flow and subsequent low-water flow is to build up a set of diverging aquifers separated by coarse pervious material in the upper part of the cone and by fine material of decreasing permeability down the slope of the cone. The typical texture produced by combined stream action and torrential activity is shown in Fig. 140.

After a channel filled with pervious material is abandoned, it is covered with material deposited by subsiding flood water, by rainwash, by mudflows generated by torrential downpour,[1] and by the wind. The relative permeability of the materials encasing the buried stream channels determines the degree of confinement of the water in the aquifers. Talus material deposited at the contact of the cone with the mountains con-

Fig. 140.—Hogsback Creek alluvial cone, Owens Valley, California. Typical structure of coarser portion of an alluvial cone. Water is confined only where fine clay layers occur or where layers of coarser material are cemented by fine silt.

stitutes a zone of permeable material at the upper boundary of the deposit which will absorb the flow of minor streams on each side of the master stream and surface and subsurface water moving down the mountain slopes. In extreme cases the entire body of the alluvial deposit may be angular and the cone may be described as a talus or debris cone. The cones at the foot of

[1] BLACKWELDER, E., Mudflow as a Geologic Agent in Semiarid Mountains, *Geol. Soc. Am. Bull.* vol. 39, no. 2, pp. 465–483, 1928.

the Inyo Mountains, Owens Valley, California, are good examples of this type of cone (Fig. 141).

If the alluvial cone is deposited at the shore of a lake, bay, or ocean, fine silt or clay may be deposited under standing water and pervious sand beaches at the water's edge. If the water level fluctuates during the upbuilding of the alluvial cone, impervious clays deposited during high-level stages of the lake or ocean may overlie the stream-laid aquifers deposited during

Fig. 141.—Section of an alluvial cone of the Inyo Mountains, Owens Valley, showing extreme angularity of material and great porosity of the deposit as a whole. The hydrologic structure of the Inyo cones differs from those on the opposite side of the valley at the foot of the Sierra Nevada which contain sorted sand aquifers set in torrential outwash with sufficient fine material to constitute confining formations.

an antecedent low-level stage of the standing water. Under these conditions confinement of water in the lower portions of the aquifers will be pronounced. The Santa Clara Valley, Santa Clara County, California, contains excellent examples of this type of alluvial cone.

Hydrologic Structure and Ground-water Movement in Alluvial Cone.—The general hydrologic structure is the same for most alluvial cones but the quantity of water absorbed and delivered to the aquifers, the velocity of subsurface motion of water, and the degree of confinement of the deeper waters are of infinite variety. Figure 142 is a stereogrammatic sketch of the areas of an alluvial cone classified according to their function in the

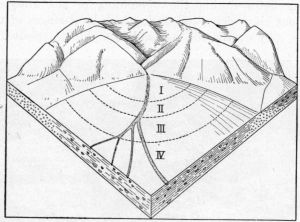

FIG. 142.—Hydrologic structure of an alluvial cone. I, intake area; II, upper conduit zone; III, artesian or pressure zone; IV, discharge zone. The pressure zone may include a portion or all of the discharge zone.

hydraulic scheme. Figure 143 is a cross section through Fig. 142 along the line of the surface stream.

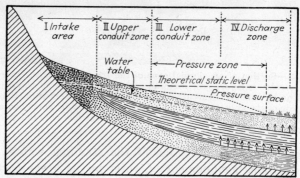

FIG. 143.—Cross section of an alluvial cone, showing hydrologic structure.

I. *The intake area* is shown as a belt covering the upper and pervious portion of the cone and extending down the present stream channel. The belt outside the stream channel absorbs rainfall and surface and subsurface runoff from the mountain watershed tributary to the cone. The quantity absorbed by

FIG. 144.—Exposure showing structure of the lower Lone Pine alluvial cone near apex. Material consists of large boulders set in sandy detritus and is pervious throughout. The scarp was formed by movement on the Lone Pine fault during the Owens Valley earthquake of March 26, 1872. Maximum height of scarp 22 ft.

this area is difficult to determine. In some cases it may be large, but it is usually considered to be small.

Influent stream seepage in the intake area is usually the chief source of supply of free and confined ground water, and in engineering estimates has often been considered the sole source. Influent seepage from stream flow can be determined by stream gaging at stations starting above the intake area and continuing down the cone, provided flood flow does not produce serious inaccuracies.

II. *Upper conduit zone* starts at the upper edge of a confining formation. The upper portion of the conduit furnishes a less satisfactory water supply than the pressure zone because (1) the water level may be drawn down below the well intake in the upper part of the conduit by overpumping, owing to the smaller quantity of water in the conduit above the well compared with the quantity of water in the conduit below the well. If the water level is lowered below the well bottom, the well goes dry. (2) Coarse material (boulders and cobble) derived from the apex of the cone may make drilling expensive. (3) The water level in the well may be a long distance below the surface.

III. *Lower conduit or pressure zone* is the zone in the alluvial cone in which the water in wells originally rose to or above the surface. The pressure surface of this zone may be nearly flat on account of slow escape at the ends of the "fingers" of the aquifers and resultant slow movement of water in the conduit and small reduction of head by friction. Occasionally it is steep and the water level in the well may be below the surface and below the water table. An example of this was noted in an aquifer in Owens Valley, California, where ready escape was afforded by open fractures due to cutting of the aquifer by faults near the base of the cone, and the rapid percolation caused by the open exit developed large friction and lowered the static level far below ground surface.

IV. *Discharge Zone.*—This is the leaking portion of the pressure zone. The aquifer may play out entirely or the constituent materials may gradually increase in fineness until equal to that of the confining material; they "finger out" in this zone like the fingers of a glove.

Confined water moves down the conduits and is discharged by leakage to the surface. *Free water* moves down the water-table slope to the point where it intersects the surface, where it is discharged. The combined discharge usually makes a swamp at the foot of the cone, and the quantity evaporated and transpired in the discharge zone may be susceptible to accurate measurement and give the total ground water available to salvage by pumping. The free water discharges at the upper edge of the swamp, and the confined water throughout the entire discharge zone.

The structure and hydrologic properties of the materials of the cone may modify the scheme outlined above, increasing water movement in certain zones or reducing the effect of some zones to a minimum. If the material of the cone is derived from mechanically disintegrated granitic formations, the deposit may

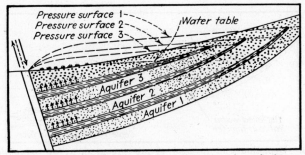

Fig. 145.—Aquifers in an alluvial cone cut by a fault.

be more permeable downslope of the cone, where large bodies of sorted sand occur, than at the apex, where heterogeneous deposits of boulders cemented with finer material occur. The intake area may cover the central portion of the cone and confinement may not be well developed. Such cones, for example, are developed against the southern and western slopes of the San Gabriel Mountains. Spreading operations in such cones are very satisfactory. Wells may produce large flows under the pump, but the pressure head may be small and the wells may function largely as water-table wells.

Individual characteristics may be the result of unusual geologic structure. For example, the alluvial cone of the Santa Ana River, southern California, is truncated by a branch of the San Andreas fault, known locally as the Bunker Hill dike. Movement on the fault occurred during the upbuilding of the alluvial cone and repeatedly raised an older and relatively impervious alluvial formation across the course of the Santa Ana River. During times of active uplift of the barrier the Santa Ana River was dammed back, resulting in deposition of silts and clays. When the barrier was deeply breached by the river, coarse and pervious sand and gravel layers were deposited over the impervious materials. The impervious fault barrier developed a zone of marked upward leakage above the fault within the area of productive artesian wells (Fig. 145). These relations gave rise to an overestimate of the importance of upward leakage in artesian systems and to curious views of artesian pressure mentioned previously (pages 323–324).

Depletion in the Average Alluvial Cone.—The aquifers in the typical confined system of an alluvial cone are normally

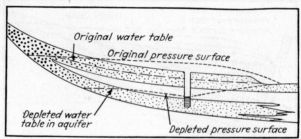

Fig. 146.—Depletion and reversal of pressure gradient by overpumping an aquifer in an alluvial cone. Impervious material is without dots.

filled with water up to the water table at the fountain head which locates the theoretical static level of the artesian basin. Upward leakage out of the finger ends of the aquifers establishes the pressure gradient, which in the main trunk portions of the aquifers may slope gently and diverge slowly from the theoretical static level and stand above the ground surface, but in the discharge area drops to the ground surface.

In the first years of pumping before depletion is large, water is furnished chiefly from the upper portion of the conduit and from free water above and tributary to the conduit (Fig. 146). If overpumping is practiced, the water level in the conduit at the intake is lowered, the pressure in the conduit is reduced, and a depleted pressure surface is developed. As pumping continues, a reverse gradient may be developed from the lower edge of the cone toward the wells, and water is drawn from the supply stored in the ends of the aquifers or squeezed out of the silt and clay by reduction of pressure due to pumping.

In the San Francisquito cone, Stanford University, California, the water level drops about 18 ft. (Fig. 147, *ab*) during the first two months of pumping (March and April). This produces the necessary hydraulic gradient to draw water from the fine material at the finger ends of the aquifers, as evidenced by the reversal of pressure gradient produced by the drop in head. Prior to the actual reversal of gradient the water is abstracted chiefly from the aquifers and the water level in the conduits is lowered thereby. From then on to September the lowering is 2½ to 3 ft. per month, or 10 ft. for seasonal pumping (Fig. 147,

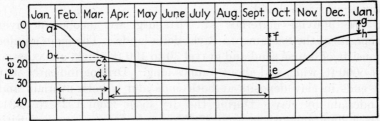

Fig. 147.—Annual water-level fluctuation caused by overpumping in the San Francisquito alluvial cone. *a-b*, depletion due to drawing down water level in conduit; *c-d*, depletion of water from fingers of aquifers and from aquicludes in lower portion of cone; *e-f*, recovery after close of pumping season; *g-h*, annual depletion; *i-j*, period of rapid lowering of water level accompanied by lowering of water level at intake of conduit; *k-l*, slow lowering of water level and production under reversed gradient.

cd). The water is drawn from the aquifers downslope from the pumps, a portion coming from the sand fingers at the ends of the aquifers and a portion from the enclosing silts and clays. If the resulting compaction of water-bearing material is permanent, the withdrawal cannot be renewed by natural recharge. Slow recovery (Fig. 147, *ef*) during the winter season brings the water level back to a point below the previous high point. During the present cycle of dry years (including 1935) the increment due to influent seepage has been small, and recovery is due largely to the slow extraction of water from the fine materials into the aquifers. The difference between the two high points of successive years (6 ft. as shown by the 1931 measurements) represents annual depletion (Fig. 147, *gh*), a portion of which may be permanent.

Isolated Sand Lens Surrounded by Incoherent Silt and Clay

The occurrence of water in sand lenses under a slight artesian head is known to those who have had experience in boring soft alluvial materials. One example of an occurrence of this type on a large scale is possibly represented by the main water sand in the Pittsburg region near the mouth of the Sacramento River in central California. The classification of these conditions as a special type of confined-water system is justified by the probability that this type exists in sand channels deposited and then truncated by a stream meandering over its partly submerged bottom lands. The residual portion of the sand is finally sealed on all sides by clays deposited in slack water, and thus the aquifer is isolated.

The alluvial materials at Pittsburg are incoherent river deposits of the Sacramento River delta lands. The main aquifer consists of coarse sand and gravel 30 to 100 ft. thick, a maximum of 6000 ft. wide, and about 5 miles long. Drilling indicates that it ends in clay deposits at both ends and is both overlain and underlain by clay. During the dry cycle from 1925 to 1931, 2½ billion gallons per year (7672 acre-feet) were pumped with an average lowering of the water level in wells of only 3 ft. per year.[1]

The lenticular sand body has a deep water-level depression shown in wells owing to overpumping, indicating that the water in the aquifer now has strong negative pressure. Drawdown tests in wells piercing the *coarse* aquifer have extremely *steep* cones of pumping depression. These unusual hydraulic relations indicate that movement of water to the wells in the coarse sand is suffering unusual resistance. This was thought at first to be due to the confining clays; some of the water may be derived from extremely slow percolation through the enveloping clays or may be squeezed out of the clays by reduction of pressure in the aquifer due to pumping. However, subsequent studies show that water enters the main aquifer through breaks in the surrounding silts and clays.[2] The location of these breaks is

[1] TOLMAN, C. F., B. C. HYDE, and C. KILLINGSWORTH, Ground Water Supply and Contamination of Pittsburg and Adjacent Industrial Area, Contra Costa County, Calif., unpublished report, 1931.

[2] TOLMAN, C. F., and J. F. POLAND, An Investigation of the Ground-water Supply of Columbia Steel Co., Pittsburg, Calif., unpublished report, 1935.

shown by the advance of contamination due to inflow of salt water from the Sacramento River during the season of high salinity. Confinement in the Pittsburg area, therefore, is less complete than was first thought.

References

CHAMBERLIN, T. C., Requisite and Qualifying Conditions of Artesian Wells, *U.S. Geol. Surv. 5th Ann. Rept.*, pp. 131–173, 1884.

DARTON. N. H., The Geology and Underground Waters of South Dakota, *U.S. Geol. Surv. Water-Supply Paper* 227, 1909.

—— Artesian Waters in the Vicinity of the Black Hills, S.D., *U.S. Geol. Surv. Water-Supply Paper* 428, 1918.

—— Geology and Underground Water Resources of the Central Great Plains, *U.S. Geol. Surv. Prof. Paper* 32, pp. 120, 151–152, 156, 165, 190–193, 1905.

—— Artesian Well Prospects on the Atlantic Coastal Plain Region, *U.S. Geol. Surv. Bull.* 138, 1896.

FIEDLER, A. G., and S. S. NYE, Ground-Water Investigations of the Roswell Artesian Basin, New Mexico, *N. Mex. State Eng., 8th Bienn. Rept.*, pp. 81–107, 1928.

FULLER, M. L., Summary of the Controlling Factors of Artesian Flows, *U.S. Geol. Surv. Bull.* 319, 1908.

KEILHACK, K., "Grundwasser und Quellenkunde," Gebrüder Borntraeger, Berlin, 3d ed., pp. 220–257, 1935.

MEINZER, O. E., Artesian Conditions and Prospects as Shown by the Survey of 1923 (Edgeley and La Moure Quadrangles, N.D.), *U.S. Geol. Surv. Bull.* 801, pp. 57–74, 1929.

MEINZER, O. E., and H. H. HARD, The Artesian Water Supply of the Dakota Sandstone in North Dakota, *U.S. Geol. Surv. Water-Supply Paper 520-E*, 1925.

PIPER, A. M., The Origin of Artesian Pressure, *Econ. Geol.*, vol. 23, pp. 683–696, 1928.

RUSSELL, W. L., The Origin of Artesian Pressure, *Econ. Geol.*, vol. 23, pp. 132–157, 1928.

SIMPSON, H. E., Geology and Ground-water Resources of North Dakota, *U.S. Geol. Surv. Water-Supply Paper* 598, pp. 45–62, 1929.

TERZAGHI, C., The Origin of Artesian Pressure, *Econ. Geol.*, vol. 24, pp. 94–100, 1929.

THOMPSON, D. G., The Origin of Artesian Pressure, *Econ. Geol.*, vol. 24, pp. 758–771, 1929.

CHAPTER XIII

WELLS

By C. F. Tolman and J. F. Poland

A water well is a vertical excavation, either a shaft or borehole, constructed for the purpose of extracting ground water. Other excavations for collecting ground water include tunnels, drifts from shafts, horizontal boreholes from wells, drainage ditches, and various types of engineering works for collecting spring water. Discussion in this chapter is limited to wells, although principles developed may be applied to production of ground water from tunnels and drainage ditches.

Well water is lifted to the ground surface in various types of containers, by hand or mechanical devices, or water is raised by pumps or by natural hydraulic pressure in artesian wells. The following discussion is restricted to hydraulics of pumped wells.

HYDRAULICS OF WELLS

The two types of wells which require separate treatment of hydraulic behavior are water-table wells and wells tapping confined water. The former draws on free ground water below the water table and the latter on confined ground water below a confining formation. Pumping of the former lowers the water level in the well, extracts water from the immediately adjacent water-bearing material, and produces a cone of water-table depression surrounding and tributary to the well. Water outside of the cone of depression but within the area of influence is diverted to replace the body of ground water which is moving into the pumping well.

Pumping of confined water reduces pressure in the water-bearing conduit and causes movement of water in the conduit toward the well. Reduction of pressure in the conduit is registered by lowering of the water level in nonproducing wells during well flow from the producing well. The depression in the pressure surface produced by pumping a well or group of wells is called the cone of pressure relief. Both the pressure surface registered by the static water level in wells piercing the confined aquifer and the pumping depression in the pressure surface are imaginary, in contrast to the water table and cone of water-table depression which are physical surfaces. The cone of pressure relief does not indicate the extraction of stored water in the conduit in the vicinity of the pumping well, unless the conduit suffers deformation by reduction of pressure due to pumping, but merely a diversion from the natural flow in the conduit coming from a distant source. The cone of pressure relief is similar in shape to the cone of water-table depression.

If a well taps both free and confined water or if the confining formation leaks, both extraction of water from the free ground water around the well and pressure relief in the confined aquifer occur. If the well taps several confined water-bearing strata, a composite pressure effect is produced in all the aquifers.

Water-table Wells

If the cone of depression caused by pumping a water-table well does not reach other wells or boreholes, only five hydraulic observations can be made.

1. The quantity of water pumped in a given time, usually expressed in gallons per minute, per hour, or per day, can be measured. This is a quantitative figure for the yield of a well without respect to drawdown or size of well.

2. The drawdown or lowering of the water level during a selected period of pumping can be determined. If the pumping level becomes stationary after a period of pumping, the natural supply of ground water to the cone of depression is equal to the quantity pumped and information is thereby furnished as to the supply available. The drawdown necessary to produce the water pumped is a direct function of permeability of the water-producing formations, and the comparative permeability of aquifers supplying a number of wells can be determined from the drawdown of the respective wells, provided the frictional entrance resistance into the various wells is equal.

3. The gallons produced per foot of drawdown can be calculated. This value is known as the *specific capacity* and furnishes the best figure for comparison of yield from two or more wells.

The specific capacity depends upon two factors: the permeability and thickness of the aquifer and the frictional resistance at the entrance to the well.

4. The static level to which the water rises after cessation of pumping can be measured. Overpumping is indicated if the water does not rise to its original level after pumping stops, and safe yield is indicated if the recovery between pumping periods is complete.

5. The rate of recovery, which depends upon, and consequently indicates, permeability of the surrounding aquifer, can be determined by means of an electric measuring line which is lowered into the well to determine the rise of the water surface. The rise in water level can also be measured by an air-line and pressure gage if the well is equipped with this device, but these measurements are not so accurate as those obtained with the electric line.

If a second well or observation hole lies within the area of pumping depression and the approximate extent of the area of depression is known, a cross section of the cone of water-table depression can be drawn. Three or more wells or boreholes showing a depression of water level during pumping of the well under consideration indicate the shape of the cone and area of pumping depression. From these data the hydraulic behavior of the well can be determined and the coefficient of permeability of the aquifers penetrated by the well can be calculated by the Thiem method.[1]

Cone of Water-table Depression and Area of Influence.— During pumping a cone of depression is formed by the removal of water and the slope of this cone of pumping depression develops slowly until it is sufficient to generate a movement of water toward the well equal to the amount of water pumped. The movement of water toward the well is normal to the contours of the cone of depression (Fig. 148A), and the cross-sectional area through which water percolates toward the well is a cylindrical surface the dimensions of which vary directly with distance from the well. The slope therefore is a maximum

[1] THIEM, G., "Hydrologische Methoden," Leipzig, 1906; WENZEL, L. K., The Thiem Method for Determining Permeability of Water-bearing Materials and Its Application to the Determination of Specific Yield, *U.S. Geol. Surv. Water-Supply Paper* 679-A, 1936. (See discussion of change in the cone of depression with time, Wenzel, pp. 50–52.)

at the well because the water pumped is moving through a minimum cross-sectional area and hence with maximum velocity.

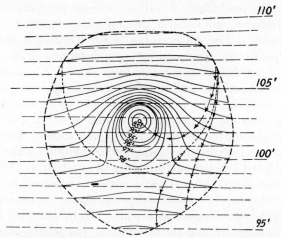

Fig. 148*A*.—Water-table contours before and during pumping of a water-table well.   Horizontal broken lines are water-table contours before pumping; solid lines water surface showing cone of depression during pumping.   Area defined by heavy broken line is area of influence; light, short-dashed line indicates the crest of the ground-water divide.   Arrows show direction of percolation.   This cone developed after 48-hour pumping test.   (*Modified after Wenzel.*)

The slope flattens at a decreasing rate with distance from the well and with corresponding decrease in velocity.

The cone of water-table depression and area of influence have been discussed in connection with ground-water litigation in order to delimit the area affected or damaged by pumping operations.   It has been commonly thought that the cone of water-table depression is an inverted cone beyond the margins of which ground-water conditions and contours are not affected.   Theoretically, if a well were pumping from a ground-water basin or reservoir which receives no ground-water additions or from which no

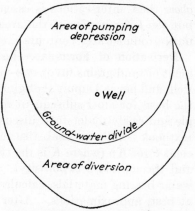

Fig. 148*B*.—Area of influence of a pumping water-table well with division into area of pumping depression and area of diversion.

discharge takes place, a cone would develop which would extend to the margins of the basin and the water table throughout the entire basin would finally be adjusted to the pumping level of the well. However, no natural ground-water basin without discharge exists. The water table is an inclined surface which slopes toward the discharge area, and pumps draw on water moving in the direction of water-table slope. A cone of depression forms around the well, the boundary of which is the ground-water divide (Fig. 148) which delimits the water moving toward the well. Beyond the divide is an area in which ground water moves in around the lower margin of the cone of depression to replenish water diverted by pumping, and ground-water contours are readjusted throughout this area to pump draft (Fig. 148A). The authors suggest that the area within the ground-water divide be called the *area of pumping depression*, the entire area within which ground-water contours are modified by pumping be named the *area of influence*, and the area outside the ground-water divide but within the area of influence be designated the *area of diversion*.

If pump discharge is less than quantity of water percolating, equilibrium is finally established and the distance between the intersections of the ground-water divide and the boundary of the area of influence is the width of the ground-water flow supplying the well. Thereafter the position of the ground-water divide *above* these intersections is essentially constant during pumping, but the *lower portion* of the area of influence gradually expands until ground-water contours are adjusted to lessened supply.

Derivation of Formulas.—Lamination and parallel arrangement of sand grains favor two-dimensional (horizontal) flow to a well, and hence Dupuit's[1] original treatment of this type of flow is the basis for most subsequent mathematical studies.[2] The simple and easily understood discussion in Turneaure and Russell's textbook is followed, substituting Meinzer's permeability coefficient P for Kp (where K is the transmission coefficient of Slichter and Hazen, and p is porosity). On account of heterogeneity of water-bearing materials, calculations prior to pumping tests are, at best, approximations. After the pump is installed pumping tests determine the yield of the well. On account of the inac-

---

[1] Dupuit, J., "Études théoriques et pratique sur le mouvement des eaux," 2d ed., Dunod, Paris, 1863.

[2] By Slichter, Thiem, Wenzel, and Theis. See references (pp. 413–414).

curacies inherent in a theoretical treatment, no consideration is given to secondary modifying factors and the simplest set of conditions are assumed to control well production.

If a water-table well extends to the bottom of the permeable material, the depth of the moving water varies directly as y, and the cross-sectional area (at any point xy) through which the water moves equals $2\pi xy$ (Fig. 149). If the well stops above the bottom of the body of pervious material, percolating water might be assumed to move in from below the intake of the well according to Slichter's theory that ground-water motions take place throughout the entire available cross-sectional area. However, as stratification and lamination tend to restrain vertical water movement, the assumption is made that appreciable supply of water does not move in from below the

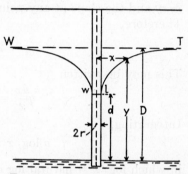

Fig. 149.—Section through water-table well showing cone of water-table depression.

well intake and y will designate the difference in elevation between points on the cone of depression and the bottom of well intake.

In Fig. 149 WT represents the water table. Let

r = radius of well.

d = depth[1] of water in well when pumping.

D = depth[1] of well below water table and below "static water level."

$(D - d)$ = drawdown.

x and y = coordinates of any point on the curve $WwlT$ referred to axes drawn through the center and bottom of the well.

q = quantity of water pumped in gallons per day.

P = permeability coefficient as defined by Meinzer (pages 207–208).

The available head used in pumping is represented by $(D - d)$ and is consumed in the following ways: (1) by friction due to percolation of water in the water-bearing materials toward the well, (2) by entrance resistance through well perforations, (3) by friction of water flowing upward in the well casing, and

[1] Measured above base of aquifer if well penetrates underlying aquiclude or above bottom of well if it ends in the aquifer.

(4) by generation of velocity head of the rising water in the well casing. For shallow wells all these factors except the first are relatively small and will be neglected in this elementary treatment.[1]

The equation for the curve $WwlT$ may be derived as follows: The cross-sectional area through which water is passing toward the well at any distance x from the center of the well is $2\pi xy$ and the slope at any point $xy = dy/dx$.

Therefore,

$$q = 2\pi Pxy\frac{dy}{dx}. \tag{1}$$

This may be written

$$q\frac{dx}{x} = 2\pi Pydy.$$

Integrating,

$$q\log_e x = \pi Py^2 + C \tag{2}$$

in which $\log_e x$ = natural log of x, and C = constant of integration.

When $x = r$ and $y = d$, from (2)

$$C = q\log_e r - \pi Pd^2.$$

Substituting and solving for y^2,

$$y^2 = \frac{q}{\pi P}\log_e \frac{x}{r} + d^2. \tag{3}$$

Substituting R for the radius of the "circle" of influence, the corresponding value of y becomes D (depth of well below water table) in equation (3), and solving for q,

$$q = \frac{\pi P(D^2 - d^2)}{2.3\log_{10}\dfrac{R}{r}}. \tag{4}$$

In order to solve for q (quantity of water in gallons per day that a well will pump for any assumed value of D and d), it is necessary to know or assume values for P, permeability, and R, radius of circle of influence. The value of R usually lies

---

[1] The second factor is measured by the difference in water level inside and outside the casing during pumping. It is often large in deep wells, especially if poorly perforated.

between **100** to **10,000** ft., but a value of **1000** may be used for R to obtain an estimate of q because large variation in the value of R makes small difference in value of q. Table **13** shows values of $\left(\dfrac{1}{\log_{10} R/r}\right)$ for several values of R and r.

TABLE 13.[1]—VALUES OF $\dfrac{1}{\log_{10} \dfrac{R}{r}}$ IN EQUATION (4)

R, feet	(2r) Well diameter, inches						
	4	6	8	12	24	48	120
100	0.36	0.38	0.40	0.43	0.50	0.58	0.77
200	0.32	0.34	0.36	0.38	0.43	0.50	0.62
500	0.28	0.30	0.31	0.33	0.37	0.41	0.50
1000	0.26	0.27	0.28	0.30	0.33	0.37	0.43
2000	0.24	0.25	0.26	0.27	0.30	0.33	0.38

[1] After Table 36 of Turneaure and Russell, p. 257.

The permeability of a sand or gravel aquifer can be determined accurately only by a pumping test or by laboratory tests on undisturbed samples. However, an arbitrary approximation of permeability can be made from inspection or, preferably, by mechanical analysis of the water-bearing material.

Table 14 of average permeabilities has been prepared as a guide to the approximate permeability of materials encountered

TABLE 14.—APPROXIMATE PERMEABILITIES OF VARIOUS TYPES OF MATERIAL

Type of material	Effective size, millimeters	Estimated permeability coefficient	
		Average	Range
Sand:			
Very fine..................	0.05 to 0.10	50	10 to 300
Fine.....................	0.10 to 0.25	300	50 to 1,000
Medium..................	0.25 to 0.5	600	100 to 3,000
Coarse..................	0.5 to 1.0	1,500	300 to 5,000
Gravel:			
Fine.....................	1 to 2	3,000	1,000 to 10,000
Medium..................	2 to 5	6,000	3,000 to 20,000

in the field. It is important to realize that this table is useful only in forming a rough estimate. The actual permeability depends upon degree of uniformity, porosity, degree of cementation, shape and size of openings, and water temperature. These factors can be accurately evaluated only by testing the material.

Example.—Assume that a test hole has been drilled through water-bearing material, supplying the following information. The aquifer is 40 ft. thick. Mechanical analyses of the samples collected from the test hole indicate an average effective size of 0.2 mm. How much water can be pumped from a 12-in. well with a 10-ft. drawdown? Assuming a permeability of 300,

$$q = \frac{\pi 300(1600 - 900)0.3}{2.3} = 86{,}400 \text{ g.p.d.}$$

Equation (4) may be used to determine the permeability of an aquifer by substituting for factors R, r, D, and d, water-level measurements of any two observation wells at distances a and a' from the pumped well but within the cone of depression.[1] The equation then becomes

$$P = \frac{2.3q}{\pi(h'^2 - h^2)} \log_{10} \frac{a'}{a} \tag{5}$$

where h and h' represent the thickness of the saturated part of the water-bearing bed at a and a', respectively, and a' is the greater distance from the pumped well. The measurement of two observation wells at distances a and a' from the pumped wells furnishes more accurate data for calculation of P than would the use of R, r, D, and d in equation (4).

Confined-water Wells

When a well is drilled into an aquifer confined by an overlying impervious bed, water flowing under pressure will rise in the well casing to a level equivalent to the hydrostatic pressure exerted at the point of well entrance into the aquifer. When the well is pumped, a cone of pressure relief is developed.

Cone of Pressure Relief.—Mathematical analysis of the cone of pressure relief indicates that it is similar in shape to the cone of water-table depression. However, the cone of pressure relief has not received the detailed field study that has been given the cone of water-table depression, as the cost

[1] Discussed in detail in *Water-Supply Paper 679-A*, pp. 10*ff*.

of sinking a large group of deep wells to reach the confined aquifer is excessive compared to that of drilling shallow test holes to the water table, and in artesian well fields the wells are usually spaced too far apart to give detailed information regarding the shape of the cone of pressure relief. The pressure contours around a pumping well develop a ridge or pressure-contour divide within which the conduit water is moving toward the well and outside of which, and within the area of influence, the conduit water is redistributed to replace that diverted by well flow. On account of the lack of data, however, it seems premature to divide the area of influence of a confined-water well into an area within and without the pressure-contour divide equivalent to the areas within and without the ground-water divide of a water-table well, but when further data are available the division can probably be made with advantage.

The form of the cone of pressure relief is modified by variations and limitations in the size of the confined aquifer, especially by its width, as it is evident that the cone of pressure relief cannot exceed the areal extent of the conduit tapped by pumping.

In shallow wells the head consumed by entrance and casing friction and by generation of velocity head within the well is relatively small and was neglected in discussion of water-table wells. The head consumed by entrance friction is the most important of the three losses. In deep wells and hence in most artesian wells these factors become larger and pumping level within the well casing may be considerably lower than the level immediately outside the casing. To measure this level it would be necessary to place a perforated pipe directly outside the casing. In practice the pumping level inside the casing is measured and often assumed to represent the level of water outside the well. This introduces an appreciable error in calculations of flow of deep wells, but as all calculations prior to production tests are merely approximations, discussion of correction for head consumed at well intake and within well casing is omitted.[1]

In Fig. 150 a well is represented as piercing a confined aquifer with entrance of water into the well only from this aquifer. *PL* represents the static pressure surface; *wl*, the pumping water level; *PwlL*, the cone of pressure relief; *r*, the well radius; *R* the

[1] See Turneaure and Russell, *op. cit.*, pp. 264–267.

radius of the cone of pressure relief; D, the static level of water in the well; d, the water level when pumping; and x and y, coordinates of any point on the curve $PwlL$. The water passes through a constant thickness m.

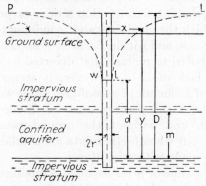

Fig. 150.—Section through artesian well showing cone of pressure relief.

Equation (1) (page 386) becomes

$$q = 2\pi Pxm\frac{dy}{dx} \tag{6}$$

By similar development

$$q = \frac{2\pi Pm(D - d)}{2.3 \log_{10} \dfrac{R}{r}} \tag{7}$$

for quantity in gallons per day pumped from an artesian well. This equation differs from equation (4) only in the substitution

of $2m$ for $(D - d)$. Values of $\left(\dfrac{1}{\log_{10} \dfrac{R}{r}}\right)$ in Table 13 and P esti-

mated as discussed on pages 387 to 388 can be used in equation (7).

Example.—Assume a test hole has been drilled into a confined aquifer and furnishes the following information:

Feet	Log
0– 6	Soil
6– 50	Yellow clay
50–100	Blue clay
100–150	Sand and pebbly gravel
150–155	Clay

Static water level is 10 feet above ground surface. The aquifer is 50 ft. thick (m). Mechanical analyses of samples of the water-bearing material in the aquifer collected from the test well indicate an average effective size of 0.4 mm. The permeability is measured in the laboratory or is estimated from Table 14 (page 387) to approximate 600. How much water can be pumped from a 12-in. well producing from this aquifer with a pumping drawdown of 40 ft. and R assumed to be 1000?

From equation (7), $q = \dfrac{2\pi 600 \times 50(160 - 120)0.3}{2.3} = 984,000$ g.p.d.

Factors Affecting Quantity of Flow

Size of Well.—The question is often asked: How much will enlarging the diameter of a well increase production? Table 13 shows that a 12-in. well will produce 10 to 15 per cent more water than a 6-in. well, all other factors being equal; while a 48-in. well will produce from 20 to 35 per cent more than a 12-in. well. If a 12-in. well produces 400 gal. with 50 ft. of drawdown, a 48-in. well should produce 480 to 540 gal. with the same drawdown if drilled and completed under identical conditions. However, there is an important modification of this general statement which should be emphasized. The production of sand-free water from fine sands is directly proportional to the size of the well, all other conditions being equal. The reason for this is explained in the following paragraph.

Effect of Diameter on Velocity of Flow into Well.—A basic formula in hydraulics is

$$q = aV$$

where q = quantity of water discharged.

a = cross-sectional area of opening.

V = velocity of water.

Therefore

$$V = \frac{q}{a}.$$

If the quantity of water equals 1 cu. ft. per second (1 sec.-ft. or 449 g.p.m.) and the effective openings equal an area of 5 sq. ft., the entrance velocity of the water into the well will be 0.2 ft. per second. If the diameter of the well and number of perforations in the casing are doubled, the effective openings will be doubled and the velocity will equal 0.1 ft. per second. In other words, with constant production the velocity of inflow is inversely proportional to the diameter of the well. If the flow into the well is turbulent, the friction loss at the time of entrance into the well varies approximately as V^2. Doubling the size of the well therefore reduces the entrance velocity to one-half and the friction loss to one-quarter. The most important effect of reduction of entrance velocity is the reduction in sand-carrying capacity of the water. It seems probable that this is a direct relationship, as there is a certain critical velocity at which sand of any given grain size will be dislodged from its bed and carried into a well under any constant set of conditions. If the size of well and the number of perforations are doubled, all other conditions remaining the same, the critical entrance velocity of the sand considered above will be reached only when the production of the well has been doubled.

TYPES OF WELLS[1]

Dug Wells

In the United States dug wells are frequently used as a source of water supply for the home, ranch, or private estate where the water table is reasonably close to the surface. Dug wells are particularly numerous in glacial and alluvial deposits which in their unconsolidated state are easy to excavate, such as the glacial deposits of northeastern United States. In former years dug wells were a common source of water supply for domestic purposes and irrigation in California, but during the dry cycle from 1917 to 1934 the overdraft on the ground-water supplies of many of the alluvial valleys lowered the level beyond the reach of shallow pits and in consequence many of these have been abandoned.

Dug wells are usually excavated by handwork, using a pick and shovel. The loose material is hoisted to the surface and the hole is followed down with well cribbing where the formation will not stand by itself. The well is lined with wood, rock, concrete, brick, or metal, depending upon the cost and availability of material. If the well is to be used for domestic purposes, the upper portion of the well lining should be made impervious to prevent bacterial pollution of the water by eliminating surface seepage through or down the outside of the well

[1] This discussion of well types is in part a summary of a mimeographed article on well-drilling methods by J. F. Poland and C. C. Killingsworth.

casing. Great care should be taken in locating a dug well with reference to possible pollution because such wells intercept water at or close to the water table and near-surface ground water is likely to be polluted. A domestic dug well should never be placed in the downslope direction of the water table from a refuse disposal point.

Kirk Bryan[1] discusses the procedure of well digging in the Sacramento Valley as follows:

A hole 4 by 6 feet is dug to water level, which is at a depth of 16 to 20 feet. The hole is then timbered with a square set of 4 by 4 inch pine or redwood and vertical logging of 1½ or 2 inch plank. A pump and motor are installed, the end of the suction pipe being equipped with a strong rubber hose and foot valve. A windlass is erected over the well and the earth is removed in a bucket as it is dug out by hand. The material stands without caving and it is easy to timber up after digging. The greatest difficulties are with the water. Large pulleys are put on the motor so as to increase the speed of the pump and enable it to handle more than its normal capacity. As digging progresses the pump and motor are moved down the pit on a series of stages erected on the square sets. When it is no longer possible to keep out the water the well is considered finished and able to supply the same pump if operated at normal speed.[2]

Bored Wells

Wells are often bored in soft unconsolidated materials by means of an auger turned by hand, by horse, or gasoline power. The size of hole may vary from 2 to 30 in. in diameter, although bored wells for domestic supplies rarely exceed 12 in. The augers used to loosen and to remove the materials are of many different shapes and sizes and usually are made locally. The auger is turned in the hole until loaded, then pulled and cleaned. If drilling in clay, the material is brought out on the bit; but if in sand below the water table, the sand is removed by means of a bailer, a hollow cylinder with a flap valve on the bottom, or a sand pump consisting of a cylinder with sliding piston. When the sand pump is dropped on bottom, the piston slides down the

[1] BRYAN, KIRK, Geology and Ground-water Resources of Sacramento Valley, Calif., *U.S. Geol. Surv. Water-Supply Paper* 495, p. 101, 1923.

[2] Near Lockford, San Joaquin County, California, wells over 100 ft. deep and 3 ft. in diameter have been dug by hand and without the use of timbers. The indurated alluvium stands without any support.

cylinder and as it is pulled rapidly to the top of the barrel, the sand is sucked in below it, raised to the surface, and dumped.

The drilling rods used to suspend and rotate the auger are usually of wood or hollow steel and may be any length from 3 to 20 ft. If the hole is drilled by hand, a tripod and windlass are

A   C

Fig. 151.—*A*, gasoline-powered well-boring rig; *B*, loaded bit; *C*, basket reamer.

used to raise and lower the tools operated by a drilling crew consisting of three men. Two men rotate the auger by pushing the handle around and around.

Casing is required soon after the well reaches the water table unless drilled in cemented material. The joints of casing are either screwed, welded, or punched together and driven down the hole. Perforated pipe or a drivepoint and screen are attached at the bottom of the string of casing and driven into the water-bearing beds or the casing is perforated in the hole by means of a perforating tool.

Wells of large diameter have been sunk in this manner to depths exceeding 500 ft., but in general this method is limited to the construction of shallow, small bore wells for small water supplies. This type of well was used extensively by the settlers who migrated westward. The auger method of boring wells is still practiced but is not ordinarily used to develop large quantities of water. With the improvement of machinery in the well-drilling industry, hand boring has been largely replaced.

Fig. 152.—Cement casing for bored well.

Boring of wells from 25 to 300 ft. deep by power auger is practiced also. This is the best method for obtaining samples of material above or below the water table in soft sediments. The auger brings out a sample of material less disturbed from its natural condition than does any other type of drilling tool, with the exception of the core drill.

Figure 151 shows a gasoline-powered boring outfit used to bore wells in central California. The largest bit used with this outfit bores a 20-in. hole, and in some cases the diameter of the hole has been enlarged to 40 in. by reaming with adjustable knives attached at the top of a catch-basket 8 ft. in length with a trapdoor on the bottom which is opened to dump the reamings after removal from the hole (Fig. 151C). Figure 152 shows the type of cement casing used in some of the wells bored by this driller. The perforated joints have side wings built out to guide the gravel which follows behind an oversize shoe on the bottom of the casing and is introduced from the surface as the casing moves down. Wells with an artificial gravel cylinder placed outside the casing are called gravel-envelope or gravel-wall wells (pages 403–406).

Drilled Wells

There are many modified types of drilled wells, but space permits description of only the two common methods—percussion and hydraulic rotary.

Percussion Drilled Wells. *Driven Wells.*—The driven well is the simplest form of percussion well. Driven wells are necessarily shallow and of small diameter because of the difficulty in driving large pipe to great depths; in consequence they develop small water supplies for domestic or ranch use. In rare cases batteries of driven wells are hooked up together and pumped as one unit to produce a large supply of municipal or irrigation water.

A piece of pipe pointed at one end and perforated for part or all of its length constitutes the casing of a driven well. The casing is driven into the ground by a wooden maul or hydraulic ram until it reaches an aquifer carrying sufficient water. Casing varying from 1 to 6 in. in diameter is used, the smaller sizes being the more common. Extra heavy pipe should be used for driven wells because standard pipe is not strong enough to withstand driving. If the well is driven into a sand horizon, the perforated portion of the pipe is covered with wire gauze of a sufficient fineness to keep out the sand, or a new screen is installed after driving the casing into the sand. To prevent injuring the gauze or screen and clogging of the perforations, the pointed end is usually made larger than the tube. In some cases the gauze is covered by a perforated jacket.

Driven wells are adapted to soft, granular formations which are easily penetrated by the pipe. On account of the ease with which the pipe can be driven, pulled up, and redriven, this type of well is suitable for prospecting for water at shallow depths and for development of temporary water supplies. Difficulties in driving the casing through boulders and other obstructions limit such wells to shallow depths, usually less than 100 ft., although they may occasionally be several hundred feet deep.

Cable-tool Wells.—The common type of water-well drilling in the United States is percussion drilling with a portable outfit. The rig is usually powered with a gasoline engine placed at the

Fig. 153.—Portable cable-tool well-drilling rig, with drill-line drum geared directly to the main drive shaft. (*Courtesy of Roscoe Moss Company.*)

front end of the frame. A mast or A-frame is so constructed that it will fold down over the front of the rig while moving from one location to another. The hole is drilled by raising and lowering a heavy bit on the end of a steel cable which is threaded over a sheave at the top of the mast and down to the drill-line drum. The broken and crushed material in the bottom of the hole is removed by means of a bailer or sand pump.

Figures 153 and 154 illustrate two types of portable well-drilling outfits. In both of these rigs the power is transmitted

Fig. 154.—Portable cable-tool well-drilling rig.

by belt drive to the band wheel which turns the main drive shaft. Figure 153 shows the drill-line drum geared directly to the main drive shaft, while the sand-line drum to the rear and the hydraulic

WELLS 399

pumps in the foreground are chain-driven. The pumps are used
to operate hydraulic jacks.

The oscillating motion of the drill cable is usually obtained
by means of a crank attached eccentrically to the band-wheel
shaft. The rig pictured in Fig. 154 has a double walking beam
attached to both ends of the band-wheel shaft. The sand line
is lighter than the drill cable and has a higher speed ratio. It
is used in handling the sand pump and bailer. Drilling is carried
on by oscillating the string of tools up and down so that the bit
will strike the bottom of the hole. Adjustment of the length
of line so that the bit will strike with the right amount of weight
and stroke requires the skill and care of an experienced driller.
The driller holds his hand on the cable and notes the character
of the jar which indicates the manner in which the tools are
operating. Each formation has its characteristic jar, and
satisfactory progress in drilling depends to a large extent upon
the ability of the driller to interpret the vibrations which come
to him through the drilling cable. The driller regulates the
length of stroke and rapidity of blows according to his interpretation of the cable vibrations. As a rule the full weight of the
tools is not allowed to drop upon the bottom of the well but is
taken up in part by stretching of the drill line. The stretch of
the line is regulated so that the tools will strike bottom and then
jump back immediately. This gives the tools less time to jam
or stick in the hole.

There are many variations in the types of bits used in drilling
with the cable-tool rig. The club drill is the most common type
and is used with reasonable success in almost any formation.
The form of the cutting edge is varied to adapt it to the character
of the formation to be drilled. For hard rock a fairly sharp
chisel edge is used, while for soft material the bit used is almost
flat on the bottom with only a blunt edge at the center. The
bit is made of a heavy bar of steel or iron from 4 to 11 ft. long
and somewhat wider than it is thick. It is dressed to a blunt
edge on one end and terminates in a tapered tool joint at the
other end. The shank of the bit is usually several inches smaller
than the cutting edge, which permits the bit to work in the hole
eccentrically, drilling a hole somewhat larger than the actual
gage of the bit. A wide groove or "water course" is cut on each
side of the bit to permit easy displacement of the fluid in the

well as the tools rise and fall. This bit combines a relatively long and moderately full body with ample clearance for the sludge and permits a maximum amount of drilling between bailings.

The bailer or sand bucket consists of a section of tubing 10 to 25 ft. long with a check valve on the bottom. The bailer used is always somewhat smaller than the well casing to allow free movement up and down in the hole. Upward pressure of the well fluid on the descending bailer raises the valve so that the fluid passes through the bailer. When the bailer is lifted the valve closes, catching the material in the tube. After reaching the bottom of the hole the bailer is then raised and dropped a few feet, the process being repeated several times in order to force as much of the sand or clay as possible through the valve. When the bailer has been filled, it is drawn to the surface and dumped.

Casing.—Types of casing used in water wells vary from heavy second-hand oil-well casing weighing 60 lb. per lineal foot to single stovepipe casing which is very light and cannot withstand much pressure. Usually the cheapest and lightest casing available is selected because the purchaser desires the least expensive installation. In rare cases this choice proves the most economical. Generally it is wiser to increase the initial cost of the well by buying good, heavy, durable casing which will give service over a longer period of years. The size of casing varies from 1 to 60 in. in diameter. Casing 6 to 16 in. in diameter is commonly used. Casing is riveted, lap-welded steel or cast-iron pipe and made up in sections varying in length from 3 to 20 ft. The sections are either screwed together with collar connections, welded by electric or acetylene torch, or in the case of the double riveted casing, either clinched by denting the outside casing against the inner casing with a pickax or bolted together. The gage or thickness of the steel varies from No. 6 to No. 20, with 10, 12, and 14 gage being considered the most practical and economical in western United States.

A casing shoe or starter leads the way for the entire line of casing, and it should be selected with this in mind. In many cases a half coupling or collar is used, but usually a good heat-tested cast-steel shoe is satisfactory. But if hard driving at considerable depth is expected, the best forged-steel shoe is a wise selection. Such a shoe should be seamless and of ample length and thickness so that it will withstand the maximum amount of driving.

California Stovepipe Method.—The California stovepipe method of well drilling was developed in California primarily for sinking water wells in unconsolidated alluvial materials consisting of alternate strata of clay, sand, and gravel. This method of drilling involves the same principles as the cable-tool method. The main differences are: (1) the use of the mud-scow bit which acts as both bit and bailer, and (2) the short joints of riveted casing.

The mud-scow bit consists of a disk-valve bailer with a sharp-edged cutting shoe on the bottom, built a little larger than the outside diameter of the bailer tube to allow free passage of the tool. Sometimes a blade is put across the bottom to chop up the formation. Each time the bit is dropped, part of the drillings are trapped in the bailer and when it is full, it is pulled to the surface and emptied. If tough or hard material is encountered, a churn-drill bit is used in place of the mud-scow.

At the bottom of a string of California stovepipe casing is a riveted-steel starter 10 to 25 ft. in length made of three or more thicknesses of sheet steel with a forged-steel shoe at the lower end. This reinforcement prevents the bottom from collapsing when pressed down under pressure. Above the starter the casing consists of two sizes of sheet steel made into riveted lengths, from 2 to 3 ft. in length. The larger size of casing is made to fit snugly over the smaller size. Each outside section overlaps the inside section half its length so that a smooth surface results both outside and inside when the casing is in place. Assembled in this way the inner and outer joints never coincide. Denting of the casing with a pointed pick serves to lock the two casings so they will stay together when a pulling strain is put on the casing string.

The casing is driven down by raising and lowering the tools with a driving head or is forced down, length by length, by hydraulic jacks anchored to two timbers buried in the ground. These jacks press upon a suitable head attached to the upper section of the stovepipe so that the end of the casing will not be telescoped.

The California rig as first developed differed from the ordinary portable cable-tool rig in the manner of developing the drilling motion.   A walking beam was attached to the top of the mast, a pitman rod connecting one end of the beam with an eccentric crank operated by the band wheel.   The drilling line was led through a sheave at the other end of the walking beam and the up-and-down motion of the beam was transmitted through the drill cable to the bit.   However, this type of operation was less practical for many purposes than the use of a straight mast with a drilling sheave at the top and consequently has been discarded by many drillers.   The use of short lengths of casing in well drilling has, however, proved very popular and has spread over much of the western part of the United States where water is produced from soft, unconsolidated alluvial deposits.

Hydraulic Rotary Wells.—The hydraulic rotary method of well drilling originated in the oil fields of Louisiana about 1890 and came into prominence in 1901 with the development of the Spindletop oil district.   Since that time it has replaced the cable-tool method of oil-well drilling to a great extent.   The hydraulic rotary method is now being used in the drilling of water wells, especially on the Pacific coast.

The essential difference between the cable-tool and rotary methods lies in the manner of abrasion and removal of material from the hole.   In the rotary method the hole is made by rapid rotation of a bit on the bottom of a string of drill pipe.   The cable-tool method uses percussion obtained by vertical oscillation of the bit as a means of abrasion.   The material is removed from the cable-tool hole by bailing, while in the rotary hole this is accomplished by circulation of mud fluid descending through the drill pipe and ascending outside the pipe.   The fluid carries the broken fragments to the surface in suspension.   Hydraulic rotary water wells are sometimes drilled by a portable rig with a drilling mast comparable to the portable cable-tool outfits, but ordinarily a wooden derrick 40 to 60 ft. high is built and heavy drilling machinery is moved in, installed on the derrick floor, and assembled.

When the drilling machinery is completely rigged up and ready to operate, a drilling bit is fastened to the drill pipe which, in turn, is screwed onto the end of the kelly, a square section of drill pipe which fits into the rotary table on the derrick floor. The gripping bushings are set around the kelly, the pump is started, and the bit is lowered in the hole.   The fluid is circulated from the mud pit for a few minutes, rotary table and drill pipe are set in motion, and the bit is slowly lowered. When the bit touches bottom, drilling begins. The amount of weight placed on the bit is governed by the amount and weight of the drill pipe above the bit, the character of the formation being drilled, the type of bit employed, and the judgment of the driller. If the formation is sticky, the driller decreases the weight or the bit will tend to become balled up. If the circulation gets clogged or too much weight is placed on the bit in sticky digging, there is great danger of a twist-off or breaking of the string of tools, usually near the bit. If this occurs, a fishing job is necessary, which may or may not be successful in the recovery of the lost tools. A great variety of tools have been invented for use in fishing jobs and a large amount of ingenuity is often necessary before the broken parts can be fished out. Fishing jobs sometimes run into weeks and months of work and obviously are very expensive. Consequently it pays the operator to keep a close watch on the working parts of the drilling equipment and to exercise all the care possible in drilling operations.

The common type of rotary drilling bit is known as the "fishtail" bit owing to its strong resemblance to a fishtail. It is usually made of special steel (sometimes chrome steel) molded into a tapering, double-wing blade which may vary in length from 15 in. to 2 or even 4 ft. The two wings are turned back slightly in opposite directions, giving a corkscrew effect when rotated. Mud fluid is flushed down both sides of the bit through $\frac{3}{4}$- or 1-in. holes in the base. In soft formations the stream of fluid under considerable pressure often loosens the material more rapidly than do the rotation and abrasion of the bit blades. The fishtail bit is only advisable in relatively soft formations, as it dulls too rapidly in hard material, necessitating frequent removal for sharpening and refacing.

Gravel-envelope Well.—The rapid progress of the rotary method in water-well drilling is due, in large part, to the development of a specialized type of well known as the gravel-wall or gravel-envelope well. This type of well as drilled by the rotary method[1]

---

[1] Gravel-envelope wells are also drilled by cable tools, following one of two methods of procedure. One practice involves the use of two casings with gravel placed between them. The outside casing is sometimes pulled but is often left in the hole. It has been found that if both casings are left in the

is ordinarily of large diameter. The hole is reamed, casing which is usually about one-half the diameter of the hole is run in and centered, and the space between the casing and well wall is filled with sorted pea gravel. Usually a test bore is first drilled to determine the geologic and hydrologic character of the formations encountered. This test bore may be drilled to any desired size, but one of the major operators in California usually drills a 12-in. test bore. The information gained from this test determines the future development of the well, or abandonment of the hole if conditions seem unfavorable. If the test shows the formation to be satisfactory, the hole is reamed smooth to a diameter commonly 24 to 28 in. but which may be between 12 and 60 in. If it is desired to shut off contaminated surface water, conductor pipe is run in to a clay stratum and cemented. If the job is successfully carried out, the water behind the conductor pipe is shut off from entrance into the well.

The hole is reamed to bottom and the casing is run into the hole joint by joint. These joints may be threaded and screwed together, or they may be welded into one solid string. Welded connections are preferable, since the joints are solid and therefore are not so subject to corrosion as are threaded joints. As the casing is made up and run into the hole, the perforated lengths are placed opposite the water-bearing strata. This slotted pipe is machine-perforated in the factory and has uniform openings. The slits in the casing are from $\frac{1}{8}$ to $\frac{1}{4}$ in. in width and 1 to 2 in. in length, with $\frac{3}{16}$ by 1 in. a common size. Opposite very fine sand strata the casing is left blank to prevent transportation of sand into the well. After the casing is landed on bottom with guides to center it in the hole, an area of mud-filled hole completely encircles the casing. This mud holds the formation in place and keeps it from sloughing down against the outside of the casing. Sorted gravel of uniform size is fed down outside the casing against the stream of rising mud fluid which prevents

---

well with gravel between them, the permeability of the gravel decreases rapidly owing to cementation and clogging of the pore spaces. The second practice depends upon the use of an oversize shoe at the bottom of the string of casing. As this shoe moves down the hole, gravel is fed in above it and moves down with the casing, filling the space between the casing and the walls of the hole. This method is similar to that described on pp. 393–396 for bored wells.

the settling gravel from lodging prematurely and bridging the hole. Usually some type of plunger is run into the casing and moved rapidly up and down simultaneously with the thinning of the mud by the addition of clear water. As the fluid in the hole gradually thins, the surging of the plunger washes the plastered mud off the walls of the hole. The rapid movement of the plunger as it is moved up and down on the end of the drill pipe enlarges the bore of the hole in loose water-bearing material and as this material is dislodged and washed out of the well, the settling gravel takes its place, serving the double purpose of holding the loose formation in place and furnishing an additional highly porous storage basin.

After the space around the casing has been filled to the surface with gravel and after as much of the drilling mud as possible has been removed by swabbing and thinning of the circulating fluid, the well is ready for a final washing and test pumping. During the test the specific capacity of the well (gallons of water per minute per foot of drawdown) is measured and the safe production is estimated. By safe production is meant the amount that can be pumped steadily over long periods without damage to the formation and transportation of too much sand, which would result in rapid wearing of the pump parts and possible collapse of the well. The test usually covers a period of from 50 to 100 hr. At the end of the test-pumping period the water pumped from the well should be clear of sand and mud. The knowledge gained from this test enables the operator to install a pump suitable to the capacity of the well. If a pump is installed without knowledge of the capacity and drawdown of the well, there is danger that it would prove inefficient and expensive to operate. The test pumping, therefore, is an integral part of the development of the well.

In this type of well the gravel layer, which averages from 4 to 12 in. in thickness, has several advantages.

1. The large diameter of the hole decreases the velocity of water entering the well from a given cross section of formation directly as the diameter of the well increases. Thus, if an 8-in. hole has 6 g.p.m. of water entering the well through a 1-ft. cross section of the wall, a 24-in. hole would have 2 g.p.m. of water percolating into the well through the same areal cross section, other factors being equal. This reduction in velocity

of water entering the well increases the production of sand-free water proportionally.

2. The gravel envelope acts as a storage basin and at the start of pumping, water is partially drawn from the gravel envelope instead of being taken entirely from the aquifers. This storage is especially important in cases where most of the water is coming from thin, sandy aquifers.

3. It decreases the drawdown by reducing entrance friction and thus reduces power bills and allows the bowls of the pump to be placed higher in the well than would be possible otherwise.

4. It prevents hollowing out around casing and eliminates the possibility of collapse as long as the gravel envelope keeps moving into cavities developing around the well.

Gravel-envelope wells are subject to contamination in areas where salt-water contamination is an actuality or a possibility. Top water and bottom water can ordinarily be shut off by proper cementing under pressure, but contaminated water entering the well through aquifers located near the middle of the well section is difficult to shut off. In some cases cementing of the entire envelope under pressure is required to seal off the contaminated aquifer. Ordinarily in the case of contaminated gravel-envelope wells the practice of well drillers is to attempt a shutoff of the salt water by cementing off top or bottom water. If the subsequent test shows continued high salt content, the wells are abandoned and often left open to free circulation of water throughout the gravel envelope. This usually results in contamination of the entire series of aquifers encountered by the well within the next few years after abandonment, with a gradually widening area of contamination spreading from the well as a center. When gravel-envelope wells are abandoned owing to contamination or in cases where contamination is a possibility, the wells should be completely sealed from top to bottom by cement introduced under pressure and in sufficient quantity to fill the gravel envelope as well as the interior of the casing.

Comparison of Cable-tool and Hydraulic Rotary Wells.—In the United States the majority of water wells are drilled by the cable-tool method, but the hydraulic rotary method is used locally. Each method has its advantages and disadvantages. Not infrequently a well produces only a small quantity of water and is short-lived because of the use of a method unsuited to the type of materials encountered in drilling. Advantages of each type of well are outlined below for the purpose of selecting the most efficient well for development of the desired quantity of water.

Advantages of Cable-tool Method.[1]—1. A more accurate sample of the formation is obtained (unless coring is used by the rotary process). However, the accuracy of the log depends upon the experience of the driller in each process.

2. It is possible to test quantity and quality of each stratum as drilling proceeds. The bad water can often be shut off by leaving blank casing through the contaminated stratum.

3. Less water is necessary for drilling operations.

4. Cost per foot of drilling is lower for relatively shallow holes in unconsolidated materials.

5. In most cases a cable-tool rig is much lighter and can be more easily transported in rough country.

Advantages of Hydraulic Rotary Method.—1. The rotary process can drill large holes up to 60 in. in diameter.

2. A test hole can be drilled as a prospect in doubtful or unknown territory and if the prospects are found to be poor, the hole can be abandoned at a minimum expense without the trouble of pulling casing or leaving one or two strings of casing in the hole.

3. Casing with uniform machine-perforated openings can be set at the desired depth after the exact log of the well is known. This assures the maximum supply of water entering the well, a minimum drawdown, and a minimum inflowing velocity which decreases sand troubles.

4. The ordinary procedure of placing a gravel envelope around the casing in a rotary-drilled hole ensures admittance into the well of water from all horizons including sandy horizons which cannot be developed by a cable-tool well.

5. The rotary can handle alternate hard and soft formations with less danger of accidents than can the cable tools. Cable tools drilling in sticky shales and clays, quicksand, and other formations likely to give trouble are in danger of freezing the

[1] Ordinarily the advantages of the cable-tool system are the disadvantages of the hydraulic rotary system; consequently to save repetition, only the advantages of the two systems are emphasized.

casing or sticking the tools owing to sloughing sands or collapse of the hole.

WELL PERFORATIONS

Importance of Perforations.—The following discussion of well perforations is applicable to virtually all types of wells. Well perforations are considered by many well drillers to be only a small factor in well production. Until recently little consideration has been given to the importance of perforations in every phase of well development. The actual drilling of a water well is only one of the two major operations in the final success of the well. The other is the method of completion and development.

The number, size, type, and distribution of perforations can practically control not only the capacity of a well but also determine the life of a well and the wear on pumping units. In some cases the perforations may be too small. An example of this is the placing of fine perforations suitable in quicksand in a well in which the aquifers consist of evenly sorted coarse sand and gravel having a high permeability. Unnecessary entrance friction is thereby developed which causes greater drawdown and greater pumping lift, increasing the cost of operation. On the other hand, if the perforations are too large, the maximum amount of water will have free entrance to the well but difficulty will be encountered in inflow of silt, sand, and small pebbles. The sediment may come into the well faster than it is pumped out and partially fill the well, shutting off good water-bearing formations. If too much material is pumped out from around the casing, there is danger of collapse.

In the cable-tool method of drilling perforation of the casing is an important problem. The formation is not known in advance, and either blank casing is put in the hole and later cut at the proper depths after the formation is known, or machine-perforated casing is used for part or all of the depth of the well. Where part of the casing is machine-perforated, the perforated area may not be opposite the good water-bearing formation. This difficulty can be eliminated by having machine-perforated casing the entire length of the well, but this adds 50 cents to a dollar per lineal foot to the cost of the completed well and is not popular, even though it may be the most economical method of construction from the standpoint of long well life and cost per gallon of water pumped.

Types of Perforations.—Perforations are of two types: (1) machine perforations which are cut in the factory, and (2) perforations made by perforating machines while the casing is in the ground.

Machine-perforated Casing.—Where it is possible to use machine-perforated casing, it is much more satisfactory than casing ripped in the well by perforating machines. The slots in the former are correctly spaced and all of the uniform desired size. The casing is not weakened measurably by the perforating as is likely to be the case when ripping is done in the hole. The perforated pipe can be placed opposite the desired point and can be depended upon to exclude all of the sand with a diameter greater than the specified slot.

Casing Perforated in the Ground.—It is difficult to control satisfactorily the size and spacing of the slots made by the perforating machine. If a pumping test indicates incomplete perforation, a second use of the cutter will probably result in overperforation and is almost sure to tear or rip the casing. In many cases old casing has been pulled from wells in which holes as big as a man's fist were torn by faulty action of the cutter blades. Such oversize holes may cause collapse of the well soon after its completion. Even if the well does not collapse, large amounts of sand may enter the well, wearing the pump bowls and runners, cutting the casing and tubing, and ultimately injuring the distribution system. On the other hand, with care and good equipment, perforation of casing in the ground is often satisfactory, especially when a well is producing from gravel.

The size of the openings is as important as the number of openings and should be adjusted to the different types of formations in which the well is drilled. If drilling samples are taken and logged as the well is drilled, a satisfactory size of perforations may be selected. In western United States where the heterogeneous alluvial formations contain most of the water, it is commonly considered that the size of perforations should be chosen so that about 60 per cent of the grains will pass through the openings and about 40 per cent of the grains will be retained outside the casing. As the finer material is pumped out of the well, the larger grains settle around the casing, forming an envelope area with greater porosity and larger passages for transmission of water to the well.

Well Screens.—Sand trouble is often overcome by the introduction of a well screen of the proper size to exclude the coarser sand and allow the fine sand to pass into the well, resulting in increased permeability in the coarse envelope developed around the well (Fig. 155). There are many types of well screens on the market today, varying from a perforated pipe wrapped with wire to a highly specialized type of screen having a continuous slot opening. When screens were first developed it was thought that their main function was to prevent sand from entering the

Fig. 155.—Development of a test well. In this test a screen of standard make was installed in a mixture of sand and gravel and the well was developed by ordinary methods. Development of an envelope of coarse material around the screen with gradation outward to the original mixture is clearly shown. (*Courtesy of Edward E. Johnson, Inc.*)

well. Consequently fine screens were used which would exclude 60 to 80 per cent of the sand. Recently, however, the coarseness of the screen has been increased with very beneficial results. It is now common practice in the Midwest to make a sieve analysis of the dried sand in which the screen is to be set. A size of screen is then used that will exclude about one-third of the dry sand unless the sand is found to be virtually homogeneous, with a low uniformity coefficient, in which case a finer screen is used.

The coarse screen permits considerable readjustment during development with removal of the finer particles which filter through the slots, their place being taken outside the screen by coarser material in a somewhat looser state. If considerable fine sand can be removed, either in the case of the gravel-envelope well or of the plain screen well, a zone of coarse material is built

up around the casing, which acts to (1) reduce velocity and sand-
carrying capacity of the water, thereby reducing wear on pumping
equipment; (2) increase the permeability of the formation
surrounding the well, thereby reducing friction losses and drawdown during pumping; and (3) give a greater capacity per foot of
drawdown.

WELL DEVELOPMENT

Proper treatment and development of a well often result in
a safe production of 25 to 50 per cent more than would hasty
methods of development, and in addition safeguard the future
of the well, whereas careless or hurried work might result in a
relatively early collapse of the casing.

Meinzer[1] gives the following discussion with reference to well
development:

If the water is obtained from hard rocks, the driller may have performed his entire duty when he has sunk the hole to the required depth.
If, however, the water occurs in beds of sand or other incoherent material
the driller's work is not complete when he has made the hole, but only
when he has so far as possible, developed or finished the well in such a
manner that it will yield a water supply without inflow of sand, silt,
or clay and will remain in good condition for a period of years.   The
process of developing or finishing the well requires quite as much skill
as the process of making the hole and if properly done, it may consume
much time.   A reliable driller will not leave a well in an unfinished condition or in a condition that will cause trouble in the future.   However,
if he is paid only at a certain rate per foot for making the hole, he can
hardly afford to spend much time in developing the well, and if he
does so he is at a great disadvantage with his less scrupulous competitors.
In localities where wells end in sand it is therefore desirable to devise a
form of contract that will give the driller adequate reward for skillful
work in finishing a well without requiring him to assume undue hazards.
Such a form of contract will also be advantageous to the persons for
whom the wells are drilled, for it will tend to give them the service of
skillful drillers on competitive terms.

The many methods of developing wells in sand and gravel
are all based on the principles of surging or agitating the water

[1] MEINZER, O. E., Problems of the Soft-water Supply of the Dakota
Sandstone, with Special Reference to the Conditions at Canton, S.D., *U.S.
Geol. Surv. Water-Supply Paper 597-C*, pp. 168–169, 1929.

in the formation for the purpose of removing the finer material near the casing and to prevent "bridging" of the sand particles. This is accomplished by any method that causes an alternate flow of water from formation to well and *vice versa*. Some of the common methods are "backwashing" (starting and stopping

Fig. 156.—Twelve-inch, thirty-foot welded well screen used in a well at Eau Claire, Wisconsin, which delivered 2,000 g.p.m. with a drawdown of 3 ft. 5 in. (585 g.p.m. per foot of drawdown) on official test at the end of a 10-hr. continuous pumping test. (*Courtesy of Edward E. Johnson, Inc.*)

the pump intermittently), "surging" the well with a surge plunger, and surging the well with compressed air.

Care should be exercised in developing the well sufficiently to obtain the maximum production, but the well should not be overdeveloped with danger of caving, sealing off the supply of water, or collapsing the well casing.

USEFUL FORMULAS

Horsepower Necessary for Pump Lift.

1. Hydraulic horsepower $= \dfrac{\text{g.p.m.} \times \text{total head in feet}}{3960}$

2. Brake horsepower $= \dfrac{\text{g.p.m.} \times \text{head in feet}}{3960 \times \text{efficiency}}$

3. Electrical horsepower $= \dfrac{\text{kw.}}{0.746}$

4. Power input (kw.) $= \dfrac{3.6 \times \text{meter constant} \times \text{disk revolutions}}{\text{time in seconds}}$

5. Over-all plant efficiency $= \dfrac{\text{g.p.m.} \times \text{pump lift}}{3960} \div \dfrac{\text{kw.}}{0.746}$

References

BOWMAN, ISIAAH, Well-drilling Methods, *U.S. Geol. Surv. Water-Supply Paper* 257, 1911.

BRYAN, KIRK, Geology and Ground-water Resources of Sacramento Valley, Calif., *U.S. Geol. Surv. Water-Supply Paper* 495, 1923.

DUPUIT, J., "Études théoriques et pratique sur le mouvement des eaux," 2d ed., Dunod, Paris, 1863.

EDSON, F. A., Diamond Drilling with Special Reference to Oilfield Prospecting and Development, *Bur. Mines, Bull.* 243, 1926.

FIEDLER, A. G., Use of Cement in Well Construction, *Water Works Eng.*, vol. 82, no. 10, pp. 587–588, 620, 623, May 8, 1929.

——— Choosing the Site and Constructing the Well, *Water Works Eng.*, vol. 84, no. 7, pp. 444–446, Apr. 8, 1931.

FLINN, A. D., R. S. WESTON, and C. L. BOGERT, "Waterworks Handbook," pp. 217–255, McGraw-Hill Book Company, Inc., New York, 1916.

HOWELL, R. R., and Co., *Howell Drillers News*, Minneapolis, Minn.

JEFFERY, W. H., "Deep Well Drilling," Gulf Publ. Co., 1925.

Jetting and Self-Cleaning Methods, *Johnson Nat. Drillers Jour.*, December, 1930.

KEILHACK, K., "Grundwasser und Quellenkunde," Gebrüder Borntraeger, 3d ed., Berlin, 1935.

MEINZER, O. E., Problems of the Soft-water Supply of Dakota Sandstone, *U.S. Geol. Surv. Water-Supply Paper* 597, pp. 168–169, 1929.

——— Past and Future of the Water Well Drilling Industry, *Johnson Nat. Drillers Jour.*, vol. 2, no. 6, pp. 1–2, 1930.

SANDERSON, R. R., "Drill Work Methods and Cost," Cyclone Drill Co., 1911.

SCHWALEN, H. C., The Stovepipe or California Method of Well Drilling as Practiced in Arizona, *Univ. Arizona, Agr. Exp. Sta. Bull.* 12, 1925.

SMITH, G. E. P., The Utilization of Ground Waters by Pumping for Irrigation, *Trans. Internat. Eng. Congress*, pp. 414–457, 1915.

SUMAN, J. R., "Petroleum Production Methods," pp. 1–305, Gulf Publ. Co., 1923

Turneaure and Russell, "Public Water-Supplies," 3d ed., John Wiley & Sons, Inc., 1924.

Uren, L. C., "A Textbook of Petroleum Production Engineering," pp. 89–258, McGraw-Hill Book Company, Inc., New York, 1924.

Wenzel, L. K., The Thiem Method for Determining Permeability of Water-bearing Materials, and Its Application to the Determination of Specific Yield, *U.S Geol. Surv. Water-Supply Paper 679-A*, 1936.

CHAPTER XIV

OIL-FIELD FLUIDS

In this short chapter are presented first the author's concepts of the movements of fluids in oil fields during accumulation of hydrocarbons and after the pool is tapped by wells. The application of data collected by ground-water hydrologists to problems of oil-field geology and engineering is then discussed. The first portion of the chapter contains much that is theoretical and as yet unproved, and alternate theories could be presented which would modify the ideas advanced here. Furthermore the migratory movements during oil accumulation are probably minor for certain local oil pools and extensive for others.[1] Inasmuch as the purpose of the chapter is to sketch for the ground-water hydrologist the complex hydraulic conditions of the predominant type of oil accumulations, it was thought better not to dim the picture by discussing alternative theories, but to permit the student to revise the concepts presented here by reference to the literature, a selected bibliography of which is included at the end of the chapter.

Occurrence.—With rare exceptions the fluids and gases of oil fields occur in pervious members of marine sedimentary rocks, principally in pervious sandstones which are interstratified or overlain by impervious shale; and less often in cavernous limestone or in fractured sedimentary formations. The gas and oil pools occur most often in sand layers of anticlinal (upfolded) structures[2] and are held therein by buoyancy in water which is displaced by the lighter components, just as gas or light oil can be caught and held in an inverted tumbler immersed in water. The favorable geologic structure may be a definite anticline with

[1] WILLIS, B., Geologic Distillation of Petroleum, *Mining and Metallurgy*, no. 157, sec. 10, pp. 2–7, January, 1920.

[2] The student is referred to the compilation of articles by various authorities in "Structure of Typical American Oil Fields: A Symposium on the Relation of Oil Accumulation to Structure," in two volumes published by the American Association of Petroleum Geologists in 1929.

reversal of dip, a mere bend without a reversal, a change in porosity of the oil sand, a lenticular body of sand in shale, or a fractured zone in impervious material. The trap must furnish sufficient resistance to hold an oil body against further rise due to buoyancy or artesian pressure until the oil becomes attached to the surfaces of the sand grains, when resistance to movement

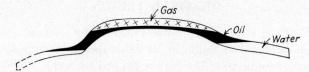

Fig. 157.—Occurrence of water, oil, and gas in an anticline. (*After Beal.*)

of the oil is increased. Where there has been little structural deformation of the oil-bearing rocks and hence no pronounced folding of the strata, hydrocarbons may accumulate in lenticular bodies of sand and gravel formed near and parallel to an ancient shore line. Such accumulations are referred to as "shore-line" or "strand-line" accumulations.[1]

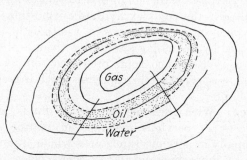

Fig. 158.—Contour map of an anticline showing distribution of gas, oil, and water. (*After Emmons.*)

Gas usually occurs in the center or highest portion of the sand layer and is backed by oil and farther down dip by water, or it may occur in higher horizons of sand where it may be backed directly by water and separated from oil-filled layers by bodies of shale. Heavy oil occurs in synclines when the strata are dry, and hence buoyancy does not affect oil segregation.[2] Over-

[1] BREWER, CHARLES, JR., Genetic Relationship of Oil Reservoirs to Shore-Line Deposits, *Amer. Assn Pet. Geol. Bull.*, vol. 12, pp. 597–615, June, 1928.

[2] MUNN, M. J., Reconnaissance of Oil and Gas Fields in Wayne and McCreary Counties, Ky., *U.S. Geol. Surv. Bull.* 579, pp. 49–50, 1914.

lying pervious layers above the retaining shale are filled with water called *top water;* water in the oil-bearing strata surrounding the oil and gas accumulation is called *edge water;* water in layers between oil horizons is *intermediate* water; and water filling the strata below the oil sand is *bottom water* (Figs. 157, 158). In certain occurrences water backing up the oil is believed to be connate water or "fossilized brines."[1]

The types of structure in which gas, oil, and water are held have been discussed exhaustively and have undergone repeated classification.[2] Some salient structural features of hydrocarbon occurrences are illustrated in Figs. 159 and 160 (page 422).

Organic Shales the Probable Source Rocks.—The outstanding result of half a century of scientific investigation and theorizing is that neither the exact nature of the source material nor the processes by which it is converted into the natural hydrocarbons is as yet understood. It is generally assumed, however, that source material is concentrated in shale of organic origin which is predominantly siliceous-bituminous in California and bituminous

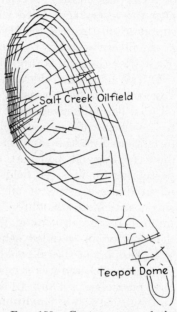

Fig. 159.—Contour map of the faulted anticlinal structure of Salt Creek Oilfield and Teapot Dome, Wyoming. Maximum width of anticline, 5 miles; contour interval 200 ft. (*Modified after Beck.*)

elsewhere, and that a minor source rock is cavernous bituminous limestone. The shale is charged with hydrocarbons at some stage prior to the folding of the rock and the formation of suitable reservoirs.

[1] WASHBURNE, C. W., The Role and Fate of Connate Water in Oil Sands, *Amer. Inst. Min. Eng. Trans.*, vol. 51, pp. 607–610, 1915.

[2] CLAPP, F. G., A Proposed Classification of Petroleum and Natural Gas Fields Based on Structure, *Econ. Geol.*, vol. 5, pp. 503–521, 1910; Revision of Structural Classification of Petroleum and Natural Gas Fields: *Bull. Geol. Soc. Amer.*, vol. 28, pp. 553–602, 1917.

MOVEMENT OF OIL-FIELD FLUIDS

Migratory movements of hydrocarbons originally stored in the source rock may be classified as follows: (1) transfer of oil from the generating shale into adjacent sand conduits; (2) movement of oil in conduits to and into the reservoir structure, and forcing of water out of the reservoir by hydrocarbons; (3) movements *after* the reservoir is filled with oil, due either (*a*) to continued supply of oil through the feeding conduits, or (*b*) to deformation of the filled reservoirs by earth movements; and (4) movements of oil after the pool is tapped by wells.

1. The lenticular character of some oil sands and supposed absence of conduits capable of conducting hydrocarbons to the oil pool has influenced some geologists familiar with such fields to postulate direct movement from adjacent oil-generating formations into the sand lens. 2. Oil movement through conduits feeding oil pools at structurally favorable localities is postulated for most oil fields. 3-*a*. Long continued addition of oil produces a series of oil horizons, one above another, in a single anticlinal structure. Features 2 and 3-*a* are of special interest to the student of fluid movement. 3-*b*. The effect of deformation of oil-filled sand is merely mentioned in passing.

4. Tapping of the oil pool by wells and the production of fluids through wells produces a new set of hydraulic conditions which have been observed and studied in detail by petroleum engineers. In the discussion of conditions during well production, the realm of theory is left and the attempt is made to explain observed phenomena.

Hydraulic Conditions during Accumulation of Oil Pool

The generating shale was either charged with hydrocarbons entrapped in the original sediment or manufactured in the organic shale at some later time. Our interest starts with the driving out of the hydrocarbons from the shale into adjacent water-bearing sand.

The most probable process effecting the expulsion of the petroleum oil and gas from shale is compaction,[2] and possibly

[1] VERSLUYS, J., Compaction an Agent in the Accumulation of Oil at the Anticlines, *K. Akad. Wetens. Amsterdam, Proc. Sec. Soc.*, vol. 33, p. 106, 1930.

later recrystallization of the shale under pressure. Compaction results in great reduction of pore space and consequently the expulsion of large quantities of fluids.[1]

The occurrence of oil in strand-line accumulations in strata that have not been deformed suggests that expulsion of hydrocarbons may take place prior to strong deformation and for such cases compaction appears to be the major process by which the hydrocarbons are driven out of the source material deposited to the seaward of the shore-line reservoir rocks.

Complete expulsion of the hydrocarbons, however, may be delayed until the strata are subjected to deformation, the oil-bearing beds are folded and the underlying source rocks deformed and recrystallized by heat and pressure. Conclusive evidence to this effect is found, for example, in the folded, fractured, and recrystallized source rocks that underlie the oil deposits of the Santa Maria and adjacent oil fields of California. Prior to recrystallization the original source rock was largely of diatomaceous origin and the predominant mineral was opal (of which the diatom tests are made) which was later recrystallized into chalcedony. The "spent" rock, now exposed, is highly contorted and fractured and contains hydrocarbon residues concentrated by metamorphism into bands and irregular aggregates and the lighter hydrocarbon fractions have been completely eliminated and delivered to the reservoir formation.[2]

It is a matter of speculation as to whether oil is squeezed out in minute or large drops. Some have assumed that a fine spray of oil may develop an emulsion of oil in water.[3] However, the

[1] Since 1916 McCoy has favored the hypothesis that water in the sands adjacent to a source shale will enter the interstices of the shale and force the oil into the sand. In recent experiments (Problems of Petroleum Geology, pp. 281–291, Amer. Assn. Pet. Geol., 1934) he observed the penetration of water, held originally in saturated sand, into adjacent oil-saturated ground shale and displacement of oil into the water sand. He thinks that this is the only important type of movement where oil sands are surrounded by oil-saturated source rocks. As the author of this text believes that the preponderance of evidence indicates migration of oil in conduits feeding oil pools and is skeptical as to the quantitative importance of this "displacement" process, these viewpoints are not considered.

[2] Photomicrographs of these residues appear in an article by C. F. Tolman, Biogenesis of Hydrocarbons by Diatoms, *Econ. Geol.*, vol. 22, no 5, pp. 454–474, Plates III, IV (1927).

[3] An emulsion of oil in water is unstable and the droplets will coalesce into

slow process of compaction probably drives out hydrocarbon drops, one at a time, which rise by buoyancy or are moved by any slow artesian current that may exist in the sand stratum receiving the oil. These two possible methods of oil transfer have given rise to two theories; namely, the hydraulic theory of oil accumulation, and the anticlinal theory which assumes that buoyancy is the principal moving force.

Objections to Original Hydraulic Theory.—Strong artesian movement calls for large head and rapid escape at the exit of the conduit. Study of the geologic structure of oil-bearing regions does not suggest that such conditions are common. Oil fields are commonly on the edge of large synclinal basins. The generating formations are presumably best developed toward the center of the basin, but probably not far from the strand line. The artesian movements postulated for oil accumulation would have to be from the basin toward the flanking oil-bearing structures, or against the hydraulic gradient of an ordinary artesian system in such a geologic structure. For shore-line accumulations bordering the ocean, where the regional dip of the oil-bearing beds has always been oceanward, there is no possibility of the existence of an artesian circulation from the ocean toward the land caused by hydraulic pressure originating at the fountain head. If sufficient quantities of water accompanied by oil are furnished by compaction of shale in the center of the basin or under the ocean, however, a slow outward movement in a direction favorable for the migration of the oil to the oil-bearing structures would be developed.

Role of Compaction and Buoyancy.—The writer's belief is that both oil and water are driven out of the great bodies of shale underlying synclinal basins by compaction,[1] that the oil moves up the structural pathways principally by the force of buoyancy, but movement is assisted by feeble water currents generated by compaction. Hydrocarbon gas dissolved in the

---

larger drops. Emulsion of water in oil (water drops surrounded by a skin of hydrocarbon oil) is stable. It may be produced at the well intake, especially where a mixture of oil and water is being pumped. It is not probable that a water-in-oil emulsion would be produced by the slow expulsion of oil from shale.

[1] BECKSTROM, R. C., and F. M. VAN TUYL, Compaction as a Cause of the Migration of Petroleum, *Amer. Assn. Pet. Geol. Bull.*, vol. 12, pp. 1049–1055, November, 1928.

oil drops probably reduces the viscosity of the oil,[1] and gas bubbles have a greater buoyancy than oil. Hence the presence of gas is probably an important factor in assisting the upward migration of the oil drops.

Experimental work shows that in a static water column movement of a drop of oil too large to pass through the throat of a pore in water-filled sand is retarded. But in a slowly upward-moving current of water the oil drop is deformed, the oil is pushed through the constriction, a dumbbell-shaped drop is formed, the lower portion of which is contracting and the upper portion expanding. When the two portions of the drop are of equal size, the entire drop jumps upward out of the constriction.[2]

The principle that the upward force exerted by buoyancy increases in direct proportion to the quantity of water displaced is the basis for the hypothesis here presented that drops tend to accumulate behind restrictions of any type in oil-conducting water sands, and as the oil accumulations increase in size, the effective force of buoyancy increases until the oil is forced through the constriction.

This principle is especially important after the oil finds lodgment in the crest of an anticline. The growing oil pool develops increasing upward buoyant pressure, directly proportional to the difference in elevation between the top and the edge of the oil pool, and this difference in elevation may be measured in hundreds of feet. This growing differential pressure may become sufficient to force the oil through the coarser portions of the retaining formation, through cracks that commonly form at the crest of the anticline; or if the shale is thick, unbroken, and impenetrable, the oil pool may develop until it backs down underneath the impervious portion of the retaining formation and spills over into an upper sand. Shale formations are often lenticular in character and it would be difficult indeed to conceive of a retaining structure so regular, extensive, and unfractured that a growing oil pool would not find a way through or around some of the retaining beds. As soon as a passageway is established through or around the first barrier, a second pool

---

[1] SOBER-FIELDS, GERTRUDE, Gas Propulsion of Petroleum, *Oil Gas Jour.*, vol. 28, (38) pp. 30, 140, February, 1930.

[2] DODD, H. V., Some Preliminary Experiments on the Migration of Oil up Low-angle Dips, *Econ. Geol.*, vol. 17, no. 4, pp. 288–289, 1922.

is formed in the next sand above the barrier, and then others, the number depending upon the quantity of oil delivered and the structure of the oil field.

Mills[1] developed experimentally a group of successive accumulations, one over the other, in the pervious members of an anti-

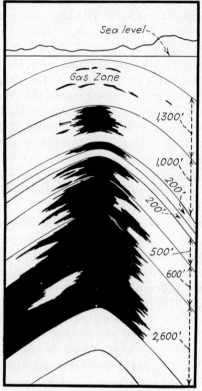

Fig. 160.—Oil zones in Ventura Avenue field, California, showing successive oil horizons overlain by gas (oil bodies in black). (*After F. W. Hertel.*)

clinal structure (Fig. 160). Some oil-field geologists,[2] however, have been skeptical regarding cross migration through thick shale formations, preferring to postulate a different source for each layer of oil. This postulate seems improbable because

[1] Mills, R. Van A., Relations of Texture and Bedding to Movements of Oil and Water through Sands, *Econ. Geol.*, vol. 16, pp. 124–141, 1921.

[2] Gester, S. H., Huntington Beach Oil Field, *Bull. Amer. Assn. Pet. Geol.*, vol. 8, pp. 41–46, 1924.

the upper horizons often contain gas which, of course, is the most mobile of the hydrocarbon accumulations. The theory calls for gas-generating source material discharging into the upper horizons overlying oil-forming source material which feeds the lower strata.

Conditions after Accumulation and before Drilling

Each stratum of oil or gas may be considered as a static fluid body subjected to great hydraulic pressure of the column of water backing up the hydrocarbon fluids. Gas is dissolved in the oil and is a source of potential energy which is probably released by pressure relief during well production.

The ancient oil bodies of the Appalachian fields in structures subjected to progressive deformation since Paleozoic time are supposed[1] to have been moved bodily out of the original anticlinal position without dissipating the fluid constituents.

The composition of mineral salts dissolved in the edge water is modified by reaction of the dissolved salts with the hydrocarbon oils and gases[2] and many years ago the penetration of an oil-bearing horizon beyond the confines of the oil body was recognized by chemical analysis of the water in the drilling well.[3]

Hydraulic Conditions under Production

When the oil stratum is pierced by a well, high pressure (popularly called rock pressure) accompanies the first production of the well and this pressure is gradually reduced by friction engendered by the moving fluids. The relation of pressure to production is controlled by the hydraulic type of fluid delivery to the well as discussed in following paragraphs.

Control of production limits oil extraction to certain of the oil horizons, and great differences in pressure are developed thereby in the different oil and water sands. This may cause cross migration of vagrant water through fractures or other structural irregularities into the producing oil sands.[4]

[1] WILLIS, B., *op. cit.*

[2] ROGERS, G. S., The Sunset-Midway Oil Field, Calif., Chemical Relation of the Oil, Gas, and Water, *U.S. Geol. Surv. Prof. Paper* 117, pt. 2, pp. 1–103, 1917.

[3] This pioneer work was done by L. A. Penn, of the Associated Oil Company.

[4] For an excellent description of water and oil movements of this type see

The edge water of each oil horizon and top, intermediate, and bottom waters have been recognized by chemical analyses, and the water horizons leaking into the well through flaws in casing and the proper locations for cementing jobs have been determined by chemical analyses and by conductivity methods.

Three types of hydraulic conditions which control the fluid delivery at the well and the motions of gas, oil, and edge water have been discussed by Herold;[1] namely, production under a constant hydraulic head, under a diminishing hydraulic head, and production by gas expansion.

The type of fluid delivery under the first-mentioned control is similar to delivery from a tank with head maintained at a constant level and is called "hydraulic control" by Herold. In nature, if replenishment of water in the formation is sufficiently rapid so that head is maintained in spite of oil and gas production, the well is under hydraulic control. Herold discusses wells, especially in Mexico, the pressure and production of which remain constant. When a second well is brought in, there is a sudden drop in pressure and production, both of which again remain constant until another well is drilled. Change from oil to water production occurs when edge water reaches the well.

A water tank producing under a lowering head illustrates the second type of control which is called "volumetric control," and the mathematical treatment worked out for fluid delivery from tanks producing under this condition applies to this type of oil-well control. Wells of this type are common especially in California. With volumetric control edge water moves in as the oil body is pumped out.

The third control was suggested by an analysis of production curves of oil and gas wells in certain Mid-Continent and Eastern fields. These curves show a significant difference in the behavior of the wells from that when hydraulic pressure governs fluid delivery. The mathematical analysis of these curves indicates that the energy causing flow is supplied by expanding gas dissolved in the oil, and that the energy thus derived is able to force oil to the well only for a definite and limited distance.

Geology and Oil Resources of the Elk Hills, Calif., by Woodring, Roundy and Farnsworth, *U.S. Geol. Surv. Bull.* 835, pp. 58–80, 1932.

[1] HEROLD, S. C., "Analytical Principles of the Production of Oil, Gas and Water from Wells," Stanford University Press, 1928.

Jamin's[1] experimental work on the resistance to fluid movement generated by a series of bubbles in a capillary tube furnished the basis for a concept of the physical conditions governing fluid delivery of wells functioning under this control which Herold designates "capillary control." The liquid and bubble-filled Jamin capillary tube represents the physical condition of the fluids in the oil-bearing formation when the relief of pressure accompanying the escape of the fluids from the well is sufficient to cause the gas that is dissolved in the oil to flash into bubbles. Thus a body of foam is formed encircling the well, increasing in diameter as the pressure decreases in the reservoir and sooner or later the Jamin resistance cannot be overcome by the hydraulic pressure on the oil and gas pool, and then the pressure that moves the fluids becomes internal and not external to the pool. The force of the expanding gas can push a line of bubbles of definite length in the capillary interstices which discharge toward the well. The length of this line of bubbles is the radius of the "area of production" around the well and no production beyond this area is possible as long as Jamin resistance[2] is sufficient to prevent movement by hydraulic pressure and, of course, there is no movement of edge water toward the well.

During production a well may change from one control to another and this change can be recognized by a mathematical analysis of pressure and rate of production curves.

The author believes that Herold's treatment is sound and furnishes an interesting picture of the functioning of oil wells under production. All modifying factors, however, are not treated by him, among them elasticity and compressibility of oil-bearing formations.

HYDROLOGIC DATA OF INTEREST TO THE PETROLEUM GEOLOGIST AND ENGINEER

The hydrology of near-surface water-bearing formations has been investigated by ground-water hydrologists, of hydrocarbons and water at greater depths in sedimentary rocks by oil-field

---

[1] JAMIN, J. C., Mémoire sur l'équilibre et le mouvement des liquides dans les corps poreux, *Compt. Rend.*, tome 50, 1860.

[2] There is a tendency at present to discount the importance of "Jamin effect" in retarding fluid movement. (Personal communication from V. H. Wilhelm.) Of course, resistance of any type, if it exceeds hydraulic pressure, will produce "capillary control."

investigators, and of water in soils by agricultural scientists. As emphasized by Meinzer[1] each group has been content to study its own literature and use its own terminology without much concern as to help that could be obtained from the other groups. Oil-field investigators have carried out more detailed laboratory studies of porosity and permeability than the ground-water group and have developed more refined methods of mathematical analysis of fluid delivery from wells. The analysis of water-table and pressure-surface maps, drawdown and recovery of pumping wells, and the hydraulic features of free and confined water have been studied in far more detail by ground-water hydrologists than by the other groups and the principles established by these studies can be reviewed with profit by oil-field engineers and geologists. The flushing of oil pools under capillary control[2] involves principles developed by study of ground-water replenishment, complicated by the physical properties of mixtures of oil, gas, and water.

The importance of an understanding of the principles of ground-water hydrology to petroleum geologists is emphasized by the attempts that have been made in southern California to use water-table maps[3] as indicators of structures buried by thick deposits of water-bearing alluvium.[4] Much must be known in respect to the contact between the water-bearing alluvium and the bedrock before any interpretation is possible. If, for example, the bedrock carrying petroliferous formations were truncated evenly by erosion before the deposit of water-bearing alluvium was laid down, there would be no relation between the water table and the structure of the bedrock series. If the bedrock projects into the water-bearing alluvium as a hill, the latter might function as a ground-water dam and affect the water-table contours.

[1] MEINZER, O. E., Movements of Ground Water, *Amer. Assn. Pet. Geol. Bull.*, vol. 20, no. 6, p. 704, 1936.

[2] ALBRIGHT, J. C., Water-flood Practices in Pennsylvania Vary but Follow Same Basic Principles, *Oil Weekly*, vol. 79, no. 9, pp. 31–34, 1935.

[3] The principles of interpretation of water-table maps are discussed on pp. 229–248 and some simple examples of geologic interpretation of them appear on pp. 249–257. The hydraulic principles governing confined water are discussed on pp. 319–328.

[4] SOPER, E. K., Limitations of Ground Water as Aid in Determination of Hidden Geologic Structures, *Amer. Assn. Pet. Geol. Bull.*, vol. 16, no. 4, pp. 335–360, 1932.

If percolating ground water is diverted around the sides of a buried anticlinal bedrock hill and the latter is reflected in surface topography, as occurs in several southern California fields,[1] this surface hill will collect influent seepage and discharge it down its sides, developing a ground-water mound which is a subdued replica of the topography of the surface hill and in this particular case of the underlying structure as well (Figs. 161, 162). These striking examples of "water-table hills" over a buried

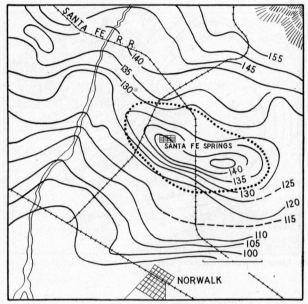

Fig. 161.—Ground-water contours in the Santa Fe Springs oil field showing a "ground-water hill" approximately coinciding with the margins of the oil pool, shown by dotted line. (*After E. K. Soper.*)

structure have led some to hope that this relation of a "water-table anticline" to a buried anticline might be general.

Important oil-bearing reservoirs occur along faults in southern California and if a fault offset is preserved in the bedrock surface, and especially if faulting has cut the alluvium, the fault is usually clearly indicated by the ground-water contours (see pages 254–256).

Many difficulties are encountered in this study, such as the selection of water levels only in true water-table wells. Most

[1] *Ibid.*, pp. 342–348.

wells that penetrate deeply in alluvium show pressure levels not water-table surfaces, and geologic interpretation of these two types of water levels in wells is quite different. Also effects of pumping and irrigation must be taken into consideration.

Interpretation of pressure surfaces in deep wells is more difficult than water-table interpretation. Each water-bearing stratum in the alluvium may have a different pressure level. If the wells penetrate a sedimentary series underneath the

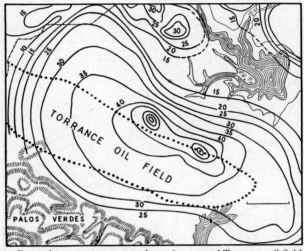

FIG. 162.—Ground-water contours and areal extent of Torrance oil field. (*After E. K. Soper.*)

alluvium and the former contains definite water horizons, each prominent horizon may be identified by a characteristic pressure surface. Hence if records are kept of pressure levels of all water horizons during drilling of wells, geologic interpretation of value might be made.

The phenomenon of higher fluid pressure at the crest of an anticline, where static oil bodies occur, than on the flanks might also occur to a lesser extent in ground-water bodies in overlying strata, as movement of the ground water at the crest of the anticline may be retarded and reduction of head due to friction of flow is lessened and pressure in the crest of the anticline may be further increased by some slight gas leakage from below reaching the overlying body of ground water.

Interpretation of water-table and pressure-surface maps without a thorough understanding of the factors that govern and modify the ground-water gradients shown by the contours, and without a knowledge of the geologic structure, is of no value. However, sound hydraulic interpretation may furnish a check on a hypothetical geologic structure, either showing it to be impossible or substantiating the structural theory under investigation.

References

General References on Origin and Accumulation

Amer. Assn. Pet. Geol., "Problems of Petroleum Geology" (Sidney Powers Memorial Volume), 1934. A compilation of articles by numerous authorities.

ANDERSON, F. M., Origin of California Petroleum, *Geol. Soc. Amer. Bull.*, vol. 37, pp. 585–614, 1926.

ARNOLD, R., and R. ANDERSON, Geology and Oil Resources of the Santa Maria Oil District, Calif., *U.S. Geol. Surv. Bull.* 322, pp. 71–91, 1907.

CLARK, F. R., Origin and Accumulation of Oil, "Problems of Petroleum Geology," pp. 309–335, 1934.

DALTON, W. H., On the Origin of Petroleum, *Econ. Geol.*, vol. 4, pp. 603–631, 1909.

EMMONS, W. H., "Geology of Petroleum," 2d ed., pp. 47–59, 72–85, McGraw-Hill Book Company, Inc., New York, 1931.

HUGHES, RICHARD V., Theories on Origin of Petroleum, *Pan-Amer. Geol.*, vol. 58, pp. 81–92, 1932.

MORREY, C. B., and E. ORTON, Origin of Oil and Gas and the Geological Conditions under Which They Are Found, *Ohio Geol. Surv. Bull.* 1, 1903.

ORTON, EDW., The Origin and Accumulation of Petroleum and Natural Gas, *Ohio Geol. Surv.*, vol. 6, pp. 60–100, 1888.

POWERS, SIDNEY, and others, Symposium on Occurrence of Petroleum in Igneous and Metamorphic Rocks, *Amer. Assn. Pet. Geol.*, vol. 16, pp. 717–858, August, 1932.

WASHBURNE, C. W., Some Physical Principles of the Origin of Petroleum, *Amer. Assn. Pet. Geol.*, vol. 3, pp. 345–362, 1919.

WHITE, C. D., and others, Geology and Occurrence of Petroleum in the United States, Petrol. Investigation, pt. 2 (U.S. 73d Cong., H. R. Committee on Interstate and Foreign Commerce, Hearings before a subcommittee on H. Res. 441), pp. 869–1086, 1934.

WHITE, DAVID, Some Relations in Origin between Coal and Petroleum, *Wash. Acad. Sci., Jour.*, vol. 5, pp. 189–212, 1915; Late Theories Regarding the Origin of Oil, *Geol. Soc. Amer. Bull.*, vol. 28, pp. 727–734, 1917.

Origin: Bacterial Theories

BASTIN, E. S., The Problem of the Natural Reduction of Sulphides, *Amer. Assn. Pet. Geol.*, vol. 10, pp. 1270–1299, 1926.

BASTIN, E. S., and F. E. GREER, Additional Data on Sulphate-reducing Bacteria in Soils and Waters of Illinois Oil Fields, *Amer. Assn. Pet. Geol. Bull.*, vol. 14, pp. 153–159, 1930.

BEYERINCK, M. W., Ueber *Spirillum desulfaricans* als Ursache von Sulfatreduktion, *Centralbl. Bakteriologie*, Bd. 1, Abt. 2, pp. 1–9, 49–59, 104–115, 1895.

ENGLER, C., Zur Bildung des Erdöls, *Ber. deutsch. Chem. Ges.*, vol. 21, 1816–1827; *Petroleum*, vol. 2, pp. 849–853, 912–916, 1021–1025, 1907.

MEYER, G., Eine Bemerkung zur Entstehung des Erdöls: *Chem. Zeitsch.*, vol. 30, 1906.

NEUBERG, C., Ueber die Entstehung optisch aktiver Fettsäuren in der Natur, *Biochem. Zeitschr.*, vol. 1, pp. 368–379, 1906.

———— Die Entstehung des Erdöls: *Ber. K. Preuss. Akad. Sitzungsber*, pp. 451–455, 1907.

POTONIÉ, H., Zur Frage nach den Ur-Materialen des Petroleums, *Jahrb. k. Preuss. geol. Landesamt.*, vol. 25, pp. 342–368, 1904.

RENAULT, B., Houille et Bacteriaces: *Soc. Hist. Nat. Autun. Bull.*, vol. 9, pp. 475–500, 1896; *Compt. Rend.*, vol. 117, p. 593, 1893.

THAYER, L. A., Some Experiments on the Biogenetic Origin of Petroleum. Unpublished dissertation for Ph.D. degree, Stanford University, 1935, Contains comprehensive bibliography and summary of bacterial theories.

Origin: Biogenetic Theories

BECKING, L. B., C. F. TOLMAN, H. C. McMILLAN, J. FIELD, and T. HASHIMOTO, Preliminary Statement Regarding the Diatom "Epidemics" at Copalis Beach, Wash., *Econ. Geol.*, vol. 22, pp. 356–368, 1927.

HACKFORD, J. E., The Chemistry of the Conversion of Algae into Bitumen and Petroleum and of the Fucosite-Petroleum Cycle, *Inst. Pet. Tech. Jour.*, vol. 18, pp. 76–123, February, 1932.

STUART, M., The Sedimentary Deposition of Oil, *Rec. Geol. Surv. India*, vol. 40, pp. 320–330, 1910.

———— "The Geology of Oil Shale and Coal," pp. 60–78, London, 1926; *Econ. Geol.*, vol. 9, pp. 594–597, 1914.

TOLMAN, C. F., Biogenesis of Hydrocarbons by Diatoms, *Econ. Geol.*, vol. 22, pp. 454–474, 1927.

Origin: Destructive Distillation

CUNNINGHAM-CRAIG, E. H., Origin of Oil and Shale, *Roy. Soc. Edinburgh Proc.*, vol. 36, pp. 44–86, 1916.

HAWLEY, J. E., Generation of Oil in Rocks by Shearing Pressures, *Amer. Assn. Pet. Geol. Bull.*, vol. 13, pp. 303–366, 1929; vol. 14, pp. 451–481, 1930.

———— II. Effects of Shearing Pressures on Oil Shales and Oil-Bearing Rocks, *Amer. Assn. Pet. Geol. Bull.*, vol. 13, no. 4, pp. 329–365, 1929.

RAND, W. P., Generation of Oil in Rocks by Shearing Pressures, IV–V. Further Studies of Effects of Heat on Oil Shales, *Amer. Assn. Pet. Geol. Bull.*, vol. 17, pp. 1229–1250, 1935.

RICH, J. L., Generation of Oil by Geologic Distillation during Mountain Building, *Amer. Assn. Pet. Geol. Bull.*, vol. 11, pp. 1139–1150, 1927.

TRAGER, E. A., Kerogen and its Relation to Oil Shale, *Amer. Assn. Pet. Geol. Bull.*, vol. 8, pp. 301–311, 1924.

TRASK, P. D., Results of Distillation and Other Studies of the Organic Nature of Some Modern Sediments, *Amer. Assn. Pet. Geol. Bull.*, vol. 11, pp. 1221–1230, 1927.

――― "Origin and Environment of Source Sediments of Petroleum," Gulf Publishing Co., 1932.

Migration and Accumulation

General Papers

ILLING, V. C., The Migration of Oil and Natural Gas, *Inst. Pet. Tech. Jour.*, vol. 19, pp. 229–274, 1933.

MUNN, M. J., Studies in the Application of the Anticlinal Theory of Oil and Gas Accumulation, *Econ. Geol.*, vol. 4, pp. 141–157, 509–529, 1909.

MUSKAT, MORRIS, Problems of Underground Water-flow in the Oil Industry, *Trans. Amer. Geophys. Union*, pp. 399–401, 1932.

MUSKAT, M., and R. D. WYCKOFF, A Theoretical Analysis of Water Flooding Networks, *Amer. Inst. Min. Eng. Tech. Publ.* 507, Petrol. Div., 1933.

WASHBURNE, C. W., and F. H. LAHEE, Oilfield Waters: "Problems of Petroleum Geology" (Sidney Powers Memorial Volume), pp. 833–840, Amer. Assn. Pet. Geol., 1934.

Hydraulic Theories

DODD, H. V., Some Preliminary Experiments on the Migration of Oil up Low-angle Dips, *Econ. Geol.*, vol. 17, no. 4, pp. 274–291, 1922.

GARRISON, A. D., Selective Wetting of Reservoir Rocks and its Relation to Oil Production, *Oil & Gas Jour.*, vol. 34, pp. 36–39, 1935.

McCOY, A. W., Notes on Principles of Oil Accumulation, *Jour. Geol.*, vol. 27, no. 4, pp. 252–262, 1919; vol. 28, no. 4, pp. 371–373, 1920.

――― A Brief Outline of some Oil-accumulation Problems, *Amer. Assn. Pet. Geol. Bull.*, vol. 10, no. 11, pp. 1015–1034, 1926.

MILLS, R. VAN A., Experimental Studies of Subsurface Relationships in Oil and Gas Fields, *Econ. Geol.*, vol. 15, no. 5, pp. 398–421, 1920; vol. 16, no. 1, pp. 52–60, 1921.

――― Relations of Texture and Bedding to the Movements of Oil and Water through Sands, *Econ. Geol.*, vol. 16, no. 2, pp. 124–141, 1921.

RICH, JOHN L., Moving Ground Water as a Primary Cause of the Migration and Accumulation of Oil and Gas, *Econ. Geol.*, vol. 16, pp. 347–371, 1921.

――― Function of Carrier Beds in Long Distance Migration of Oil, *Amer. Assn. Pet. Geol. Bull.*, vol. 15, pp. 911–924, 1931.

――― Further Notes on the Hydraulic Theory of Oil Migration and Accumulation, *Amer. Assn. Pet. Geol. Bull.*, vol. 17, No. 3, pp. 213–225, 1923.

Anticlinal Theories

ANDREWS, E. B., Rock Oil, Its Geological Relations and Distribution, *Amer. Jour. Sci. Arts*, 2d ser., vol. 32, November, 1861.

HOWEL, J. V., Historical Development of the Structural Theory of Accumulation of Oil and Gas, "Problems of Petroleum Geology," pp. 1–23, 1934.

KEYES, CHARLES, Buoyancy Law of Petroleum Pooling, *Pan-Amer. Geol.*, vol. 58, pp. 107–118, 1932.

ORTON, EDW., Preliminary Report upon Petroleum and Inflammable Gas, *Geol. Surv. Ohio*, 1886.

—— First Annual Report of the Geological Survey of Ohio, 1890.

—— The Origin and Accumulation of Petroleum and Natural Gas, Chap. II, vol. 6, *Geol. Surv. Ohio*, 1888.

—— Report on the Occurrence of Petroleum, Natural Gas and Asphalt Rock in Western Kentucky, *Geol. Surv. Kentucky*, 1891.

ROGERS, H. D., On the Distribution and Probable Origin of Petroleum, or Rock Oil, of Western Pennsylvania, New York, and Ohio, *Proc. Phil. Soc. Glasgow*, vol. 4, no. 2, May 2, 1860.

WHITE, I. C., The Mannington Oil Field, with Appendix on the "Anticlinal Theory" of Natural Gas, *Geol. Soc. Amer. Bull.*, vol. 3, pp. 187–215, 1892.

—— Petroleum and Natural Gas, *West Va. Geol. Survey.*, vol. 1, 1899.

Source Material

ANDERSON, R., Origin of Oil from Marine Plankton Shales in California, *Geol. Soc. Amer. Bull.*, vol. 38, pp. 119–200, 1927.

GOLDMAN. M. I., "Black Shale" Formations in and about Chesapeake Bay, *Amer. Assn. Pet. Geol. Bull.*, vol. 8, pp. 195–201, 1924.

HASEMAN, J. D., Origin and Environment of Source Sediments, *Amer. Assn. Pet. Geol. Bull.*, vol. 14. pp. 1465–1468, November, 1930.

ORTON, EDW., The Trenton Limestone as a Source of Petroleum and Inflammable Gas in Ohio and Indiana, *U.S. Geol. Surv. 8th Ann. Rept.*, pt. II, 1886.

PECKHAM, S. F., Examination of the Bituminous Substances Occurring in Southern California, *Geol. Surv. Calif.*, vol. 2, Appendix, 1882.

RAE, COLIN, Organic Material in Carbonaceous Shales, *Amer. Assn. Pet. Geol. Bull.*, vol. 6, pp. 333–341, 1922.

STOUT, WILBER, Source Material for Petroleum and Natural Gas, *Amer. Assn. Pet. Geol. Bull.*, vol. 20, no. 6, pp. 797–804, 1936.

TAKAHASHI, J. R., The Marine Kerogen Shale from the Oil Fields of Japan, *Science Repts. Tohoku Imp. Univ.*, ser. 3, vol. 1, no. 2, pp. 63–156, Sendai, 1922.

TOLMAN, C. F. Summary of Progress in the Microscopic Study of the Siliceous Shales, *Geol. Soc. Amer. Bull.*, vol. 38, no. 1, pp. 196–197, 1927.

Compaction

ATHY, L. F., Compaction and Oil Migration, *Amer. Assn. Pet. Geol. Bull.*, vol. 14, no. 1, pp. 25–35, 1930.

—— Compaction and Its Effect on Local Structure, "Problems of Petroleum Geology," pp. 811–823. 1934.

HEDBERG, H., The Effect of Gravitational Compaction on the Structure of Sedimentary Rocks, *Amer. Assn. Pet. Geol. Bull.*, vol. 10, no. 11, pp. 1035–1072, November, 1926; vol. 11, no. 8, pp. 875–886, 1927.

────── Gravitational Compaction of Clays and Shales, *Amer. Jour. Sci.*, vol. 31, pp. 241–287, 1936.

VERSLUYS, J., Compaction an Agent in the Accumulation of Oil at the Anticlines, *K. Akad. Wetens. Amsterdam Proc. Sec. Sci.*, vol. 33, no. 9, 1930.

Structure

Amer. Assn. Pet. Geol., "Structure of Typical American Oil Fields," A Symposium on the Relation of Oil Accumulation to Structure, 2 vols., 1929.

EMMONS, W. H., "Geology of Petroleum," 2d ed., pp. 86–132, McGraw-Hill Book Company, Inc., New York, 1931.

LAHEE, F. H., and others, Symposium on Reservoir Conditions in Oil and Gas Pools, *Amer. Assn. Pet. Geol. Bull.*, vol. 16, pp. 861–942, 1932.

TWENHOFEL, W. H., Marine Unconformities, Marine Conglomerates, and Thickness of Strata, *Amer. Assn. Pet. Geol. Bull.*, vol. 20, no. 6, pp. 677–703, 1936.

Hydraulics of Production

HEROLD, S. C., "Analytical Principles of the Production of Oil, Gas, and Water from Wells," Stanford University Press, 1928.

UREN, L. C., "A Textbook of Petroleum Production Engineering," McGraw-Hill Book Company, Inc., New York, 1934.

Chemistry of Oil-field Waters

BAKER, C. L., Panuco Oil Field, Mexico, *Amer. Assn. Pet. Geol. Bull.*, vol. 14, pp. 295–441, 1926.

ESTABROOK, E. L., Analyses of Wyoming Oil-field Waters, *Amer. Assn. Pet. Geol. Bull.*, vol. 9, pp. 235–246, 1925.

GINTER, R. L., Causative Agents of Sulfate Reduction in Oil-well Waters, *Amer. Assn. Pet. Geol. Bull.*, vol. 14, pp. 139–152, 1930.

GRIZZLE, M. A., Geochemical Relations of Waters Encountered in the Huntington Beach Field, *Calif. State Bur. Mines*, vol. 9, no. 6, pp. 17–28, 1923.

MILLS, R. VAN A., Protection of Oil and Gas Field Equipment against Corrosion, *U.S. Bur. Mines Bull.* 233, 1925.

────── and R. C. WELLS, The Evaporation and Concentration of Waters Associated with Petroleum and Natural Gas, *U.S. Geol. Surv. Bull.* 693, 1919.

NEAL, R. O., Petroleum Hydrology Applied to Mid-Continent Fields, *Am. Inst. Min. Eng. Trans.*, vol. 61, pp. 565–579, 1920.

PALMER, CHASE, California Oil-field Waters, *Econ. Geol.*, vol. 19, pp. 623–635, 1924.

REISTLE, C. E., JR., Identification of Oil-field Waters by Chemical Analysis, *U.S. Bur. Mines Tech. Paper* 404, 1927.

—— and A. C. LANE, A System of Analysis for Oil-field Waters, *U.S. Bur. Mines Tech. Paper* 432, 1928.

ROGERS, G. S., The Sunset-Midway Oil Field, Calif., pt. II, Geo-chemical Relations of the Oil, Gas, and Water, *U.S. Geol. Surv. Prof. Paper* 117, 1919.

—— Chemical Relations of the Oil-Field Waters in the San Joaquin Valley, Calif., *U.S. Geol. Surv. Bull.* 653, 1917.

TAYLOR, F. M., The Bearing of Base-exchange on the Genesis of Petroleum, *Jour. Inst. Pet. Tech.*, vol. 14, pp. 825–840, 1928.

WASHBURNE, C. W., Oil-field Brines, *Trans. Amer. Inst. Min. Eng.*, vol. 65, pp. 269–281, 1921.

CHAPTER XV

SPRINGS

A spring is concentrated ground-water flow issuing at the surface as a current of flowing water. A spring, therefore, issues from the outcrop of an aquifer or where an aquifer is overlain by a pervious alluvial or detrital cover. The water of the spring may be supplied by free water moving under the control of the water-table slope (water-table spring), by confined water rising under hydraulic pressure (artesian spring), or by water forced up from moderate or great depths by other forces than hydraulic pressure (geysers, volcanic and thermal springs).

Diffuse effluent seepage may occur without giving rise to springs, although slow seepage may be accompanied by outflow sufficiently concentrated and localized to form springs. Such springs are usually at the upper edge of the area of effluent seepage and often mark the outcrop of the water table. Combined surface flow of water from springs and diffuse effluent seepage may maintain a swamp, discharge from which is by evaporation, transpiration, or surface flow from the lower edge, or in channels draining it.

Water collected in depressions or stream courses by drainage from a swamp probably should not be classified as spring water, as it is supplied by drainage of surface water and not wholly by ground water. In order to differentiate pools or water currents draining from swamps from the (true) feeding or source springs, the former may be designated as *drainage springs*. Drainage springs are subject to mineralization, contamination, and pollution by all the mineral and organic substances in solution in the swamp water.

Capillary rise may bring water to the surface but does not form ground-water springs.

A spring is often a pool of clear water in a depression (pool spring)[1] sometimes delicately tinted by sky reflection, micro-

[1] BRYAN, KIRK, Classification of Springs, *Jour. Geol.*, vol. 27, p. 530, 1919; MEINZER, O. E., Ground Water in Juab, Millard, and Iron Counties, Utah; *U.S. Geol. Surv., Water-Supply Paper* 277, p. 44, 1911.

organisms, mineral salts in solution or precipitated substances in suspension.[1]   In the arid Southwest the term "ojo de agua" and "ojo" (eye) for spring is doubtless based on the occurrence of springs as round clear pools.   The less euphonious American term waterhole usually refers to a spring, and the term "cienega" refers to both a swamp and the springs feeding a swamp.[2]

The spring depression may be in alluvial material or solid rock. In either case it is usually floored with dancing sand, and the pool is agitated by the ascending water currents or is bubbling with escaping gases, chiefly carbon dioxide, hydrogen sulphide, and hydrocarbon gases (*bubbling springs*).   Springs discharging underneath a water body such as a stream, lake, or ocean may be registered at the surface of the water by upwelling currents.

Springs may also issue from cracks in solid rock and from solution cavities in soluble rocks such as gypsum and limestone. Occasionally spring water under pressure may shoot out of an opening like water from the nozzle of a hose.

Effluent seepage may take place throughout the outcrop of a pervious formation.   Spring flow, however, is usually concentrated at the base of a water-bearing stratum and above the contact with less pervious material.   Such springs are called *contact springs*.

Spring Deposits.—Springs, especially hot springs and geysers, deposit travertine, siliceous sinter, sulphur, and other deposits at their orifices.   Deposits around geysers may form large basins with tubular connections with the subterranean source of hot water and heat.   Hot springs build up a series of basins, the sides of which extend a little above the outlet of the water.   A group of such basins may constitute a spring terrace, and the spring deposit may include a series of terraces built up successively or simultaneously at various discharge levels.   Such springs have been called *terrace springs*.

In arid regions springs may issue from the top of a small mound.   These have been called *mound springs*[3] and *knoll springs*.[4]   Windblown dust is deposited in the moist area around

[1] MEINZER, O. E., Large Springs in the United States: *U.S. Geol. Surv. Water-Supply Paper 557*, pp. 9, 10, 1927.

[2] BRYAN, *op. cit.*, p. 525.

[3] *Ibid.*, p. 529.

[4] MEINZER, *Water-Supply Paper 277, op. cit.*, p. 44.

the spring and is held in position by surrounding vegetation. The mound may be built up to the elevation of the artesian head of the spring water. If the water finds a lower exit, the mound may be abandoned; and if it dries out and vegetation dies, it may be eroded by the wind.[1]

Constant, Irregular, and Periodic Discharge.—Springs are *perennial* if they discharge throughout the year, *temporary* or *intermittent* if they discharge throughout a portion of the year either after rains or during a high-water-table stage, and *periodic*

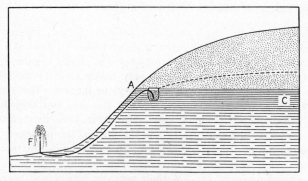

Fig. 163.—Artificial "geyser spring" illustrating principle of natural siphon spring. *A*, normal point of emergence of spring; *C*, impervious stratum; *F*, geyser spring; dashed line, water table developed by burial of barrel and pipe. (*After Fuller.*)

if they discharge at intervals not directly related to the occurrence of rain.

Periodic flow may be due to (1) the decrease of transpiration and evaporation at night which results in a nocturnal rise of the water table; (2) to high-water subterranean flows chiefly in limestone caves and conduits which raise the level of the sub-surface stream to some exit out of reach in the lower water stages; (3) to variation in barometric pressure where artesian pressure can bring the water to the surface only during low baro-metric pressure;[2] (4) to tides which may either dam back ground water at high tide, causing spring flow in the zone affected along

[1] Meinzer, O. E., and R. F. Hare, Geology and Water Resources of Tularosa Basin, New Mexico, *U.S. Geol. Surv. Water-Supply Paper* 343, pp. 52–53, 1915.

[2] Veatch, A. C., Fluctuations of the Water Level in Wells, with Special Reference to Long Island, N.Y., *U.S. Geol. Surv. Water-Supply Paper* 155, pp. 10, footnote, 63–69.

the coast, or to an increase in head due to the weight of the water of high tides on a flexible artesian aquifer (pages 334–337); (5) to superheating and the periodic ejection of water (geyser action); and (6) to siphon action[1] (Fig. 163) which develops the interesting and unusual ebbing and flowing springs.

Ebbing and flowing springs are to be distinguished from ordinary intermittent springs the flow of which increases in wet seasons and decreases markedly or ceases in dry seasons, and also from variable artesian springs affected by changes in atmospheric or tidal pressure. Meinzer[2] states:

An ebbing and flowing spring has periods of flow, when it flows vigorously, and periods of ebb, when it ceases to flow or flows at a greatly reduced rate. The periods of flow may occur at nearly regular intervals or at very irregular intervals; they may occur at intervals of a few minutes or a few hours or even a few days or longer. The springs of this type are nearly all situated far from the sea, and they have no relation whatever to oceanic tides. In their periodic action they resemble geysers, but their water has the normal temperature of ordinary ground water, and they do not generally emit any noticeable amount of gas. All or nearly all ebbing and flowing springs issue from limestone, and as early as 1724 their periodic action was ascribed to natural siphons in the rock.[3]

Discharge varies greatly as to both quantity and regularity. A spring near Fairfield, Tennessee, has an average discharge of 500 g.p.m., flow increasing during $4\frac{1}{2}$-min. periods with maximum flow for 1 min., decreasing flow for 5 min. 50 sec., and minimum flow for 2 min. 15 sec. During exceptionally wet seasons the flow is constant.[4] The discharge of a spring near Broadway, Virginia, is shown in Fig. 164. The dormant period may be brief or may last weeks or months. The spring may function regularly for a few days and then erratically. Extra-

[1] FULLER, M. L., Construction of So-called Fountain and Geyser Springs, *U.S. Geol. Surv. Water-Supply Paper* 145, pp. 46–50, 1905; GEIKIE, A., "Textbook of Geology," p. 405, New York, 1902.

[2] MEINZER, O. E., Ebbing and Flowing Springs, p. 52, "Ground-Water Resources of Shenandoah Valley," by R. C. Cady, *Virginia Geol. Surv. Bull.* 45, 1936.

[3] DESAGULIERS, J. T., *Royal Soc. London Phil. Trans.*, vol. 33, no. 384, p. 132, 1724; abridged ed., vol. 7, pp. 39–41, 1809.

[4] STOW, M. H., An Ebb and Flow Spring near Fairfield, Va.; *Virginia Geol. Surv. Bull.* 46-F, 1936.

ordinarily large flood flows may be developed after a period of quiescence.[1]

The principal feature of ebbing and flowing springs is siphon action which seems to be characteristic of solution conduits in limestone. A continuous variable flow develops if a spring is fed by both a siphon conduit and by steady flow from another source. Meinzer[2] states:

The variations in water supply are produced chiefly by the alternation of wet and dry seasons and successive freezing and thawing of the

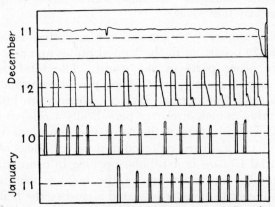

Fig. 164.—Hydrograph of ebbing and flowing spring near Broadway, Virginia. This spring was dormant from July 19 to December 7, after which it discharged continuously for nearly three days. The horizontal broken line shows the level at which overflow from the lip of the basin begins. The hydrograph shows the fluctuating water level in the basin during periods of flow. During periods of ebb the basin is generally empty. The average discharge of the spring when flowing was about 1,000 g.p.m. (*After Meinzer, Courtesy of Geological Survey of Virginia.*)

ground. In seasons of abundant water an ebbing and flowing spring may lose its periodic character and may flow continuously because the supply exceeds the capacity of the siphon; on the other hand, in dry seasons it may cease to flow because the small supply of water escapes elsewhere, or it may have a continuous flow that is too small to prime the siphon or that comes from other sources. . . .

Irregularities in the periodic action may result from variations in the air-tightness of the siphon system. The influence of air leaks on the siphon system was investigated experimentally by

[1] Meinzer, O. E., Ebbing and Flowing Springs, *op. cit.*
[2] *Ibid.*, p. 54.

Josiah Bridge.[1]   Minor irregularities in periods of flow may be due to surges produced by variations in the pressure of entrapped air as the system discharges.

The system is likely to be more nearly air-tight when the interstices of the soil and rocks are filled with water than when they are dry or only partly filled, and also probably more nearly air-tight when the ground is frozen than otherwise.   The variations in air-tightness may determine whether the system of caverns is discharged completely by the siphon or whether the siphon action is interrupted by air leaks before the discharge is completed.   Obviously a great variety of irregularities in discharge may thus result.[2]

The total number of ebbing and flowing springs is very small, only about 20 occurring in the United States and a comparable number in other parts of the world.   The total number in existence may be greater, but they are rare and unusual features.

Thermal and Nonthermal Springs.—*Geysers* are intermittent thermal springs which discharge periodically a column of boiling water.   The classic explanation of geyser eruptions was given by Bunsen[3] and has been repeated in most textbooks of geology. The essential feature is a tubular opening in consolidated lava with internal temperature above the boiling point of water. The inflowing surface water is heated almost to the boiling point at the surface, and above 212°F. below the surface, but the water is prevented from boiling by the weight of the overlying column of water.   At some point below the surface the temperature of the water reaches the boiling point for that depth, steam is formed, and the overlying water is lifted and overflows.   The relief of pressure caused by the overflow reduces the pressure on the entire superheated column of water which bursts into steam and causes eruption of the geyser.   The eruptions are periodic, and the period is determined by the time necessary to fill the tube and superheat the water.

The mineralized water of the geyser is rich in silica which is deposited on the sides of the tube and builds up the basin surrounding the geyser.   The mineral content of the water reduces convection currents and thereby aids superheating.   The depo-

---

[1] BRIDGE, J., Ebb and Flow Springs in the Ozarks, *Schools Mines Metal. Univ. Missouri Bull.*, Tech. Ser., pp. 15–26, November, 1923.

[2] MEINZER, Ebbing and Flowing Springs, *op. cit.*, p. 54.

[3] BUNSEN and DESCLOISEAUX, *Compt. Rend.*, vol. 23, p. 934, 1846.

sition of silica in the basin is brought about largely by hot water algae.

The three best known large geyser fields are in Yellowstone National Park, United States,[1] in New Zealand, and in Iceland. Smaller geyser fields also exist as "The Geysers" and "The Little Geysers" in California.[2]

The temperature of hot springs in lavas of Tertiary, Quaternary, and recent ages is usually attributed to volcanism, but other sources must be sought for hot springs in regions where recent volcanism has not occurred. These are chemical alteration of rocks which produces heat, such as kaolinization of feldspar, deep-seated rocks which are hot because rock temperature increases with depth, and heat generated by movement and rock crushing along recently active faults.[3]

The majority of springs are nonthermal; that is, the average temperature of spring water is not far from the average temperature of the superficial rock. This indicates that water feeding the spring is not of deep-seated origin or that the water movements are so slow that the water has cooled to the temperature of the rocks through which it passed as it approached the surface. Springs may be classified in respect to temperature as cold springs, nonthermal or ordinary temperature springs, and thermal springs which may be warm, hot, or boiling.[4] Cold springs may originate from melting snow or ice, especially from glaciers and snow banks and from snow that has accumulated in caves, or the spring water may be cooled by air circulation and evaporation in caverns and other openings above the water table. The division between thermal and nonthermal waters is usually fixed at 70°F., but 20° to 25° above the mean for the region might be preferable.[5]

Mineral Springs.—*Mineral springs* are either highly mineralized with salts common in the ground water of the region or

[1] HAGUE, ARNOLD, The Origin of the Thermal Springs in the Yellowstone National Park, *Geol. Soc. Amer. Bull.*, vol. 22, pp. 103–122, 1911.

[2] ALLEN, E. T., and A. L. DAY, Steam Wells and other Activity at "The Geysers," Calif., *Carnegie Inst. Wash. Publ.* 378, 1927.

[3] MEINZER, *Water-Supply Paper* 277, *op. cit.*, p. 43.

[4] The term boiling spring is also popularly applied to springs issuing with sufficient force to agitate violently the water and bottom sand and to springs discharging large quantities of gas with the water.

[5] BRYAN, *op. cit.*, p. 527.

contain an uncommon salt or salts. Nonmineral springs are usually spoken of as *common springs*.

Mineral springs may be classified according to the principal salt or group of salts, or according to the gases with which they are charged. More complicated classification based on the groups of radicals in solution has been suggested.[1]

The common varieties of mineral springs are *saline springs* (carrying chiefly common salt), bromine and iodine springs (carrying salts of bromine and iodine), epsom springs (carrying magnesium sulphate), calcareous springs (precipitating calcium carbonate), gypsum springs (carrying calcium sulphate), borax or boron springs (carrying borax), chalybeate springs (carrying and usually precipitating iron hydroxide), acid springs (usually carrying an acid sulphate radical), alum springs (carrying aluminum sulphate), soda springs (carrying sodium carbonate and bicarbonate), hydrogen sulphide, stinking, or sulphur springs (giving off hydrogen sulphide and precipitating sulphur), carbonated springs (giving off carbon dioxide), inflammable gas springs (giving off hydrocarbon gases), oil springs (carrying liquid hydrocarbons), fake oil springs (carrying an organic or mineral material that forms an iridescent film on the surface of the water).[2]

Medicinal springs are those of reputed therapeutic properties. In a single spring field individual springs may vary remarkably in taste and to a less extent in mineral content. If a sanatorium or health resort is established in the neighborhood of such a group or springs, special therapeutic properties may be attributed according to the variation in taste of the spring water.

Radioactive Springs.—Certain spring waters, especially mineral and hot springs, have an abnormally high and easily measurable radioactivity. Waters thus charged are reputed to have valuable medicinal properties. The radioactive impurities are supposed to be derived from the formations through which the water has passed.[3] Prospecting for radioactive springs by the use of the radioscope has been undertaken in Russia (pages 276–277).

[1] CLARKE, F. W., The Data of Geochemistry, *U.S. Geol. Surv. Bull.* 770, pp. 181–217, 1924.

[2] PEALE, A. C., The Natural Mineral Waters of the United States, *U.S. Geol. Surv. 14th Ann. Rept.*, pt. II, pp. 64–68, 1894.

[3] The extensive literature on radioactive springs is listed by Richard Ambronn, translated by M. C. Cobb in "Elements of Geophysics," McGraw-Hill Book Company, Inc., p. 131, 1928.

Size of Springs.—Springs vary from a trickle of a few drops a minute, which, caught in a prospector's pan, may furnish him the only available water for many miles around, to the great flows from tubular openings in limestone or from porous lava. The largest known maximum spring flow exceeds

Fig. 165.—Waterfalls developed by Thousand Springs, Snake River, Idaho. (*Photograph by C. F. Bowen. Courtesy of U. S. Geological Survey.*)

4000 sec.-ft. (Fontaine de Vaucluse in France).[1] The average flow of a number of very large springs may exceed 500 sec.-ft. "A single spring of this type issuing chiefly from one opening (in limestone) may give rise to a river that is navigable by good-sized passenger and freight boats."[2]

In the stretch of about 40 miles along the canyon of the Snake River below Shoshone Falls, Idaho, where the river has cut through the water-bearing lava beds, an aggregate of more than 5000 sec.-ft. of ground water is discharged. . . . Farther up the river are the Portneuf Springs which altogether discharge about 1400 sec.-ft.[3]

Many of the springs along the Snake River issue on the side of the canyon between 125 and 200 ft. above the river, and these "ground-water torrents" form mighty waterfalls, some

[1] Keilhack, K., "Grundwasser und Quellenkunde," 3d ed., pp. 286–287, Gebrüder Borntraeger, Berlin, 1935.

[2] Meinzer, *Water-Supply Paper 557, op. cit.*, p. 8.

[3] Meinzer, *op. cit.*, pp. 42–43.

of which have been utilized for the development of electric power.[1]

Meinzer's[2] classification of springs according to size is as follows:

Magnitude	Average Discharge
First.........	100 sec.-ft. or more
Second......	10 to 100 sec.-ft.
Third.......	1 to 10 sec.-ft.
Fourth......	100 g.p.m. to 1 sec.-ft. (449 g.p.m.)
Fifth........	10 to 100 g.p.m.
Sixth........	1 to 10 g.p.m.
Seventh.....	1 pt. to 1 gal. a minute. About 200 to 1500 gal., or 4 to 40 barrels, a day.
Eighth......	Less than 1 pt. a minute. Less than about 200 gal., or 5 barrels, a day.

CLASSIFICATION OF SPRINGS

Factors in Classification.—In the preceding paragraphs springs have been described according to various features, some of which are important and others incidental. These special features are not suitable as a basis for a general classification of springs, the purpose of which is (1) to arrange and classify all data so that the processes that cause spring flow and the factors that affect it may be discovered, and (2) to group together springs of like origin and characteristics for the purpose of description.

The important factors controlling the location of springs, the direction of movement of the effluent water currents, and the quantity of outflow are (1) rainfall, (2) hydrologic character (chiefly permeability) of the material at the ground surface, (3) topography, (4) hydrologic character of the water-bearing formations, and (5) geologic structure.

The hydraulic features of spring flow due to the previously-mentioned controls are (1) percolation of free ground water to the surface (water-table springs), (2) overflow of ground-water reservoirs, (3) outflow of subsurface streams, and (4) effluent percolation or flow of confined water, including confined water rising under hydraulic pressure and deep water forced upward by other forces than hydraulic pressure. These

[1] *Ibid.*, pp. 47–50.
[2] *Ibid.*, p. 3.

features, in respect to source of water, may be stated as follows: Spring water supplied by (1) free ground water, (2) artesian water, (3) volcanic water, and (4) deep water of unknown origin.

In addition to the great variety of factors involved in the formation of springs, a further difficulty in applying a complete and orderly classification is the lack of information regarding the character and structure of the aquifers feeding certain springs, especially those issuing from a soil or alluvium-covered area. In some cases even detailed study may not discover all the factors involved in the genesis of a spring. As a result of the complex interaction of the many factors in spring formation, not only is there no satisfactory general classification of springs, but also it is not likely that such a classification will ever be developed.

Each author describing a group of springs, or the springs of a region studied by him, has described and classified them according to the salient features that impressed him during his investigation. The two best general classifications of springs by K. Keilhack and by Kirk Bryan[1] are founded on the properties of springs or on selected factors governing the concentration and outflow of spring water. For example, the main divisions of Keilhack's classification are founded on origin or source of spring water ("descending" and "ascending" springs), and subdivisions are based on a combination of hydraulic and geologic factors governing spring flow. Bryan emphasizes origin for the first main subdivisions, and subheads are made according to geologic formation and structure.

[1] Keilhack's classification of springs is followed fairly closely by later German writers. His examples are taken chiefly from Europe. He classifies springs in two main groups; namely, (A) *Absteigende Quellen* (descending springs), and (B) *Aufsteigende Quellen* (ascending springs). The chief emphasis, therefore, is laid on the source of water and direction of movement. Descending springs are fed by percolation of free water, occurrences commonly called *water-table springs*. Ascending springs are artesian springs which are forced upward by hydrostatic pressure or by heat and expansion of gases. His subdivisions of these two groups, generally accepted in Germany, are given on pages 257–320 of his book on ground water (3d ed.).

The classification of Kirk Bryan is probably the most valuable one offered to date and was used freely in the preparation of this chapter. He emphasizes the source of water in his two main divisions; namely, I. Springs due to deep-seated water, and II. Springs due to shallow waters. (Bryan, Kirk, Classification of Springs, *Jour. Geol.*, vol. 27, pp. 522–561, 1919.)

Classification Adopted in This Text.—In the present writer's attempts to develop a satisfactory classification of springs, especially for descriptive purposes, it was discovered that a classification according to the type of water-bearing formation (where granular, pervious materials are involved), or according to the type of opening (fractures or solution channels), also brought together spring groups of similar hydraulic behavior and offered a fairly satisfactory basis for descriptive purposes.

The major groups selected are as follows:

 I. Springs issuing from pervious veneer formations.
 II. Springs issuing from thick pervious formations.
 III. Springs issuing from interstratified pervious and impervious formations.
 IV. Springs issuing from solution openings.
 V. Springs issuing from lava.
 VI. Springs issuing from fractures.

Controlling Factors in Each Group.—I. The controlling factor for springs issuing from pervious veneer formations is the near approach to the surface of the impervious basement. As explained by Keilhack,[1] this causes a reduction in the cross-sectional capacity of the aquifer to transmit water and forces it to the surface. In other words, the water moves in a formation of limited capacity, and overflow occurs at points of diminished transmission capacity or at the termination (lower edge) of the aquifer.

II. In thick pervious formations the position of bedrock does not materially affect spring flow or effluent seepage. Springs occur at the outcrop of the water table which, in turn, is controlled by topography, decrease in permeability of the water-bearing material, and quantity of ground water in motion.

III. For springs in interstratified pervious and impervious formations the chief controls are the outcrops of the aquifers (and hence topography) and the geologic structure. Springs are usually located above impervious members (outcrop and contact springs).

IV. Springs occur at the lowest exit to the surface of main solution conduits. The quantity of flow depends upon the capacity of the interconnected conduit system and the quantity of water supplied to the conduit.

[1] KEILHACK, *op. cit.*, pp. 259–262.

V. Springs in lava are controlled by vertical flow in fractures, horizontal permeability due to gas-inflated zones, flow tunnels and other flow textures, permeable ash and tuff beds; and interruption of permeability by impervious lava flows, tuff beds, and dikes and sills, concentrating water currents which may be furnished exit by canyons and deep valleys.

VI. Springs flowing from fractures fall into several groups. Fractures, especially faults intersecting pervious granular material, may dam free ground water (fault-dam spring) or may guide pressure water to the surface (artesian fault spring). The superficial fracture system opened up by weathering in impervious rock is fed by surface water, often delivered by an overlying body of detrital or alluvial material. The principal springs issue from the larger fractures draining many smaller feeding fractures. Deep fractures, especially faults cutting impervious formations, may conduct volcanic water or deep water of unknown origin to the surface.

DESCRIPTION OF SPRINGS

Class I. Springs Issuing from Pervious Veneer Formations

Characteristic Features.—Surface material pervious; basement formation impervious; aquifer is a flat or gently dipping capping formation; bedrock surface usually irregular; basement outcrop or near approach to the surface is controlling feature of spring development.

Formations are thin, pervious deposits of all kinds, including volcanic tuffs, thin alluvial formations, talus and detrital deposits, landslide material and pockets of residual soil, or alluvial and wind-deposited material in depressions in the bedrock. The superficial pervious deposit may cover an old erosion surface on the top of a mountain range, form surface caps on hills, occur as talus and detrital deposits on mountain and hill slopes, as wind deposits on stream terraces (loess), or may fill older valleys dissected by later stream channels. In general this class of springs occurs in all thin and irregular pervious deposits on a basement formation which stands above the level of the main valleys.

Description.—This class of springs has been called in general *contact springs* and *gravity springs*.[1] The former term has been

[1] FULLER, M. L., Underground Waters for Farm Use, *U.S. Geol. Surv. Water-Supply Paper* 255, p. 22, 1910.

applied also to springs from interbedded pervious and impervious materials.[1] The term gravity spring is not satisfactory, as all springs, except possibly some thermal springs and those contain-

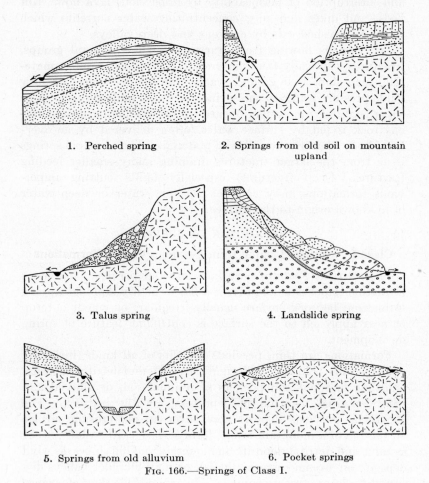

1. Perched spring

2. Springs from old soil on mountain upland

3. Talus spring

4. Landslide spring

5. Springs from old alluvium

6. Pocket springs

Fig. 166.—Springs of Class I.

ing large quantities of dissolved gases, are brought to the surface by gravity.

[1] PURDUE, A. H., Water Resources of the Contact Region between the Paleozoic and Mississippi Embayment Deposits of Northern Arkansas, *U.S. Geol. Surv. Water-Supply Paper* 145, pp. 93, 113, 1905.

This class includes (1) *perched springs*[1] except those from a series of interstratified pervious and impervious deposits; (2) springs from the lower edge of an old soil on a mountain upland or peneplain; (3) *talus springs;* (4) springs at the edges of landslides; (5) springs from a body of old alluvium cut by more

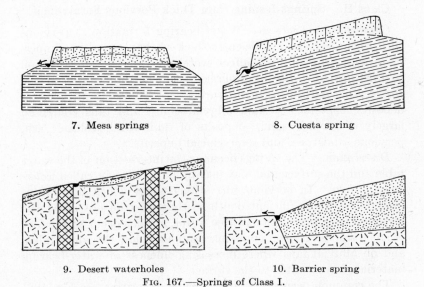

7. Mesa springs   8. Cuesta spring

9. Desert waterholes   10. Barrier spring

Fig. 167.—Springs of Class I.

recent canyons; (6) *pocket springs* from the lower edge of any deposit of pervious material filling an irregular depression in the bedrock[2] (see Fig. 166); (7) *mesa springs;* (8) *cuesta springs*[3] (9) waterholes of the desert above rock reefs which cut across and may protrude above the sands of dry washes; (10) *barrier springs* formed above a fault between a raised bedrock block and a depressed block covered with a thick deposit of alluvium (see Fig. 167); (11) springs from pervious caps of wind-blown sand, volcanic ash, or pervious sandstone; and (12) springs issuing at the edges of thin morainic material.

[1] VEATCH, A. C., Underground Water Resources of Long Island, N.Y., *U.S. Geol. Surv. Prof. Paper* 44, p. 57, 1906.
[2] LEE, C. H., An Intensive Study of the Water Resources of a Part of Owens Valley, Calif., *U.S. Geol. Surv. Water-Supply Paper* 294, p. 44, 1912.
[3] Springs fed by tubular aquifers in alluvial cones fall into Class III.

The size of this class of springs depends upon the extent and hydrologic properties of the water-bearing capping formation, the slope and configuration of the basement formation, especially at the point of spring outflow, and the rainfall. Most of these springs are small but some are large.

Class II.   Springs Issuing from Thick Pervious Formations

Characteristic Features.—Water-bearing formation is pervious throughout, flat, and sufficiently thick so that underlying impervious material does not affect water movement; stratification is unimportant. The controlling feature is intersection of the water table with the ground surface. Formations are alluvial deposits, especially certain alluvial cones and fans composed largely of granitic sand,[1] deposits of dune sand, volcanic ash, pervious sandstone, and some glacial deposits.

Description.—The springs occur at the intersection of the water table and the surface and may usually be accurately called *water-table springs*. In pervious formations under which impervious materials are at sufficient depth so that they do not affect the water table or percolation of free water, springs occur at the foot of steep slopes, in any depression reaching below the water table, and on alluvial fans where increasing fineness of water-bearing materials forces water to the surface.

The common occurrences of this type of springs (see Fig. 168) are as follows:

1. *Channel springs* occur on the banks of streams which have cut channels below the water table.[2]

2. *Valley springs* are developed on the sides of valleys at the outcrop of the water table.[3]

3. *Cliff springs* are developed at the intersection of the water table with a cliff.

4. *Dimple springs* are formed in any small depression reaching below the water table.

5. *Boundary* or *alluvial-slope springs* occur on the lower slope of an alluvial cone at the point where the water-table slope and the surface gradient are equal (pages 231–234). Below this

---

[1] GREGORY, H. E., The Navajo Country, *U.S. Geol. Surv. Water-Supply Paper* 380, pp. 140–141, 1916.

[2] BRYAN, *op. cit.*, pp. 536–537.

[3] *Ibid.*, p. 536.

point surface topography does not permit the development of a
water-table slope steep enough to carry the supply of ground
water.   This point is often located at the point of gradation from
pervious sand with a flat water-table slope to less pervious alluvial
material which calls for a steep slope to carry the water supplied

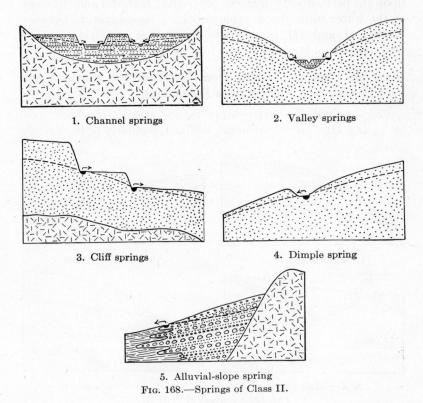

1. Channel springs   2. Valley springs

3. Cliff springs   4. Dimple spring

5. Alluvial-slope spring
Fig. 168.—Springs of Class II.

from above.   Therefore the springs have been called *boundary
springs*.[1]   *Alluvial-slope spring* is probably the better descriptive
term, as these springs are often located some distance above the
toe of the alluvial cone.   Keilhack[2] describes springs of this
character in the glacial outwash deposits of Europe.

[1] Meinzer, O. E., Geology and Water Resources of Big Smoky, Clayton
and Alkali Spring Valleys, Nev., *U.S. Geol. Surv. Water-Supply Paper* 423,
pp. 86–87, 89, pl. II, 1917.
[2] Keilhack, *op. cit.*, pp. 262–265.

6. If the alluvial materials are intersected by a fault which is less pervious than the alluvium because of gouge, precipitation of salts along its course, or interruption of stratification, a *fault-dam spring* may be developed.[1]

In general springs of Class II are not large. Their size depends upon the permeability of the water-bearing material and the slope of the water table toward the spring. The separation between Classes II and III is indefinite because of gradations in the development of layering in pervious granular deposits.

Class III. Springs Issuing from Interstratified Pervious and Impervious Formations

Characteristic Features.—Aquifers are stratiform; beds may be at any attitude—horizontal, inclined, regularly or irregularly

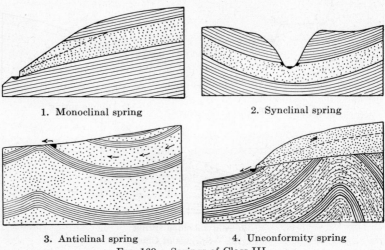

1. Monoclinal spring   2. Synclinal spring

3. Anticlinal spring   4. Unconformity spring
Fig. 169.—Springs of Class III.

folded and faulted. Unconformities may control spring flow. Springs issue where aquifers have been uncovered by erosion, often on sides of valleys and near the foot of cliffs. Formations are chiefly stratified sedimentary rocks and alluvial and glacial materials. Springs issue usually from the basal portion of outcropping aquifers and hence are called *contact springs*. These

[1] CLARKE, W. O., Ground Water Resources of Niles Cone and Adjacent Areas, Calif., *U.S. Geol. Surv. Water-Supply Paper* 345, pp. 130–132, 150, 1915.

may be perched springs drawing on perched ground water. An essential feature is a steepened topographic slope which truncates the aquifer or a structural attitude that brings the aquifer to the surface.

Description.—This class of springs may be subdivided according to the structure of the water-bearing formation. It includes (1) monoclinal springs, (2) synclinal springs, (3) anticlinal springs, and (4) unconformity springs. (Fig. 169.) All may draw on confined water. This type of springs has also been called overflow springs[1] if the geologic structure holding the water functions as a reservoir and the water flows out at the lowest discharge point.

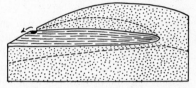

Fig. 170.—Hardpan spring.

Common varieties of contact springs are *hardpan springs* which occur above a single layer of hardpan developed in horizon *B* of an old soil (Fig. 170), and glacial-drift springs issuing from lenticular sand and gravel deposits, from stream-channel deposits surrounded by less pervious unassorted till, or outwash glacial sands and gravels covered by unassorted till. A large gravel channel overlain by drift may produce large springs.

Class IV. Springs Issuing from Solution Openings

Characteristic Features.—Aquifers are solution conduits and caverns formed along fractures and joint systems (Chap. X), connected with the surface by sinkholes or tunnels at the base of cliffs. Solution channels at and below the water table discharge water-table streams or confined flow from subwater-table conduits.

Description.—The springs usually form a pool filling a solution basin connected with a tubular aquifer in which the water moves as a subsurface stream. The underground drainage may be considered as a subsurface stream system, or if the conduit is below the water table, as subwater-table flow. Surface streams often plunge underground through sinkholes, and rainfall is delivered rapidly to the aquifer through large openings. The springs therefore are variable in discharge, and the water may be

[1] KEILHACK, *op. cit.*, pp. 284–295.

contaminated and polluted by infiltration of surface water.
Meinzer[1] states

The present study has shown that the fluctuations of the large limestone springs, whether in Florida, Missouri, or Texas, are as a rule
much greater and more sudden than those of the springs in volcanic
rock, whether in Idaho, California or Oregon.

There are, however, considerable differences in the behavior of limestone springs of different regions, which can be attributed to several
causes. Probably the chief cause of differences in fluctuation is the
position of the water table or of the underground and surface drainage
with respect to the water levels of the past. Where the land has not
subsided and nothing has occurred to raise the level of the streams and
the water table, a nearly complete and perfect underground drainage
system may be developed, with very cavernous rock above the level of
the underground drainage and very tight rock below this level. Such
an underground drainage system resembles a surface drainage system
that is well developed on impervious rock without lakes or swamps. It
lacks storage capacity and discharges its water swiftly after a rain.
Its outlets form springs that fluctuate violently, in extreme cases discharging torrents of muddy water in wet periods and becoming entirely
dry in periods of drought.

Where a limestone country has subsided with reference to sea level,
great systems of caverns may be submerged beneath the water table
and may function as huge subterranean reservoirs that equalize the
spring discharge somewhat as a lake equalizes the discharge of a stream
that flows through it. Limestone springs of this type are perennial
and relatively constant, and they discharge clear water even at times of
heaviest rainfall.

This class includes many very large springs and has received
much attention from European investigators. Vaucluse spring
in southern France is the classic example of a mighty spring
formed by overflow of a water body stored in solution openings
in limestone. After heavy rains it probably is the largest
ground-water torrent in existence, but in dry seasons its discharge
falls considerably below a number of large springs in the United
States. The spring flows out at the foot of cliffs 200 meters high
which encircle the head of the charming valley excavated by
outflow from the spring. It wells up in a wide, circular and
funnel-shaped basin which lies in a deep, arched hollow. This

---

[1] MEINZER, *Water-Supply Paper* 557, *op. cit.*, p. 7.

spring has reached a volume of 120 cubic meters per second (over 4000 sec.-ft.). The extreme low of 1869 did not fall far below 200 sec.-ft., and the average flow from 1874 to 1878 was about 600 sec.-ft.

This spring supplies the Sorgues River which turns 200 mills and waters about 5000 acres. In dry years the body of water in the basin is small in circumference and only 10 or 12 meters deep, and one can see an opening in the east wall which is the entrance of the feeding waters. The spring drains the limestone mountains of the Neocomian region, full of fractures and fissures and underlain by impermeable strata. Sixty per cent of the rainfall over the drainage area of the spring discharges at the spring orifice. Open fractures represent 5 per cent of the volume of the Neocomian limestone at the surface. From 24 to 48 hr. after rainfall the effect is noticed at the spring.[1]

Large Limestone Springs in the United States.—Large springs, including several of first magnitude, occur in central Florida and adjacent parts of Georgia and Alabama. They discharge from solution openings in soft cavernous limestone of Tertiary age. Many issue from deep pools filling limestone caverns uncapped by erosion, and some give rise to rivers navigable by passenger and freight boats. Some of these springs fluctuate greatly with rainfall but remain clear during times of greatest discharge due to low relief of land, dense vegetation, and mantle of sandy soil through which the water passes before entering the solution channels. The water in the large pools is blue and so transparent that fish and objects on the bottom can be observed. The water is only moderately hard; total dissolved solids of eight large springs averages 232 p.p.m. The temperature of the springs is approximately the mean air temperature. The table on page 456 shows the discharge of some of the largest springs in Florida.[2]

Large springs also occur in the Paleozoic limestone east of the Mississippi River, but the only known first-magnitude springs are the Big Springs at Tuscumbia, Alabama, of special interest because of its proximity to Muscle Shoals dam, and the Huntsville, Alabama, spring which furnishes the water supply of that city.

[1] KEILHACK, *op. cit.*, pp. 285–290.
[2] MEINZER, *Water-Supply Paper 557, op. cit.*, p. 11.

TABLE 15.—DISCHARGE OF LARGE SPRINGS IN FLORIDA (*After Meinzer.*)

Name of spring	County	Temperature, °F.	Discharge, second-feet
Silver...............	Marion	70	822 (Dec. 1898) 545 (May 1906) 608 (Feb. 1907)
Blue...............	Marion	74	342 (Feb. 1917) 778 (Dec. 1898)
Wakulla............	Wakulla	70	716 (Dec. 1904) 847 (Feb. 1907) 738 (Feb. 1917)
Itchatucknee..........	Columbia	74	326 (Feb. 1917) 403 (Dec. 1898) 44 (Feb. 1917)

In the Ozark region of Missouri and Arkansas is a group of springs exceeded in size only by those of Florida. The Ozark

FIG. 171.—Water flowing from Big Spring, Missouri. (*Photograph by H. C. Beckman. Courtesy of U. S. Geological Survey.*)

uplift is structurally a dome. The basal formation is cavernous, cherty and dolomitic limestone of Cambrian and Ordovician age. The margin of the uplift is deeply dissected by box canyons which tap the subsurface conduit system and hence contain large springs. The area underlain by the Cambrian and Ordovician limestone is marked by sinkholes and dry, deep valleys. On account of greater relief in this region than in Florida the subsurface drainage is more vigorous, the springs rise promptly after heavy rain and snowfall, and the discharge then becomes turbid or muddy. Seven springs in this area are of first magnitude, ranging from 100 to 700 sec.-ft.

Springs occur in the Cretaceous limestone of Texas in the Balcones fault zone which separates the coastal plain and the Edwards Plateau. Both the plateau and the coastal plain are underlain by Lower Cretaceous limestone which dips gently toward the coast, the conduit system of which supplies the springs. The springs in the fault zone are generally considered artesian and those of the Edwards Plateau are "overflow" or gravity springs. Both types of springs are less flashy than those of the Ozark region.

Class V. Springs in Lava

Characteristic Features.—The principal aquifers are porous strata or horizons overlain by thin flows of lava, with considerable vertical permeability due to fractures, cascade-flow lines, craters, blowholes, and spatter cones. The aquifer may consist of pervious breccia or tuff, or interstratified sand and gravel overlain by lava, and may be underlain by impervious material such as shale or dense lava.[1]

Description.—The great springs of this type issue from the edges of lava plateaus or in canyons that have been excavated in them. The attitude of the flows is fairly flat with slight inclination toward the margin of the plateau. The collecting area is the surface of the lava plateau and is very large. Downward movement through an infinite variety of openings regulates the supply to the main water-bearing stratum, hence the discharge of the springs is usually fairly constant.[2] Heavy irrigation on the lava plateau has been known to increase greatly the flow of the springs.[3] The temperature of the springs is also fairly constant. It registers the average temperature of the lavas of the plateau. Large springs issue from gravel channels buried under lava flows.

Important groups of volcanic springs issue from the Tertiary and Quaternary lavas of Idaho, Oregon, Washington, and

---

[1] MEINZER, *Water-Supply Paper 557, op. cit.*, p. 6.

[2] *Ibid.*, p. 7.

[3] *Ibid.*, p. 47.

California. Meinzer describes the springs in the Snake River basin, Idaho, as follows:

The drainage basin of Snake River is notable for the numerous very large and spectacular springs which it contains. These springs issue chiefly from volcanic rocks or closely related deposits. The water-bearing volcanic rocks are largely basalt, but they also include jointed obsidian and rhyolite. A large part of the basin of Snake River above King Hill, Idaho, was inundated with basaltic lava during the Tertiary and Quaternary periods, and the lava rock is in many parts so broken or vesicular that it absorbs and transmits water very freely. Hence, much of the water that falls as rain or snow on the extensive lava plain or that flows upon this plain from the numerous streams that rise in the bordering mountains finds its way into the lava rock and percolates to localities of lower levels, where it reappears in large springs. In a stretch of about 40 miles along the canyon of Snake River below Shoshone Falls, where the river has cut through the water-bearing lava beds, an aggregate of more than 5,000 second-feet of ground water is discharged. In this stretch occur eleven springs of the first magnitude and four that yield more than 500 second-feet each. Farther up the river are the Portneuf Springs, which altogether discharge about 1,400 second-feet. There are also many other large springs in other parts of the drainage basin of Snake River or in adjacent country, the largest of which are the Big Springs, at Big Springs, Idaho, the only springs of first magnitude that are known to issue from rhyolite and obsidian.[1]

At most of the springs the water issues at considerable heights above river level. Thus the Blue Lakes lie about 160 feet above river level, Niagara Springs and the springs that feed the Clear Lakes issue at points about 125 feet above river level, most of the water in the Box Canyon issues at the head of the canyon about 200 feet above river level, the Sand Springs issue near the top of the canyon nearly 200 feet above river level. Thousand Springs issue about 30 feet below the rim rock and 195 feet above the river level (Fig. 165, page 443), most of the Bickel Springs issue 140 to 150 feet above river level, and much of the water of the Malade Springs also issues far above the level of Snake River.

On account of the notable height above the river at which most of these springs issue, together with the great volume of water which they discharge, they are capable of developing a great amount of water power. Large power plants have already been installed at Malade Springs and at Thousand and Sand Springs, and other large plants could be installed at other springs. . . .

[1] MEINZER, *Water-Supply Paper* 557, *op. cit.*, pp. 42–43.

Some of the springs, such as Thousand, Bickel, Crystal, and Niagara springs, issue sheer from the canyon wall or occupy only slight alcoves; others, such as Blue Lakes, the Box Canyon Springs, and Malade springs, occupy deep, narrow branch canyons of considerable length, with precipitous walls at their sides and head. These branch canyons were apparently formed by the action of the springs themselves, though the precise process of excavation is difficult to explain. (See explanation of I. C. Russell, Geology and Water Resources of the Snake River Plains of Idaho, *U.S. Geol. Surv. Bull.* 199, pp. 127–130, 1902.)[1]

At the Thousand springs the water can be seen gushing from innumerable openings in the exposed edge of a scoriaceous zone below a more compact sheet of lava rock. At Sand, Box Canyon, and Blind Canyon springs the water, according to Russell (*U.S. Geol. Surv. Bull.* 199, *op. cit.*, p. 165), comes from a stratum consisting largely of white sand which is overlain by a thick sheet of lava. At most of the springs there is so much talus that the true source of the water can not be observed, but it probably issues chiefly from the large openings in scoriaceous or shattered basalt where the basalt overlies more dense rocks. The fact that most of the springs are confined to rather definite localities and issue at points far above the river indicates that the flow of the ground water to the springs is governed by definite rock structure. The great body of ground water is obviously held up in the very permeable water-bearing rocks by underlying impermeable formations. It may be that the underlying surface which holds up the water is a former land surface and that the principal subterranean streams which supply the springs follow down the valleys of this ancient surface.

The water of these springs does not contain much mineral matter. It is generally very clear, although the water of some of the springs, such as the Blue Lakes, has beautiful blue color and a slight opalescence due to minute particles in suspension. So far as is known, all the springs have about normal temperatures. . . .

The lava plain lying north and northeast of these large springs extends over a few thousands of square miles and receives the drainage of a few thousand square miles of bordering mountainous country. The great capacity of the broken lava rock to take in surface water is well established and is, moreover, shown by the fact that in the entire stretch of more than 250 miles from the head of Henrys Fork of Snake River to the mouth of Malade River no surface stream of any consequence enters Henrys Fork or the main river from the north. The greater part of this vast lava plain discharges no surface water into the Snake, and a number of rather large streams that drain the mountain area to the north lose themselves on this lava plain. A part of the water that falls on the plain and adjoining mountains is lost by evapora-

[1] MEINZER, *Water-Supply Paper* 557, *op. cit.*, pp. 47–49.

tion and transpiration, but a large part percolates into the lava rock and thence to the large springs. Contour maps of the water table in parts of this region show to some extent the course of the ground water, but when the entire region has been studied the limits of the area contributing water to these springs will be better known. . . . [1]

The great region of Tertiary basalt and related volcanic rocks in which the large springs of Idaho are found extends into northern Nevada and northeastern California and includes most of Oregon and Washington. Large springs occur in other parts of this region, especially in California and Oregon, and some of these rival the large springs on the Snake River. The springs of northern California are an important source of water for the Pitt River which maintains a large constant flow throughout a cycle of dry years.

Class VI.   Springs Issuing from Fractures

This class includes three main groups: springs issuing from (*A*) fractures intersecting pervious materials, (*B*) fractures in impervious material, and (*C*) fractures supplied largely or in part by water of deep-seated unknown origin.

A. SPRINGS FROM FRACTURES INTERSECTING PERVIOUS MATE-RIAL. *Characteristic Features.*—Materials are pervious veneer formations or thick pervious formations, from which fault-dam springs[2] may issue, or interstratified pervious and impervious members, from which artesian springs rise from fissures tapping confined water. This group includes all springs issuing from fractures of all types cutting pervious material.

Artesian fault springs are developed on fault-conduits cutting the lower portion of an alluvial cone and intersecting any type of geologic structure carrying confined water. A *spring line* is a group of springs along a line which may represent a geologic structure, often a fault. Fault springs issuing from nonindurated alluvial material are usually not large. Those issuing from pervious sedimentary formations may be large.[3]

B. SPRINGS FROM FRACTURES IN IMPERVIOUS ROCK.   1. **Springs Issuing from the Superficial Zone of Fracture Opened**

---

[1] MEINZER, *Water-Supply Paper* 557, pp. 50–51.

[2] Fault-dam springs have been referred to under Classes I and II but could be put here with propriety.

[3] MEINZER, *Water-Supply Paper* 557, p. 6.

Up by Weathering. *Characteristic Features.*—Aquifers are fractures in impermeable formations, such as intrusive igneous rocks (granite, diorite) and metamorphic rocks (quartzite, schist, and gneiss). Fractures may be regular or irregular, including joints and joint systems, shears and shear zones, faults and fault zones. The fissure which supplies a spring is usually fed by intersecting fractures that connect with some pervious superficial formation acting as a supply reservoir, such as talus and landslide material, soil pockets, a body of regolith or severely fractured and weathered rock. Examples of such springs are illustrated in Fig. 97, page 299.

2. Springs Receiving Water Largely from Deep Unknown Sources.—These are often thermal and mineral. Thermal springs developed near volcanic vents are usually highly mineralized by volcanic emanations and therefore the origin is fairly well known. They include salfataras, boiling springs, hot mud springs, geysers, and terrace hot springs.

Deep water may be of (*a*) meteoric or (*b*) juvenile origin, or (*c*) may be furnished by the processes of metamorphism and compaction (rejuvenated water) which slowly squeeze water out of deeply buried formations into fractures or other available aquifers.

a. Descending (meteoric) water moves through numberless small fractures and fissures, gradually draining into the larger deep fissures. Return movement may be due to hydraulic pressure, expansion of dissolved gases, and heat.

b. Juvenile water may be forced out of solution in a magma and upward through the overlying rocks by forces connected with the intrusion and crystallization of a molten body of rock. Temperature may be a secondary force causing the ascension of water if the water passes through an overheated body of rock. The superheating of surface waters penetrating heated lava rock forms geysers and many hot springs. Gases dissolved in the water under pressure may escape from solution upon relief of pressure as the water ascends and the pressure exerted by the expanding bubbles of gas combined with the lessened weight of the column of mixed gas and water may assist the upward movement of water. The common gases are steam, carbon dioxide, hydrogen sulphide, and hydrocarbon gases.

INVESTIGATION AND DEVELOPMENT OF SPRINGS

Only a small proportion of the springs of the world are developed to full capacity and the spring flow utilized. It is not strange that this should be so in the humid regions where there is an excess of water, but it is an astonishing fact that in the semiarid and arid regions the springs are rarely fully developed. Spring water is allowed to accumulate in a swamp to be polluted by men and animals and wasted by evaporation and transpiration. The development and diversion of water from a single large spring usually involve no geological investigation and little engineering work except possibly improvement of the spring orifice and installation of the necessary diversion ditches or conduits. A spring house built over the spring often affords cold storage for perishable goods.

For suggestions on the development and protection of small springs see *Water-Supply Paper* 255, Underground Waters for Farm Use, by Myron L. Fuller, pages 22 to 27. The full development of a group of small springs and the accompanying diffuse effluent seepage may involve an estimate of the water available, a geological investigation to determine the source of the water, and an application of the methods of drainage engineering to collect and conduct the water to the place where it is to be used. The ultimate quantity of water available for development can not usually be determined by measurement of flow from the various springs of a group because diffuse seepage may furnish a considerable portion of the water. The amount available may be estimated by a measurement of the area of the swamp fed by effluent seepage and a determination of the transpiration coefficient of the assemblage of plants living in the swamp either by actual experiment or from evaporation and transpiration studies reported in the literature.[1] This quantity added to the water drained from the swamp will give the total supply of available water. The drainage ditch should usually be dug a short distance downslope from the spring line and to a sufficient depth so that the trench or depression in the water table developed by the ditch will not discharge water to the surface by capillarity and will extend underneath most of the swamp, as illustrated in

[1] See references, pages 93–94.

Fig. 72, page 239. The trench may be open or lined with perforated pipe or filled with clean sand and gravel.

Large spring zones have been developed and spring water
collected by drainage works for municipal use. For example,

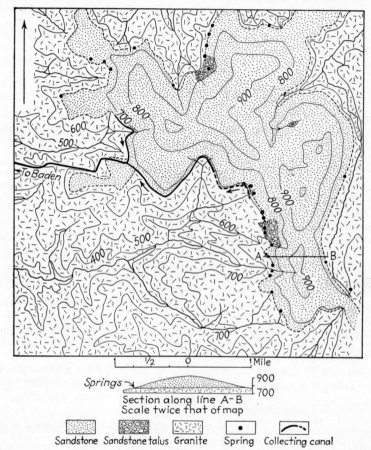

Fig. 172.—Map of area near Baden-Baden, Germany, showing collecting canal
fed by inclined gravity springs. (*After Bryan.*)

the water supply of the municipality of Baden-Baden, Germany,
is derived from a zone of contact springs issuing at the base of
a sandstone formation overlying granite[1] (see Fig. 172).

[1] Eck, H., Geognostische Beschreibung der Gegend von Baden-Baden,
Rothenfels, Gernsbach und Herrenalb, *K. preuss. geol. Landesanstalt Abh.*,
Neue Folge, Heft 6, pp. 653*ff.*, 1892.

References

General References

MEINZER, O. E., Large Springs in the United States, *U.S. Geol. Surv. Water-Supply Paper* 557, 1927.

BRYAN, KIRK, Classification of Springs, *Jour. Geol.*, vol. 27, pp. 522–561, 1919.

WARING, G. A., Springs of California, *U.S. Geol. Surv. Water-Supply Paper* 338, 1915.

KEILHACK, K., "Grundwasser und Quellenkunde," 3d ed., pp. 257–359, Berlin, 1935.

FULLER, M. L., Underground Waters for Farm Use, *U.S. Geol. Surv. Water-Supply Paper* 255, pp. 22–27, 1910.

FULLER, M. L., Underground Waters of Eastern United States, *U.S. Geol. Surv. Water-Supply Paper* 114, 1905. This paper contains many references to and examples of springs.

Classification of Springs

MEINZER, O. E., Large Springs in the United States, *U.S. Geol. Surv. Water-Supply Paper* 557, pp. 2–4, 1927.

KEILHACK, K., *op. cit.*, pp. 257–258.

BRYAN, KIRK, *op. cit.*, pp. 559–561.

PURDUE, A. H., Water Resources of the Contact Region between the Paleozoic and Mississippi Embayment Deposits of Northern Arkansas, *U.S. Geol. Surv. Water-Supply Paper* 145, pp. 93–113, 1905.

LEE, C. H., Water Resources of a Part of Owens Valley, *U.S. Geol. Surv. Water-Supply Paper* 294, pp. 44–45, 1912.

GREGORY, H. E., The Navajo Country, *U.S. Geol. Surv. Water-Supply Paper* 380, pp. 140–141, 1916.

MEINZER, O. E., Geology and Water Resources of Big Smoky, Clayton and Alkali Springs Valleys, Nev., *U.S. Geol. Surv. Water-Supply Paper* 423, pp. 86–89, pl. II, 1917.

CLARKE, W. O., Ground Water Resources of Niles Cone and Adjacent Areas, Calif., *U.S. Geol. Surv. Water-Supply Paper* 345, pp. 130–132, 150, 1915.

Thermal and Mineral Springs

ALLEN, E. T., and A. L. DAY, Hot Springs of the Yellowstone National Park, Carnegie Inst. of Washington, 1935.

BROWN, J. S., The Hot Springs of Haiti, *Jour. Geol.*, vol. 32, no. 5, pp. 384–399, 1924.

BRYAN, KIRK, The Hot Springs of Arkansas, *Jour. Geol.*, vol. 32 no. 6, pp. 449–459, 1924.

BUNSEN and DESCLOISEAUX, *Compt. Rend.*, vol. 23, p. 934, 1846.

DARTON, N. H., The Hot Springs at Thermopolis, Wyo., *Jour. Geol.*, vol. 14, pp. 194–200, 1906.

DAY, A. L., Hot Springs and Fumeroles of "The Geysers" Region, Calif., *Jour. Geol.*, vol. 32, no. 6, 1924.

DAY, A. L., and E. T. ALLEN, The Source of the Heat and the Source of the Water in the Hot Springs of the Lassen National Park, *Jour. Geol.*, vol. 32, no. 3, 1924.

GAUTHIER, A., The Genesis of Thermal Waters and their Connection with Volcanism, *Econ. Geol.*, vol. 1, pp. 688–697, 1906.

HAGUE, ARNOLD, The Origin of the Thermal Springs in the Yellowstone National Park, *Bull. Geol. Soc. Amer.*, vol. 22, pp. 103–122, 1911.

HAYDEN, F. V. The Hot Springs and Geysers of the Yellowstone and Fire-hole Rivers, *Amer. Jour. Sci.*, vol. 3, pp. 105–115, 1872.

JAGGAR, T. A., Some Conditions Affecting Geyser Eruption, *Amer. Jour. Sci.*, vol. 5, pp. 323–333, 1898.

MEINZER, O. E., Origin of the Thermal Springs of Nevada, Utah and Southern Idaho, *Jour. Geol.*, vol. 32, no. 4, 1924.

PEALE, A. C., The Natural Mineral Waters of the United States, *U.S. Geol. Surv. 14th Ann. Rept.*, pt. II, pp. 64–68, 1894.

SOSMAN, R. B., General Summary of the Symposium on Hot Springs, *Jour. Geol.*, vol. 32, no. 6, 1924.

STEARNS, N. D., H. T. STEARNS, and G. A. WARING, Thermal Springs in the United States, *U.S. Geol. Surv. Water-Supply Paper* 679-D, 1936.

WARING, G. A., Springs of California, *U.S. Geol. Surv. Water-Supply Paper* 338, pp. 32–311, 1915.

WASHINGTON, H. S., Notes on the Sofatara of Sousaki, A Recent Eruption of Methana, and Recent Macculube at Vulcano, *Jour. Geol.*, vol. 32, no. 6, 1924.

WRIGHT, F. E., The Hot Springs of Iceland, *Jour. Geol.*, vol. 32, no. 6, 1924.

ZIES, E. G., Hot Springs of the Valley of Ten Thousand Smokes, *Jour. Geol.*, vol. 32, no. 4, 1924.

Spring Deposits

ALLEN, E. T., and A. L. DAY, Steam Wells and Other Activity at "The Geysers," Calif., *Carnegie Inst. Wash. Publ.* 378, 1927.

ALLEN, E. T., Geyser Basins and Igneous Emanations, *Econ. Geol.*, vol. 30, no. 1, pp. 1–13, January–February, 1935.

—— The Agency of Algae in the Deposition of Traver ine and Silica from Thermal Waters, *Amer. Jour. Sci.*, vol. 28, no. 167, pp. 373–389, November, 1934.

CLARKE, F. W., Data of Geochemistry, *U.S. Geol. Surv. Bull.* 770, pp. 176–217, 1924.

WARING, G. A., Springs of California, *U.S. Geol. Surv. Water-Supply Paper* 338, pp. 124, 134, 154–155, 1915.

WEED, W. H., Formation of Travertine and Siliceous Sinter by the Vegetation of Hot Springs, *U.S. Geol. Surv. 9th Ann. Rept.*, pp. 613–676, 1890.

Constant and Irregular Discharge

BRIDGE, J., Ebb and Flow Springs in the Ozarks, *School Mines Metal., Univ. Missouri Bull.*, Tech. Ser., pp. 15–26, November, 1923.

FULLER, M. L., Construction of So-called Fountain and Geyser Springs, *U.S. Geol. Surv. Water-Supply Paper* 145, pp. 46–50, 1905.

MEINZER, O. E., Ebbing and Flowing Springs, in "Ground-water Resources of Shenandoah Valley," by R. C. Cady, *Virginia Geol. Surv. Bull.* 45, pp 52–55, 1936.

STOW, M. H., An Ebb and Flow Spring near Fairfield, Va., *Virginia Geol. Surv. Bull.* 46-*F*, 1936.

VEATCH, A. C., Fluctuations of the Water Level in Wells, *U.S. Geol. Surv. Water-Supply Paper* 155, pp. 57, 63–69, 1906.

CHAPTER XVI

THE GROUND-WATER INVENTORY

The ultimate goal of quantitative hydrologic measurements is to determine additions of water to the ground-water reservoir of the area under investigation from all sources (ground-water increment) and discharge of every kind from the ground-water body (ground-water decrement). The balancing of the one against the other is called the *ground-water inventory*. The inventory should be continued for as long a period as critical data are available; and, of course, the longer the period, the more reliable the conclusions derived therefrom. Inasmuch as the items measured, such as influent seepage, evaporation, transpiration, pumpage, and other factors vary from year to year, season to season, and even day to day, Meinzer recommends that short-period inventories, which he terms trial balances, be taken monthly[1] or for each wet and dry season.[2] If an inventory period can be selected at the end of which the water table or water level in wells returns to the level at which it stood at the beginning of the period, the increment and decrement for that period are equal (provided compaction due to overpumping does not change the capacity of the reservoir) and evaluation of the factors not susceptible to measurement may be rendered possible.[3]

The general ground-water equation, rainfall = evaporation and transpiration + runoff + ground-water increment, is of little or no value in detailed studies because of the general character of the factors and the difficulties in evaluating them. In each investigation the factors actually important in supplying and removing ground water are determined by collection and

[1] Meinzer, O. E., and N. D. Stearns, A Study of Ground Water in the Pomperaug Basin, Conn., *U.S. Geol. Surv. Water-Supply Paper* 597-B, pp. 73–146, 1928.

[2] Meinzer, O. E., The Source and Disposal of Ground Water in the Mokelumne Area, Calif., pp. 183–189; Supplemental Report to *Water-Supply Paper* 619 (released in manuscript form).

[3] See pp. 495–498.

analysis of the geologic and hydrologic data bearing on the recharge, discharge, and motions of the ground-water body, and the quantity of water in storage at the time the inventory is taken. A special ground-water equation, or equations, are evolved in terms of the factors selected which apply to the particular region under investigation. The list of factors that may be measured and used in the inventory are as follows:

Ground-water increment:

1. Rainfall penetration to the water table.

2. Natural influent seepage from streams, lakes, and ponds.

3. Artificial influent seepage from irrigation, reservoirs, spreading operations, including feeding water down wells.

4. Inflow of free or confined ground water from outside the area investigated.

Ground-water decrement:

1. Effluent seepage and spring flow of free ground water and discharge by surface flow, evaporation and transpiration, or artificial removal by drainage works.

2. Effluent seepage and spring discharge of confined water along faults or slow leakage from the lower portions of aquifers holding confined water.

3. Artificial discharge by pumping.

4. Subsurface discharge of free or confined water from underneath the area.

Only certain of the above-mentioned factors may be important in any one area and occasionally can be determined in several different ways. In the natural state, before artificial draft on ground water has been made by pumping or drainage, equilibrium is generally established between ground-water increment and decrement. If subsurface inflow and outflow beneath the area under investigation are small, influent and effluent seepage are equal. Lowering of the water table by pumping reduces and may completely cut off effluent seepage and therefore the available water may be measured either by influent seepage or by the original effluent seepage.

If the supply is not overpumped, a second equilibrium is reached which is registered by a stationary water level after a considerable period of pumping. The quantity of water that can be pumped without a continued lowering of the water level, therefore, may measure the quantity of water available. Also, as previously stated, a stationary water level in a pumping confined-water well indicates equilibrium between extraction and supply.

It must not be concluded that a considerable lowering of the water table is serious or is detrimental to the water supply. Just as a surface reservoir must be drawn down in order to catch and preserve flood flow, so the subsurface-reservoir level (water table) must be lowered sufficiently to prevent loss by effluent seepage. A decrease in the area of effluent seepage increases the area of influent seepage (absorptive area) and in turn increases the rate of ground-water recharge. A depleted reservoir at the end of the dry season or cycle of dry years is necessary if the water is to be salvaged in the following wet season or cycle. In legal controversies an unreasonable view has been taken in the past in regard to the necessity of maintaining the water table at the "natural level."

A well tapping confined currents of water diverts water escaping from the conduit below the well, which, under natural conditions, often supports a high water table in swamp areas, and lowering of the water table may reclaim the swamp land. Extreme overpumping may salvage water locked up in clays (pages 470 to 472). Of course, unreasonable lowering of the water table or depletion of artesian aquifers may increase the cost of pumping and make ground water unavailable to those who are not financially able to sink deep wells and pump from the greater depths.

In making a ground-water inventory special care is necessary in the selection of the boundaries of the area to which the method is to be applied. If possible, it should consist of a hydrologic and geologic unit and contain a water body the sources and losses of which can be segregated and evaluated. For example, if the water resources of a portion of a piedmont alluvial deposit are to be evaluated, each alluvial cone of the piedmont slope should be selected as a unit. Each cone has an individual feeding stream, the influent seepage capacity of which may differ from those of adjacent cones. Usually poor hydraulic connection exists between the aquifers of adjacent cones. An intermontane valley, a bolson, or a stretch of river valley the surface and subsurface inflow and discharge of which can be evaluated make good "units" for this type of study.

If the water-bearing materials function as a conduit rather than as a reservoir, the quantity of water moving in the conduit can be determined if geologic data (usually derived from well logs) are sufficient to determine the cross-sectional area of the conduit and if the velocity of percolation is known. The latter may be determined by direct measurements of velocity of percolation by electrolytic or dye methods (pages 217–219) or from the hydraulic gradient shown by the static levels of wells piercing the aquifer and permeameter measurements of permeability (pages 207–217). Recently the quantity of water supplied by aquifers consisting of pumice and glass sand was satisfactorily estimated from permeameter measurements of permeability of these formations and from the hydraulic gradient determined from the static level of wells penetrating these strata. The cross-sectional areas of aquifers were determined from geologic cross sections of the region drawn from abundant well-log data and checked by samples collected during the drilling of the wells.[1]

Importance of Water of Compaction.—Recent studies have emphasized the importance of the process of compaction by which silt and clay are converted gradually into hard dense shale.[2] The degree of compaction depends on the type of material and the amount and duration of load. Water must be evacuated before reduction of pore space is possible, and the process of compaction is slow because of resistance to passage of water through and out of the compacting aquicludes.

If noncompacted alluvial-cone deposits are overpumped, the hydraulic pressure in aquifers is reduced in proportion to the lowering of the water level (a lowering of 100 ft. in water level in wells reduces the hydraulic pressure in the aquifers by 43 lb. per square inch). Such reduction of water pressure in the aquifers reduces the hydraulic pressure resisting the squeezing out of water from the aquicludes by the weight of overlying material. Also, as shown by Meinzer,[3] the aquifer is compacted because of reduction in the hydraulic pressure which supports part of

[1] Private unpublished report by C. H. Lee.

[2] ATHY, L. F., Compaction and its Effect on Local Structure, "Problems of Petroleum Geology," A Symposium, Amer. Assoc. Pet. Geol., p. 815, 1934.

[3] MEINZER, O. E., Compressibility and Elasticity of Artesian Aquifers, *Econ. Geol.*, vol. 23, pp. 263–291, 1928.

the weight of the overlying material, and the load on the sand and gravel constituents of the aquifer is thereby increased.

That compaction is a process capable of supplying large amounts of water is indicated by several phenomena observed in connection with overpumping of alluvial cones. (1) Overpumping of confined water in the San Francisquito alluvial cone, Santa Clara County, California, has reversed the normal hydraulic gradient from the hills toward the bay so that the static-pressure level now slopes from San Francisco Bay toward the hills, indicating that ground water is moving from under the bay to the wells and is probably being drawn from the finger ends of the aquifers and out of the surrounding clays (pages 376–377). (2) Spreading operations of the Santa Clara Valley Water Conservation District, Santa Clara County, California, are building up the water level more rapidly than was calculated from specific yield, which was determined by quantity of water pumped and accompanying water-level depression;[1] in other words, specific absorption is less than specific yield. This result suggests that pore space has been decreased during the period of overpumping, and less water is required to restore the water level than was originally abstracted during lowering.[2] (3) The extraordinary sinking of the land in the overpumped area in the Santa Clara Valley is further indication of the extent to which compaction may be induced by overpumping (pages 341–345).

The first ground-water inventory containing a quantitative estimate of water produced by compaction of nonindurated

[1] TIBBETTS, F. H., Water-conservation Project in Santa Clara County, *Trans. Amer. Geophys. Union*, pp. 458–465, 1936.

[2] Specific yield determined by ratio of volume of water pumped to volume of sediments dewatered is increased by compaction, and specific absorption determined by volume of water fed underground to volume of sediments saturated is decreased. Spreading data collected by the Santa Clara Valley Water Conservation District indicate that the volume of sediments saturated by spreading is larger than the volume of sediments previously dewatered by pumping a like quantity of water. This difference may be due in part to slow draining of fine sediments during a long period of overpumping compared with the short recharge period, but the excessive yield compared with absorption is probably due to compaction. However, interpretation of this difference between yield and recharge capacity is complicated by the fact that confined aquifers are dewatered at the intake and spread water is first added to the water table and may have no immediate effect on the water level in pressure wells. A satisfactory and complete interpretation can only be gained after long-continued measurements are available.

alluvial water-bearing materials known to the writer was made by M. B. Smith for the Livermore Valley, Alameda County, California.[1] A summary of some of the results of this investigation appears on pages 495–498.

Development of Inventory Methods.—Up to the present time the methods of making a ground-water inventory have not reached the accuracy necessary to make them acceptable to all investigators. They often require investigations so extensive and long-continued that they cannot be applied except to studies of importance. This work has been carried on extensively by the United States Geological Survey, and to the hydrologists of that organization we are indebted for many of the recent refinements of this type of research. Meinzer has been in charge of this work in recent years and has written the only general summary and discussion of the methods of making a ground-water inventory.[2] Space forbids quoting his contribution in full, but selected quotations and a condensed summary of his discussion of methods of investigation applicable to making a ground-water inventory are given. His excellent bibliography and also references to discussions in this text are included to assist those engaged in this work in finding detailed descriptions of methods successfully applied in the past.

The making of a ground-water inventory may involve all methods of hydrologic research; therefore this chapter is a summary review of the practical value of data treated in this text and in ground-water literature.

SUMMARY OF METHODS FOR ESTIMATING GROUND-WATER SUPPLIES

"The most urgent problems in ground-water hydrology at present are those relating to the rate at which the rock formations will supply water to wells in specified areas—not during a day, a month, or a year but perennially. The permeable rock formations may be regarded as underground reservoirs or as underground conduits. Some water-bearing formations function chiefly as reservoirs, others chiefly as conduits, but all of them

---

[1] SMITH, M. B., Ground Water in the Livermore Valley, California, Master's Thesis, Stanford University, May, 1934.

[2] MEINZER, O. E., Outline of Methods for Estimating Ground-water Supplies, *U.S. Geol. Surv. Water-Supply Paper* 638-C, 1932.

have some of the properties of both. . . . Quantitative methods based on the reservoir conception are applicable chiefly, though not exclusively, to formations or parts of formations that have water tables; methods based on the conduit conception are applicable most largely to artesian formations, in which the water moves laterally considerable distances from the intake to the discharge area.

Methods Based on Concept of Formations as Reservoirs

"The natural reservoirs formed by rock formations generally have very great capacity compared with that of ordinary artificial surface reservoirs, just as most other natural features are of huge size in contrast to the works of man. However, if the water derived from them is taken chiefly out of storage without being replaced the supply will eventually fail.

"The 'safe yield' of an underground reservoir, or the practicable rate of withdrawing water from it perennially for human use, may be estimated by methods that are comparable to those used in estimating the safe yield of a surface reservoir, although different in technique. It is necessary to measure the rate of inflow (intake methods) or the rate of discharge (discharge methods), or else these rates must be estimated by determining changes in storage (water table or storage methods).[1] In many areas the most effective method of studying the ground-water supply is the inventory method, in which all available methods are used to make periodic inventories of the entire water supply of the area, from its entrance into the area as precipitation, stream flow, or underground percolation to its exit as evaporation, transpiration, runoff, or underground leakage."

Intake from Surface Streams.[2]—"The principal intake method consists of establishing gaging stations on influent streams and

[1] MEINZER, O. E., Quantitative Methods of Estimating Ground-water Supplies, *Geol. Soc. Amer. Bull.*, vol. 31, pp. 329–338, 1920.

[2] Experimental determinations of stream seepage are described in the following references. Bailey developed curves and an empirical formula for computing recharge from records of stream flow and temperature.

BAILEY, PAUL, Engineering Investigation of Percolation from Alameda Creek and Ground-water Studies on Niles Cone, *Calif. State Water Comm. 3d Bienn. Rept.*, pp. 95–131, 1921.

CLAPP, W. B., in J. C. HOYT, Report of Progress of Stream Measurements for the Calendar Year 1903, pt. 4, Interior Basin, Pacific, and Hudson

determining the quantities of water lost between successive stations. The quantity of water that reaches the water table consists of this amount minus the loss by evaporation and transpiration either directly from the stream or from soil moisture supplied by the stream . . . " The seepage method gives the most reliable results for streams with relatively constant flow and with heavy losses in proportion to the total flow. " . . . It is generally not applicable in times of flood, when the measurements of flow are relatively inaccurate and the percentage of loss is small. It is not applicable or only difficultly applicable to perennial streams in which the loss is small in comparison to the total flow, because with such streams small percentage errors in the measurements of the flow may produce large percentage errors in the computed seepage losses. [It is not applicable] . . . for determining recharge from intermittent and ephemeral streams and is wholly inapplicable for determining recharge directly from rain or melting snow. In humid regions almost no streams except the ephemeral ones are influent, and therefore this method obviously has little application . . . "

Intake Directly from Rain and Melting Snow.—Mariotté[1] in the seventeenth century measured influent seepage from rainfall

---

Bay Drainage, *U.S. Geol. Surv. Water-Supply Paper* 100, pp. 339–356, 1904.

CONKLING, HAROLD, San Gabriel Investigation, *Calif. Dept. Pub. Works Div. Water Rights Bull.* 5, pp. 52–72, 1927.

GRUNSKY, C. E., Irrigation Near Fresno, Calif., *U.S. Geol. Survey Water-Supply Paper* 18, pp. 71–79, 1898.

LEE, C. H., An Intensive Study of the Water Resources of a Part of Owens Valley, Calif., *U.S. Geol. Surv. Water-Supply Paper* 294, 1912.

MENDENHALL, W. C., The Hydrology of San Bernardino Valley, Calif., *U.S. Geol. Surv. Water-Supply Paper* 142, pp. 50, 51, 1905; Ground Waters and Irrigation Enterprises in the Foothill Belt, Southern California, *U.S. Geol. Surv. Water-Supply Paper* 219, pp. 28, 29, 1908.

POST, W. S., Santa Ana Investigation, Flood Control and Conservation, *Calif. Dept. Pub. Works Div. Eng. Irrig. Bull.* 19, pp. 165–179, 1929.

PRITCHETT, H. C., and others, Seepage Loss and Gain of the Mokelumne River, Calif., *U.S. Dept. Int. Memo for Press*, Release for June 5, 1934.

SMITH, G. E. P., Ground-water Supply and Irrigation in the Rillito Valley, *Ariz. Univ. Agr. Exp. Sta. Bull.* 64, pp. 118, 119, 1910.

WHITE, W. N., Preliminary Report on the Ground-water Supply of Mimbres Valley, N. Mex., *U.S. Geol. Surv. Water-Supply Paper* 637, pp. 77–80, 1931.

[1] MARIOTTÉ, EDMÉ, Traités du mouvements des eaux et des autres corp fluides, 1686.

(pages 18–19). Lysimeters and other methods of measuring influent seepage are described on pages 164–171. " . . . Since Mariotté's work the most common method of estimating ground-water recharge has probably been to determine approximately the quantity of water that annually falls as rain or snow on a given area and apply to this quantity the percentage that is assumed to reach the zone of saturation. This method is of little value, however, except to give an idea of the maximum possibilities, unless there is a reliable basis for the percentage that is assumed. Commonly the assumed percentage and therefore also the computed recharge are much too large.

"Attempts have been made to compute the recharge in an intake area by deducting the runoff and the evaporation (including transpiration) from the precipitation, but the results have generally been unreliable, especially because of uncertainty as to the amount of evaporation and transpiration[1] (pages 84–92). . . . "

In a detailed study by Blaney estimated quantities of runoff, evaporation and transpiration were deducted from rainfall. " . . . Tests of soil moisture proved that the remaining water was stored in the soil to satisfy the deficiency of soil moisture in the root zone. After this deficiency had been completely supplied and the soil moisture had been brought up to the specific retention, or quantity of water that the soil can hold by molecular

---

[1] Recent studies include the following:

BLANEY, H. F., Disposal of Rainfall, in Post, W. S., Santa Ana Investigation, *op. cit*, pp. 152–157.

BLANEY, H F., and others, Rainfall Penetration and Consumptive Use of Water in Santa Ana River Valley and Coastal Plain, *Calif. Div. Water Res. Bull.* 33, 1931.

KUNESH, J. E., Surface, Spring, and Tunnel Water Investigations, *Honolulu Sewer and Water Comm. Rept.*, pp. 85–92, 1929.

McCOMBS, JOHN, Methods of Estimating Safe Yield of Honolulu Artesian Area, *Honolulu Sewer and Water Comm. Rept.*, pp. 55–61, 1927.

SONDEREGGER, A. L., Water Supply from Rainfall on Valley Floors, *Am. Soc. Civ. Eng. Proc.*, vol. 55, pp. 1144–1150, 1929.

STEARNS, H. T., T. W. ROBINSON, and G. H. TAYLOR, Geology and Water Resources of the Mokelumne Area, Calif., *U.S. Geol. Surv. Water-Supply Paper* 619, pp. 174, 175, 1930; also more recent report released in manuscript form (on file in public library, Lodi, Calif.).

TAYLOR, G. H., Investigations Relating to the Absorption of Precipitation and its Penetration to the Zone of Saturation, *Amer. Geophys. Union Trans.*, pp. 206–211, 1931.

attraction against the pull of gravity, any remaining surplus was assumed to (seep) downward beyond the reach of plant roots and ultimately to reach the water table . . . "

"The method of following the movements of water in the soil by making periodic borings with soil augers and determining the moisture content of soil samples obtained from different depths has been extensively used in connection with agricultural investigations and less frequently to determine the ground-water recharge."

Discharge by Overflow.—"An underground reservoir, like a surface reservoir, may lose water by overflow, evaporation, diversion, and underground leakage. The overflow of an underground reservoir may appear in definite springs or in general seepage that contributes to the flow of the surface streams. If it appears in a few large and definite springs the ground-water discharge can be determined by measuring the flow of these springs. If the springs are relatively constant, it may be sufficient to make occasional measurements with current-meter, weir, or other device; if they are relatively variable it may be necessary to establish gaging stations in order to obtain records of daily or continuous rate of flow . . . [1]"

"If the overflow of the underground reservoir appears in many small, widely scattered springs or in general seepage, its quantity may be estimated by establishing gaging stations on the effluent streams to measure the total runoff and then differentiating between the two components of the total—the direct runoff and the ground-water runoff. This differentiation can best be made by studying small representative drainage basins rather than by gaging the trunk stream of a large drainage basin, because the large basin is likely to have more frequent rainfall in some parts of its area and a longer and less definite period for complete delivery of the direct runoff."

A gaging station was established near the mouth of the Pomperaug River, Connecticut,[2] and from consideration of

[1] The following references describe spring-flow gaging:

CRANDALL, LYNN, The Springs of Snake River Canyon, *Idaho Irr. Eng. Agr. Soc. Joint Confer., Proc.*, pp. 146–150, 1918–1919.

MEINZER, O. E., Large Springs in the United States, *U.S. Geol. Surv. Water-Supply Paper 557*, pp. 17–41, 42–47, 1927.

[2] MEINZER, O. E., and N. D. STEARNS, A Study of Ground Water in the

channel storage, velocity of flow, and rate of movement of flood crests it was concluded that " . . . the direct runoff is nearly all delivered from the basin within a week of the time the water falls as rain, and that therefore the stream flow a week or more after the latest rain is virtually all derived from ground water. A hydrograph was constructed of the total runoff for the years covered by the investigation, 1913 to 1916, and a hydrograph of the ground-water runoff was then made which coincided with that for total runoff in periods of prolonged fair weather and was interpolated between these periods. The ground-water runoff was computed from this hydrograph . . . "[1]

An evaluation of the channel-storage method of estimating ground-water overflow is discussed by Meinzer[2] as follows:

"The channel-storage method is based on the simple law that in any period when there is no overland runoff, that is when no storm or snow-water is running into the stream system from the surface, the quantity of water derived by effluent seepage into a given stream system equals the quantity of water discharged from the stream system minus the decrease or plus the increase in channel storage during the same interval. The law thus stated does not take into account the quantities of stream water that are lost during the period by evaporation from the stream system. If any part of the stream system is influent, the law gives the net effluent seepage. It includes the seepage derived from bank storage, perched ground water, and spring flow.

Discharge by Evaporation and Transpiration.—"Where the water table is near the surface the underground reservoir loses water by evaporation from the soil and by transpiration from plants. In some arid regions all or nearly all the ground water is disposed of in this way, and little or no water remains to be discharged through springs and seeps. In humid regions, however, the ground-water recharge is greater, and more soil moisture is supplied directly by the rains and melting snow, with the result that evaporation from the soil and transpiration from plants

---

Pomperaug Basin, Conn., with Special Reference to Intake and Discharge, *U.S. Geol. Surv. Water-Supply Paper* 597, pp. 107–116, pl. 19, 1929.

[1] This general method was used earlier by I. E. Houk, Rainfall and Runoff in Miami Valley, Ohio, *Miami Conserv. Dist. Tech. Repts.*, pt. 8, 1921.

[2] MEINZER, O. E., and others, The Channel-Storage Method of Determining Effluent Seepage, *Amer. Geophys. Union Trans.*, pp. 415–418, 1936.

make less heavy demands on the ground water. For these reasons in humid regions there is generally an excess of ground-water discharge over the consumption by soil evaporation and transpiration, and this excess feeds the streams and maintains their flow during dry seasons.[1]"

"Not much work has yet been done to establish the relations of the rate of soil evaporation to the factors that determine the rate. In most tank experiments data are obtained as to the atmospheric conditions and the depth to the water table, which give some basis for generalizations as to the variations of soil evaporation with variations in these factors. Generally records are also obtained of the rate of evaporation from a free water surface, so that the data as to soil evaporation can be expressed in terms of evaporation opportunity, or ratio of soil evaporation to evaporation from a free water surface. [Sleight made mechanical analyses of five soils used in evaporation tests, and] these analyses gave a basis for determining the evaporation opportunity for different sizes of grain with each of several depths to the water table. It is desirable that in future tank experiment tests be made of the mechanical composition, porosity, permeability, and capillary range of the soils used.

"The rate at which soil discharge occurs may be controlled either by the rate at which the water can be lifted by capillarity to the level at which it is evaporated or by the rate at which it can be evaporated. The rate at which water is lifted through the soil from the water table to the point at which it is evaporated depends chiefly on the permeability of the soil, the height the water is lifted, and the capillary head or difference between the potential and actual capillary lift. In other words, the law of

[1] Tests of rate of ground-water discharge by capillary rise and evaporation from the soil are described in the following publications. The investigations of Lee and White are described in this text, pages 86–88 and 89–92.

LEE, C. H., An Intensive Study of the Water Resources of a Part of Owens Valley, Calif., *U.S. Geol. Surv. Water-Supply Paper* 294, pp. 57, 119, pl. 15, 1912.

SLEIGHT, R. B., Evaporation from the Surfaces of Water and River-bed Materials, *Jour. Agr. Res.*, vol. 10, pp. 209–261, 1917.

SLICHTER, C. S., The Underflow in Arkansas Valley in Western Kansas, *U.S. Geol. Surv. Water-Supply Paper* 153, pp. 43, 44, 1906.

WHITE, W. N., A Method of Estimating Ground-water Supplies based on Discharge of Plants and Evaporation from Soil; Results of Investigations in Escalante Valley, Utah, *U.S. Geol. Surv. Water-Supply Paper* 659-A, 1932.

capillary rise is essentially Darcy's law of flow, in which the energy is furnished by capillary attraction instead of by hydrostatic head. Therefore, if the water table is very near the surface and the soil is very permeable, the rate of discharge is determined by the possible rate of evaporation; but if the water table is at greater depth and the soil is less permeable, the limiting factor may be the possible rate of capillary rise. Further investigation of the processes involved in soil discharge and of the controlling laws should help to make the field methods more applicable and exact.

"As a rule, vegetal discharge, which is effected by transpiration, is greater than soil discharge and occurs over wider areas, because the roots of certain plants lift water much higher than it is lifted by the capillary interstices of the soil. In arid regions nearly all the vegetal discharge of ground water is accomplished by plants of a few dominant and well-recognized species.[1] To determine the quantity of ground water discharged by the ground-water plants in any particular area it is necessary to make a map of the area showing, so far as may be practicable, the distribution, density, and growth of the principal species, and to determine the rate at which they discharge water.[2] Holes should also be dug to investigate the root habits of different species of plants and to determine to what depths their roots

---

[1] MEINZER, *Water-Supply Paper 577, op. cit.*, p. 1.

[2] Maps showing areas of ground-water discharge and distribution of dominant species of ground-water plants appear in the following publications. Information regarding construction of such maps is given in *Water-Supply Papers* 423, pp. 92–102, and 577.

CLARK, W. O., and C. W. RIDDELL, Exploratory Drilling for Water and Use of Ground Water for Irrigation in Steptoe Valley, Nev., *U.S. Geol. Surv. Water-Supply Paper* 467, pl. 2, 1920.

LEE, C. H., An Intensive Study of the Water Resources of a Part of Owens Valley, Calif., *U.S. Geol. Surv. Water-Supply Paper* 294, pl. 25.

MEINZER, O. E., and F. C. KELTON, Geology and Water Resources of Sulphur Springs Valley, Ariz., *U.S. Geol. Surv. Water-Supply Paper* 320, pls. 1, 2.

MEINZER, O. E., Geology and Water Resources of Big Smoky, Clayton, and Alkali Springs Valleys, Nev., *U.S. Geol. Surv. Water-Supply Paper* 423, pl. 2, 1917.

MEINZER, O. E., Plants as Indicators of Ground Water, *U.S. Geol. Surv. Water-Supply Paper* 577, 1927.

WHITE, W. N., *Water-Supply Paper 659-A, op. cit.*, pl. 1.

extend to reach the capillary fringe and feed on water from the zone of saturation."

"The rate of vegetal discharge has generally been determined by means of tanks in which the different species are grown with measured quantities of water and in some investigations with different depths to the water table. . . .[1] The method was also introduced of obtaining the dry weight of vegetable matter produced in the tank experiments and determining the ratio of weight of water consumed to weight of dry matter produced. This ratio was then applied to data on dry matter naturally produced in order to compute the natural discharge of ground water. . . . "[2]

Storage Methods in General.—"If a capacity table or curve has been developed for a surface reservoir, a gage showing the changes in its water level will indicate for any period the net increase or decrease in storage. When the water level is rising it will register the excess in rate of recharge over rate of discharge, and vice versa. If it is known that there is no discharge in a certain period the record of rise will show the total rate of recharge during that period.

"Because of the frictional resistance of water-bearing materials to the flow of the water from the intake to the discharge area of an underground reservoir the water table is almost nowhere a level surface, such as the water surface of an ordinary reservoir. Therefore, when this storage method is applied to underground reservoirs the depths to the water level in numerous wells are measured every week or month, or at other more or less frequent intervals, and continuous records are generally obtained on a few representative wells by means of automatic water-stage recorders. Levels are usually run to the observation wells, and a series of contour maps of the water table at successive dates are constructed. From these maps or from the base data it is possible to compute the volume of water-bearing material that became saturated or drained in a given period.[3]

[1] Important investigations of this type are described in:

LEE, C. H., Evaporation and Transpiration with Special Reference to a Salt-water Barrier: Appendix *C*, pp. 247–307, *State of Calif., Div. Water Res. Bull.* 28, 1931.

WHITE, *Water-Supply Paper 659-A, op. cit.*, pp. 64–71.

[2] LEE, *Water-Supply Paper 294, op. cit.*, pp. 62–63.

[3] Investigations of water-level fluctuations are described in the following

"In order to evaluate these results in terms of water instead of water-bearing material it is necessary to apply a factor generally known as the specific yield. This factor represents the interstitial space that is emptied when the water table declines, expressed as a percentage of the total volume of material that is dewatered. The same factor generally represents the space that is occupied by water going into storage when the water table rises. If, however, the material into which the water rises has been further desiccated by soil evaporation or vegetal discharge the amount of recharge is greater for each unit of rise.

"The water level in a well is sensitive to every force that acts upon the body of water with which the well communicates. Hence, in most wells the water level fluctuates almost constantly, often in a complicated manner. The curve produced by an automatic water-stage recorder over a well gives an accurate record of the resultant of the forces that act upon the ground water. A well that extends only slightly below the water table generally records faithfully both recharge and discharge, but great care must be taken in applying this method to use only wells in which the water level is a continuation of the water table and not the upper surface of a column of water that is supported by artesian pressure in the water-bearing formation and that therefore fluctuates as a result of atmospheric or other changes in pressure. Even in a true water-table well there may be fluctuations produced by changes in temperature which affect

references (see also pages 257–259 of this text):

Amer. Geophys. Union Trans., Symposium on Fluctuation of Ground-water Levels, pp. 337–390, 1936.

CLARK, W. O., Ground-water Resources of Niles cone and Adjacent Areas, Calif., *U.S. Geol. Surv. Water-Supply Paper* 345, pp. 149–162, pl. 10, 1915; Ground Water for Irrigation in the Morgan Hill Area, Calif., *U.S. Geol. Surv. Water-Supply Paper* 400, pp. 66–68, 76–105, pls. 6, 7, 1917; Ground Water in Santa Clara Valley, Calif., *U.S. Geol. Surv. Water-Supply Paper* 519, pp. 58–75, 129–183, pls. 10–19, 1924.

ELLIS, A. J., and C. H. LEE, Geology and Ground Waters of the Western Part of San Diego County, Calif., *U.S. Geol. Surv. Water-Supply Paper* 446, pp. 121–155, pls. 20–25, 1919.

STEARNS, H. T., T. W. ROBINSON, and G. H. TAYLOR, Geology and Water Resources of the Mokelumne Area, California, *U.S. Geol. Surv. Water-Supply Paper* 619, pp. 112–172, 185–188, 292–398, pls. 6–8, 13, 1930; also later report released in manuscript form (on file in public library, Lodi, Calif.).

capillarity, by confinement of air in the interstices of the overlying zone of aeration by rain or frozen ground, or by other
causes that have nothing to do with recharge or discharge (page
258)."

[In investigations of water-level fluctuation measurements were
made of water levels in wells], " . . . data were obtained for
estimating the specific yield, maps were prepared showing the
contours of the water table at different dates, and computations
were made of the seasonal increase in storage represented by
the rise in the water table.   More recently the same method has
been used in making computations of net semiannual additions
of water to or removals of water from the underground reservoir.
. . . On account of uncertainties as to the specific yield and as
to pressure effects in observation wells there may be large
percentage errors in the computed recharge in all these investigations, and in the present stage of development of this
method it is impossible even to state what may be the limits
of error."

Specific Yield in Relation to Storage Methods.—"Perhaps
the greatest difficulty in the application of quantitative methods
lies in the variability in the texture and hence in the hydrologic
properties of the water-bearing materials. The hydrologic
properties vary greatly, even with apparently slight differences
in texture. Hence the ordinary geologic descriptions are quite
inadequate for hydrologic purposes, and quantitative descriptions based on laboratory determinations have become essential.
However, the hard rocks that yield their water largely from
joints or crevices are not amenable to laboratory tests, and the
incoherent materials are difficult to handle without disturbing
and repacking, which may considerably change their texture
and hydrologic properties.

"The two hydrologic properties of greatest significance are
specific yield and permeability. Mechanical analyses and determinations of porosity and moisture equivalent are useful chiefly
as indirect means of determining these two essential hydrologic
properties. Any quantitative method that does not involve
either of these properties has a great advantage in avoiding the
complications that result from the heterogeneity of the water-
bearing materials. Most storage methods involve the perplexing
problem of specific yield."

Seven methods to determine specific yield are described by Meinzer[1] and are summarized briefly in the following pages.

1. "*The laboratory saturation and drainage method* consists of draining high columns of saturated materials by gravity and determining both the volume of material drained and the volume of water yielded. The volume of water yielded can be measured directly or can be computed from the porosity and the moisture content after draining. The columns must be high enough to avoid the vitiating effects of the capillary fringe, and care must be taken to prevent loss by evaporation. As molecular forces vary with the temperature of the water, the tests must be made at a uniform temperature, or corrections for temperature must be applied. As drainage continues for a long time at a diminishing rate, the specific yield should be determined for specified periods of draining. If the material is fine, appreciable drainage may occur during a period of several weeks."[2]

2. "*The method of field saturation and drainage* is similar in principle to the laboratory method. A plot of land is selected where the water table and capillary fringe are at sufficient depth below the surface. The material underlying the plot is thoroughly wetted by applying water at the surface and is then allowed to drain, care being taken to avoid much evaporation. After a sufficient period of draining, samples are taken for determination of moisture content and porosity, and the specific yield

[1] MEINZER, O. E., The Occurrence of Ground Water in the United States, with a Discussion of Principles, *U.S. Geol. Surv. Water-Supply Paper* 489, pp. 67–76, 1923; *Water-Supply Paper* 638-C, *op. cit.*, pp. 113–114.

[2] This method has been used by the following investigators. See also pp. 200–204, 207–213 of this text.

HAZEN, ALLEN, Experiments upon the Purification of Sewage and Water at the Lawrence Experiment Station, *Mass. Board of Health 23d Ann. Rept.*, pp. 428–434, 1892.

KING, F. H., Principles and Conditions of the Movements of Ground Water, *U.S. Geol. Survey 19th Ann. Rept.*, pt. 2, pp. 86–91, 1899.

MEINZER, O. E., *Water-Supply Paper* 489, *op. cit.*, pp. 53–57, 1923. This paper gives a concise presentation and discussion of the Hazen and King experiments.

STEARNS, H. T., T. W. ROBINSON, and G. H. TAYLOR, Geology and Water Resources of the Mokelumne Area, Calif., *U.S. Geol. Surv. Water-Supply Paper* 619, pp. 151–172, 1930.

WHITE, *Water-Supply Paper* 659-A, *op. cit.*, pp. 74–76.

is computed as the difference between these two.[1] . . . If the
specific yield of material below the soil that is more representative
of the water-bearing material is desired, it is necessary to apply
enough water to wet this deeper material and to obtain samples
from it.   In some situations it might be advantageous to dig
pits to the material to be tested.

3. "In the *direct sampling method* samples are obtained by
boring into the material immediately above the capillary fringe
after the water table has declined appreciably, and the moisture
content and porosity of the samples are determined.[2] . . . The
essential feature in this method is to take a sample where the
water table has gone down, as it generally does during the dry
summer season in California.   For the most conclusive results
the sample should be taken from a point which in the preceding
wet season was below the water table and which at the time of
taking the sample is far enough above the water table not to be
seriously affected by the capillary fringe.   Where the fluctuation
of the water table is less than the thickness of the capillary fringe
the most significant samples are those taken just above the fringe.
As in practice this position can not be very definitely determined,
it is advisable to take samples at several levels, as was done by
Lee.   In making tests of this kind it is essential to ascertain that
the part of the deposit from which the sample is taken has not
received any recent contribution of water from rain or irrigation
and has not been exposed to evaporation or to absorption by
plants, both of which consume water that is retained against
gravity by molecular attraction.

4. "The *pumping method* consists in observing the lowering
of the water table and hence the volume of sediments drained
by pumping a measured volume of water.   The specific yield
is, of course, the ratio of the volume of water pumped to the
volume of material drained.   Serious errors may be introduced
by pumped water returning to the water table and by other

[1] This method used by Israelson and other soil scientists.

ISRAELSON, O. W., Studies in Capacities of Soils for Irrigation Water,
Jour. Agr. Research, vol. 13, pp. 1–28, Apr. 1, 1918.

[2] The direct sampling method was employed by A. J. Ellis and C. H. Lee,
Geology and Ground Waters of the Western Part of San Diego County,
Calif., *U.S. Geol. Surv. Water-Supply Paper* 446, pp. 121–123, 1919.

percolation into or out of that part of the underground reservoir which is supplying the pumped water. . . . [1]

5. "The *recharge method*, which is the converse of the pumping method, consists of observations on the seepage losses from streams or canals and on the resultant rise of the water table, from which is computed the volume of material saturated. It is, of course, merely the storage method of determining recharge, with the specific yield instead of the quantity of water as the unknown factor.

6-7. "The *moisture-equivalent and mechanical-analysis methods* are based on investigations by Briggs, Veihmeyer, and others[2] on the relations between the moisture equivalent or mechanical composition of the water-bearing materials, on one hand, and the specific retention, on the other hand. The specific yield is computed as the difference between porosity and specific retention as determined by one of these indirect methods. Both of these methods are valuable, at least in giving a general check on the results from other methods, and they deserve further investigation."

A refinement of the seventh method was developed by Eckis[3] in his investigation of the South Coastal basin of California. He averaged calculated specific yield of water-bearing materials in combined groups of well logs.

Estimates of Discharge from Daily Water-table Fluctuations.— In most localities in which plants draw water from the zone of saturation there are daily fluctuations of the water table, ranging

[1] The pumping method is applicable in areas having heavy seasonal pumpage from unconfined ground water and was used by W. O. Clark, Ground Water for Irrigation in the Morgan Hill Area, Calif., *U.S. Geol. Surv. Water-Supply Paper* 400, pp. 84–86, 1917.

[2] BRIGGS, L. J., and J. W. McLANE, The Moisture Equivalent of Soils, *U.S. Dept. Agr. Bur. Soils Bull.* 45, 1907; BRIGGS and H. L. SHANTZ, The Wilting Coefficient for Different Plants and Its Indirect Determination, *U.S. Dept. Agr. Bur. Plant Ind. Bull.* 230, 1912; BRIGGS, MARTIN and PEARCE, The Centrifugal Method of Mechanical Soil Analysis, *U.S. Dept. Agr. Bur. Soils Bull.* 24, 1904; VEIHMEYER, F. J., and A. H. HENDRICKSON, The Moisture Equivalent as a Measure of the Field Capacity of Soils, *Soil Sci.*, vol. 32, pp. 181–194, 1931.

[3] ECKIS, R., South Coastal Basin Investigations: Geology and Ground-water Storage Capacity of Valley Fill, *State of Calif., Div. Water Res. Bull.* 45, pp. 109–114, 1934.

from a small fraction of an inch to several inches. Water-stage recorders are used to obtain curves of these fluctuations[1] and from these the rate of ground-water discharge is calculated.

Ground-water Rating Curve.—"In the Pomperaug investigation weekly measurements were made of the depths to the water levels in a number of observation wells, and the average depth for each week was plotted against the corresponding ground-water runoff. It was, of course, found that the runoff for a given stage of the water table was much less in summer, when vegetal discharge and soil evaporation were active, than in the colder part of the year, when there was very little loss by these processes. A curve was drawn through or near the coordinate points for winter weeks, according to the empiric method used in making rating curves for surface streams. This gave a rating curve for ground-water runoff during the winter. It was hoped that the curve would show approximately the total ground-water discharge in summer and that the ground-water evaporation could be obtained by subtracting the ground-water runoff from the total discharge as shown by the curve. In fact, however, this difference seems to give minimum rather than actual figures for ground-water evaporation, because the roots of plants and the soil capillaries do not wait for the water to appear at the surface but pump it up from some depth.[2] Further investigation will be required to determine whether it will be practicable under any circumstances to use the stage of the water table as an index either of ground-water runoff or of total ground-water discharge."

Safe Yield Compared with Natural Intake and Discharge.— "The safe yield of a water-bearing formation, or the practicable rate of withdrawing water from it perennially for human use, may be either greater or less than the rate of natural recharge or discharge as determined before heavy withdrawals are begun.

---

[1] This method was applied in the following studies (see also pp. 85–92).

SMITH, G. E. P., The Effect of Transpiration of Trees on the Ground-water Supply (unpublished). See *Wash. Acad. Sci. Jour.*, vol. 14, p. 160, 1924.

TROXELL, H. C., The Diurnal Fluctuation in the Ground-water and Flow of the Santa Ana River and its Meaning, *Trans. Amer. Geophys. Union*, pp. 496–504, 1936.

WHITE, *Water-Supply Paper 659-A, op. cit.*, pp. 20–61; Notes in Regard to Work in Escalante Valley *U.S. Geol. Surv. Water-Res. Bull.*, pp. 22–29, Mar. 10, 1927; see also *Wash. Acad. Sci. Jour.*, vol. 17, pp. 238–240, 1927

[2] MEINZER, and STEARNS, *Water-Supply Paper 597-B, op. cit.*, Fig. 13.

It may be less because natural discharge can not be wholly prevented, even by heavy withdrawals through wells. On the other hand, it may be greater because of artificial increase of the rate of recharge."

"In order to utilize fully the flow of a stream, storage is required to hold the excess water of high stages for use in times of small flow or whenever there may be need for the water. Many of the underground reservoirs are so large that they have capacity to carry over great quantities of water not only from a wet season to the following dry season but also from a period of wet years to a period of dry years. However, to utilize these reservoirs fully it is necessary to pump enough water out of them to make room for all the inflow during the wettest seasons and during the periods of successive years of heavy precipitation. This was well illustrated by some of the underground reservoirs of southern California, whose water tables, under heavy pumping for irrigation, went down a little lower each summer than they had risen in the previous winter, until it appeared that excessive depletion must inevitably compel reduction in irrigation. Then came a period of wet winters when recharge occurred to a remarkable extent and the water levels rose beyond all expectations."[1,2]

"Artificial recharge can be accomplished in some places by draining surface water into wells, spreading it over tracts underlain by permeable material, temporarily storing it in leaky reservoirs from which it may percolate to the water table, or storing it in relatively tight reservoirs from which it is released as fast as it can seep into the stream bed below the reservoir . . . "[3]

Storage Methods Applied Where Use Has Become Large.— "If an underground reservoir is heavily pumped, a study of the relations of the water levels to the amount of pumpage is likely to give more reliable information as to the safe yield than can be obtained by any method of studying an undeveloped reservoir.

[1] This principle of increasing recharge by use was recognized by G. E. P. Smith, *op. cit.*, p. 189; and H. C. Wolff, The Utilization of the Underflow near St. Francis, Kans., *U.S. Geol. Surv. Water-Supply Paper* 258, pp. 104–107, 1911.

[2] EBERT, F. C., Records of Water Levels in Wells in Southern California, *U.S. Geol. Surv. Water-Supply Paper* 468, pls. 2, 3, 4, 1921.

[3] See pp. 173 to 187 for discussion of spreading operations and pp. 188 to 189 for comprehensive list of references on various methods of artificial recharge.

If the water levels in the wells remain virtually stationary during a considerable period of pumping it may be concluded that during this period the rate of recharge has been about equal to the rate of discharge, including both natural discharge and withdrawals from wells . . ."[1]

"Regardless of the manner in which the water levels fluctuate, if at the end of any period they return approximately to the position they had at the beginning of the period, the record of pumping furnishes a measure of the recharge during the same period minus the natural loss[2] . . ." neglecting water furnished by compaction (pages 495–498).

"The great advantage in basing computations on a period of stationary water levels or on a period in which the water levels are about the same at the end as at the beginning of the period is that there is no net withdrawal from or addition to the storage, and consequently the specific yield of the water-bearing material is not involved. If, however, the water table declines persistently or if it is desired to make monthly or annual estimates of the recharge, it becomes necessary to determine the specific yield or at least the capacity of the underground reservoir for each foot of saturation within the belt through which the water table migrates. In regions that have distinct wet and dry seasons, such as California and parts of the Hawaiian Islands, the recharge during the dry season may be negligible in quantity. If natural discharge has become relatively small, the pumpage in the dry season may therefore represent approximately the reduction in storage. If both the pumpage and the average decline of the water table are known, the approximate capacity of the underground reservoir for each foot of depth can be computed, and this figure can be used in computations of recharge during the wet season . . . "[3]

Leakage Methods.—"In some places there is good evidence of leakage from one underground reservoir into another. If the leakage occurs as underflow through a relatively definite underground channel, it can be estimated by one of the conduit

[1] This principle was utilized by W. C. Mendenhall, The Hydrology of San Bernardino Valley, Calif., *U.S. Geol. Surv. Water-Supply Paper* 142, pp. 56–67, 1905.

[2] See inventory of ground-water supply of Niles cone; Bailey *op. cit.*, pp. 105–106.

[3] Method used by McCombs, *op. cit.*, pp. 61–65.

methods described . . . (in following pages). If, however, the leakage occurs by percolation through the rocks at considerable depths it may be quite impracticable to estimate the quantity of water that is lost . . . ''[1]

Methods Based on Concept of Formations as Conduits

"Ground water travels laterally from the intake areas to the discharge areas. On account of the viscosity of the water and the small size of the interstices of the water-bearing material through which it usually percolates, there is a very appreciable resistance to its flow. Hence the rate of recharge is controlled not only by the intake facilities and the quantity of surface water that reaches the intake area but also by the capacity of the formation to carry water from the intake area to the area of natural discharge or to the wells where the water supply is to be recovered. If the distance from the intake area to the discharge area is great, as it is in some of the large artesian basins, the problem of safe yield relates to the capacity of the formation as a conduit rather than to its capacity as a reservoir. Quantitative methods are therefore required to estimate the transmission capacities of water-bearing formations."

Field Tests of Velocity.—Direct measurement of velocity of percolation in conduits can be made by Thiem's salt method, Slichter's electrolytic method, or by dye methods (pages 217–219).[2] To estimate by electrolytic, channel, or dye methods

[1] Descriptions of leakage methods appear in:

SLICHTER, C. S., Observations on the Ground Waters of Rio Grande Valley, *U.S. Geol. Surv. Water-Supply Paper* 141, pp. 9–13, 1905.

MEINZER, O. E., *Water-Supply Paper* 423, *op. cit.*, pp. 147–150.

McCOMBS, JOHN, and A. G. FIEDLER, Methods of Exploring and Repairing Leaky Artesian Wells, *U.S. Geol. Surv. Water-Supply Paper* 596, pp. 1–32, 1927.

[2] Determination of velocity of percolation by these methods is described in the following publications:

A. Thiem Method:

THIEM, A., Verfahren für Messung natürlicher Grundwassergeschwindigkeiten, *Poly. Notizblatt*, vol. 42, p. 229, 1887.

SLICHTER, C. S., Theoretical Investigation of the Motion of Ground Waters, *U.S. Geol. Surv. 19th Ann. Rept.*, pt. II, pp. 297–384, 1898; The Motions of Underground Waters, *U.S. Geol. Surv. Water-Supply Paper* 67, pp. 46–48, 1902.

the quantity of water moving it is necessary to ascertain with some degree of accuracy the cross section through which water percolates, the velocity of movement through each unit of cross section[1] and the effective porosity of the formation (pages 215–217).

Channel Underflow Measured by Water-table Slope and Effluent Seepage.—A method has recently been proposed[2] for estimating the quantity of ground water moving through a channel filled with pervious alluvium underlain by impervious bedrock, without determination of velocity, permeability, or cross-sectional area. Ground water moving under the San Gabriel Valley converges and passes through the Whittier narrows where the alluvium is

---

Electrolytic Method:

SLICHTER, *Water-Supply Paper* 67, *op. cit.*; The Underflow in Arkansas Valley in Western Kansas, *U.S. Geol. Surv. Water-Supply Paper* 153, 1906; Field Measurements of the Rate of Movement of Underground Waters, *U.S. Geol. Surv. Water-Supply Paper* 140, pp. 65–85, 1905.

VEATCH, A. C., and others, Underground Water Resources of Long Island, N.Y., *U.S. Geol. Surv. Prof. Paper* 44, pp. 86–115, 1906.

Dye Method:

DOLE, R. B., Use of Fluorescein in the Study of Underground Water, *U.S. Geol. Surv. Water-Supply Paper* 160, pp. 73–85, 1906.

HAMLIN, HOMER, Underflow Tests in the Drainage Basin of Los Angeles River; *U.S. Geol. Surv. Water-Supply Paper.* 112, 1905.

SLICHTER, *Water-Supply Paper* 140, *op. cit.*, pp. 50–64; Observations on the Ground Waters of Rio Grande Valley, *U.S. Geol. Surv. Water-Supply Paper* 141, pp. 9–13, 1905.

SLICHTER, C. S., and H. C. WOLFF, The Underflow of the South Platte Valley, *U.S. Geol. Surv. Water-Supply Paper* 184, pp. 9–12, 1906.

STABLER, HERMAN, Fluorescein an Aid to Tracing Waters Underground, *Reclamation Record*, vol. 12, pp. 122, U.S. Recl. Service, 1921.

STILES, C. W., H. R. CROHURST, G. E. THOMSON, and N. D. STEARNS, Experimental Bacterial and Chemical Polution of Wells via Ground Water, with a Report on the Geology and Ground-water Hydrology of the Experimental Area at Fort Caswell, N.C., *U.S. Pub. Health Service Hyg. Lab. Bull.* 147, 1927.

WOLFF, H. C., The Utilization of the Underflow near St. Francis, Kan., *U.S. Geol. Surv. Water-Supply Paper* 258, pp. 98–119, 1911.

[1] HOYT, J. C., and N. C. GROVER, "River Discharge," 4th ed., pp. 3, 4, 44–81, John Wiley & Sons, Inc., 1927.

[2] KIMBLE, J. C., Underflow at Whittier Narrows, San Gabriel River Valley, Los Angeles County, California, *Trans. Amer. Geophys. Union*, pp. 521–525, 1936.

approximately one mile wide with a maximum depth of about 1000 ft. The alluvium is composed of sand, gravel, and clay with coarser material predominating. No extensive clay blankets exist and it is postulated that the ground water moves vertically with about the same freedom as it moves laterally. Part of the ground water rises at the narrows as effluent seepage into the river channel and the remainder percolates as "underflow" through the narrows. Percolation through the narrows has been practically constant from 1924 to 1934. The method is based on Darcy's law that velocity of percolation varies directly with water-table slope. As the cross-sectional area occupied by underflow and area discharging effluent seepage are constant, the sum of the underflow and effluent seepage is a direct measure of velocity and therefore varies directly as water-table slope. In December, 1923, the average ground-water slope immediately above the area of effluent seepage was 18 ft. per mile and stream flow produced by effluent seepage was 112 sec.-ft. In December, 1933, the water-table slope was 9 ft. per mile and stream flow 40 sec.-ft. Using Darcy's law, $18/(112 + x) = 9/(40 + x)$, where the numerators measure hydraulic gradient in feet per mile and denominators are the sum of rising water and underflow (the latter designated as x). Solving, $x = 32$ sec.-ft. = the constant underflow in the narrows.

Laboratory Determination of Permeability.—Laboratory methods of determining permeability and quantity of water moving in a conduit or water-bearing formation when the hydraulic gradient and cross-sectional area of the aquifer are known are discussed in detail in Chap. VIII.

The hydraulic gradient can be satisfactorily determined only by measuring the depth to water level in nonpumping wells distributed over the area. The measured wells must be outside the area of influence of pumping wells and must penetrate a single confined-water body.

" . . . A well should not be yielding water at the time it is measured or for some time prior to its measurement; otherwise there will be a local drawdown that will introduce an error. There may also be a drawdown caused by heavy flow or pumping from other wells in the same vicinity, and precautions must be taken with respect to errors that might be produced by changes in atmospheric pressure or other causes. The water levels are measured from definite bench marks, or reference points, to which levels are run. A contour map of the pressure-indicating surface is then constructed. Such a map shows approximately the direction of movement of the ground water and the hydraulic gradient at every point, the direction in any locality being at right angles to the contour and the gradient being the ratio of the contour interval to the distance between successive contours.

"The area of cross section can be estimated from well records and outcrops that show the thickness and extent of the formations. A cross section that is pertinent for this purpose must obviously have the same general trend as the contours of the pressure-indicating surface, in order to be approximately at right angles to the direction of flow.

"The most serious difficulty with this method and one that up to the present time has not been effectively overcome is that of determining the true average permeability of the material that constitutes the water-bearing formation.[1] Laboratory methods are available to determine accurately the permeability of the samples that are tested, but the difficulty lies in obtaining representative samples. Even apparently slight differences in texture may make great differences in permeability. A rather inconspicuous admixture of colloidal clay to an otherwise permeable sand may cut down greatly its capacity to conduct water. In a sand formation a few thin strata of coarse, clean sand may conduct more water than all the rest of the formation. These permeable strata may be overlooked in the sampling, or if samples from them are taken it may be impossible to give them the proper weight in comparison with samples from other parts of the formation. Consolidated rocks are likely to contain joints and crevices which conduct much of the water and which therefore render laboratory methods inapplicable. On the other hand, unconsolidated samples can not easily be recovered and tested without disturbing the texture of the material and thus introducing errors of unknown but conceivably great amount. Moreover, samples taken at the outcrop of a formation may not be representative because of changes produced by weathering, and samples obtained from wells are generally nonvolumetric and

[1] Where water-bearing materials consist of regular beds of volcanic sand interstratified with impervious materials, this difficulty is overcome (page 470).

greatly disturbed and may be either washed or mixed with clay of foreign origin. If the conditions of drilling can be controlled it may be possible to obtain an undisturbed or only moderately disturbed sample, especially if a core barrel is used, but such favorable conditions are rarely obtainable. In spite of the difficulties, the laboratory tests are of value in giving general limits of permeability, and it will be highly desirable to complete the project, now in progress, of making a set of permeability tests of all the leading formations in this country that conduct water through their pore spaces.

"Efforts have been made by Hazen, King, Slichter, and others[1] to compute the permeability of water-bearing material from its mechanical composition and porosity. . . . These indirect methods of computing permeability are useful for some purposes but have not always given consistent results and are not in general to be recommended. Direct tests of permeability require no more work and are generally more satisfactory (pages 201–215)."

Permeability Determined from Discharge and Drawdown of Wells.—"One of the most promising methods of determining permeability is a field method . . . based on the performance of wells that enter the water-bearing formation.[2] In order to make a test by this method it is necessary to have one well from which water can be withdrawn, either by pumping or by artesian flow, at a rate that will produce considerable drawdown, and two or more other wells that are located at different distances from the discharge well and near enough to it to have appreciable drawdown when it is discharging. This method has the advan-

---

[1] For a review of the work of Hazen, King, and Slichter on this subject see Stearns, *Water-Supply Paper* 596-F, *op. cit.*, pp. 170–176. See also pages 201–207 of this text.

[2] Proposed by G. Thiem, "Hydrologische Methoden," Leipzig, 1906, and discussed in detail by L. K. Wenzel, The Thiem Method for Determining Permeability of Water-bearing Materials, and its Application to the Determination of Specific Yield, *U.S. Geol. Surv. Water-Supply Paper* 679-A, 1936. See also pp. 213–215 of this text. The method was used by Theis in a survey of Portales Valley, New Mexico. He compares results obtained by this method with those obtained by laboratory methods. (Theis, C. V., Progress Report on the Ground-Water Supply of the Portales Valley, New Mexico, *New Mexico State Engineer 11th Bienn. Rept.*, 1932–1934, pp. 87–108, 1935; Progress Report on the Ground-water Supply of Lea County, New Mexico, *ibid.*, pp. 127–153.)

tage over the laboratory methods in that it deals with all the water-bearing materials in the vicinity of a well, undisturbed and in place."

Area of Influence of Wells.—Meinzer discusses the cone of pressure relief and the area of influence due to pumping confined water.[1] The cone of pressure relief enlarges and contracts with increase and decrease of quantity of water pumped. When equilibrium occurs, drawdown is constant and the cone diverts a ground-water stream equal in quantity to that pumped. The body of moving water diverted is equal in width to the width of the area of influence measured at right angles to the direction of artesian percolation and in thickness to that of the aquifer. No appreciable amount of water is withdrawn from storage until the area of influence reaches the fountain head, or unless there is elastic deformation or compaction of the conduit or confining strata. The results may be expressed in gallons per minute per foot of width of ground-water stream diverted. If the aquifer is stratiform and of uniform thickness, flow per square foot of aquifer can be calculated.[2] Neither porosity nor specific yield need enter into the calculations.

Movements of Water Levels in Wells in Relation to Rates of Withdrawal.—Meinzer discusses the determination of the rate at which confined water will move to the well under the gradient that will be established by the drawdown involved in the permissible lift (determined by well depth, equipment, and economical conditions).[3] If pumping rate does not exceed salvageable recharge, the water level will approach as a limit some point above the bottom of the well. If the pumping level declines persistently, excessive ultimate drawdown is indicated. If pumping or artesian discharge decreases, the water levels may begin to rise and therefore the point of equilibrium has been reached and passed. "By critical study of this game of tag between the water levels and the rates of withdrawal a number of points of equilibrium (between drawdown and quantity of water pumped) can be approximately determined, but exact

[1] MEINZER, *Water-Supply Paper* 638-C, *op. cit.*, pp. 136–137.

[2] This method is probably not applicable for pressure water in alluvial deposits on account of the heterogeneity of water-bearing materials and variable size of aquifers.

[3] *Ibid.*, pp. 138–140.

determination is complicated by the lag in the movements of the water levels due to storage, and further study needs to be given to this subject to develop a systematic method of interpretation that is mathematically sound. These points of equilibrium are points on a rating curve of the inflowing stream of ground water. To the extent that this curve can be projected it will indicate the drawdown that will be caused by increased rates of withdrawal and will thus establish the safe yield.[1]

Evaluation of Extraneous Influences on Water Levels.—"The movements of the water levels in wells are not the effects of simple forces acting singly but rather the resultants of a complex of interacting forces. This complexity, of course, increases the difficulties of interpretation. For example, a study of the effects produced by different rates of pumping may be complicated through changes produced by variations in atmospheric pressure or by the ebbing and flowing of oceanic tides. The barometric or tidal effects must be evaluated, and corrections must then be made for them. These extraneous agencies are, however, not wholly a detriment, for if they are studied in a time and place where other agencies are absent or can be eliminated, they are likely to afford valuable information on the ground-water conditions." The modifying effects—barometric pressure, tidal load, and more recently studied effect of compaction due to overpumping—are discussed on pages 331–345.

Estimates of Water Yielded by Compaction[2]

The ground-water hydrology of Livermore Valley, Alameda County, California, has probably been studied in detail for a longer period than any other locality in the United States. Ground water in the valley supplies local demands and is a source of water supply for San Francisco, and surface flow out of the valley supplies ground water to Niles alluvial cone which has been pumped by local consumers and by the Bay Cities Water Company. Legal disputes in regard to the distribution of the

---

[1] The rating-curve method was developed by D. G. Thompson and applied in his survey in the Atlantic City region. Ground-water Supplies in the Atlantic City Region, *New Jersey Dept. Conserv. Devel. Bull.* 30, pp. 35–88, 1928.

[2] The following discussion is a summary of results presented in a thesis for the M.A. degree at Stanford University by M. B. Smith, Ground Water in the Livermore Valley, California, 1934.

water led to taking of continuous measurements of surface and ground water.[1]

Ground-water fluctuations are due primarily to variations in rainfall and pumping. The latter is heavy in dry periods and therefore accentuates natural cyclic fluctuations. The ground water and pressure level stood at the high or overflow point in 1898 prior to ground-water development and utilization, dropped to a low point in 1905, and was brought back to a high level in 1907 as a result of two seasons of heavy rainfall. These fluctuations constitute the first known cycle. The water-level records of the seasonal high of 1907 are available, but data regarding stream flow and pumping are incomplete. The next major cycle is from 1907 to 1916. Complete data on runoff, water withdrawals, and water levels in wells are available since 1916 and therefore the 1916 level is an important reference point in the study of ground-water inventories in this area. Subsequent variations in water levels in wells are as follows: The general water level rose during the wet periods of 1919, 1921–1923, 1926–1928, and declined during the dry periods of 1916–1918, 1920, 1923–1925, 1929–1931.

The first general inventory was made for the period of Jan. 1, 1916, to Apr. 24, 1923. The water levels at the end of this period closely approximated those at the beginning, fluctuations during the period were moderate (maximum water-level fluctuation 10± ft. and pressure surface 20± ft.), and the average ground-water level was much higher than in the second period selected. The second period, Feb. 1, 1925, to Apr. 24, 1930, followed the abrupt drop in water levels of 1923 and 1924 (a maximum of 65 ft. in the Pleasanton basin) and the water level remained below the depressed 1925 level, returning to that level at the end of the period. During this second period, therefore, ground water functioned under a lowered water table and a depleted pressure surface.

The third period selected was from May 1, 1916, with water level at the highest recorded level, to Jan. 1, 1932, with lowest recorded water level. This inventory was made in order to estimate specific yield and will not be discussed here.

[1] WILLIAMS, C., Report on Water Supply of Alameda Creek Watershed with Particular Reference to Livermore Valley Underground Supply, Unpublished report, 1912; Lee, Charles H., Spring Valley Water Company, The Future Water Supply of San Francisco, 1912.

Inventory for the first period Jan. 1, 1916, to Apr. 24, 1923:

GROUND-WATER INCREMENT

	Million Gallons
Influent seepage from streams (measured)	12,744
Rainfall increment (from detailed analysis)	1,100
Subsurface additions from pervious Tertiary rocks exposed in drainage basin, dipping under and underlying alluvial deposits of the valley. Since no large lowering of water level or pressure surface occurred which would cause compaction of water-bearing materials, the quantity added by subsurface percolation into the area is measured by the deficit between supply and withdrawals	7,581
	21,425

GROUND-WATER DECREMENT

Withdrawals by pumping (largely measured)	20,199
Evaporation and transpiration (estimated by study of relation of water table to ground surface)	1,226
	21,425

Inventory for the low-water-level period from Feb. 1, 1925, to Apr. 24, 1930:

GROUND-WATER INCREMENT

Influent seepage from streams (measured)	10,067
Rainfall increment (small because of depressed water level and light rainfall)	311
Return water from gravel plants (measured with 85 per cent return)	2,490
Subsurface additions from underlying Tertiary rocks (calculated from comparison of rainfall on rocks of drainage basin compared with that of first period)	5,679
Deficit interpreted as representing water furnished from compaction of alluvial material during low-water-level period (21.8 per cent of total pump yield)	5,166
	23,713

GROUND-WATER DECREMENT

Withdrawals by pumping	23,713
Evaporation and transpiration	0
	23,713

This deficit of 5166 million gallons during a period of lowered water table and pressure conditions represents water derived from compaction of alluvial materials, probably both aquifers and aquicludes, and possibly also furnished in small part by long drainage of very fine material the specific yield of which is very small.

The reduction of pressure in all the aquifers caused their compaction by increasing the load sustained by the sand and gravel aggregates, and also reduced the back pressure acting on the aquicludes and thus accelerated the squeezing out of water from them by pressure of overlying material and increased the rate of compaction of the clay members.

The lowering of water level in Livermore Valley is less than that recorded in other areas in California. This study indicates that where water levels have been similarly lowered by overpumping, water may be furnished by compaction of alluvial material in sufficient amounts to revise all prior estimates of specific yield and capacity of ground-water reservoirs and introduces a new factor in the ground-water inventory. The excess water produced by compaction may be regenerated in small part by recharge of ground-water reservoirs, but Terzaghi's[1] experimental work suggests that a considerable portion of the water of compaction is permanently abstracted from the water-bearing materials and cannot be replenished either naturally or artificially. Data from spreading operations, especially in the Santa Clara Valley, Santa Clara County, California, may furnish information regarding the permanency of compaction.

A new field has been opened up by the discovery of the importance of the process of compaction of water-bearing alluvial materials in furnishing water to wells when overpumping occurs and it is hoped that the data necessary for quantitative estimates will be collected in the near future.

[1] TERZAGHI, CHARLES, Principles of Soil Mechanics, *Eng. News-Record*, vol. 95, pp. 987–990, 1925.

CHAPTER XVII

GROUND-WATER PROVINCES OF THE UNITED STATES AND HAWAIIAN ISLANDS

A regional classification of ground water is based upon the selection of areas characterized by a general similarity in the principal occurrences. Such a regional classification of the mode of occurrence of ground water is of value for comparative and descriptive purposes. The probable characteristics of ground-water bodies are thus established for each province, and successful methods of exploration of ground water in localities within the region can be applied to the entire province, with limitations due to local variations. As further information becomes available in regard to differences in ground-water occurrence within a general province, the latter may be subdivided, and the methods of ground-water extraction applicable to each smaller area determined.

Ground water is held in superficial materials or in underlying bedrock formations. Meinzer uses the areal extent of either the important superficial water-bearing formations or important bedrock formations, or a combination of the two if both hold important water supplies, to locate his ground-water provinces.[1]

Important Superficial Water-bearing Formations

1. Glacial materials of semicontinental extent cover northern United States and control the distribution of the most available ground water of that region. These deposits overlie bedrock formations of many different types. Local glacial deposits occur in the Rocky Mountains, Cascade Mountains, and the Sierra Nevada, and outwash gravels of glacial origin occur beyond the southernmost continental glacial moraine. The areal extent of the glacial drift is shown in Fig. 173. Within the glaciated region is the "driftless area" of Wisconsin which was never

[1] MEINZER, O. E., The Occurrence of Ground Water in the United States, *U.S. Geol. Surv. Water-Supply Paper* 489, pp. 309–314, 1923.

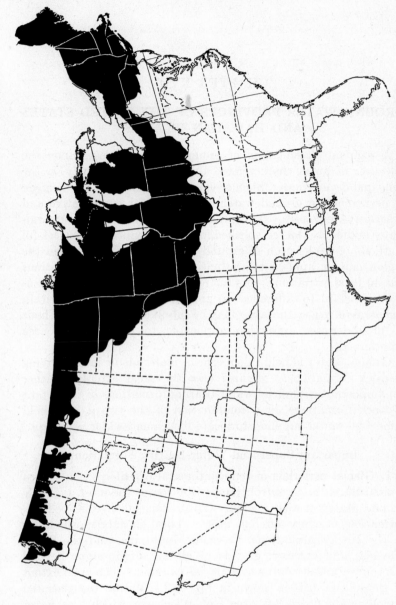

FIG. 173.—Extent of Pleistocene ice sheet in the United States.   (After unpublished map compiled by W. C. Alden.)

covered by the continental ice sheets, but the river valleys of which contain outwash glacial gravels. The basement formation of the driftless area is of lower Paleozoic age. The Potsdam and St. Peter sandstones are the principal aquifers.

Glacial Epochs.—Five glacial advances occurred during Pleistocene times, all but the first following interglacial epochs in which the continental ice sheet was melted and withdrawn beyond the boundary of the United States. Each ice sheet eroded and redistributed, in part, the deposits of the older glaciers, especially north of the United States, but laid down successive deposits of drift within the United States. The interglacial time intervals were probably vastly longer than the glacial intervals, and the length of the interglacial epochs became successively shorter after each advance of the ice sheet. If the time since the last glacial advance (the late Wisconsin stage) be taken as unity, the intervals between the progressively older glacial advances can be represented approximately by the numbers 1, 2, 4, 8, 16.[1]

Structure and Hydrologic Properties of Glacial Drift.—The term *glacial drift* includes all types of deposits laid down by glaciers and by streams issuing from them or dammed by them. The bulk of the material is *till,* a heterogeneous formation consisting of boulders of all sizes incased in the more finely ground glacial débris or flour, much of which is of the fineness of silt and clay. The permeability of the till is low. The pervious members (aquifers) of the drift are (*a*) sorted deposits laid down by glacial streams which issue at the edge of the ice sheet (*glacial outwash* and *glacial aprons*), (*b*) deposits of sand and gravel laid down by subglacial streams (*eskers* and *kames*) and by streams flowing upon the ice and glacial drift, (*c*) stratified deposits laid down in glacial lakes, and (*d*) materials redeposited by the wind (*loess*).

The gravel and sand deposited by glacial streams are the important aquifers of the glacial drift. Large artesian flows have been encountered in river gravels overlain by till. The unassorted till usually furnishes only small supplies of water, sufficient for domestic purposes, and the ground water contained therein is subject to pollution. The pervious members are usually concentrated either at the base or at the top of the sheets

---

[1] CHAMBERLIN, T. C., and R. D. SALISBURY, "Geology," vol. III, Earth History, p. 414, Henry Holt and Company, Inc., New York, 1906.

of material laid down by each successive glacier. Therefore the contacts between the deposits of each glacial epoch are usually water-bearing, and the contact horizon may be marked by springs. Glacial outwash aprons and valley trains deposited beyond the terminal moraines in New England, Rhode Island,

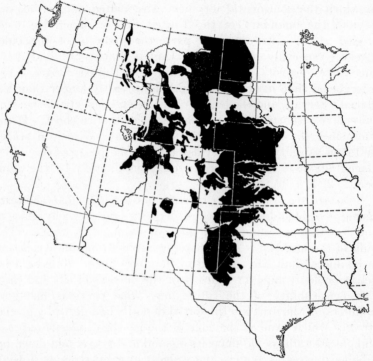

Fig. 174.—Sheet of Tertiary alluvium overlying central Great Plains area. (*After Meinzer.*)

and Long Island, and also well developed in the drainage system of the Mississippi River from Pennsylvania to the Dakotas, supply large quantities of good water to Brooklyn and to many other municipalities and to industrial plants.[1]

Irving Crosby[2] comments upon the variable hydrologic properties of glacial drift. He states that the drift varies greatly in different parts of the country; in the southern peninsula of

[1] Meinzer, *Water-Supply Paper* 489, *op. cit.*, p. 285.
[2] Crosby. Irving, personal communication.

Michigan it is predominantly sandy and very thick, and in other regions, such as New England, it is predominantly clayey, variable in thickness and very thin on the average. In parts of this region many wells produce water from underlying bedrock.

A good discussion of the hydrologic properties of glacial drift and the utilization of the water supply therein will be found in Meinzer's *Water-Supply Paper* 489, pages 282 to 291.

2. A great sheet of Tertiary alluvium[1] (Fig. 174) derived from erosion of the central Rocky Mountains overlies the central portion of the Great Plains area. Meinzer states:

The Great Plains are largely underlain by gravelly, sandy, and clayey materials that were spread smoothly over them in the later part of the Tertiary period by streams from the Rocky Mountains. These alluvial deposits, nowhere more than a few hundred feet thick, are in most areas porous enough to furnish at least some water, and they contain abundant irregularly distributed lenses and stringers of gravel and sand that yield large quantities of good water to many wells. They constitute one of the most valuable aquifers in the United States, ranking among the first in quantity of water, quality of water, number of wells supplied, and extent of productive area. The water supply of these beds is one of the most attractive features and one of the leading assets of the great semiarid region which they underlie. They give rise to only a few flowing wells, but the pumping lifts are generally not great.[2]

The Great Plains also contain important Quaternary aquifers consisting of alluvial gravel and sand. These deposits were apparently laid down chiefly in the Pleistocene epoch. They are found mainly in the valleys which lead from the mountains and which trench the Tertiary and older formations that underlie the Great Plains. They are extensively developed in the valleys of Arkansas and Platte rivers and many other streams and are also found in a few areas from which the streams that produced them have been diverted. These deposits extend for hundreds of miles from the mountains and in some places expand to considerable widths. In the part of the Platte River valley . . . the belt of alluvium ranges from 5 to 20 miles in width. This alluvium contains large quantities of good water which it yields very freely to wells. It is heavily drawn upon for many purposes, including irrigation.[3]

[1] See discussion by Meinzer, *Water-Supply Paper* 489, *op. cit.*, pp. 271–282.

[2] MEINZER, *Water-Supply Paper* 489, *op. cit.*, p. 278.

[3] *Ibid.*, pp. 303–305.

The alluvial deposits overlap Paleozoic formations in the south, chiefly "red beds" of Paleozoic (and Triassic) age which are deficient in potable water; hence where the alluvial deposits have been eroded, ground-water supplies are poor. Tertiary alluvium overlies the Cretaceous rocks to the north. The most important deep aquifer is the Dakota sandstone which is nearly

Fig. 175.—Areas of western United States underlain by Quaternary valley fill. (*After Meinzer.*)

coextensive with the Cretaceous formations underlying the alluvium. However, the Dakota sandstone is too deep to permit exploitation within the area covered by the Great Plains alluvium.

3. The Alluvial Deposits of the Semiarid Southwest (Fig. 175).—The chief water bearers are the deposits of valley fill of which alluvial cones and fans are the most important. Their structure depends upon the bedrock formation of the adjacent mountains from which they are derived and upon the geologic processes by which they were formed, which vary chiefly with climate. The ground water of the Great Basin region is largely in alluvial deposits of this type, as are the principal deposits of ground water in the Great Valley of California and in the inter-montane valleys of the Pacific Coast ranges. The hydrologic

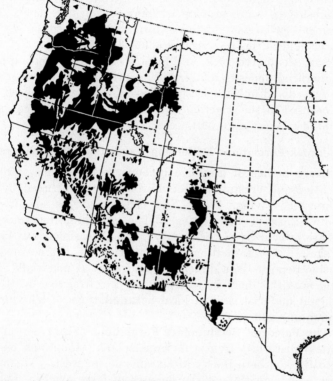

FIG. 176.—Areas of western United States underlain by Tertiary or Quaternary volcanic rocks. (*After Meinzer.*)

properties of the valley fill of the West are well described by Meinzer[1] and are discussed in this text, pages 364–376, 532–538.

4. Superficial lava formations (Fig. 176) control the occurrence of ground water and delimit an important ground-water province. The largest continuous area of lava is that constituting the Columbia Plateau and its extensions covering portions of Idaho,

[1] MEINZER *Water-Supply Paper* 489, *op. cit.*, pp. 291–294, 297–303.

Washington, Oregon, and California. A second large area, the Gila River lava field, covers a portion of the Colorado Plateau in eastern Arizona and western New Mexico. Innumerable smaller areas of porous lava outcrop west of the Rocky Mountains. The Gila River lava field should probably be classified as a definite ground-water region and each smaller lava field as a ground-water area characterized by ground-water movements and subsurface water storage peculiar to volcanic rocks. The hydrologic properties of lava formations are discussed by Meinzer[1] and in this text on pages 309–312, 543–548.

5. Soil, weathered rock, and local accumulations of alluvium are superficial deposits too erratic in distribution and character to be considered in the selection of ground-water provinces, but may be used in the selection of subdivisions of provinces, such as ground-water regions and areas.

Bedrock Formations Delimiting Ground-water Provinces

1. Large bodies of intrusive igneous rocks, such as granitic batholiths, and crystalline metamorphic rocks intruded by the igneous rocks[2] (Fig. 177). The latter may be of all ages including those of Tertiary age. The crystalline metamorphic rocks are principally of pre-Cambrian and occasionally of Paleozoic age. These formations are important if not covered by extensive deposits of sedimentary and alluvial materials. The ground water is held in fractures, in the irregular mantle of weathered material, and in local accumulations of alluvium in intermontane valleys.

2. The Paleozoic Sedimentary Formations (Fig. 178).—These are little disturbed from the Appalachian Mountains on the east to the southern Rocky Mountains on the west. The major structures are gentle and the flexures of large extent. Locally the Paleozoic formations are sharply folded near the eastern boundary of the region and in the Ouachita Mountains of Oklahoma and Arkansas. The entire region where Paleozoic rocks occur near the surface contains a rather unsatisfactory ground-water supply and wells more than a few hundred feet deep are apt to encounter salty water.[3] Good water is generally

---

[1] Meinzer, *op. cit.*, pp. 279–282.

[2] See discussion by Meinzer, *op. cit.*, pp. 196–201.

[3] *Ibid.*, p. 203; see also pp. 201–204 for discussion of Paleozoic systems.

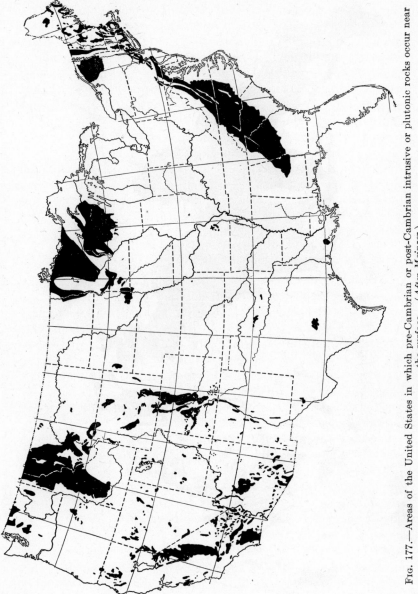

Fig. 177.—Areas of the United States in which pre-Cambrian or post-Cambrian intrusive or plutonic rocks occur near the surface. (*After Meinzer.*)

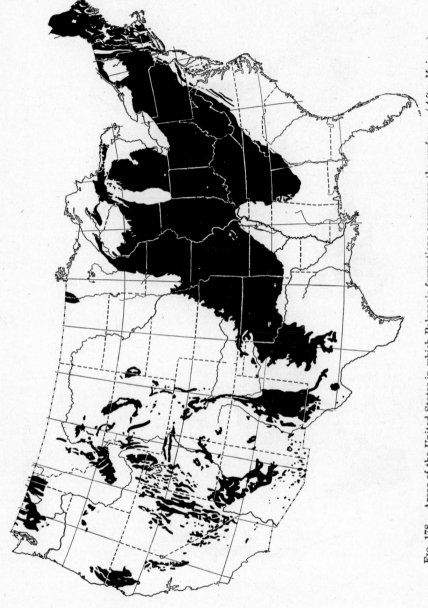

Fig. 178.—Areas of the United States in which Paleozoic formations occur near the surface. (*After Meinzer.*)

encountered within 200 to 300 ft. of the surface except in Kansas, Oklahoma, and Texas where salty water extends up to the water table. The best supplies are in alluvial deposits of the stream courses.

Several water-bearing sandstone formations occur, the most important of which are the Potsdam sandstone of Cambrian

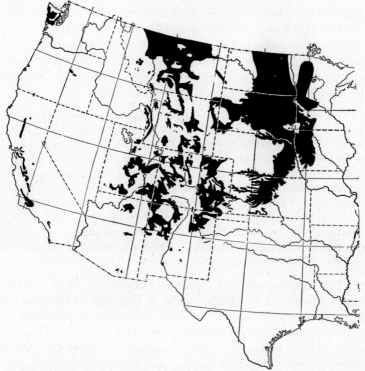

Fig. 179.—Areas of northwest Great Plains region, Rocky Mountains, and Colorado Plateau in which rocks of Upper Cretaceous series occur near the surface. (*After Meinzer.*)

age, the St. Peter sandstone of Ordovician age, and the Pottsville sandstone and its equivalents at the base of the Pennsylvanian series. Limestone and dolomite beds of Ordovician, Silurian, Devonian, and Carboniferous ages carry water in solution openings, but only where conditions have been favorable for the development of such openings. Flowing wells are obtained where structural and topographic conditions are favorable.

3. Cretaceous Formations of the Northwest Great Plains Region, the Rocky Mountains, and Colorado Plateau[1] (Fig. 179).—These are chiefly thick shale formations with interstratified sandstone. Where these formations are not covered with alluvial material, there are only scanty supplies of near-surface ground water, as the greater portion of the Cretaceous-Tertiary sedimentary sequence consists of shale. The great aquifer is the Dakota sandstone formation which underlies most of North and South Dakota and Nebraska, and also the western portions of Kansas, Iowa, and Minnesota. The structure is an irregular synclinal basin with dips so flat that the water-bearing beds can be reached over an area of thousands of square miles. The aquifer is described by Meinzer[2] as follows:

. . . the basal formation of the Upper Cretaceous is the Dakota sandstone, one of the most valuable aquifers in the United States and a notable source of artesian water. It is approximately equivalent in age to the Woodbine sand of Texas. Above the Dakota sandstone, which is generally not much more than 100 feet thick, lie Upper Cretaceous formations which in some places aggregate several thousand feet in thickness. These overlying formations are predominantly shaly and include much dense, plastic, impervious shale that will yield no water but is very effective in confining the copious supplies of the Dakota sandstone under artesian pressure. There are, however, several fairly good water-bearing beds at various horizons above the Dakota.

4. The Cretaceous and Tertiary Formations of the Atlantic Coastal Plain and the Embayment of the Gulf of Mexico (Fig. 180).—The sedimentary rocks are nonindurated and were laid down when the ocean transgressed upon the eastern and southern shores of the North American continent. They are covered locally by terrace deposits and by ancient stream deposits. The ocean transgressions were limited to a zone of about 100 miles in width on the east, but extended far up the Mississippi Valley and over southeastern Texas, forming an enlarged Gulf of Mexico known as the embayment of the Gulf of Mexico.

The catchment area of each pervious marine formation is the outcrop area, and the depth to the aquifers is shown by geologic

[1] See descriptions by Meinzer, *Water-Supply Paper* 489, *op. cit.*, Upper Cretaceous series, pp. 266–270; Tertiary system, pp. 271–276; Eocene and later Tertiary deposits, pp. 277–279.

[2] MEINZER, *op. cit.*, p. 268.

structural cross sections. The aquifers are porous sandstone and pervious limestone formations of Cretaceous and Tertiary age. Artesian water is commonly encountered down the dip of the sandstone aquifers. The quality of the ground water in some of the aquifers is ruined by formational saline contamination, especially in Texas.

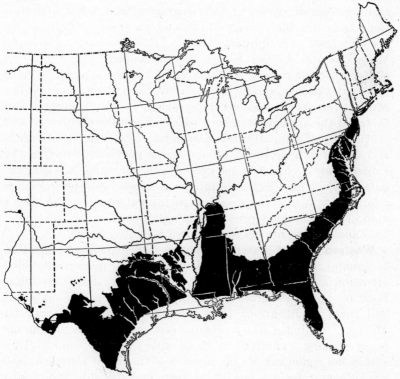

Fig. 180.—Areas of Atlantic and Gulf coastal plains in which Cretaceous and Tertiary formations occur near the surface. (*After Meinzer.*)

5. Eocene and Later Tertiary Deposits of the Great Plains, Rocky Mountains, and Colorado Plateau Region.[1]—This thick sequence of formations, including marine sandstone, lacustrine deposits, and some alluvial materials, contains water-bearing horizons of varying extent and thickness.

[1] See descriptions by Meinzer, *Water-Supply Paper* 489, *op. cit.,* Upper Cretaceous series, pp. 266–270; Tertiary system, pp. 271–276; Eocene and later Tertiary deposits, pp. 277–279.

CLASSIFICATION OF GROUND-WATER PROVINCES

Ground-water provinces of the United States have been delimited and described by Ries and Watson,[1] and by Meinzer,[2] who has kept closely in touch not only with the investigations of the Division of Ground Water of the United States Geological Survey carried out under his direction, but also those of various state geological surveys, state engineers, and other organizations and individuals engaged in ground-water investigations. In his important contribution entitled The Occurrence of Ground Water in the United States are assembled typical geologic columns for the regions in which ground water is procured from sedimentary rocks, and he has described the hydrologic properties of the various formations represented in the columns, and sketched the geologic structure which affects the occurrence and movements of ground water in each province. He then bounds and describes a group of ground-water provinces covering the United States. Space is not available to summarize the geologic data on which his selection of provinces is based and the student is referred for further information to his publication. Meinzer's map of ground-water provinces is reproduced in this text (Fig. 181) and his description of provinces is quoted in full.

Western Ground-water Provinces.—The regional classification of ground water in western United States receives detailed attention and original treatment in this text. Some modifications of Meinzer's provinces within this region are suggested and these modifications have been approved, in general, by Meinzer.[3] Intense study of ground-water occurrences and the many striking variations in topography, geology, and climate within the region call for the division of the major provinces into ground-water regions, which in turn may be subdivided into ground-water areas. A general description of the ground-water province of the Hawaiian Islands has been prepared by R. G. Sohlberg who has recently been engaged in studying ground-water geology in that region.

---

[1] RIES, H., and T. L. WATSON, "Engineering Geology," John Wiley & Sons, Inc., pp. 330–337, 1915.

[2] MEINZER, *Water-Supply Paper* 489, *op. cit.*, pp. 309–314.

[3] Personal communication.

GROUND-WATER PROVINCES DESCRIBED BY MEINZER

In order to summarize effectively the occurrence of ground water in the United States the country has been divided into twenty-one ground-water provinces, the approximate boundaries of which are shown in (Fig. 181). Any such division is necessarily somewhat arbitrary, both as to the number of provinces and as to their boundaries, but it serves a very useful purpose for concise presentation of the conditions of the entire country.

In making the division consideration is given to the several important groups of aquifers in the country, namely, glacial drift, valley fill of the western basins, Tertiary lava, Miocene and Pliocene (upper Tertiary) formations of the Great Plains, Eocene formations of the interior, Cretaceous formations (chiefly the Upper Cretaceous of the interior, including the Dakota sandstone), Paleozoic sedimentary formations, and pre-Cambrian and other crystalline rocks. The general rules for classification are as follows:

1. A large area in which only one of these groups of aquifers exists or is important, constitutes a province. The provinces of this class are the Piedmont province (*C*), the South-central Paleozoic province (*E*), the Wisconsin Paleozoic province (*G*), the Black Hills Cretaceous province (*J*), the Trans-Pecos Paleozoic province (*M*), the Columbia Plateau Lava province (*S*), and the Southwestern Bolson province (*T*).

2. Where more than one of the principal groups of aquifers occurs, the coextension of the two most important of these groups determines the limits of a province. The provinces of this class are the Northeastern Drift province (*B*), the North-central Drift-Paleozoic province (*F*), the Superior Drift-Crystalline province (*H*), the Dakota Drift-Cretaceous province (*I*), the Great Plains Pliocene-Cretaceous province (*K*), the Great Plains Pliocene-Paleozoic province (*L*), and the Montana Eocene-Cretaceous province (*O*). Modifications of this rule are represented by the Atlantic Coastal Plain province (*A*), the Northwestern Drift-Eocene-Cretaceous province (*N*), and the Montana-Arizona Plateau province (*Q*), in which at least three of the principal groups of aquifers are present and are so nearly equal in importance that they must all be taken into account.

3. In rugged and lofty mountainous regions the topography and, to some extent, the climate produce radical changes in ground-water conditions, which eclipse the differences due to the presence of different groups of aquifers. Such a mountainous region constitutes a ground-water province. The provinces of this class are the Blue-Ridge-Appalachian Valley province (*D*), the Southern Rocky Mountain province (*P*), the Northern Rocky Mountain province (*R*), and the Pacific Moun-

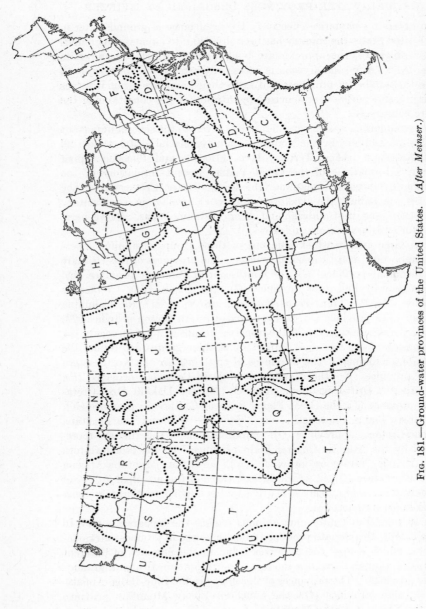

Fig. 181.—Ground-water provinces of the United States. (*After Meinzer.*)

A. Atlantic Coastal Plain province
B. Northeastern Drift province
C. Piedmont province
D. Blue Ridge-Appalachian Valley province
E. South-central Paleozoic province
F. North-central Drift-Paleozoic province
G. Wisconsin Paleozoic province

I. Dakota Drift-Cretaceous province
J. Black Hills Cretaceous province
K. Great Plains Pliocene-Cretaceous province
L. Great Plains Pliocene-Paleozoic province
M. Trans-Pecos Paleozoic province
N. Northwestern Drift-Eocene-Cretaceous province

O. Montana Eocene-Cretaceous province
P. Southern Rocky Mountain province
Q. Montana-Arizona Plateau province
R. Northern Rocky Mountain province
S. Columbia Plateau Lava province
T. Southwestern Bolson province
U. Pacific Mountain province

tain province (*U*).   The last-named province is not, however, a very satisfactory unit.

A. Atlantic Coastal Plain province.—Water is derived in rather large quantities from Cretaceous, Tertiary, and Quaternary strata, chiefly sand and gravel interbedded with clayey beds.   Very large supplies are obtained from alluvial gravels in Mississippi Valley and adjacent areas.   The province includes extensive areas of artesian flow.   The ground water ranges from low to high in mineral content.

B. Northeastern Drift province.—Principal ground-water supplies come from glacial drift.   The till yields small supplies to many springs and shallow wells; the outwash gravels yield very large supplies, notably on Long Island.   Many drilled rock wells receive small supplies, chiefly from joints in crystalline rocks or in Triassic sandstone.   Ground water is generally soft and otherwise low in mineral matter.

C. Piedmont province.—Water that is generally low in mineral matter is supplied in small quantities by the crystalline rocks and locally by Triassic sandstone.   Many shallow dug wells are supplied from surface deposits or from the upper decomposed part of the bedrock.   Many drilled wells of moderate depth are supplied from joints in the crystalline rocks.   Some wells in Triassic sandstone yield rather large supplies.

D. Blue Ridge-Appalachian Valley province.—This is a region of rugged topography with numerous springs which generally yield water of good quality from Paleozoic strata, pre-Cambrian crystalline rocks, or post-Cambrian intrusive rocks.   The water supplies are derived chiefly from springs, spring-fed streams, and shallow wells.

E. South-central Paleozoic province.—The ground-water conditions are in general rather unsatisfactory.   The principal sources of supply are the Paleozoic sandstones and limestones.   Throughout considerable part of the province the Paleozoic supplies are meager or of poor quality. Deep Paleozoic water is highly mineralized.   In many of the valleys large supplies are obtained from glacial outwash and other alluvial sands and gravels.

F. North-central Drift-Paleozoic province.—Most water supplies are derived from the glacial drift.   Numerous drilled wells obtain large supplies from glacial outwash or from gravel interbedded with till. The water from glacial drift in this province is generally hard but otherwise good.   In many small areas the drift gives rise to flowing wells.   Many drilled wells end also in Paleozoic sandstone or limestone and receive ample supplies of water.   The deeper Paleozoic waters are generally highly mineralized and in many places are unfit for use; the shallower Paleozoic waters are commonly of satisfactory quality except that they are hard.   In many valleys flowing wells can be obtained from Paleozoic aquifers.

G. Wisconsin Paleozoic province.—Most of the water supplies are obtained from wells of moderate depth drilled into Cambrian or Ordovician sandstone or limestone. These wells as a rule yield ample supplies of hard but otherwise good water. In many of the valleys artesian flows are obtained from the Paleozoic aquifers. The region is devoid of water-bearing drift except in the valleys, where there are water-bearing outwash gravels.

H. Superior Drift-Crystalline province.—In most parts of this province satisfactory water supplies are obtained from glacial drift. Where the drift is thin water supplies are generally scarce, because the pre-Cambrian crystalline rocks in most places yield only meager supplies, and as a rule there are no intervening Paleozoic, Mesozoic, or Tertiary formations that are thick enough to yield much water. The drift and rock waters range from soft waters of low mineralization, in Wisconsin, to highly mineralized waters—some of them unfit for use—in the western and especially the northwestern part of the province.

I. Dakota Drift-Cretaceous province.—The two important sources of ground water are the glacial drift and the Dakota sandstone. The drift supplies numerous wells with hard but otherwise fairly good water. It is available for water supply in nearly all parts of the province. The Dakota sandstone has extensive areas of artesian flow. It supplies many strong flowing wells, a considerable number of which are more than 1000 feet deep. The Dakota sandstone waters are highly mineralized but are used for domestic supplies. The water from most parts of the formation is very hard, but the water from certain strata is soft, although rich in sodium sulphate and sodium chloride.

J. Black Hills Cretaceous province.—The conditions in this province are, on the whole, unfavorable with respect to shallow-water supplies because most of the province is underlain by the Pierre shale or by shales of the White River group (Oligocene). The principal aquifer is the Dakota sandstone, which underlies the entire region except most of the Black Hills. This sandstone will probably yield water wherever it occurs, and over considerable parts of the province it will give rise to flowing wells. Throughout much of the province it is, however, far below the surface. In some localities underlain by shale small supplies are obtained from shallow wells. In the Black Hills water is obtained from a variety of sources, ranging from pre-Cambrian crystalline rocks to Cretaceous or Tertiary sedimentary rocks.

K. Great Plains Pliocene-Cretaceous province.—The principal aquifers of this province are the late Tertiary sands and gravels (Ogalalla formation and related deposits) and the Dakota sandstone. The Tertiary deposits underlying the extensive smooth and uneroded plains supply large quantities of water to shallow wells. The Dakota sandstone underlies nearly the entire province and gives rise to

various areas of artesian flow. Throughout much of the province, however, it lies too far below the surface to be a practical source of water.
Where the Tertiary beds are absent or badly eroded and the Dakota
sandstone is buried beneath thick beds of shale, as in parts of eastern
Colorado, it may be very difficult to develop water supplies for even
domestic and live-stock uses. Many of the valleys contain Quaternary
gravels, which supply large quantities of good water. Considerable
Tertiary and Quaternary well water is used for irrigation.

L. Great Plains Pliocene-Paleozoic province.—The principal aquifers of
this province are the late Tertiary and Quaternary sands and gravels,
which give the same very favorable conditions as the Tertiary and
Quaternary deposits in province *K*. The Tertiary deposits are underlain through practically the entire province by Permian or Triassic
"Red Beds," which in most places do not yield much water or yield only
highly mineralized water. In the localities where the Tertiary deposits
are thin or absent or where they have been badly eroded the ground-
water conditions are generally unfavorable.

M. Trans-Pecos Paleozoic province.—The bedrock consists of Carboniferous and Triassic strata, including limestone, gypsum, red beds of
shale and shaly sandstone, and some less shaly sandstone. In most of
the province these rocks yield only meager supplies of highly mineralized
waters to deep wells. In the Pecos Valley, however, Carboniferous limestones and sandstones yield very large supplies to numerous flowing
wells; the water is very hard but good enough for irrigation and for
general domestic and live-stock uses. Locally the bedrock is overlain
by Quaternary water-bearing gravels.

N. Northwestern Drift-Eocene-Cretaceous province.—Ground-water
supplies are obtained from glacial drift and from underlying Eocene and
Upper Cretaceous formations. Where the drift is absent or not water-
bearing wells are sunk into the underlying formations with variable
success. The Eocene and latest Cretaceous, which underlie most of the
eastern part of the province, generally include strata or lenses of sand,
gravel, or coal that yield water. The Cretaceous formations that occur
in the western part consist chiefly of alternating beds of shale and sandstone. The sandstones generally yield water, but the shales are
unproductive, and where a thick shale formation immediately underlies
the drift or is at the surface it may be very difficult to get successful
wells. In certain localities upland gravels yield water to shallow wells.

O. Montana Eocene-Cretaceous province.—Fairly good water in quantities adequate for domestic and live-stock supplies and generally also
adequate for small municipal supplies is obtained from strata and lenses
of sand, gravel, and coal in the Fort Union (Eocene) and Lance (late
Cretaceous or Eocene) formations which underlie most of the province.
These formations in this province usually rest on the Pierre shale, a

thick dense shale of Upper Cretaceous age that yields no water or only meager amounts of water, generally of poor quality. Hence, locally, where the Fort Union and Lance are absent or do not yield adequately, there is great difficulty in obtaining satisfactory water supplies. In the northern part of the province there is little water-bearing glacial drift.

P. Southern Rocky Mountain province.—In this lofty mountain province, underlain for the most part by crystalline rocks, water supplies are obtained chiefly from springs, from streams fed by springs and melted snow, or from very shallow wells near the streams.

Q. Montana-Arizona Plateau province.—The question may properly be raised whether the large region included in this province is sufficiently homogeneous to be regarded as a unit with respect to ground water. It is, for the most part, an arid to semiarid plateau region underlain by sedimentary formations ranging in age from Paleozoic to Tertiary, not violently deformed but sufficiently warped and broken to produce a close relation between rock structure and the occurrence of ground water and to cause rather rapid variation in ground-water conditions from place to place. On the whole, water supplies are not plentiful and not of very satisfactory quality. Where thick formations of nearly impervious material, such as the Mancos shale, are at the surface, or where the plateau is greatly dissected, as in the Grand Canyon region, water supplies are scarce. Locally, however, sandstone aquifers, such as the sandstones of the Kootenai formation, the Dakota sandstone, or the Mesaverde formation, are within reach of the drill and may yield very satisfactory supplies, in some places giving rise to flowing wells. Locally there are also water-bearing gravels of Quaternary age.

R. Northern Rocky Mountain province.—This is a relatively cold region, chiefly mountainous but with extensive intermontane valleys and plains. It is underlain by a great variety of rocks with complicated and diverse structure. As in other mountain regions, the water supplies are obtained largely from mountain springs and streams. Considerable water is in places available from valley fill, chiefly ordinary alluvial sand and gravel and the outwash deposits of mountain glaciers. A few supplies are also obtained from wells drilled into various rock formations—for example, the Belt series, of pre-Cambrian (Algonkian) age, and the sedimentary beds of Tertiary age.

S. Columbia Plateau Lava province.—The principal aquifers of this province are the widespread Tertiary and Quaternary lava beds and interbedded or associated Tertiary sand and gravel, such as those of the Ellensburg formation. In general, the lava yields abundant supplies of good water. It gives rise to many large springs, especially along Snake River in Idaho. Locally the lava or the interbedded sand and gravel give rise to flowing wells. However, much of the lava is so permeable and the relief of the region is so great that in many places the water table is too far below the surface to be reached except by deep wells. In certain parts of the province glacial outwash and ordinary valley fill are also important sources of water.

T. Southwestern Bolson province.—The principal source of water supply in this arid province is the alluvial sand and gravel of the valley fill underlying the numerous intermontane valleys that characterize the region. These water-bearing beds of sand and gravel not only provide numerous desert watering places and domestic, live-stock, mining and municipal supplies, but in many places they also yield important irrigation supplies. In the elevated marginal parts of the valleys the water table may be very far below the surface or ground water may be absent; in the lowest parts, underlain by clayey and alkaline beds, ground water may be meager in quantity and poor in quality; at intermediate levels, however, large supplies of good water are generally found. The province includes the Valley of Southern California and the Great Valley of California, in both of which water from the valley fill is extensively used for irrigation. Most of the water in the valleys of this province is recovered by means of wells, but there are also many springs, some of which are large. There are numerous areas of artesian flow, but most of the water for irrigation as well as other purposes is pumped. In mountain areas of the province there are, in the aggregate, many springs, small streams, and shallow wells that furnish valuable supplies. As a rule, the most favorable areas in the mountains for springs and shallow wells are the areas underlain by granitic rocks.

U. Pacific Mountain province.—This is a somewhat heterogeneous province, characterized chiefly by lofty mountains with some intermontane valleys and by heavy precipitation. Water supplies are obtained largely from the numerous streams. Many shallow wells are supplied from crystalline rocks in the Sierra Nevada and other parts of the province. The lowland areas of the northern part of the province are underlain largely by glacial drift that yields water freely. Tertiary formations, which are well developed in Oregon and Washington, would doubtless also yield much water.

GROUND-WATER PROVINCES OF WESTERN UNITED STATES

The writer has modified Meinzer's classification of the ground-water provinces of western United States to some extent and has treated in detail the water-bearing formations of California. The western provinces as treated and named here are as follows:

    I. The Great Basin ground-water province.

    II. The Columbia Plateau ground-water province.

    III. The Great Valley of California ground-water province.

IV. Ground-water province of the Coast ranges of Central and Southern California.

V. The Northern Coast range ground-water province.

These provinces are bounded on the east by Meinzer's Trans-Pecos Paleozoic province (*M*), Montana-Arizona Plateau

FIG. 182.—Ground-water provinces of western United States adopted in this text. I, Great Basin province; II, Columbia Plateau province; III, Great Valley of California province; IV, Coast Ranges of Central and Southern California province; V, Northern Coast Ranges province; *M*, *Q*, and *R*, Meinzer's Trans-Pecos Paleozoic province, Montana-Arizona Plateau province, and Northern Rocky Mountain province, respectively.

province (*Q*), and the Northern Rocky Mountain province (*R*) (Fig. 182).

The *Great Basin province* corresponds to the geologic and structural province of the same name and to Meinzer's "Southwestern Bolson province" except as to the western boundary. Meinzer includes southern California and the Sacramento Valley in his Bolson province and places the Sierra Nevada and northern Coast ranges of California in his "Pacific Mountains province."

The western boundary adopted for the Great Basin province follows the crest line of the Sierra Nevada, the eastern slope of which is the collecting area for the western group of basins of the Great Basin region, and the western slope the principal source of ground water for the Great Valley of California. South of the Sierra Nevada the boundary is the divide between the Mojave and Salton deserts and the Pacific Ocean and follows the crest of the Tehachapi Mountains, the San Gabriel and San Jacinto mountains, and the southern Coast ranges of California.

The *Columbia Plateau ground-water province* corresponds to Meinzer's "Columbia Plateau Lava province" except that the province has been extended on the southwest to include the volcanic plateau and mountains of northeastern California.

The *Great Valley of California* province includes the drainage area of the San Joaquin and Sacramento valleys. It contains a great water body in the central alluvial deposits which is fed by the drainage of the encircling mountains. The importance, extent, and characteristic features of this area deserve recognition as a ground-water province.

The *ground-water province of the Coast ranges of Central and Southern California* includes the intermontane valleys of the Coast ranges and the Pacific coastal plains. The northern boundary is the Sacramento River where it breaks through the Coast ranges to San Francisco Bay. Each valley has ground-water bodies of individual characteristics and hence the province is subdivided into areas enclosing each characteristic ground-water occurrence.

The *Northern Coast range ground-water province* includes the Pacific Coast ranges of northern California, Oregon, and Washington including the intermontane valleys. It includes the Willamette Valley which is structurally similar to the Great Valley of California and contains a large central body of water-bearing alluvium. This area should probably be separated from the Northern Coast Range province either as a separate province or at least as a ground-water region.

I. The Great Basin Ground-water Province

Extent and General Structure.—The Great Basin region lies between the Colorado Plateau and the Rocky Mountains on the east, the Columbia Plateau on the north, and the Sierra Nevada, the Tehachapi Mountains, and southern Coast ranges of California on the west. It is endowed with unique structural, topographic, and climatic characteristics. Structurally it consists of a mosaic of fault blocks, from a score to more than 100 miles long, in some cases, and from a few to a score or more miles wide. These blocks have been affected by unequal vertical displacement. The elevated blocks constitute the present mountain ranges and the depressed blocks or the lower portions of tilted blocks, the intermontane basins. The elevated blocks have been attacked by the processes of disintegration and erosion intensified by aridity, and the depressed blocks have been covered by the debris shed by the mountains. Normally the basins are undrained but may spill over one into the other with the development of a longitudinal drainage system traversing a group of basins.

Topography.—The area within centripetal drainage of the sunken block is designated as a *bolson*. If drained by an intermittent longitudinal stream, it is a *semibolson*. The alluvial slope flanking the mountains and leading down to the central mud flat or temporary lake is a *bajada*, and the flat area occupied temporarily by water is the *playa*.[1]

The Valley Fill.—The material filling these basins is called *valley fill*. It consists of alluvial cones flanking the mountains and usually coalescing into the *piedmont alluvial deposit*. The central portion of the basin may contain lacustrine deposits or playa deposits often intermixed with saline evaporation products. If a strong longitudinal, temporary or permanent stream traverses the valley, it may deposit pervious stream gravels in the center of the valley and parallel to its longer axis. Otherwise playa or lacustrine deposits of small permeability occupy the center of the valley.

Alluvial cones are the chief bearers of available ground water. These are by far the most important source of water in the arid and semiarid Southwest. The structure and hydrologic properties of alluvial cones have been discussed (pages 365–376). Both vary with the type of rock furnishing the material for the cone and the processes of weathering, erosion, transportation,

---

[1] Tolman, C. F., Erosion and Deposition in the Southern Arizona Bolson Region, *Jour. Geol.*, pp. 136–163, 1909.

Fig. 183.—Typical undrained basin or bolson south of Las Vegas, Nevada, with playa in centerground and regularly sloping bajadas (compound alluvial cones) stretching from the mountain slopes to the center of the valley. (*Photograph by Eliot Blackwelder.*)

and deposition.   Each alluvial cone has its own structure and hydrologic character, and each should receive individual study. One may be pervious (sand derived from disintegrating granitic mountains) and another largely impervious (material supplied by formations disintegrating into clay and silt).

The size of the alluvial cone depends upon the quantity of material removed from the parent mountain range and therefore usually, but not always, on the present height of the mountain range.   Detailed studies of certain important alluvial cones[1] have shown that much of the valley fill has been derived from an older mountain range eroded to a peneplain, and the more recent superficial gravels are the result of the elevation and erosion of the present range.   The study of the structure and development of an alluvial cone may indeed be fascinating and lead back to the tectonic and physiographic history of the range itself.

The water supply of an alluvial cone depends upon the size of the drainage area tributary to the stream building the cone and upon the rainfall.   Large water supplies, therefore, are found in the cones along the higher ranges, such as the Sierra Nevada and Wasatch Mountains.   Deficient water may be expected in the smaller basins flanked by small ranges.   The quantity of water that actually gets underground, however, is controlled by the geologic structure of the cone, especially the permeability of the channel of the feeding stream, as discussed on pages 168–172 and 365–376, and by the distribution of the rainfall.

The motions of ground water, especially of confined water, in alluvial cones have been discussed.   The methods of estimating the supply of available ground water have been discussed repeatedly in preceding chapters.   The methods of making a ground-water inventory (Chap. XVI) were developed in connection with the study of the water supply of enclosed basins and are best applicable to the basins of this region.

[1] For example, recent investigations of the San Francisquito alluvial cone, Santa Clara County, California, indicate that the *older* or Santa Clara gravels, over 1000 ft. thick as shown in two recently drilled wells, are derived from the erosion of a late Tertiary mountain range, and the superficial, recent gravels are derived from the present mountain range.   Also observations have been made regarding the great age and complex origin of materials of the alluvial cones both east and west of the Sierra Nevada.

FIG. 184.—Owens Valley and the Sierra Nevada from the Inyo Mountains. Symmetrical alluvial cone developed at the base of the Inyos shown in foreground. On the right are the lava flows of the great lava plateau through which the Owens River has cut a deep Quaternary and post-Quaternary canyon (see Fig. 102, page 310). Underlying the lava plateau are the glass sands which extend under Owens Valley and constitute one of the principal aquifers of the region in the vicinity of Bishop, California.

Lake Beds and Axial Stream Gravels.—Lake beds in the center of bolsons are usually aquifers of secondary importance only. Even the extensive beds deposited in the Pleistocene lakes Bonneville and Lahontan are not productive aquifers. Ancient lake beds may be important locally as in the upper Owens Valley near Bishop, California, where stratified beds of pumice and "glass sand" are important water bearers. The conditions are entirely dissimilar in lower Owens Valley where the small

Fig. 185.—Exposure of pumice beds (glass sand) in Chalfant Valley, Owens Valley region, California. These underlie the lava plateau (Fig. 184) and constitute an important aquifer in the Bishop area.

specific yield of the fine lake beds of the Quaternary Owens Lake furnishes only small flows to deep wells. These vital differences were discovered by drilling, and show the great differences that may exist in the same region where superficial examination indicates similarity in occurrence of ground water.

Occasionally the gravels deposited by streams flowing down the axis of the valley are of importance, as in upper Owens Valley, or they may be of little importance where deposits of limited extent only have been laid down in channels cut in clay and silt, as in lower Owens Valley.

II. The Columbia Plateau Ground-water Province

This province is characterized by the occurrence of great sheets of lava, the largest and most important of which is the Columbia River basalt. The volcanic cones and flows of the Cascade Range and the volcanics of Mt. Shasta and the northeastern portion of California are also included in this province. The region may be considered broadly as a great plateau.

The Blue Mountains of Oregon, which rise above the surrounding region flooded with lava, are not of sufficient extent or importance to be segregated into a separate province but constitute a ground-water region.

The hydrologic properties of lava, the ground-water motions therein, and the description of spectacular ground-water torrents issuing from the lavas of this region are described on pages 457 to 460.

III. The Great Valley of California Ground-water Province

The Great Valley of California, including the Sacramento and San Joaquin valleys, is a definite ground-water province. The valley fill encloses a vast ground-water body with characteristic features due chiefly to the structure and the way in which water is supplied to the fill (Fig. 186). The complicated structure of this body of valley fill has been discussed recently,[1] and no attempt is made here to describe it in detail or to discuss the history of its formation and the varied geological processes involved, but merely to summarize a few of its hydrologic characteristics.

Location and Topography.—The Great Valley occupies the center of the State of California and constitutes the largest single area of arable land in the West. It is surrounded by mountains, the Sierra Nevada on the east, the Tehachapi Mountains on the south, the Coast ranges on the west, and Mt. Shasta, Mt. Lassen, and the volcanic plateau on the north. The chief supply of water is furnished by the mountains to the north and east, the lofty peaks of which are covered with snow

[1] STEARNS, H. T., T. W. ROBINSON, and G. H. TAYLOR, Geology and Water Resources of the Mokelumne Area, Calif., *U. S. Geol. Surv. Water-Supply Paper* 619, 1930; TOLMAN, C. F., A Report on the Geology of the Mokelumne Region, pp. 20–46, unpublished report.

throughout the year.   The Tehachapi and Coast ranges furnish only small contributions to either the surface or ground-water supplies.

Fig. 186.—Ground-water provinces of California and ground-water areas of Coast Ranges of Central and Southern California province. I, Great Basin province; II, Columbia Plateau province; III, Great Valley of California province; IV, Province of Coast Ranges of Central and Southern California; IV-1 San Diego County; IV-2, Los Angeles basin; IV-3, Ventura basin; IV-4, Santa Barbara area; IV-5, Santa Maria basin; IV-6, Salinas Valley; IV-7, Santa Clara Valley; V, Northern Coast Range province.

Topographically the valley is a semibolson.   The Sacramento and San Joaquin rivers flow south and north down the axis of the valley, join in the center and break westward through the Coast ranges to the Pacific Ocean via Suisun Bay, Carquinez Straits, San Pablo and San Francisco bays and the Golden Gate.[1] For more than 100 miles north and south of their confluence the two rivers flow as anastomosing or braided streams through the basin and delta regions which were originally occupied by tule swamps, but are now reclaimed into the most productive land of the United States. This area represents the playa portion of the typical bolson.

Structure and Ground-water Supply.—The bajada or sloping piedmont plains surround the flood plains of the two rivers and rise gently to the encircling mountains. The piedmont deposits are made up of coalescing alluvial cones. Available ground water is found chiefly in the alluvial cones built by the streams debouching from the Sierra Nevada, with maximum yield in a belt about one-third the width of the cones located midway between the flood plains of the Sacramento and San Joaquin rivers and the foothills of the Sierra. The yield of the cones flanking the Coast ranges is small and the water is poor in the southern and central Coast range piedmont deposits, but better wells are obtained in the north.

It was formerly assumed that the piedmont deposits flanking the Sierra Nevada were of the nature of normal alluvial cones, of great thickness, deposited chiefly since the last westward tilting and uplift of the Sierra Nevada at the beginning of the Quaternary period. Recent detailed studies and sampling of drilling wells in the vicinity of the Mokelumne River have shown that the piedmont deposits of that area consist of marine, lacustrine, and alluvial formations. The older lacustrine and alluvial formations are composed entirely of volcanic debris and the younger consist of ordinary stream sediments. These piedmont formations vary in age from Eocene (locally Cretaceous) to Recent. The two volcanic horizons, one of Miocene and one of probable Pliocene age, can be identified in samples from wells, and can usually be recognized in the written logs of the drillers. As the older formations are widely distributed along the edge

[1] For the geology of this outlet see Appendix *D*, Geology of Upper San Francisco Bay Region, with Special Reference to a Salt Water Barrier Below Confluence of Sacramento and San Joaquin Rivers, by C. F. Tolman in *State of Calif., Div. Water Res. Bull.* 28, 1931.

of this foothill region, and as the entire eastern area is a topographic unit and has had a similar topographic history, the
writer believes that the complicated structure of the piedmont
alluvial deposits discovered in the Mokelumne area probably
characterizes these deposits for the length of the Sierra Nevada.

The upper horizon of volcanic detritus, older lacustrine and
alluvial deposits, and a recent alluvial formation are good water
producers. The water sands and gravels represent chiefly
stream deposits, and the encasing materials are aquicludes. The
percentage of water-bearing sand and gravel to silt and clay,
as shown by a comprehensive study of the well logs, is 16.5 per
cent for the younger alluvial material, 15.1 per cent for the
older alluvial and lacustrine deposits, and 10.8 per cent for the
alluvial and lacustrine material made up largely of volcanic
detritus. On account of the great number of wells which intersect and interconnect the various aquifers in the Lodi region, there
is no apparent confinement of water, and the ground water
functions as a single water body filling innumerable artificially
interconnected tubes or layers.

It is interesting to note that the streams in the Mokelumne
region that deposited the gravel channels in the volcanic detritus,
and probably those that laid down some of the older river
alluvium, did not debouch from the Sierra Nevada at the same
points as the present-day streams.[1] Therefore the aquifers do
not converge under the present stream, and the upper portions
of the alluvial cones are not uniformly pervious. This explains
in part the low seepage loss of the Mokelumne River.[2] (For
further discussion of influent seepage of the Mokelumne River
see pages 169–171.)

Irrigation and Ground Water.—Extensive irrigation in the
southern part of the San Joaquin Valley has built up the water
table, and furnishes ground water which is brought into use a
second time by pumping. The most striking example is the
great ground-water mound built up by irrigation on the alluvial
cone apexing at the point where the San Joaquin River debouches
from the Sierra Nevada.

[1] For description of the ancient drainage of the Sierra Nevada, see Walde-
mar Lindgren, Tertiary Gravels of the Sierra Nevada of California, *U.S.
Geol. Surv. Prof. Paper* 73, 1911.

[2] TOLMAN, C. F., Report on the Geology of the Mokelumne Region,
Unpublished report, pp. 44–46, 1930.

Water Conservation and Flood Control.—The engineering studies of the past 12 years have shown that there is an excess of water over irrigation requirements in the Sacramento River but a deficient supply in the San Joaquin River and in the southern portion and western slopes of the San Joaquin Valley. In dry years saline water moves up the lower reaches of the Sacramento and San Joaquin rivers and injures the productive delta region.[1]

A comprehensive plan of flood control by dams, redistribution of the water conserved, and maintenance of a minimum discharge in dry seasons to prevent the intrusion of saline waters up the rivers has been adopted by the State Legislature,[2] and construction has been started. Ground-water storage will result from increased irrigation and should be utilized as an auxiliary method of conservation of water wherever practical.

Valley Fill of Willamette Valley and Puget Sound Trough.— A large body of alluvium fills the structural trough crossing central Oregon and Washington. This depression is similar in many respects to the Sacramento Valley, and its valley fill encloses a large body of available water. However, the larger rainfall of the region and the abundant supply of surface water have delayed until recently extensive exploitation of the ground-water resources. The lack of development, and therefore of detailed information, renders it unnecessary to consider this region, although it undoubtedly is a distinct ground-water region.

IV. GROUND-WATER PROVINCE OF THE COAST RANGES OF CENTRAL AND SOUTHERN CALIFORNIA

The eastern boundary of this province follows the divide between the Pacific Ocean and the Salton Sink, the Mojave Desert and the San Joaquin Valley. The northern boundary is selected somewhat arbitrarily as coinciding with the course

[1] Economic Aspects of a Salt Water Barrier, *State of Calif., Div. Water Res. Bull.* 28, 1931; Report on Salt Water Barrier Below Confluence of Sacramento and San Joaquin Rivers, Calif.: *State of Calif., Div. Water Res. Bull.* 22, vol. 1, 1929.

[2] Report to Legislature of 1931 on State Water Plan, *State of Calif., Div. Water Res. Bull.* 25, 1930.

of the Sacramento River across the Coast ranges including Carquinez Strait, San Pablo and San Francisco Bay, and the Golden Gate (Fig. 186).

Structure and Ground-water Supply.—The principal ground-water bodies are in the mountain valleys of San Diego County, with but scanty water in the terraces fronting the ocean, in the valley fill of the Los Angeles basin, the Ventura basin, and the tributary Santa Clara Valley of Ventura County, the Santa Maria Valley, and the longitudinal valleys of the Coast ranges between Santa Barbara and San Francisco, the most important of which are the Salinas Valley, and the Santa Clara Valley of Santa Clara County. The large water bodies are without exception in valley fill.

The formations consist of a basement of granitic and intrusive rocks, metamorphic or cemented rocks of the Franciscan formation of Jurassic age, and an immense thickness (50,000 ft.) of Cretaceous, Tertiary, and Quaternary sedimentary rocks. None of these is an important aquifer in comparison with the valley fill, although locally good water supplies are pumped from the younger Tertiary sandstones. The demand for water has led to careful geological investigation of the Tertiary formations as a possible source of water. The sedimentary rocks are closely folded and all are cut by a great system of faults, some of which are still active and are progenitors of earthquakes. The trend of the main structural feature is shown in the topography. The ridges are mostly upraised folds or fault blocks and the valleys are sunken blocks filled with alluvium. The chief importance of the older formations is the type of valley fill derived therefrom. The detritus from the granitic rocks is built into a pervious valley fill. Alluvial material derived from shale is characterized by low permeability.

1. *San Diego County.*—In San Diego County the coast is lined with narrow beaches, and the streams have excavated deep cuts through upraised terraces and discharge directly into the ocean without laying down extensive alluvial deposits. In the granitic mountains which they drain, however, streams descend through narrow gorges from one open valley to another and have floored the valleys, excavated during more ancient cycles of erosion, with fairly thick deposits of pervious sand and gravel. These alluvial basins act as regulating reservoirs which are filled with

ground water in times of occasional floods, and drain slowly, maintaining stream flow far into the dry season.[1]

2. *The Los Angeles Basin.*—The Los Angeles basin, or South Coastal basin of California,[2] includes the coastal plain of Los Angeles and Orange counties, and the piedmont valleys of the Los Angeles, San Gabriel, and Santa Ana rivers between low hills protruding above the plain and valleys—the San Pedro, Potrero, and Puente hills. This area is bounded by the San Fernando, San Gabriel, San Jacinto, and Santa Ana mountains and the Pacific Ocean. The area is approximately 2,500,000 acres, about 45 per cent of which is underlain by productive ground-water basins.[3]

Diverted surface flow of streams and stored surface waters are able to furnish only about 10 per cent of the summer water supply; about 90 per cent originating within the South Coastal basin comes from the ground-water reservoirs. The capacities of most of the ground-water basins are so great that large excesses of ground water are stored during years of heavy rainfall to be utilized during years of subnormal rainfall. The total surface area of those portions of the ground-water basins in which the water level fluctuates is about 840,000 acres, and in this area it is estimated that every foot average rise or fall of the water table represents approximately 70,000 acre-ft. change in the amount of underground water.[4]

When development of ground water first began in this region, there was an excess rising to the surface at the outlets of all the principal basins and artesian pressures existed in many places. Pumping has depleted the artesian pressure and the areas characterized by flowing wells have been greatly reduced.

The Los Angeles basin is so called because it was occupied during the Tertiary period by an embayment of the ocean which

[1] ELLIS, A. J., and C. H. LEE, Geology and Ground Waters of the Western Part of San Diego Co., Calif., *U.S. Geol. Surv. Water-Supply Paper* 446, pp. 34–46, 1919.

[2] ECKIS, ROLLIN, Geology and Ground-water Storage Capacity of Valley Fill, South Coastal Basin Investigation, *State of Calif., Div. Water Res. Bull.* 45, 1934. This excellent contribution furnishes a wealth of information in regard to the hydrologic properties of the basin of especial interest to those engaged in spreading operations.

[3] *Ibid.*, p. 17.

[4] *Ibid.*, p. 18.

extended up to, and in places overtopped, the low granite mountains of the area.   Great thicknesses of marine sediments were deposited in this basin.   The sedimentary rocks were folded and, together with the basement rocks, were severely faulted, with the result that the region was broken into a complex system of fault blocks, and finally the blocks on the northern and eastern margins, some in the central portion, and the San Pedro block on the extreme southwest were elevated.   The present precipitous San Gabriel mountain range received its principal elevation in relatively recent times.   The granite mass of which it is composed was intensively faulted and fractured. The Santa Ana and San Gabriel rivers, and the tributaries of the Los Angeles River and other streams draining this upraised block carried down large amounts of alluvium, chiefly gravel and granitic sand, and floored the basin with an unusually pervious valley fill.   This alluvium completely buried the depressed fault blocks, those of intermediate elevation are either buried or their apices overtop the alluvium, and the higher blocks protrude well above the valley floor as ridges or low mountain ranges, such as the San Pedro Mountains, Potrero Hills, Puente Hills, and the Santa Ana Mountains (see Fig. 187).

The valley fill has been segmented into boxlike compartments or basins by the upraised fault blocks and by faults cutting the alluvium.   For example, the Santa Ana River has filled a depression between the San Andreas fault and the San Jacinto fault (Bunker Hill dike).   In this interfault segment is the San Bernardino artesian basin.   The Riverside artesian area overlies an old canyon system excavated in granitic rock.   These canyons were tributary to the Santa Ana River and were later buried with alluvium deposited by the master stream.   They slope toward the present river and their slope and restriction in width of bedrock canyons force pressure water in the alluvial fill to the surface.   Movement along the next important fault has elevated the Santa Ana Mountains and their continuation, the San Juan Hills, athwart the course of the river and forced it to excavate the Santa Ana canyon, from which the river debouches on the coastal plain where the final and most southerly alluvial cone has been built with a prominent artesian area near its margin and above the Inglewood fault zone.

FIG. 187.—Map of the Los Angeles basin showing mountains (depth of shading indicates elevation); alluvial fill, dotted; upper portions of cones, coarse dots; artesian areas (after Mendenhall), darker dotted and lined area; and faults, black lines (probable faults dashed). Important faults are numbered as follows: 1, San Andreas fault zone; 2, San Jacinto fault zone; 3, Chino fault; 4, Riverside (possible fault); 5, Whittier fault; 6, Chapman (probable fault); 7, Inglewood fault zone; and 8, San Pedro fault. The faults which have controlled the location of the more important artesian basins are as follows: *a*, the San Andreas and San Jacinto fault system between which occurs the San Bernardino artesian basin; *b*, the Chino fault above which is the Chino artesian area; *c*, Inglewood fault system above which is the Coastal Plain artesian area. According to Eckis the Riverside fault does not exist. The alluvium of the Riverside basin fills old channels cut in bedrock and water is forced to the surface by bedrock conditions.

Limitation in space forbids detailed discussion of the various faults and basins and the characteristics of the alluvial deposits in each basin. The general picture is shown in Fig. 187 and much more in detail in the map accompanying the report by Eckis. A list of the basins, showing area, specific yield, and ground-water storage capacity also appears on page 21 of the Eckis report.

The important hydrologic property of the alluvial deposits is their general pervious character due to the sandy detritus furnished by the disintegration of granitic rock of the San Gabriel and San Jacinto mountains. A somewhat unusual feature of the alluvial deposits is described by Eckis as follows:

Although it is true of the alluvial cones in this region, as it is of those in other localities, that the coarsest material is deposited at the canyon mouths, with the finer materials distributed farther out upon the cones, well logs show very clearly that the quantity of clay present in vertical section does not increase as a function of distance from cone apex. The reason for this is that the clays and clayey gravels were in large part formed by decomposition of alluvium above the water table and were not deposited as original clays. Compact red, yellow, and brown residual clay, conglomerate partly altered to clay, and occasional thin beds of calcite-cemented conglomerate, interbedded with water-yielding sand and gravel, comprise the alluvial deposits beneath the upper slopes of the cones.[1]

The alluvial cone may be considered to have two zones of deposition: (1) the upper part (near the cone apex) beneath which weathered materials predominate over unweathered materials, or the zone of intermittent deposition; (2) the lower part (toward the distal part of the cone), beneath which the gravels, sands, and clays are unweathered or only slightly weathered, the zone of continued deposition.[2]

The central portions of the upper alluvial cones and the upper and central portions of the coastal alluvial cones, which extend to the ocean shoreline, are pervious and are the principal areas of recharge and the most satisfactory for spreading operations. The distal portions of the lower cones contain much fine silt and the ground water is strongly confined. These deposits of valley fill constitute capacious subsurface reservoirs which more than compensate for the deficiency in surface storage due to unsatis-

[1] Eckis, *op. cit.*, p. 99.
[2] *Ibid.*, p. 103.

factory dam sites. Descriptions of spreading operations in this region appear in Chap. VII.

Other Important Deposits of Valley Fill.—3. The *Ventura basin* and the Santa Clara River valley, Ventura County, are north of the Los Angeles basin. The embayment in the vicinity of Ventura carries the thickest known deposits of Pliocene marine sediments. The alluvium is not thick and carries a rather poor quality of ground water; however, farther inland the alluvium of the Santa Clara Valley is an important aquifer.

4. At *Santa Barbara* the alluvial deposits near the coast carry a water body that has a very small natural recharge, and it has been recommended that this water supply be held in reserve for dry years when the city's supply of surface water fails.[1] The city also obtains water from a tunnel piercing the Tertiary sedimentary rock (Doulton tunnel).

5. The *Santa Maria basin* is fed by the Santa Maria and Sisquoc rivers. The alluvial deposits are thin and of low permeability. The ground water is mineralized by impurities derived from oil-bearing sedimentary rocks and brea deposits.

6. The *Salinas Valley*[2] is the longest of the intermontane valleys of the southern Coast ranges and carries a good water supply in the recently deposited sands of the river.

7. The *Santa Clara Valley* (Santa Clara County) is a structural depression, the northern portion of which is occupied by the Bay of San Francisco.[3] It receives a good supply of surface water from the Santa Cruz Mountains and the Mount Hamilton range. This region has received as intensive ground-water development as any in the state. Recent study shows that there is considerable variation in the structure and ground-water movements in the individual cones of this area. On the west side of the valley an older gravel formation (the Santa Clara gravels), dating back possibly to Pliocene times, holds most of the water. In the San Francisquito cone of this region there are three distinct water bodies—free ground water, an upper and a lower confined water body. Eighty-three per cent of the

[1] TOLMAN, C. F., and A. E. SEDGWICK, Unpublished reports on water supply of the City of Santa Barbara.

[2] HAMLIN, HOMER, Water Resources of the Salinas Valley, Calif., *U.S. Geol. Surv. Water-Supply Paper* 89, 1904.

[3] CLARK, W. O., Ground Water in Santa Clara Valley, Calif., *U.S. Geol. Surv. Water-Supply Paper* 519, 1924.

pumped water was derived from the lower confined water (1932).[1]
Overpumping has been carried on to such an extent on this cone
that stored water drawn from under San Francisco Bay is
now the chief source of pumped water. The unusual sinking
of the valley in this region and its probable relation to overpumping are discussed on pages 341–345.

V. THE NORTHERN COAST RANGE GROUND-WATER PROVINCE

This province is bounded by the Pacific Ocean on the west and
by the Sacramento Valley divide and the Columbia Plateau
province on the east. The region includes the northern Coast
ranges of California, Oregon, and Washington, including the
Klamath and Siskiyou mountains of Oregon and the Olympic
Mountains of Washington.

In California, except in the northern part of the region, structural valleys containing alluvial fill are fed by influent seepage
from the main longitudinal streams, such as the Trinity, Mad,
Eel, and Russian. A small area of volcanic cones and lava flows
contains bodies of heated ground water, hot springs, and geysers
in Napa, Lake, and Solano counties.

In northern California and Oregon the principal streams have
excavated deep canyons across the range on their way to the
ocean and the large intermontane structural valleys are not
developed. These rivers include the Klamath, Rogue, Umpqua,
and Columbia. The important body of alluvium in the Willamette and Puget Sound depression has been mentioned and is
included here on account of its geographic position.

All but the southern portion of this region receive heavy rainfall. Surface water is abundant. Most of the region is unsettled
and covered with extensive forests. Therefore the use of ground
water is not as yet fully developed and little detailed information
is available regarding ground-water conditions.

North of Carquinez Straits, near the mouth of Napa Valley,
large quantities of ground water are pumped and exported
for industrial purposes. In a lawsuit (John M. Ratto *et al. vs.*
California-Hawaiian Sugar Refining Co. *et al.*) regarding the
rights to the water, interesting geological and ground-water
data were described. Napa Valley is a syncline underlain by

---

[1] KILLINGSWORTH, C. C., and B. C. HYDE, A Report on the Underground
Water Supply of Stanford University and Vicinity, unpublished report, 1932.

porous and fractured lava rock. The hills on either side are
made up largely of formations that yield clay rather than sand
on disintegration, and therefore the valley fill is not pervious
and does not yield good supplies of water, although the region
is favored with fairly abundant rainfall.

The lava rock, however, furnishes good supplies of artesian
water. This volcanic aquifer underlies most of the valley, and
the temperature of the water in deep wells increases toward the
north, where the water has to be cooled before being used for
irrigation. At Calistoga the lava is sufficiently hot to produce
hot springs and small geysers. The outcrop of the porous
lava on the sides of the mountains is narrow, and if this were
the only source of recharge, the ground-water supply would
be small. The high temperature of the artesian water indicates
a small supply and slow ground-water movements. However,
reduction of pressure due to pumping of the deep water in lava
may draw water from the relatively impervious overlying
alluvium. On account of the large areal extent of the volcanic
aquifer, a very slow downward movement would contribute a
large volume of water. This may explain why heavy pumping
has not as yet seriously depleted this unique water body.

THE HAWAIIAN GROUND WATER PROVINCE

By R. G. Sohlberg[1]

The Hawaiian Islands ground-water province is characterized
by unusual climatic and geologic conditions which have developed
water bodies of peculiarly limited extent. The ground-water
resources of the islands have been intensely developed and interesting methods are employed to recover for use relatively small
amounts of water that would be considered insignificant even
in the semiarid western United States.

The manner of occurrence of ground water in the Hawaiian
Islands is intimately connected with the geologic structure and
erratic rainfall. No region anywhere, regardless of extent in area,
has as many variations in climate as this group of islands, although
they lie entirely within the equable trade-wind belt. The wide
variation in rainfall is due to the unidirectional character of the

[1] The writer acknowledges assistance given by the engineers and geologists
engaged in development of the water supply of the Hawaiian Islands.

prevailing winds which always blow from the northeast and therefore greatly increase the amount of precipitation falling on the
northeastern and eastern mountain slopes having an elevation of
1500 ft. and over. The leeward slopes are correspondingly dry
and the average annual variation in rainfall is as much as 400 in.
within a distance of 10 miles.

The main igneous complex of the islands is composed of count-
less thin flows of olivine basalt dipping gently away from the old
eruptive centers. The latter have been extensively eroded and
the feeder dikes and multiple flow planes often serve to guide
and localize the ground water coursing rapidly downward through
the permeable basalts. Because of the extensive joints and
cooling cracks traversing almost every bed, downward movement is very rapid. Owing to the uniformly vesicular texture,
the basalt will, when once saturated, retain a surprisingly large
supply of ground water. An important but adverse effect of
the high permeability is the consequent scarcity of tight reservoir
sites. This requires the most intelligent use of subsurface basins
for the impounding of ground water.

Location and General Geology.—The Hawaiian archipelago
lies about 2100 miles to the southwest of the California coast and
consists of a windward group, embracing the eight islands of
Hawaii, Maui, Molokai, Oahu, Kauai, Lanai, Niihau, and
Kahoolawe extending between latitudes 18°54′ and 22°15′ north
(see map, Fig. 188), and a leeward group composed of atolls,
reefed islands, banks and stacks located between latitudes 23°
and 28°15′ north. The entire chain of islands has a northwest-
southeast trend, is more than 1900 miles long, and is situated
on the northern margin of the tropical zone. Except for the
cable station and a recent air base on Midway Island, the 13
islets of the leeward group are not inhabited and are relatively
unimportant save as a game refuge.

The present-day islands are the extreme peaks of an immense
submarine volcanic ridge rising about 30,000 ft. above the ocean
floor, and they may therefore, in their entirety, be said to be
the largest mountain mass on earth. Volcanic activity probably
commenced in the Tertiary period along a pre-existing line of
weakness and has continued periodically to the present day.
All available data suggest that volcanism progressed southward,
being extinguished first in the northern members of the group.

All islands in the windward group have been formed by accumulation of thin flows of vesicular olivine basalt. This lava has, in general, been extruded from one or more vents or rift zones and has flowed successively outward in a quiet manner over the previously deposited and at least partially cooled beds. Numerous cracks appeared while the flows were cooling and these, coupled with the extreme vesicularity and great number of bedding or contact planes, combine to make the Hawaiian basalt one of the most permeable rocks known.

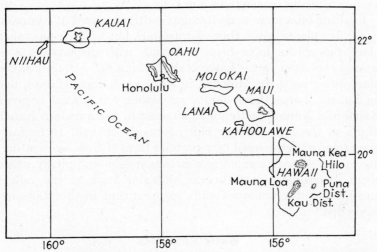

Fig. 188.—The Hawaiian Islands, windward group.

During Pleistocene time erosion was active, especially along the flanks of the major mountain masses, forming spacious amphitheater-headed valleys generally arranged in a transverse or radial manner in respect to the main range or peak. Alluvium was deposited partly as a thick blanket on the floors of the valleys and in part carried seaward and dropped in the coastal shallows. In later Pleistocene time, when the whole island group was extensively submerged, the valleys were further alluviated and also subjected to marine erosion. Old strand lines and submarine shelves that attest to former stands of the sea can probably be safely correlated with the interglacial periods.

During late Pleistocene and Recent times a great number of valley-filling flows have appeared, slightly different in mineral composition from the earlier flows. In certain districts, such as southwestern Oahu, southeastern Kauai, and southern Hawaii, tuff cones with accompanying driblet basalt were ejected as an aftermath of the main disturbance.[1] On Oahu these attain great size, examples being Diamond and Koko heads, Punchbowl, and the Salt Lake craters. These craters were thrown up near the margins of the islands as a result of the violent steam explosions occurring when the hot lava flows encountered the sea water. According to some authorities[2] such explosive eruptions were practically complete in 5 or 6 hr.

Faulting on a large scale has apparently occurred at comparatively few places in the Hawaiian Islands, but where it has taken place the effects have been profound, with displacements of several thousand feet. Large-scale faulting has certainly taken place along northern Molokai, in the Kau district, Hawaii, and on Lanai. Large throw faults are strongly indicated between Kauai and Niihau[3] and on a small scale in northwestern Kauai. Many of the high palis or cliffs, formerly thought to be fault scarps, have been formed by a peculiar form of chemical weathering combined with competitive stream erosion and piracy which result in coalescence of the amphitheater heads of the valleys and produce the scalloped cliffs so prominent in the Hawaiian landscape.[4]

Water Resources

Temperature and Rainfall.—Temperature and rainfall are direct opposites in Hawaii; the former deviates very slightly from a yearly mean, whereas the latter varies within short distances from one extreme to the other. The maximum temperature recorded, in the neighborhood of Aiea, was 97°F. and the mini-

---

[1] HINDS, N. E. A., The Geology of Kauai and Niihau, *B. P. Bishop Museum Bull.* 71, 1930; STEARNS, H. T., and W. O. CLARK, Geology and Water Resources of the Kau District, Hawaii, *U.S. Geol. Surv. Water-Supply Paper* 616, 1930; WENTWORTH, C. K., Pyroclastic Geology of Oahu, *B. P. Bishop Museum Bull.* 24, 1930.

[2] WENTWORTH, *op. cit.*

[3] HINDS, *op. cit.*

[4] PALMER, H. S., Soil Forming Processes in the Hawaiian Islands from the Chemical and Mineralogical Points of View, *Soil Sci.*, vol. 31, no. 4, 1931; WENTWORTH, C. K., Principles of Stream Erosion in Hawaii, *Jour. Geol.*, vol. 36, p. 385, 1928.

mum was registered at Humuula, Hawaii, as 25°F., a total range of 72°F. On Mauna Kea and Mauna Loa (each nearly 14,000 ft. above the sea) freezing conditions prevail during part of the year, but frost rarely descends below the 4000-ft. level and probably never below 2500 ft. The wettest place in the islands and one of the rainiest in the world is Mt. Waialeale, Kauai, where the annual rainfall averaged at least 476 in. during the period from 1911 to 1917. In 1920 rainfall amounted to 549 in. at this place. Mt. Kukui, West Maui, has an annual rainfall of about 400 in., whereas 7 miles away at Alawalu, Maui, the precipitation amounts to only 8 in. a year. In 1915 at Hana, on the same island, 24 in. fell in 4 hours.

Occurrence of Ground Water.—Ground water in the islands occurs as five distinct types, each occurrence requiring a different method of treatment for recovery and utilization. These will be discussed briefly in the following order:

1. Basal ground water.
   a. Unconfined (occurring according to the Ghyben-Herzberg principle).
   b. Confined (artesian).
2. Perched or high-level ground water.
   a. Confined between dikes.
   b. On old alluvial deposits.
   c. On beds of ash or tuff.

Unconfined basal ground water floats on salt ground water derived from the ocean (pages 245–248). The specific gravity of the salt water is 1.024 and from the Herzberg[1] equation the thickness of the fresh ground-water body below sea level is $41\frac{2}{3}$ times the depth of ground water above sea level. The curvature of the water table varies inversely with the permeability of the water-bearing material and, as the lavas are extremely permeable, the water table is nearly flat and the depth of fresh ground water below sea level is small. Hence in the absence of some structural dam the fresh-water lenses produce water tables extending only a few inches to a foot or so above mean sea level, and the bottom of the lenses are 10 to 40 ft. below sea level.

In some cases, however, peculiar structural conditions may either guide and localize rainwater from large surface areas or

[1] Herzberg, Die Wasserversorgung einiger Nordseebäder, *Jour. Gasbeleuchtung Wasserversorg.*, Jahrg. 44, Munich, 1901.

restrain fresh ground water from taking its usual lateral course to the sea. An instance of the first case is mentioned by Lindgren for Molokai[1] where the general dip of the lava beds of the east Molokai volcano is to the south, thus conducting the waters of the rainy northern upland plateau to the southeastern part of the island where, as a result, the water table is raised several feet.

Confined Basal Ground Water.—Where basal ground water is restrained from its usual free lateral migration to the sea, a special artesian condition is created sufficiently important to warrant discussion as a distinct type. On Oahu and Kauai erosional agents such as waves and running water have modified the surface and general outline of the island more than in the other major land masses in the group. This is probably due to the fact that volcanism suffered extinction in these islands long before it did in the other large members of the windward chain, and to greater relative rate of weathering on these two islands. Streams and waves have combined to deposit sedimentary coastal prisms of considerable depth on the southwestern and northern coasts of Oahu and, to a less extent, on the southeastern and probably the western coasts of Kauai.

The sedimentary beds consist of coral limestone, coral sand, and mud with contained disintegrated basalt flows and cinders. The most important member of the series is a clay deposit found just above the weathered surface of the older basalt and therefore the lowest member of the prism. The clay member is composed for the most part of lateritic soil, derived from the basalt, and submarine stream deposits, both of which have been compacted and are sufficiently impermeable to form the confining cap rock necessary in an artesian system. The beds thicken markedly seaward so that the shape of the cross section is prismatic. Uplift of the islands has resulted in the exposure of the upper surface of the prism which now forms the prominent coastal plain, such as that bordering the southwestern coasts of Oahu.

In 1926 Palmer[2] made an extensive examination of the artesian area known to exist in the Honolulu district and came to the

[1] LINDGREN, W., The Water Resources of Molokai, Hawaiian Islands, *U.S. Geol. Surv. Water-Supply Paper* 77, p. 27, 1903.

[2] PALMER, H. S., The Geology of the Honolulu Artesian Basin, *Honolulu Sewer and Water Comm., Suppl. Report*, pp. 39–44, 1927.

conclusion that four distinct isopiestic areas exist, owing to the separating V-shaped deposits of old alluvial valley fill. These act as underground dams, dividing the areas overlying a common reservoir in the Koolau range. The impermeable lower surface of the coastal prism acts as a barrier to the movement of fresh ground water oceanward, elevating the water level about 25 ft. (Fig. 189).

Little is known concerning the exact structure of the artesian areas on Kauai except that artesian water is found inland from the sedimentary beach deposits along the eastern, southeastern, and western shores of the island.

Ground Water Confined between Dikes.—In the Koolau range, on the island of Oahu, large quantities of ground water have been developed by tunneling (notably the Waiahole bore), piercing the dike complex encountered below the crest of the range. These dikes are usually found throughout the islands in various numbers and attitudes near the old volcanic vents and along the main rift zones. The Koolau dikes are exceptional in their number, more or less parallel arrangement, and nearly vertical attitude (Fig. 189). Other areas are known to exist in central Kauai, northeastern Molokai, and high-level springs indicate another system in the Kahala Mountains of Hawaii. The Mauna Kea-Mauna Loa massif is evidently insufficiently eroded as yet to expose these dikes in great numbers.[1]

As a rule, dike systems, when intelligently pierced, will yield copious flows of water at the outset, decreasing to a remarkably steady flow varying little from month to month. The 10-year record in the main Waiahole tunnel shows an average flow of 6 m.g.d. for the period 1917–1927. During this time the absolute minimum and maximum average percolation into this tunnel amounted to 3.5 and 8.5 m.g.d., respectively.[2]

The dikes are extremely fine-grained basalt and have been intruded into the more pervious vesicular basalt characteristic of the group as a whole. The material between dikes constitutes vertical aquifers. That the water storage obtained between these dikes is large is shown by tests conducted during drilling operations on the Waiahole tunnel. Gages on drill holes registered pressures up to 65 lb. to the square inch, indicating a water

[1] STEARNS, and CLARK, *op. cit.*
[2] *Report Honolulu Sewer and Water Commission*, 1929.

table 150 ft. above tunnel level or 900 ft. above sea level. Stearns[1] maintains that these bodies of ground water probably extend downward to sea level, being held at that point by the

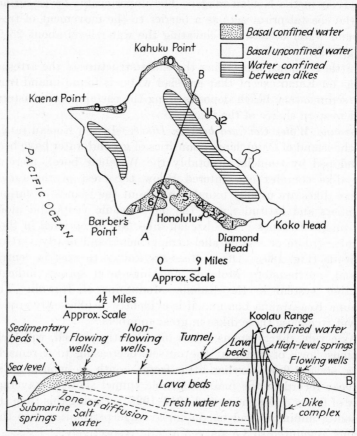

FIG. 189.—Map of Oahu showing various types of occurrence of ground water and isopiestic areas. Cross section along line A-B shows structure of water-bearing deposits. Vertical scale of cross section exaggerated. (*Modified after Stearns.*)

roots of the dike system. According to this theory, the best results will be obtained by driving the tunnels at the lowest possible elevation. Little has been done outside of Oahu in

[1] STEARNS, H. T., K. N. VAKSVIK, The Geology and Ground Water Resources of the Island of Oahu, Hawaii, *Terr. Div. Hydrography Bull.* 1, pp. 65–66, 401, 446, 1935. *Bull.* 2 contains the geologic map.

developing the water caught and held in the igneous complex of the rift zones.

Ground Water Perched on Old Alluvial Deposits.—In the Honolulu district a number of fairly large valleys transverse to the main axis of the Koolau range have been filled to considerable depth with post-Koolau volcanics, which consist of vesicular basalt flows, clinker, and *aa* interbedded with ash and tuff and floored by thick deposits of consolidated alluvium deposited on the land surface of former drainage systems. Usually the surface of this alluvium, where it is overlain by permeable beds. offers a favorable horizon for the gathering of perched ground water. If, in addition, the basins have a fairly large drainage area located in a region of heavy precipitation and at a sufficiently high altitude so that ground water may be delivered to the point of consumption without excessive pumping, the probable success of any project to recover this water is good. Four of the larger Honolulu valleys satisfy these conditions; namely, Kalihi, Nuuanu, Pauoa, and Manoa. Up to the present time, however, none of these valleys has been tunneled according to any comprehensive plan. Several tunnels in Nuuanu Valley draw considerable water from the surface of interbedded and highly consolidated tuffs that are sufficiently impermeable to constitute good aquicludes, and perched water horizons lie above one another and the basal water table.

Recently the Board of Water Supply of Honolulu has been engaged in an extensive diamond-drilling program, particularly in upper Nuuanu Valley, to determine the exact nature and extent of the perching structure and to observe fluctuations of the water table. The drill cores found an extensive alluvial deposit, ranging in thickness from 60 to 130 ft., underlying a series of basalt flows, ash beds, cinder and tuff cones having an average aggregate thickness of about 350 ft. The zone of saturation apparently is approximately 110 ft. thick with a thin perched body of water spilling into this zone from near the surface. The water table was found to fluctuate slightly with rainfall, with a lag of about three weeks. Various attempts have been made to measure the rate of movement of this underground water body in order to determine the volume to be expected if developed, but these investigations have unfortunately been unsuccessful to date.

In Kalihi and Pauoa valleys various tunnels have been driven into the late volcanic flows considerably above the central axis of the alluvial floors. In Manoa Valley several tunnels penetrate the Koolau basalt, obtaining both perched ground water from the local tuffs and the seepage usually encountered in fractured and cracked basalt located in the rainy belt. Present indications are that tunnels driven in the old alluvial floors and contacting the lower surface of the post-Koolau volcanics, along the central axis of the valleys, would develop perched ground water.

Ground Water Perched on Ash or Tuff.—Throughout the Hawaiian Islands are more or less continuous beds of red ash that have been thrown out from nearby vents and carried by the wind over considerable areas. In only one place, however, are the beds of sufficient thickness and areal extent to offer a good perching surface for ground water. In the Kau district,[1] on the island of Hawaii, large ash beds are found, varying in thickness from a few inches to as much as 55 ft. The beds may also entirely disappear owing to erosion prior to deposition of the later lava flows. At other places ash beds of small areal extent may be intercalated with several lava flows, or several thin ash beds may persist for great distances. The water moves rapidly downward through the pervious basalt found in this region to the ash beds, coursing along their upper surfaces to a main drainage channel and finally emerging as a cliff spring. This perched ground water is, unfortunately, very irregular in occurrence owing to the variation in thickness and extent of the ash beds and to the abrupt changes often encountered in the permeability of the ash.

The method of development recommended by Clark,[1] who has made a special study of this problem, consists of driving tunnels into the ash and contacting the overlying water-bearing basalt, meanwhile keeping the line of the tunnel perpendicular to the old drainage lines of the surface on which the ash was deposited. This method has been found to be very effective in recovering such small bodies of perched water as exist in the district.

Development of Ground Water. *Island of Maui.*—Unconfined basal ground water has been developed to a greater extent on Maui than on any other member of the group, because on this

[1] STEARNS, and CLARK, *op. cit.*

island no confining structure exists capable of producing an artesian condition, nor has Maui any large streams or large bodies of perched water. Because of the very slight hydraulic gradient, wells when drilled must be carried to considerable depth to produce effectively. At such depths they draw upon the lower portion of the fresh ground-water lens and, when subjected to heavy pumping, upon the brackish zone of diffusion between the fresh- and salt-water bodies. Hence either batteries of wells must be drilled or some other method devised to extend the cone of depression.

The East Maui Irrigation Company has pioneered in a unique method for the recovery of basal ground water, originally developed by digging inclined shafts down to and below sea level not far inland and locating the pumps in the shafts. Recently this ground water has been obtained by sinking vertical shafts to approximate sea level farther inland, building pump chambers at the bottom of the shafts, and extending large horizontal tunnels slightly below sea level to skim off the fresh water. The most effective method is to drive these tunnels in a general inland direction, perpendicular to the strike of the formation, so that they cut across the dip of the lava beds. A total of 200 m.g.d. are withdrawn by the East Maui Irrigation Company from 17 such developments. At Nahiku, East Maui, a little perched water is recovered from 16 tunnels at an elevation of 1300 ft., yielding in aggregate somewhat above 5 m.g.d.

Island of Oahu.—The City of Honolulu and various sugar and pineapple plantations are the chief consumers of water on this island. Several methods of development are used: (1) Drilled wells penetrating both confined and unconfined basal ground-water bodies; (2) tunnels recovering ground water confined between dikes; (3) tunnels and springs drawing on ground water perched on alluvium or tuff; (4) surface water recovered and impounded in the upper parts of stream drainage areas; and (5) comparatively shallow wells tapping gravel and other pervious layers in the coastal sedimentaries. The latter supply is largely derived from return irrigation water and possibly overflow from the artesian reservoir, although most of the excess artesian water is thought to escape seaward underneath the confining sediments of the coastal prism, rising to the surface as submarine fresh-water springs.

Owing to the scarcity of tight surface storage sites in the islands, any future plan of water development must emphasize storage in natural underground reservoirs, as the water supply of the territory is affected by periods of dry years. Clark and Stearns[1] have recommended sealing of large bores, obtaining ground water from the dike complex, in such a way that they may be opened as the ground water is needed. One such operation has recently proved successful; enormous quantities of water were stored between the dikes and used periodically for irrigation purposes.

Stearns[2] believes that at present the ground water perched on the old alluvium of the higher valleys in the Honolulu region empties into the sea and never reaches the artesian reservoir, and thus is completely wasted. Effective tunnel systems would, presumably, prevent this wastage. Also it is believed that by abandoning the present wells for shafts of the Maui type, the yield of the four isopiestic areas in the Honolulu district could be markedly increased. Kunesh[3] calculates that the ultimate yield is around 41 m.g.d., whereas at present only about 32 m.g.d. are used.

Island of Kauai.—Very little detailed or systematic ground-water data exist for this island at the present time. It is known, however, that artesian conditions similar to those on Oahu prevail along the eastern coastal plain and on the extreme western and southwestern part of the island. Undoubtedly much stream detritus has been swept seaward along the eastern marine platform as is shown by the littoral deposits exposed along the coast from Hanamaulu to Kapaa. Another and similar area may be present on the southwestern shores near the mouth of the Waimea River. That these deposits are as thick as the sedimentary prisms of the Honolulu region is doubtful; they certainly are not so effective as a confining medium for the basal ground water, as is shown by the considerably lower water table in these areas. Most of the water used by Kauai is pumped from drilled wells tapping the basal ground-water reservoir. It follows, therefore, that most of developments are located on the lowlands comparatively near the coast.

[1] STEARNS and VAKSVIK, *op. cit.*

[2] *Ibid.*

[3] KUNESH, J. F., Surface Water Supply on the Island of Oahu, 1909–1928, *Honolulu Sewer and Water Comn. Suppl. Rept.*, 1929.

Near Eleele on the southwest coast of Kauai the McBryde Sugar Company operates two pumps obtaining water from tunnels located fairly close to the sea. The static head is about 2 ft., indicating a depth of about 85 ft. to salt water. Throughout the region there is a very dense basalt flow extending from sea level to a maximum depth of 40 ft. below sea level. The tunnels serving one of the above-mentioned pumps are cut at a depth of 50 ft. below sea level, finding water in the clinker and lava tubes below this apparently confining flow. The operating drawdown at this pump is 35 to 40 ft., yet the salt content of the water does not run more than 40 grains per U.S. gallon. The length of this particular tunnel system is about 4000 ft. Detailed geological examination would doubtless reveal a very interesting confining structure at this point, capable of protecting the fresh ground water from salt-water invasion to a greater depth than would be expected were no such structure present.

Island of Hawaii.—The only permanent streams on the island are located on the northeastern coast from Hilo to Upalu Point. This is also the windward and rainy side and is therefore by far the best watered land on Hawaii, extensive ground-water development being unnecessary. In the Kau district[1] to the south, sugar cane is grown on the higher flats and, owing to the steep surface grade in all but a few areas, the cane must be transported to the mill in flumes with the aid of water. The flume water is used again at the mills in the process of crushing and boiling the cane. As a result ground-water development has reached a more advanced stage in this district than anywhere else on the island.

No perched water has been found in the Kau district except that encountered on the upper surfaces of the ash beds. This, though limited and liable to extreme fluctuations, is the only available water in the district because of its high elevation.

Basal ground water can be used on Hawaii but, because of the comparatively high elevation of most of the agricultural land, the wells would be exceedingly deep—in most cases over a thousand feet—and therefore not economically feasible.

Island of Molokai.—Like Maui, Oahu, and Kauai-Niihau, Molokai is a doublet cone consisting of the relatively low mass of Mauna Loa in the west and an arcuate mountain range to the

[1] STEARNS and CLARK, *op. cit.*

east, attaining an elevation of 5000 ft. Between these two high areas is a low saddle or gap containing 14,000 acres of the most fertile land on the island. The problem on Molokai is to bring water in sufficiently large quantities to this elevated region, which is suitable for the growing of sugar cane. The three principal streams of the island are situated in the mountainous northeastern part farthest away from the cane land. As there is no perched water developed on Molokai as yet, the entire supply must be obtained from spring and stream sources and brought to the saddle region in flumes and canals or pumped at great cost from wells near the seacoast. A system of tunnels and canals could probably be constructed through the eastern range so as to tap the water likely to be encountered between the dikes and divert surface waters from the rainy northern slopes, but such a system would probably far exceed allowable costs.

Lanai, Niihau, and Kahoolawe are too small to support large plantations and so have none but the very simplest arrangements for the recovery of stream flow and rain water. On Lanai, for example, tarpaulins are spread at night to catch the dew.

References

Ground-water Provinces of the United States

Fuller, M. L., Underground Waters of Eastern United States, *U.S. Geol. Surv. Water-Supply Paper* 114, pp. 35–40, 1905.

Meinzer, O. E., The Occurrence of Ground Water in the United States, *U.S. Geol. Surv. Water-Supply Paper* 489, Chap. IV, pp. 193–309, 1923.

Ries, H., and T. L. Watson, "Engineering Geology," John Wiley & Sons, Inc., pp. 330–337, 1915.

Glacial Drift Ground-water Province

Fuller, M. L., *op. cit.*, Glacial Drift in Eastern United States.

Meinzer, O. E., *Water-Supply Paper* 489, *op. cit.*, pp. 283–291. See list of publications regarding water in the glacial drift of the United States on p. 283.

Appalachian Ground-water Province

Fuller, M. L., *op. cit.*

Meinzer, O. E., *op. cit.*, pp. 196–204. See list of publications on p. 196 regarding water in pre-Cambrian rocks in the United States.

Atlantic Coastal Plains Ground-water Province

Fuller, M. L., *op. cit.*

LONSDALE, J. T., Geology and Ground-water Resources of Atascosa and Frio Counties, Texas, *U.S. Geol. Surv. Water-Supply Paper* 676, 1935.

MEINZER, O. E., *op. cit.* See list of publications on p. 271 regarding ground water in Tertiary rocks in the United States.

STEPHENSON, L. W., W. N. LOGAN, and G. A. WARING, Ground-water Resources of Mississippi, *U.S. Geol. Surv. Water-Supply Paper* 576, 1928.

Survey of the Underground Waters of Texas: *Dept. of Interior, Memo. for the Press*, Release for Feb. 16, 1931.

Ground-water Resources of the Houston-Galveston Area, Texas, *Dept. of Interior, Memo. for the Press*, Release for Oct. 17, 1932.

Paleozoic Ground-water Province of the Central Mississippi Valley

FULLER, M. L., *op. cit.* Contains accounts of the underground supply of individual states.

MEINZER, O. E., *op. cit.*, pp. 201–244. Discussion of Paleozoic systems.

Great Plains Cretaceous Ground-water Province

MEINZER, O. E., *op. cit.* For bibliography pertaining to ground water in Cretaceous rocks, see pp. 251–252.

—— Problems of the Soft Water Supply of the Dakota Sandstone, *U.S. Geol. Surv. Water-Supply Paper* 597, pp. 147–170, 1929.

SIMPSON, H. E., Geology and Ground-water Resources of North Dakota, *U.S. Geol. Surv. Water-Supply Paper* 598, 1929.

Great Basin Ground-water Province

CLARK, W. O., and C. W. RIDDELL, Exploratory Drilling for Water and Use of Ground Water for Irrigation in Steptoe Valley, Nevada, *U.S. Geol. Surv. Water-Supply Paper* 465, 1920.

LEE, C. H., Water Resources of a Part of Owens Valley, Calif., *U.S. Geol. Surv. Water-Supply Paper* 294, 1912.

MEINZER, O. E., *Water-Supply Paper* 498, *op. cit.*, pp. 291–305.

—— Geology and Water Resources of Big Smoky, Clayton, and Alkali Spring Valleys, Nevada, *U.S. Geol. Surv. Water-Supply Paper* 423, 1917.

Columbia Plateau Ground-water Province

LANDOS, H., Preliminary Report on the Underground Waters of Washington, *U.S. Geol. Surv. Water-Supply Paper* 111, 1905.

MEINZER, O. E., *Water-Supply Paper* 489, *op. cit.*, pp. 279–282, 313.

RUSSELL, I. C., Geology and Water Resources of Nez Perce Co., Idaho, *U.S. Geol. Surv. Water-Supply Paper* 53, 1901; *U.S. Geol. Surv. Bull.* 199, Geology and Water Resources of Snake River Plains, 1902; Preliminary Report on Artesian Basins of Southwestern Oregon, *Water-Supply Paper* 78, 1903; Geology and Water Resources of Central Oregon, *U.S. Geol. Surv. Bull.* 252, 1905.

Great Valley of California Ground-Water Province

BRYAN, KIRK, Geology and Ground-Water Resources of Sacramento Valley, Calif., *U.S. Geol. Surv. Water-Supply Paper* 495, 1924.

MEINZER, O. E., *Water-Supply Paper* 489, *op. cit.*, pp. 291–295.

MENDENHALL, W. C., R. B. DOLE, and H. STABLER, Ground Water in San Joaquin Valley, Calif., *U.S. Geol. Surv. Water-Supply Paper* 398, 1916.

STEARNS, H. T., T. W. ROBINSON, and G. H. TAYLOR, Geology and Water Resources of the Mokelumne Area, Calif., *U.S., Geol. Surv. Water-Supply Paper* 619, 1930.

Ground-water Province of the Coast Ranges of California

CLARK, W. O., Ground Water in Santa Clara Valley, Calif., *U.S. Geol. Surv. Water-Supply Paper* 519, 1924.

ECKIS, ROLLIN, Geology and Ground Water Storage Capacity of Valley Fill, South Coastal Basin Investigation, *State Calif. Div. Water Res., Bull.* 45, 1933.

ELLIS, A. J., and C. H. LEE, Geology and Ground Waters of the Western Part of San Diego County, Calif., *U.S. Geol. Surv. Water-Supply Paper* 446, 1919.

HAMLIN, HOMER, Water Resources of the Salinas Valley, Calif., *U.S. Geol. Surv. Water-Supply Paper* 89, 1904.

MENDENHALL, W. C., The Hydrology of San Bernardino Valley, Calif., *U.S. Geol. Surv. Water-Supply Paper* 142, 1905; Ground Waters and Irrigation Enterprises in the Foothill Belt, Southern Calif., *Water-Supply Paper* 219, 1908.

Ventura County Investigation, *State Calif. Div. Water Res., Bull.* 46, 1933.

Hawaiian Ground-water Province

BRANNER, J. C., Notes on the Geology of the Hawaiian Islands, *Amer. Jour. Sci.*, vol. 14, 1903.

DAVIS, W. M., The Island of Oahu, *Jour. Geog.*, vol. 22, no. 9, 1923.

DUNHAM, K. C., Crystal Cavities in the Lavas from the Hawaiian Islands, *Amer. Mineralogist*, vol. 18, p. 372, 1933.

HINDS, N. E. A., The Relative Ages of Hawaiian Landscapes, *Univ. Calif. Dept. Geol. Sci. Bull.*, vol. 20, 1931.

—— The Geology of Kauai and Niihau, *B. P. Bishop Mus. Bull.* 71, 1930.

HITCHCOCK, C. H., The Geology of Oahu, *Bull. Geol. Soc. Amer.*, vol. 11, 1900.

—— Hawaii and Its Volcanoes, *Hawaiian Gazette*, 2d ed., 1911.

Report Honolulu Sewer and Water Comm., 1929.

KUNESH, J. F., Surface Water Supply of the Island of Oahu, 1909–1928: *Honolulu Sewer and Water Comm. Suppl. Rept.*, 1929.

LINDGREN, W., The Water Resources of Molokai, Hawaiian Islands, *U.S. Geol. Surv. Water-Supply Paper* 77, 1903.

MCCOMBS, J., and A. G. FIEDLER, Methods of Exploring and Repairing Leaky Artesian Wells, *U.S. Geol. Surv. Water-Supply Paper* 596-A, pp. 4–24, 1927.

PALMER, H. S., The Geology of the Honolulu Artesian Basin, *Honolulu Sewer and Water Comm. Suppl. Rept.*, 1927.

———— Soil Forming Processes in the Hawaiian Islands from the Chemical and Mineralogical Points of View, *Soil Sci.*, vol. 31, no. 4, 1931.

STEARNS, H. T., and W. O. CLARK, Geology and Water Resources of the Kau District, Hawaii, *U.S. Geol. Surv. Water-Supply Paper* 616, 1930.

STEARNS, H. T., and K. N. VAKSVIK, The Geology and Ground Water Resources of the Island of Oahu, Hawaii, *Bull.* 1 *Terr. Div. Hydrography,* 1935; *Bull.* 2 contains the geologic map.

U.S. Geol. Surv. Water-Supply Papers, Surface Water Supply of Hawaii, issued annually.

WENTWORTH, C. K., Pyroclastic Geology of Oahu, *B. P. Bishop Museum Bull.* 30, 1926.

———— The Geology of Lanai, *B. P. Bishop Museum Bull.* 24, 1925.

———— Estimates of Marine and Fluvial Erosion in Hawaii, *Jour. Geol.*, vol. 35, p. 117, 1927.

———— Principles of Stream Erosion in Hawaii, *Jour. Geol.*, vol. 36, p. 385, 1928.

WILLIAMS, HOWELL, Notes on the Characteristics and Classification of Pyroclastic Rocks, *Proc. Liverpool Geol. Soc.*, vol. 14, 1926.

GLOSSARY

Aeration, Zone of, or Zone of Suspended Water. The zone above the water table in which interstices are partly filled with ground air except in the saturated portion of the capillary fringe.

Air-mass Analysis. A method of weather forecasting based on the assumption that all large-scale meteorological phenomena can be traced to a region of discontinuity existing between two adjacent masses of air possessing unlike physical properties.

Alluvial Cone. A body of alluvial material deposited by a stream debouching from the region undergoing erosion above the apex of the cone.

Apparent Specific Gravity (Volume-Weight). The ratio of the weight of a unit volume of oven-dry soil to that of an equal volume of water under standard conditions. This term may be applied to natural undisturbed field samples or to laboratory samples.

Aquiclude. A formation which, although porous and capable of absorbing water slowly, will not transmit it fast enough to furnish an appreciable supply for a well or spring.

Aquifer. A geologic formation or structure that transmits water in sufficient quantity to supply pumping wells or springs.

Aquifuge. A rock which contains no interconnected openings and therefore neither absorbs nor transmits water.

Area of Diversion. That portion of the area of influence of a pumping well outside of the ground-water divide. In this area the modified contours indicate that ground water is drawn in from beyond the margins of the cone of depression to replace water diverted by the pump.

Area of Influence. The area beneath which ground-water or pressure-surface contours are modified by pumping.

Area of Pumping Depression. The area overlying the cone of pumping depression, or cone of water-table depression. (See Water-table depression, Cone of.)

Artesian Well. A well tapping a confined or artesian aquifer in which the static water level stands above the water table. The term is sometimes used to include all wells tapping confined water, in which case those wells with water level above the water table are said to have *positive artesian head* (pressure) and those with water level below the water table, *negative artesian head.*

Attached Ground Water. The portion of ground water adhering to the pore walls. It is assumed to be equal in amount to the residual water left after draining (pellicular water) and is measured by specific retention.

Available Moisture. See Soil Moisture.

Average Velocity. Measured by the volume of ground water passing through a unit cross-sectional area divided by the porosity of the water-transmitting material.

Bank Storage. Storage of water in alluvial deposits adjacent to a stream during high-water stage of stream flow. The water is gradually discharged at low-water stage.

Bolson. A topographic basin with centripetal drainage system.

Capillarity. The property of tubes with hairlike openings when immersed in a fluid to raise (or depress) the fluid in the tubes above (or below) the surface of the fluid in which they are immersed.

Capillary Fringe. The zone immediately above the water table in which water is held above the water table by capillarity.

Capillary Head. The difference between capillary lift and the position of the meniscus in a capillary opening.

Capillary Interstice. An opening small enough to produce appreciable capillary rise.

Cavern Flow. Sub-surface turbulent flow partly filling caverns or large open conduits.

Channel Storage. Surface water stored between stream banks. It varies with stream level.

Circle of Influence. See Area of Influence. The latter term is preferred.

Climatic Cycle. Periodic fluctuation of climate, including a series of dry years and a preceding or following series of years with heavy rainfall.

Climatic Year. A period used in meteorological measurements, usually beginning after the end of the rainy season.

Compaction, Water of. Water furnished by destruction of pore space owing to compaction of sediments.

Confined Ground Water. A body of ground water overlain by material sufficiently impervious to sever free hydraulic connection with overlying ground water except at the intake. Confined water moves in conduits under the pressure due to difference in head between intake and discharge areas of the confined water body.

Connate Water. Water entrapped in the interstices of a sedimentary rock at the time it was deposited.

Cosmic Water. Juvenile water that comes in from space with meteorites.

Critical Velocity. For porous media, the maximum velocity under which laminar flow can occur. In pipe flow, the velocity at which eddying commences is called the *higher critical velocity*. The velocity at which eddies in turbulence die out is the *lower critical velocity*.

Dilation, Water of. Water in excess of water of saturation held by sedimentary material in an inflated state (water of supersaturation as defined by C. H. Lee).

Drawdown. Lowering of water level caused by pumping. It is measured for a given quantity of water pumped during a specified period, or after the pumping level has become constant.

Effective Porosity. The portion of pore space in saturated permeable material in which movement of water takes place. It is measured with satisfactory accuracy by specific yield.

Effective Size of Grain of Water-bearing Material. The grain size of a theoretical body of homogeneous material of one grain size that would transmit water at the same rate as the material under consideration. It is also defined (by Hazen) as the diameter of a grain of such size that 10 per cent of the material (by weight) consists of smaller grains and 90 per cent of larger grains.

Effective Velocity. The actual or field velocity of ground water percolating through water-bearing material. It is measured by the volume of ground water passing through a unit cross-sectional area divided by effective porosity.

Effluent Seepage. Diffuse discharge of ground water to the ground surface.

Evaporation. Vaporization that takes place at a temperature below the boiling point, limited by some writers to the physical process and used by others to include the biological process of transpiration. Evaporation is also commonly used to designate the quantity of water that is evaporated. The rate is expressed in depth of water removed per unit of time.

Evaporation Opportunity. The ratio of the rate of evaporation from a land or water surface to the potential rate of evaporation (evaporativity) under existing atmospheric conditions.

Evaporativity (Potential Rate of Evaporation). Rate of evaporation under existing atmospheric conditions from a surface of water that is chemically pure and has the temperature of the atmosphere.

Field Capacity. The capacity of the soil to hold pellicular water, measured by the soil scientist as the ratio of weight of water retained by the soil to the weight of the dry soil. (See Specific Retention as used by ground-water investigator.)

Fixed Ground Water. Water held in saturated material with interstices so small that it is permanently attached to the pore walls or moves so slowly that it is usually not available as a source of water for pumping.

Fixed Moisture. Moisture held in the soil below the hygroscopic limit.

Fountain Head. The elevation of water surface in a conduit if the overlying confining stratum extends above the water table, or elevation of water table above the upper termination of the confining stratum where the latter is below the water table.

Free Ground Water. Water in interconnected interstices in the zone of saturation down to the first impervious barrier, moving under the control of the water-table slope.

Gravity Water. See Vadose Water. Gravity water is also used in the literature for irrigation water derived from stream flow and drainage ditches, as distinguished from pumped water, and water furnished by a water-table well in contrast to water produced from a confined-water well.

Ground Air. Air in the zone of aeration.

Ground Water. The water in the zone of saturation.

Ground-water Cascade. Descent of ground water on a steep hydraulic gradient to a lower and flatter water-table slope. A cascade occurs below a ground-water barrier or dam which may develop effluent seepage above it, and at the contact of less permeable material with more permeable material downslope.

Ground-water Decrement. Water abstracted from the ground-water reservoir by evaporation, transpiration, spring flow, and effluent seepage, pumping wells, and outflow of ground water from underneath the area under consideration.

Ground-water Divide. The boundary of the cone of pumping depression, shown by the water-table contours as a ridge separating the area of depression and the area of diversion.

Ground-water Equation (General). A mathematical statement of the disposition of rainfall; $R = E + S + I$, where R is rainfall; E, evaporation and transpiration; S, stream flow; and I, ground-water increment.

Ground-water Equation (Local). An equation expressing the relation of ground-water losses to ground-water gains applicable to a particular area.

Ground-water Hydrology. The branch of the science of hydrology that treats ground water; its occurrence and motions, its replenishment and depletion; the properties of rocks that control ground-water movement and storage; and methods of investigation and utilization of ground water.

Ground-water Increment. Water added to the ground-water reservoir from all sources—influent seepage from streams, rainfall, and irrigation and inflow of ground water from outside the area under consideration.

Ground-water Inventory. A detailed estimate of the amount of water added to the ground-water reservoir of a given area (ground-water increment) balanced against estimates of amounts abstracted from the ground-water reservoir of the area (ground-water decrement).

Ground-water Mound. A mound-shaped or ridge-shaped addition to the ground-water body built up by influent seepage.

Ground-water Province. An area characterized by a general similarity in the mode of occurrence of ground water.

Ground-water Ridge. A ridge-shaped addition to ground water built up beneath an influent stream. See also Interstream Ground-water Ridge.

Ground-water Trench. A trench-shaped depression of the water table caused by effluent seepage into a stream or drainage ditch or by movement of ground water to a thalweg underlying a stream.

Ground-water Turbulent Flow. Turbulent flow which occurs in large openings in the zone of saturation under high velocities.

Hydraulic Gradient. A profile showing the static level of water at all points on the profile. Hydraulic gradient of ground water records the head consumed by friction of flow between any selected points on the profile. For percolating water the slope is expressed by h/l, where h is the difference in elevation between any two points and l is the distance between them. The water table registers the hydraulic gradients of free ground water, and the pressure surface those of confined water

Hydrograph. A graphic plot of changes in flow of water or in elevation of water level against time.

Hydrologic Cycle. All movements of water and water vapor in the atmosphere, on the ground surface, below the surface, and return to the atmosphere by evaporation and transpiration.

Hydrologic Properties. Those properties of rocks which control the entrance of water, capacity to hold, transmit, and deliver water. They include porosity, effective porosity, specific retention, permeability, and direction of maximum and minimum permeability.

Hygroscopic Moisture. Moisture that is held in the soil in equilibrium with atmospheric water vapor at the ground surface.

Influent Seepage. Movement of gravity water in the zone of aeration from the ground surface toward the water table.

Interstream Ground-water Ridge. A ridge in the water table formed between two effluent streams, produced by percolation toward the surface streams with the development of a residual ground-water ridge between them.

Isohyetal Map. A map on which precipitation is plotted by connecting points of equal precipitation (*isohyetal lines*) and which shows rainfall distribution in the area mapped.

Isopiestic Line. A contour of the pressure surface of a confined aquifer.

Juvenile Water. New water of magmatic, volcanic, or cosmic origin added to the terrestrial water supply.

Laminar Flow. Motion of a fluid the particles of which move substantially in parallel paths. This type of flow always occurs below the lower critical velocity and may occur between the lower and higher critical velocities. Also called straight-line, streamline, or viscous flow.

Lysimeter. A vessel placed below ground surface to collect influent seepage.

Magmatic Water. Water driven out of magma during crystallization.

Metamorphic Water. Water that is driven out of rocks by the process of metamorphism.

Meteoric Water. Water derived from the atmosphere.

Meteorology. A branch of applied physics treating the atmosphere and its phenomena, especially variations of temperature and moisture, winds, storms, etc.

Moisture Equivalent. The ratio between the water a soil will retain against a centrifugal force 1000 times the force of gravity and the weight of the soil when dry.

Pedalfer. A soil which contains more Al_2O_3 and/or Fe_2O_3 than the parent material.

Pedocal. A soil with fully developed profile in which calcium carbonate is found in some horizon in higher percentage than in the parent material.

Pellicular Front. The even front, developed only in pervious granular material, on which pellicular water depleted by evaporation, transpiration, or chemical action is regenerated by influent seepage.

Pellicular Water. Water adhering as films to the surfaces of openings and occurring as wedge-shaped bodies at junctures of interstices in the zone of aeration above the capillary fringe.

Perched Ground Water. Ground water occurring in a saturated zone separated from the main body of ground water by unsaturated rock.

Percolation. A type of laminar flow occurring in interconnected openings of saturated granular material under hydraulic gradients commonly developed underground.

Permeability. The capacity of water-bearing material to transmit water, measured by the quantity of water passing through a unit cross section in a unit time under 100 per cent hydraulic gradient.

Permeability Coefficient. As defined by Meinzer, the rate of flow in gallons a day through a square foot of the cross section of material, under 100 per cent hydraulic gradient, at a temperature of 60°F. In field terms it is expressed as the number of gallons of water per day at 60°F. that is conducted laterally through each mile of the water-bearing bed under investigation (measured at right angles to the direction of percolation) for each foot of thickness of the bed and for each foot per mile of hydraulic gradient.

Phreatic or "Well" Water. See Ground Water.

Phreatophytes. Plants that habitually send their roots to the capillary fringe and feed on ground water.

Piedmont Alluvial Deposit. A group of impinging alluvial cones built up by streams debouching from a mountain range.

Porosity. The property of a rock of containing interstices without regard to size, shape, interconnection, or arrangement of openings. It is expressed as percentage of total volume occupied by interstices.

Pressure Relief, Cone of. An imaginary surface indicating pressure-relief conditions in a confined aquifer due to pumping.

Pressure Surface. The surface to which confined water will rise in non-pumping wells which pierce a common conduit and the water levels of which are not affected by a pumping well. It is a graphic representation of the pressure exerted by confined water on the conduit walls.

Pressure-surface Map. A map showing the contours (isopiestic lines) of the pressure surface of a confined-water system.

Primary Openings. Those interstices that were made contemporaneously with rock formation as a result of the processes which formed the rocks that contain them.

Pumping Depression, Cone of. See Water-table Depression and Pressure Relief, Cone of.

Rainfall Province. An area characterized by similarity in distribution and seasonal concentration of precipitation and by a similar wind system.

Regolith. Decomposed and weathered rock in place.

Rejuvenated Water. Water returned to the terrestrial water supply by geologic processes of compaction and metamorphism. It is divided into *water of compaction* and *metamorphic water*.

Runoff. *Surface Runoff.* That portion of runoff which flows to stream channels over the surface of the ground.

    Ground-water Runoff. Stream runoff supplied by spring flow and effluent seepage.

Saturation, Water of. The total water that can be absorbed by water-bearing materials without dilation of the sediments.

Saturation, Zone of. The zone below the water table in which all interstices are filled with ground water.

Secondary Openings. Openings in rocks that were developed by processes that affected the rocks after they were formed.

Seepage. Seepage is used in this text in two distinct and different meanings: (1) The accepted usage up to the present time; *i.e.*, the appearance and disappearance of water at the ground surface. (2) As proposed in this text seepage (verb, to seep) designates the *type of movement* of water *in unsaturated material*. It is to be distinguished from percolation, which is the predominant type of movement of water in saturated material.

Soil. The layer or mantle of mixed mineral and organic material penetrated by roots. It includes the surface soil (horizon *A*), the subsoil (horizon *B*), and the substratum (horizon *C*) which is the basal horizon and is limited in depth by root penetration.

Soil Moisture. Pellicular water of the soil zone. It is divided by the soil scientist into available and unavailable moisture. *Available moisture* is water easily abstracted by root action and is limited by field capacity and the wilting coefficient. *Unavailable moisture* is water held so firmly by adhesion or other forces that it cannot usually be absorbed by plants rapidly enough to produce growth. It is commonly limited by the wilting coefficient.

Soil Water. Water in the soil zone, including gravity water and pellicular water (soil moisture).

Soil Water, Belt of. The upper portion of the zone of aeration limited to the soil zone. The water of the belt is soil water.

Specific Absorption. The capacity of water-bearing material to absorb water after all gravity water has been removed. It is the ratio of the volume of water absorbed to the volume of material saturated.

Specific Capacity. The number of gallons of water produced by a pumping well per foot of drawdown.

Specific Retention. The ratio of the volume of water which a rock or soil will retain against the pull of gravity to its own volume.

Specific Yield. The ratio of the volume of water a rock or soil will yield by gravity to its own volume.

Spring. Concentrated discharge of ground water issuing at the surface as a current of flowing water.

Standing Level. The water level in a nonpumping well. The term is used without regard to whether the well is within or outside the area of influence of pumping wells. If outside the area of influence, the term is equivalent to static level; if within the area of influence, the standing level registers one point on the cone of pumping depression.

Static Level. The water level in a nonpumping well outside the area of influence of any pumping well. This level registers one point on the water table in a water-table well or one point on the pressure surface in a confined-water well.

Subcapillary Interstice. One smaller than a capillary interstice in which molecular attraction spans the entire space and water is held immovable against the force of gravity by adhesion.

Subirrigation, Natural.   The delivery of water to plant roots by the capillary fringe.

Subsurface Perched Stream.   Vadose water concentrated in fractures or solution openings flows toward the water table in subsurface perched streams.

Subsurface Water.   All water occurring below the ground surface.

Supercapillary Interstice.   One larger than a capillary interstice in which surface tension develops no appreciable capillary lift and through which movement of water may be turbulent under hydraulic gradients occasionally existing underground.

Surface Tension.   The free energy in a liquid surface produced by the unbalanced inward pull exerted by the underlying molecules upon the layer of molecules at the surface.

Suspended Water.   Water in the zone of aeration including seeping water (gravity water) and stored water (capillary and pellicular water).

Thalweg.   A subsurface ground-water stream percolating beneath and in the general direction of a surface stream course or valley.

Transmission Constant.   An expression of hydraulic permeability of a rock or soil.   It has been expressed as the discharge in cubic feet per minute through each square foot of cross-sectional area under 100 per cent hydraulic gradient.

Transpiration.   The exhalation of water vapor by organisms; as far as the ground-water investigator is concerned, by plants.

Turbulent Flow.   The motion of a fluid which always occurs above the higher critical velocity and which may occur down to the lower critical velocity.   The particles of the fluid move in sinuous paths.

Unavailable Water.   See Soil Moisture.

Underground Water.   See Subsurface Water.

Uniformity Coefficient.   A ratio expressing variation in grain size of granular material.   It is usually measured by the sieve aperture that passes 60 per cent of the material divided by the sieve aperture that passes 10 per cent of the material.   This ratio was proposed by Hazen as a quantitative expression of degree of assortment of water-bearing sand as an indicator of porosity.   The value of the coefficient for complete assortment (one grain size) is unity; for fairly even-grained sand it ranges between 2 and 3; for heterogeneous sand the coefficient may be 30.

Vadose Water.   Water in excess of pellicular water seeping toward the water table; used in this text as a synonym for gravity water.

Velocity Head.   Energy of flow expressed as head.

Viscosity, Coefficient of.   The amount of force necessary to maintain a unit difference in velocity between two layers of water a unit distance apart.

Volcanic Water.   Juvenile water furnished by lava flows and volcanic centers.

Water Spreading.   Retention of water behind dams or in basins, maintenance of flow in ditches or stream channels, or feeding water down wells and shafts in order to develop influent seepage.

Water Table. In pervious granular material the water table is the upper surface of the body of free water which completely fills all openings in material sufficiently pervious to permit percolation. In fractured impervious rocks and in solution openings it is the surface at the contact between the water body in the openings and the overlying ground air.

Water-table Depression, Cone of. A cone of depression in the water table developed around a pumping well, the periphery of which (ground-water divide) delimits the ground water moving toward the well.

Water-table Map. A contour map of the upper surface of the saturated zone.

Water-table Stream. Concentrated ground-water flow at the water table in a formation or structure of high permeability.

Wilting Coefficient. The ratio of the weight of water in the soil when the leaves of plants first undergo permanent reduction in their water content as the result of deficiency in the supply of soil moisture to the weight of the soil when dry.

HYDRAULIC CONVERSION FACTORS

1 sec.-ft. =   7.48 gal. per second.
            449 gal. per minute.
       646,317 gal. per day.
         60 cu. ft. per minute.
    86,400 cu. ft. per day.
       0.9917 acre-in. per hour.
       1.98347 acre-ft. per day.
      40 miner's inches in California.[1]
1 ft. of head = 0.43 lb. per square inch.
1 lb. per square inch = 2.309 ft. of head.

Conversion of Units of Volume
(From King, "Handbook of Hydraulics")

U. S. gallons to cubic feet: 1 gal. = 0.1337 cu. ft.
Cubic feet to gallons: 1 cu. ft. = 7.481 gal.
Millions of gallons to acre-feet: 1 million gallons = 3.07 acre-ft.
Acre-feet to millions U.S. gallons: 1 acre-ft. = 0.326 million gallons.
Millions U.S. gallons per day to second-feet: 1 million gallons per day = 1.547 sec.-ft.
Second-feet to millions U.S. gallons per day: 1 sec.-ft. = 0.646 million U.S. gallons per day.

Weight

Maximum density of water is at 39.3°F. At this temperature 1 cu. ft. of water weighs 62.4 lb., 1 gal. weighs $8\frac{1}{3}$ lb.

Area

1 acre = 43,560 sq. ft.

Approximate Equivalents

1 sec.-ft. (per day) = $\frac{2}{3}$ million gallons = 2 acre-ft.
1 million gallons = $1\frac{1}{2}$ sec.-ft. per day = 3 acre-ft.
1 acre-ft. = $\frac{1}{2}$ sec.-ft. per day = $\frac{1}{3}$ million gallons.
450 gal. per minute = approximately 1 sec.-ft. (1 sec.-ft. = 449 gal. per minute).
1 cu. ft. per second at 1 ft. head = approximately 0.1 horsepower (0.113).
1 lb. per square inch pressure = 2.3 ft. of head.

$$\text{horsepower} = \frac{\text{g.p.m.} \times \text{head in feet}}{4500}.$$

[1] One California miner's inch has been defined as $\frac{1}{40}$ sec.-ft. by law, or 11.2 gal. per minute. In southern California it is locally interpreted as $\frac{1}{50}$ sec.-ft., or 9 gal. per minute.

INDEX

A

Ab-i-diz River, kanats, 13
Adam, N. K., capillary rise, 151
  surface tension, 151–152n.
Aeration, zone of:
  capillary fringe in, 40n., 224
  definition, 557
  fractures in, 45–46, 100–101, 112–
    113, 173, **294–295**, 297
  hydrologic character, 140–141 (*see
    also* Soil, permeability)
  water occurrence and movements
    in, 31–32, **38–42**, 45–48, **140–
    161** (*see also* Capillary fringe;
    Influent seepage; Pellicular
    water; Perched water)
  weathering in (*see* Weathering)
Air-mass analysis, 68
  definition, 557
Alabama, springs in, 455
Alluvial cone, artesian pressure in,
  322–323, **371–377**, 532–538
  definition, 365, 557
  discharge area of, 62, 85, **374–376**
    (*see also* Swamps in)
  materials of, source and type, 249–
    251, 367, 375, 504–505, **522–
    524**, 534, 536
  pumping from, effects, 61–62,
    353–355, 376–377 (*see also*
    Compaction, water of, yield;
    Confined-water well; Water-
    table well, hydraulic phe-
    nomena)
  springs in, 450–452
  structure, geologic and hydrologic,
    • 14–15, 37, 62, 102–103, 178–
    179, 344–345, **365–376**, 522–
    525, 529–530, 533–537

Alluvial cone, water table in, 231–
  234, 372–375
  (*See also* Piedmont deposits)
Alluvial material, ground-water
  provinces in, 503–505, 515,
  518, 519, 521–526, 527–538
  hydrologic character, 37, **110–112**,
    115–116, 223 (*see also* Allu-
    vial cone, structure)
  soils, alluvial, 123, 133–134, 141
  springs in, 447–452
  water table in (*see* Water table, in
    granular material)
  (*See also* Alluvial cone; Clay)
Anticline, ground water and oil in,
  415–417, 421–423, 426–429
Aquiclude, clay and silt as, 21, 53,
  64–66, 115, 117, 118, 170–
  171, 224
  in alluvial cones, 178, 365–367,
    369–371
  surrounding lenticular aquifers,
    359–360, 378–379
  compaction of (*see* Compaction)
  as confining formation (*see* Con-
    fined water)
  definition, 36–37, 557
  dikes, as, 237, 545–546
  drainage due to overpumping (*see*
    Compaction, water of, yield)
  fixed ground water in, 2, 32, 37, 43,
    224
  pressure effects (atmospheric,
    etc.), 331–338
  water table, absence in, 224, 225
Aquifer (confined):
  compaction of (*see* Compaction)
  compressibility and elasticity, 43,
    61, 319, 326, 328–330, **331–
    345**, 352–353 (*see also* Com-
    paction)

569

J

Jakosky, J. J., geophysical investigation, 281–282, 284
  geophysical methods, 260–263
Jamin, J. C., capillary resistance, 425
von Jentzsch, artesian pressure, 330
Jerusalem, rainfall records, 78–79
Juvenile water, 2, 27, 461
  definition, 27, 561

K

Kanats, 12–15
Keilhack, K., artesian systems, 316, 324, 361–362
  springs, 445–446, 451
Kepler, J., origin of springs, 17
King, F. H., capillary lift, 154
  compressibility of sand, 341
  development of ground-water hydrology, 19
  effective porosity, 217
  percolation, 203, 493
  water-level fluctuation, 258
Königsberger, J., geophysical methods, 272, 278, 282
Kunesh, J. F., Hawaiian province, 550

L

Laboratory studies, compressibility, 340–341
  hydrologic properties, 6, 21, **116–118, 207–213,** 220, 483, 491–493
Lacustrine deposits, 63–65, 296, 522, 526, 529
Lafayette dam, clay in, 51
Landslides, 48–52
  springs from, 448–449
Lane, R. A., seepage rate, 241, 243
  spreading through wells, 184–185
Laterite, 130

Lava, fractures in, 309–312, 540
  ground water in, 194–196, **309–312,** 505–506, 518–519, 527, 538–539, **543–552**
  perched water in, 165*n*.
  permeability and porosity, **99–100,** 223, **309–312,** 540, 541
  springs in, 194–196, 311, 447, **457–460**
Lee, C. H., evaporation and transpiration, 86, 89–92
  water-level fluctuation, 349–355
Lee, F. W., geophysical methods, 286
Leggette, R. M., and G. H. Taylor, water-level fluctuation, 338
Leonardon, E. G., and I. B. Crosby, geophysical methods, 284
Limestone, fractures in, 302, 304, 312–313
  ground water in, 511, 515, 516, 517
    (*see also* Solution openings)
  solubility of, 301, **303–304,** 308
    (*see also* Solution openings)
  springs in, 100, 447, **453–457**
Lindgren, W., Hawaiian Islands, 544
Litigation, application of ground-water hydrology, 59–66
  artesian pressure theories, 323–324, 375–376
  comparison of pumping effects, 59–62, 346–355, 380–381
  effluent seepage due to spreading, 177–178
  flow and percolation, use of terms, 190–191
  ground-water supporting stream flow, 60, 245
  landsliding, 50
  lowering of water table, in fractured rock, 299
  mine water, 312–313
  natural water table, 61, 469, 487
    (*see also* Water table, fluctuation, seasonal or cyclic)
  pumping and exportation, 61–62, 63–66, 158, 253, **353–355,** 495–496, 538–539

Mills, R. Van A., oil accumulation, 422

Mimbres River, N. M., influent seepage, 171–172

Mineral water, 29, 171–172, 250–251, 295
  in oilfields, 423, 424
  in solution conduits, 303–307
  (*See also* Springs, types, mineral)

Mines, water in, 113, 295, 300–301, 303, **312–313**, 364
  geophysical location, 286

Mississippi Valley, ground water in, 510–511
  (*See also* Atlantic Coastal Plain province, South Central Paleozoic province; North Central Drift-Paleozoic province)

Missouri, springs in, 455–457

Modena, Italy, wells in, 12

Moisture capacity, normal, 146
  (*See also* Field capacity)

Moisture equivalent, 147, 148*n*.
  definition, 147, 561
  used in inventory, 485

Moisture-holding capacity (*see* Field capacity)

Mokelumne River Valley, aquifers in, 38, 117, **169–171**, 529, 530
  feeding water in wells, 185
  hydrologic properties of materials, 117, 118
  influent seepage, 169–171
  stream gaging, 80
  water-level fluctuation, 336, 337
  water-table map, 251–253

Montana-Arizona Plateau province, 514, 518

Montana Eocene-Cretaceous province, 514, 517

Montrose flood, 80–81

Morgenthau, H., Santa Clara Valley, 24

Morris, S. B., water-level fluctuation, 337–338

Mudflow, 48, 70, 80–81, 370
  porosity of, 112

N

Napa Valley, 538–539

Newell, F. H., flow experiments, 203

Niles cone, spreading in, 174
  water-table map, 253–256

Niles-Irvington fault, 254–255

Nineveh, kanats in, 13

Nondischarging permeameter, 209–210

Norderney, Friesian Islands, fresh ground-water lens, 246–247

Normal moisture capacity, 146

North-Central Drift-Paleozoic province, 514, 515

Northeastern Drift province, 514, 515

Northern Coast Range ground-water province, 520, 521, 538–539
  (*See also* Pacific Mountain province)

Northern Rocky Mountain province, 514, 518

Northwestern Drift-Eocene-Cretaceous province, 514, 517

Norton, W. H., well drilling, 12

O

Oil well, hydraulic conditions, 423–425

Oilfield waters, 1, 28, **415–429**

Ojuela mine, Mexico, ground water in, 312–313

Openings in rocks (*see* Interstices)

Ore solutions, 1, 2

Oregon, springs in, 457, 460

Orvieto, Italy, well in, 11–12

Overflow in fractures, 297–298

Overpumping (*see* Compaction, water of, yield; Depletion)

Owens Valley, alluvial cones and aquifers in, 61–62, 194–196, 370–371, 373, 374, 525, 526
  evaporation study in, 86
  influent seepage in, 167
  lava flows in, 194–196, 310, 525